19-25

LAUGHING GULLS
From a painting by Earl L. Poole

# BIRD STUDIES AT OLD CAPE MAY

## AN ORNITHOLOGY OF
## COASTAL NEW JERSEY

### BY WITMER STONE

With a new introduction by

ROGER TORY PETERSON

author of numerous ornithological works and
editor of the " Field Guide " Series

IN TWO VOLUMES

VOLUME II

DOVER PUBLICATIONS, INC., NEW YORK

Published in Canada by General Publishing Company, Ltd., 30 Lesmill Road, Don Mills, Toronto, Ontario.

Published in the United Kingdom by Constable and Company, Ltd., 10 Orange Street, London W.C.2.

This Dover edition, first published in 1965, is an unabridged republication of the work first published by the Delaware Valley Ornithological Club in 1937, to which have been added a new Introduction written especially for this edition by Roger Tory Peterson; a List of Additional Species Recorded in Cape May County since the original publication of this book, compiled by Ernest A. Choate; a biographical note on Witmer Stone by James A. G. Rehn, reprinted with permission from the *Proceedings* of the Delaware Valley Ornithological Club, No. XXXI, 1938–41; and a detailed table of contents.

The frontispieces to Volumes I and II were reproduced in color in the original edition. The endpaper maps from the first edition are here reproduced as full-page illustrations (see page 2 and 5a and b).

This edition is published by special arrangement with the Delaware Valley Ornithological Club.

Library of Congress Catalog Card Number: 65-15517

Manufactured in the United States of America

Dover Publications, Inc.
180 Varick Street
New York, N. Y. 10014

# CONTENTS

## VOLUME TWO

# CONTENTS

## STILT SANDPIPER

Micropalama himantopus (Bonaparte)

The Stilt Sandpiper seems to be of irregular occurrence on the New Jersey coast, present in some years and rare or absent in others. It is moreover an autumnal migrant like the Lesser Yellow-legs and Pectoral Sandpiper, the main flight passing up the Mississippi Valley in spring; in fact we have no spring record whatever for the Cape May region.

Our first Cape May records were in 1897 when William Baily secured specimens on August 11 and 20 from little flocks of three and four and we have no records from then until 1924. But this is not remarkable when we consider the lack of observers and of familiarity with the bird as well as the irregularity of its occurrence. On August 3, 1924, Julian Potter identified a specimen on the shallow pond at the Lighthouse and others were found there until August 24. In 1926 they were present from August 23 to 28; in 1927, July 31 to August 21; in 1930 from July 12 to August 23; on August 25, 1931; and from August 5 to September 5 in 1934. A few were seen on August 7, 1935, and August 23, 1936. Julian Potter saw one at Camden on the Delaware River on October 20, 1929, which would indicate that more continuous observations at Cape May would show the birds present there much later in the autumn. On Brigantine Beach the Stilt Sandpiper would seem to be much more common in years when it is of general occurrence, as Potter found no less than forty there on July 26, 1930.

Charles Urner's records for the more northern section of the coast from Brigantine to Newark Meadows, where the Stilt Sandpiper seems to occur much more frequently than at Cape May, are presented below. They show extreme dates, period of regular or common occurrence, and maximum count for one day at a single locality.

1928.   July 3–September 30 (August 29–September 30).   Fourteen on Sept. 9.
1929.   July 14–September 15 (August 30–September 8).   Four on Sept. 8.
1930.   July 6–September 21 (July 16–August 10).   Forty on July 26.
1931.   July 9–September 27 (August 8–30).   Thirty-five on August 30.
1932.   July 7–October 12 (July 16–September 18).   Thirty on August 31.
1933.   July 12–October 7 (July 19–September 30).   Sixty on September 2.
1934.   July 7–October 12 (July 14–September 23).   Thirty on August 5.

Urner also saw a single bird on May 12, 1934, the only spring record for New Jersey so far as I know. In his grouping of the shore birds as to relative abundance he regards the Stilt Sandpiper as "irregularly and locally tolerably common."

Alexander Wilson was not acquainted with this bird and we owe our first account of it to Charles Lucien Bonaparte who tells us that "he met with it in July, 1826, near a fresh water pond at Long Branch being in company with Mr. Cooper. We observed a flock flying about at which I fired and killed the one here represented." (American Ornithology, IV, p. 89.) Turnbull (1869) states that it occurs in May and August and a specimen in his collection is labeled Brigantine. Dr. Jonathan Dwight secured ten specimens at Squan Beach between July 15 and September 15, 1879, which seem to be the only other early records for the New Jersey shore.

Julian Potter's bird of August 3, 1924, was associated with some Lesser Yellow-legs and there were from one to five present there throughout the month. In general form they resemble the Yellow-legs but are distinctly smaller, a difference easily recognized when they are feeding side by side or when flying together; the general color is somewhat paler, too, the prominent eye strip is distinctive and the legs are black instead of yellow. One individual showed traces of the barring on the flanks which is characteristic of the breeding season when it covers the entire under parts. Others in this plumage were seen by John Gillespie on July 31, 1927, on Two Mile Beach and by Charles Urner on July 18, 1928, at Barnegat.

In feeding the Stilt Sandpiper pokes its bill into the mud or sand several times in one spot without withdrawing it and often submerges its head in the operation resembling the Dowitcher in both particulars.

Julian Potter saw Stilts at Camden on the Delaware River on October 28, 1929, and found a flock of fifty feeding on a recent dredging at the same spot on September 17, 1932. On August 13, 1934, there were twelve at Cape May Point.

On August 23, 1926, I found a single Stilt with a large assemblage of Lesser Yellow-legs and other smaller species on a shallow rain water pool which had formed on a bit of meadow a little north of the beach drive above Broadway where they were sheltered from the nearby traffic by a dense growth of bayberry bushes. In this seclusion the flock remained for several days and many excellent opportunities for comparison of the Stilt with the other birds were offered. Its body was slightly smaller than that of the Yellow-legs and the bird was not quite so tall; legs and bill black and the latter seemed actually a trifle longer than that of the Yellow-legs. This was determined a number of times when the birds were in a position for accurate comparison. The back of the Stilt was much paler than that of any of the other birds with which it was associated and a Solitary Sandpiper looked black in comparison. When the Stilt Sandpiper flew its expanded tail was dull white. Another Stilt Sandpiper was seen that same day which had sustained a broken leg and was feeding in another rain water pool at South Cape May along with Semipalmated Sandpipers, Killdeers and a Pectoral Sandpiper. It showed very clearly the dark banding on the flanks.

On August 25, 1931, a rain water pool formed on a patch of grass stubble back of South Cape May and for several days was well populated with a host of shore birds. There were five Stilt Sandpipers present which waded into the water until it was up to their bodies and in feeding repeatedly plunged the head under, probing into the bottom of the pool. Their actions were very different from those of the delicate stalking Lesser Yellow-legs which held their heads up and their necks constantly moving, or from the sluggish Pectorals which seemed more plover-like in action. Some of these Stilts showed the barring below while others, probably birds of the year, were plain gray above and white below.

On August 7, 1927, a group of shore birds was studied on a meadow pool back of Seven Mile Beach which contained several Stilt Sandpipers; they not only submerged their heads but tipped up like ducks in order to reach the bottom, the water being rather deep. The Dowitchers that were present also tipped up and submerged but the Lesser Yellow-legs fed entirely from the surface.

## SEMIPALMATED SANDPIPER

**Ereunetes pusillus (Linnaeus)**

PLATE 45, p. 496

The most abundant shore bird about Cape May is undoubtedly the little Semipalmated Sandpiper, the smallest of the tribe with the exception of the Least Sandpiper, its frequent associate, and so like it in general coloration and habits, that, unless close at hand, we often find it difficult to distinguish them. Apart from the slightly larger size, however, the black instead of olive legs, lack of buffy tints on the breast (the ground color white throughout) and less blended colors above, will enable one to recognize the present bird although the two latter characters are most conspicuous in springtime. The partial webbing between two of its toes, to which its name is due, is not visible in life except under unusual conditions.

From early July throughout the summer the Semipalmateds occur in ever increasing numbers usually dwindling away again during September although small bunches may remain until November and we have records for December. In the spring flight they are with us from April to June and it is quite possible that if one were on the spot continuously they could be found in every month of the year.

They first appear on the mud flats of the sounds or on the muddy banks of salt ponds on the meadows and may be seen about the shallow pond at the Lighthouse or on the bottoms of smaller ponds which become entirely dry with the ebbing of the tide. The fresh pond formerly existing at the old race track, with its broad muddy margins, and the shores of Lake Lily at Cape May Point, also furnished satisfactory feeding grounds for these active little birds. About the middle of July or even earlier they occur in numbers on the sea beaches where they later associate with the Sanderlings and Ring-necked Plover, the three constituting the bulk, of our "beach birds."

The Semipalmated Sandpipers are typically gregarious, feeding together in rather close assemblages and taking wing simultaneously in that curious and puzzling manner of flocking birds, the individuals being able in some way to signal to each other so that the flock moves as a unit, instantaneously and with a definite objective. As one of these flocks circles about over the meadows, or wheels out over the surf, its actions are marked by the same unanimity, the individuals all turning, rising, or falling, together. The turning of their bodies in the air while in full flight produces a curious effect; at one moment one sees a series of brown backs exposed to view with rapidly vibrating wings and a slight flicker of white and then, presto, there is a sudden flash of silvery white as they turn their white bellies to the light. For a moment or two they sparkle and then with another turn they are gone and we have trouble in finding the flock at all. At a distance one may lose them completely so closely do their brown backs merge with the dark color of the marsh or water. In a fog, or in dull light with gray skies, passing flocks are practically invisible until they turn their bodies over and we catch the magic flash of white.

When they alight all are facing the same way, and when flying down the beach with the wind, they turn and face it as they come to rest. While they always occur in flocks there are some individuals that have become detached from their fellows and scattered birds may be seen all through the summer passing overhead, and what would, at a casual glance, be put down as a swallow in springtime, will now doubtless prove to be one of these little sandpipers.

On the exposed flats or on the grassy meadows, when feeding, they are all action from the moment their feet touch the ground, moving about in every direction like a colony of fiddler crabs, although even now the individuals somehow keep in close touch with one another and the flock keeps fairly well together. They walk deliberately with head lowered, probing with the bill every few seconds, now to the right and now to the left. Now and then two individuals will engage in an encounter fluffing up the plumage and jumping in the air like miniature gamecocks, the victor often pursuing his antagonist for short distances, their tails elevated throughout the performance.

On the beach they seem even more active than on the meadows, spurred on perhaps by the constantly recurring waves from which they must retreat, and also by the greater activity of their prey. They keep well down on the wet sand and run rapidly, sometimes through the shallow water of a receding wave, although this seems to be accidental and not habitual as it is in the case of the Sanderling. The latter, however, has always a closer association with the waves and water than has the present species.

At high water, when the coastal mud flats are flooded and the feeding on the beach is poor, the Semipalmated Sandpipers resort to the dry sand flats behind the dunes to rest until the turn of the tide. Here on August 30, 1920, I came upon several large flocks and by advancing slowly and silently I was able to get within fifteen feet of them and, so long as I stood rigid, they sensed no danger and went right on with their activities. It is only at such close quarters that one realizes the beauty and trimness of these little birds. They were now all in fully molted fresh plumage. Many were at rest squatting on the sand often in little depressions, some with heads turned back and bills buried in the scapular feathers, apparently asleep. A whole flock resting in this position looked precisely like little lumps of dark wet sand. Other birds were standing but with heads turned back as just described and still other with bills directed forward. Many of them were on one foot only and went hopping about preferring to advance in this way rather than to put the other foot down, although it would come into action when I started to follow them and kept them on the move. Occasionally one of the standing birds would lower the leg that had been drawn up and give it a rapid shake, as if in this cramped position it had "gone to sleep." When a bird squatted down on its belly it always placed its feet together and bending the legs at the heel (tibio-tarsal joint) would allow the body to settle down upon them. Other individuals would raise their wings high over their backs as terns and Yellow-legs so often do, and bring the axillary feathers into view.

There were little pools of water here and there and in these some of the birds were bathing. A few stood in the water and dipped their heads into it possibly seeking food. Others sat down and repeatedly ducked the whole head under, at the same time churning up the water by slightly spreading the wings at the shoulders and working them up and down. On another occasion bathing birds fluttered rapidly in the water and then raised up and did the same in the air, sometimes leaping six inches or more above the surface, possibly with the object of shaking off the water and drying the plumage. On August 28, 1933, just after the great storm and hurricane which flooded much of the Cape May district and drove salt spray far inland killing much of the vegetation, I watched a number of Semipalmated Sandpipers feeding in a flooded field north of Cold Spring, some of which submerged their heads completely in probing for food.

At a distance a large flock of these sandpipers at rest often completely escapes notice so perfectly do the birds resemble their background, and when they suddenly take wing it seems as if hundreds of the clam and oyster shells, that we supposed we had been looking at, had come to life and developed the power of flight.

On the large shallow pond to the east of the Lighthouse flocks of Semipalmated and Least Sandpipers are often seen feeding late in July or in early August when the water has become stagnant through lack of rain and is covered with a thick scum of vegetation which offers only partial support to the many shore birds that attempt to walk upon it. At every few steps the Semipalmated Sandpipers would sink in and immediately raise their wings over their backs and flap them to aid in regaining their footing. When one hundred or more were so engaged their wings made a continual flicker. On a small pond near South Cape May, under similar conditions, the sandpipers gathered on a submerged log to rest, crowding onto it in such numbers that there was not foot room for another individual.

During the northward migration the Semipalmated Sandpipers seem to be even more abundant on the sounds and meadows than they are in summer, on the return flight, or possibly their time is shorter and they are more concentrated. From one of the little gunning shacks standing on stilts back of Two Mile Beach, from which many of my studies were made, they are almost constantly in view, flying past singly or in small bunches like swallows, or gathering on the exposed flats in flocks of from twenty-five to several hundred, feeding, rising and settling again in restless activity. On May 20–24, 1922, Walker Hand and I watched them coming in to feed on the mussel beds of Jarvis Sound, as the water ebbed away and left acres of exposed mud and sand. Upwards of fifteen hundred Semipalmated Sandpipers gathered here every day exceeding the combined total of all other species of shore birds which frequented the spot. On May 22, no less than 276 came in during the first forty-five minutes of our count as against 245 of all other kinds and the same proportion was maintained, so far as we could judge, when the main body arrived. The Semipalmateds preferred the mussel beds and but few were to be seen on the smooth black mud, which the Black-bellied Plovers and certain other species frequented. They came in groups of six to thirty herding close together on the small area that first showed above the water, standing shoulder to shoulder, the outer ones with feet submerged, waiting patiently until the tide would subside sufficiently to make feeding practicable; then they would scatter in every direction and resume their characteristic activity. When the in-coming tide again began to flood the flats they reluctantly left in small flocks to seek the little salt ponds in the grass, or to rest on the dry sand stretches behind the beaches and on the higher parts of the meadows. On May 18, 1924, during a strong wind these resting birds sought shelter behind every tuft of grass or sedge on the dry sand that was large enough to act as a windbreak, or behind clods of mud or large shells which stood above the surface of the ground. It was comical to see them standing, mostly on one foot, one behind another in close packed lines, three or four feet long to leeward of the grass tuft, the first in line sheltered by the grass itself the others by the birds immediately in front.

In the spring they are more conspicuously colored than during the southward flight and are all definitely streaked on the breast with black, the elimination of the plain-breasted young birds moreover, makes identification more easy.

The Semipalmated Sandpiper arrives at Cape May during the last week of April or the first of May, the fact that some of the birds winter here, or only a short distance to the south, makes it difficult to decide just when the true transients arrive. Our records are as follows:

| | | | | | |
|---|---|---|---|---|---|
| 1903. | April 29. | 1912. | May 8. | 1925. | May 8. |
| 1904. | April 30. | 1913. | April 18. | 1931. | May 9. |
| 1905. | May 2. | 1916. | April 22. | 1932. | April 30. |
| 1907. | April 25. | 1917. | April 19. | 1933. | May 6. |
| 1908. | April 28. | 1920. | May 1. | 1934. | May 5. |
| 1910. | May 1. | 1924. | May 9. | | |

These dates may not be entirely accurate as I have never been present continuously at the Cape during the spring, but I have found birds plentiful in several years by April 30. Their height of abundance is in May and they begin to decrease by the 25th of that month. We have however many records for June: June 7, 1914; June 4, 1916; June 12, 1921; June 21, 1923; June 5, 1925; June 19, 1926; June 12 and 26, 1927; June 10 and 24, 1928; June 9, 1929; June 25, 1932; June 17, 1933; June 30, 1935. Just how these dates are to be interpreted it is difficult to say. They may represent very late north-bound migrants, or, as seems more likely, non-breeding birds which never reached their summer homes. Within a week or two from the last June record we begin to get the van of the south-bound birds my arrival dates being:

| | | | | | |
|---|---|---|---|---|---|
| 1916. | July 8. | 1926. | July 16. | 1932. | July 10. |
| 1921. | July 2. | 1927. | July 4. | 1933. | July 8. |
| 1923. | July 3. | 1928. | July 7. | 1934. | July 13. |
| 1924. | July 12. | 1929. | July 15. | 1935. | July 13. |
| 1925. | July 4. | 1931. | July 6. | 1936. | July 4. |

Our latest autumn dates are:

| | | | | | |
|---|---|---|---|---|---|
| 1930. | November 9. | 1932. | November 13. | 1934. | November 3. |
| 1931. | November 7. | 1933. | November 19. | | |

The only December records were obtained on the Christmas census of the Delaware Valley Ornithological Club on December 24, 1933—nine seen by Richard Miller on Seven Mile Beach and two by Fletcher Street from a boat on the sounds, and three on December 22, 1935.

I saw several Semipalmated Sandpipers on the meadows west of Seven Mile Beach on March 18, 1933, and fifty on March 28, 1936, our only records for that month which leaves only two months in the year—January and February, in which these little sandpipers have not been recorded from Cape May.

Charles Urner's records of the migration of the Semipalmated Sandpiper for the region between Brigantine and Newark Meadows on the northern seaboard of the state are given below and show the extreme dates and period of regular or common occurrence, as well as the maximum count for one day at a single locality.

Northward migration:

> 1929.   to June 22 (May 11–30). 4000 on May 19.
> 1930.   to June 22 (May 11–31). 3500 on May 31.
> 1931.   May 3–May 31 (May 17–31). 2000 on May 17.
> 1932.   May 1–June 4 (May 5–25). 4000 on May 18.
> 1933.   April 29–June 4 (May 5–June 4). 2500 on May 21.
> 1934.   May 5–June 18 (May 12–27). 800 on May 16.

Southward migration:

1928. July 1–October 14 (July 1–October 14). 6000 on August 1.
1929. July 4–October 20 (July 13–October 6). 4000 on July 31.
1930. July 7–October 12 (July 7–September 21). 3000 on August 3.
1931. July 4–October 4 (July 11–September 27). 1400 on August 2.
1932. July 4–November 12 (July 9–October 15). 2700 on July 31.
1933. July 2–December 24 (July 2–October 8). 4000 on July 30.
1934. July 7–December 23 (July 11–September 30). 4000 on August 26.

In point of numbers the Semipalmated Sandpiper stands at the head of the six species grouped by Urner as "abundant" on our coast (see page 385).

## WESTERN SANDPIPER

Ereunetes mauri Cabanis

PLATE 45, p. 496

While there is no question as to the distinctness of this Western race from the Semipalmated Sandpiper it seems probable that, with our changing conception of the differences between species and sub-species, the two forms may eventually be regarded as differing only subspecifically, as has already been done in the case of the Eastern and Western Dowitchers, birds which have exactly the same relation to one another.

The older writers up to the time of Baird, Cassin and Lawrence's classic "Birds of North America" did not recognize two forms although the latter authors did comment upon the extraordinary variation in the length of the bill. The two birds were apparently first separated by Lawrence in 1864 and while recognized by Ridgway in 1887, Coues in the same year regarded the western form: as "an alleged variety, probably untenable." Ridgway moreover stated that this race was "chiefly restricted" to the West, thereby implying that it also occurred in the East. C. W. Beckam (Auk 1885, p. 110) recorded one specimen taken in Virginia in 1884 saying that eastern records were few, and Hugh M. Smith mentioned fourteen collected at Piney Pt., Md., in 1885. Other records followed as collectors learned to separate skins of the two forms. The species was apparently first definitely recorded from New Jersey in my "Birds of Eastern Pennsylvania and New Jersey" (1894) on the basis of one taken and identified by Norris DeHaven at Atlantic City, May 17, 1892, and one found in Dr. W. L. Abbott's collection, Cape May Co., September 14, 1880. Other specimens previously regarded as Semipalmated Sandpipers were found in various collections, one obtained as early as 1885, by George Morris, at Beach Haven; one on Seven Mile Beach by David McCadden on September 5, 1898, and another by Dr. William E. Hughes on July 23, 1899, while William Baily secured a series of thirty-five little "peeps" on Two Mile Beach, Cape May Co., on September 1, 1895, of which he identified twenty as Westerns. (Auk, 1896, p. 174). All of the New Jersey specimens with one exception were taken in the autumn and Ludlow Griscom states (Birds of N. Y. Region) that "no specimens have been *collected* there in spring."

With the advent of "sight records" on such a large scale as we have to-day, we are confronted with numerous occurrences of Western Sandpipers on every hand.   Charles Urner records them in numbers on the Newark Meadows, Barnegat and Brigantine in his reports on the shore bird migration on the New Jersey coast.   In connection with his first year's record he adds "difficulty of satisfactory field identification with many individuals reduced the number of records," but the number increased in the later years and he had apparently found identification characters satisfactory to himself.

As Charles Urner is one of our most experienced students of the living birds we feel that his figures probably present as near an approximation to the relative abundance and time of occurrence of these two birds on the New Jersey coast as it is possible to reach.   For ordinary observers, however, only a small proportion of the Semipalmated Sandpipers that one sees can be identified as Westerns with any pretense to scientific accuracy.   And we agree with Griscom that "only the merest handful of ornithologists who have given special study to these birds are competent to make a sight record worthy of serious consideration."

In order to better appreciate the problem presented by these birds we may quote from two of the leading authorities on field identification.   Roger T. Peterson says: the Western Sandpiper is "one of the most difficult species to identify in the field.   When mixed with Semipalmateds it appears a little larger and more coarsely marked.   The bill is very noticeably longer and thicker at the base.   In the breeding plumage it is much rustier on the back and crown than the Semipalmated.   A trace of this rusty is often evident in the fall.   In late summer or early fall the more complete band of breast streaking is a good point.   The breast band in the Semipalmated is reduced at this season to a dusky smudge at each side of the breast.   The black feet distinguish it from the Least which is more or less rusty on the upper parts."

Ludlow Griscom in his "Birds of the New York Region" says: "An even more difficult proposition is to determine the Western Sandpiper.   The greater average length of bill is not a field character.   There remains simply color.   In summer the Western differs from the Semipalmated exactly as does the Least but the difference is slightly more intensified (i. e. rustier on the back and more streaked below).   I have yet to be convinced that it is possible to distinguish the two species satisfactorily in winter plumage."

The bill measurements given by Ridgway are, for the Semipalmated males .68–.75 in., females .80–.90 in. and for the Western, males .68–.90, females .85–1.15 in.   As we manifestly cannot determine the sex in the field we have a range of .68–.90 in. against .85–1.15 in.   The largest Semipalmateds therefore exceed the smallest Westerns and there must be a consider-able number of individuals on either side of the 85–90 series that the human eye could not possibly determine.   I am unable to say just how many hun-dredths of an inch difference in length can be so recognized but it is easy to see the meaning of Griscom's statement regarding bill length as a field char-acter.   All that can be done with regard to the length of bill is to refer the manifestly long bills in any flock to the Western and leave the others as Semipalmated, even though we know that some of them belong, almost certainly, to the former.   Thickness of bill at base is a better character. Fortunately many of our late summer migrants are still in more or less complete breeding plumage and the rusty tints of these are diagnostic.

With regard to identifications by our Cape May observers: Fletcher Street finds the Western Sandpipers on Ludlam's Beach present every summer after the middle of July in association with the Semipalmated and has a few spring records; Julian Potter has recorded a number on the southward flight but none in spring and one on Seven Mile Beach on December 26, 1932.   He has seen a flock of twenty as late as October 25, 1933, on the beach, where they seem more common than on the meadows after mid-September.

Personally I have every summer during July and August picked out a certain number of individuals with decidedly long bills and very rusty backs which I have felt sure were Westerns.   One of these studied on July 28, 1929, with John T. Nichols, on the meadows back of Five Mile Beach possessed these characters while it was also very fully streaked below.   It also kept to itself out on the end of the flock and did not mingle with the other birds. Ernest Choate and I found another with Semipalmateds on an overflowed field at Cold Spring on August 29, 1933, after the great storm of that month, which seemed slightly longer and more slender than the other species.   It seemed to prefer to feed in the deeper water a peculiarity mentioned by Urner.

Charles Urner's records for the northern beaches and meadows from Brigantine to Newark indicate that this species, as he identifies it, is very much more plentiful there than in the Cape May region.   It is also, as we have found it in the southern areas, rare in spring, at which season his records are meager.   He saw five on May 12, 1929; and a few others May 11 and 26; two on June 22, 1930; six on May 24, 1931; one on May 25, 1932; five on May 7, 1933 with a few more until the 21st and one on May 12, 1934.

On the southward migration his extreme dates, period of regular or common occurrence and maximum count for one day at a single locality are:

| | | |
|---|---|---|
| 1928. | July 22–October 12 (August 29–September 15). | 10 on September 15. |
| 1929. | July 7–November 2 (July 13–September 15). | 50 on September 13. |
| 1930. | July 16–October 12 (July 16–September 28). | 30 on August 10. |
| 1931. | July 12–October 4 (July 12–September 20). | 66 on August 30. |
| 1932. | July 4–November 8 (July 16–September 11). | 25 on August 28. |
| 1933. | July 19–November 5 (July 19–October 1). | 500 on September 10. |
| 1934. | July 14–November 11 (August 4–September 30). | 100 on September 16. |

Urner regards the Western Sandpiper as one of the ten "common" species standing just below the group of six designated as "abundant" but relegates it to last place in the group (see page 385).   In southern New Jersey we should not give it nearly so high a rating.

## BUFF-BREASTED SANDPIPER
Tryngites subruficollis (Vieillot)

My personal experience with this rare little sandpiper is limited to one individual found on September 25, 1926, on a shallow rain water pool back of the low dunes at South Cape May. I came upon a bunch of six Pectorals and some Semipalmateds and with them was a bird that I had never before seen in life but I at once recognized it as a Buff-breasted Sandpiper.

The general buffy tone of coloration was very characteristic. The under parts were entirely uniform buff, with strong buff tints above, while the dark markings of the upper parts formed a peculiar shell pattern. The bill was very short and slender, shorter in proportion than in any other sandpiper. All things considered it recalled the Upland Plover more than any other species and it is, in fact, a miniature of it in many respects. In size it seemed intermediate between the Pectoral and the Semipalmated Sandpipers with which it was associated.

The bird had one leg broken and hanging useless and it stood perfectly still on the other leg or occasionally hopped a few steps. It flew a few yards when I tried to approach still closer and then took wing and disappeared in the direction of the Delaware coast. It was not to be found in the afternoon nor on the following day although a diligent search was made.

On September 9, 1928, Julian Potter was fortunate enough to find six of these birds on Brigantine Beach. He first saw two and then two more.

"Their small heads, thin necks, brown and buff plumage and yellowish brown legs told me at once that they were Buff-breasted Sandpipers. Scarcely had I secured a good look at them when they flew and settled among

PLATE 45

*William Vogt*

*Wharton Huber*

1. WESTERN SANDPIPER, LONG ISLAND, N. Y.
2. FLOCK OF SEMIPALMATED SANDPIPERS, CORSON'S INLET, N. J.

PLATE 46

*J. F. Street*

*William Vogt*

1. SANDERLING ON THE BEACH AT SOUTH CAPE MAY, AUGUST, 1920.
2. DOWITCHERS ON LONG ISLAND, N. Y.

a mixed flock of shore birds some forty yards distant. The striking white, dark edged under wing pattern noticed in the first birds was also shown by these. There were nineteen species of waders on the edges of the pool, among them thirty Willets, six White-rumped Sandpipers and a Baird's Sandpiper but not race of my Buff-breasted birds.

"Returning to where I had first seen them I found that the first two had returned and brought two more with them. Upon alighting they had immediately frozen but soon relaxed and while four started to feed in a rather indifferent manner, the others bathed. This was not a vigorous process as is the rule with most waders. One dipped the rear portion of its body in the water by teetering exactly like a Spotted Sandpiper; the other just wet the under side of its body by a series of squats. The wings were fluttered without touching the water, and both birds seemed in fear of disarranging their immaculate plumage. They moved about in a very deliberate manner, the folded wings extending just beyond the tail. Suddenly one uttered a short throaty err, err. Immediately alert, they all took flight, settling on the Brigantine Golf Course. Here two of them indulged in the curious performance of stretching one wing straight up over the back, apparently they were the bathers pluming themselves." (Auk, 1929, p. 109.)

This sandpiper was quite unknown to Wilson and Bonaparte and Audubon never saw a live one. It was discovered in Louisiana by the French ornithologist Vieillot, when visiting America about 1818, and Nuttall tells us that in 1834, a few were found in some seasons in the Boston markets in August and September. In 1844 Giraud had procured it on Long Island but I find no mention of its occurrence in New Jersey until Turnbull's brief statement in 1869 and little or nothing since them.

The first New Jersey specimens that I ever saw were two shot by W. M. Swain and presented to the Academy of Natural Sciences of Philadelphia, one secured on Barnegat Bay below Cedar Creek between the 7th and 21st of September, 1898, and the other at Toms River on September 9, 1899.

Charles Urner saw one on Brigantine Island on September 24, 1926, the day before I found mine at Cape May, another at the same spot on September 4, 1927, and a third on September 16, 1928; Potter's birds already mentioned were seen on September 9, of the same year.

In 1931, one was found on the Newark Marshes on September 6 (Kassoy and Herbert) while there are seven additional records in 1932 from the same locality on September 8, 18, 19, 22, 28, October 1 and 8 (Urner, Kuerzi and Edwards) and one for Brigantine golf course on September 11 (Henry Collins). In 1933 Clifford Marburger found a dead specimen on Brigantine on September 10 and one was seen there on August 24, possibly the same bird. In 1934 Charles Urner has three records for the Newark Marshes, August 30, September 15 and 23 and on August 30, 1935, F. W. Loetscher saw one on Brigantine.

In his list showing the comparative abundance of New Jersey shore birds Charles Urner places the Buff-breasted Sandpiper in the "rare" group (cf, p. 385).

# MARBLED GODWIT

### Limosa fedoa (Linnaeus)

Wilson tells us that in his time, about 1810, this splendid bird was found on the salt marshes of Cape May "in May and for some time in June, and also on their return in October and November; at which last season they are usually fat, and in high esteem for the table." He found them cautious and watchful and only to be approached by imitating their call or whistle. They were "much less numerous than the Short-billed Curlews [i. e. Hudsonian Curlew], with whom, however, they not unfrequently associate."

To the Cape May gunners the Marbled Godwit was known as the "Marlin."

Examining our scanty sources of subsequent information we find that on Long Island Giraud (1844) regarded it as not abundant but of regular occurrence in spring and autumn. Turnbull (1869) calls it "not uncommon" and W. E. D. Scott, in 1877, secured an adult in May and two young birds late in July on Long Beach. Dr. William L. Abbott on his many trips to Five Mile Beach, obtained but two specimens both taken on September 14, 1880. While old gunners, when I first visited Cape May in the "nineties," told me of shooting "Marlin," as these birds were known along the New Jersey coast, and did not seem to realize that they had become scarce, I was unable, however, to locate any specimens or secure any definite records. On Long Island, two had been shot on August 10, 1910, and a single individual seen by a reliable observer on August 20, 1909. In view of the apparent disappearance of the species on our coast I was astonished to find one near Cape May Point on August 9, 1920. As I was walking down the beach below South Cape May I noticed a large brown shore bird with a very long straight bill coming across the meadows on set wings with the apparent intention of alighting on the strand but some persons walking there caused it to change its mind and it continued on beyond the Lighthouse and disappeared. I had a good look at it as it passed me and was in no doubt as to its identity. About half an hour later when I was standing at almost the same spot the bird reappeared sailing in on set wings as before, from the northwest, directly toward me, and alighted on the meadow in a patch of short dead grass. I had a splendid view of it, if only of short duration, and could see the slight up-curve of the bill at the tip, the very black narrow border to the front edge of the wing and the dark brown and buffy brown mottling on the back. The rump was plain buffy brown. Although I sank at once to the ground the bird apparently saw me and after a few moments was off again in the direction of the Race Track Pond where on set wings it again alighted. It was gone again, however, before I could reach the spot. On August 14, following, John T. Nichols and Charles Rogers saw a single individual on Long Island, perhaps the same bird or an associate!

For several years following these observations we find no record of this species in New Jersey but on August 22, 1928, J. S. Edwards saw two on the Newark Marshes where the same birds or others were found on August 29, 31, and September 1, of the same year. On September 2, 1928, Charles Urner and J. M. Johnson saw three on a fresh water pond on the Brigantine golf course, they wrote: "They were feeding within a few feet of the car in which we sat, running about on the partly submerged sidewalks, and we had opportunity to observe their method of drinking, curving the lowered neck apparently enough to allow the water to run into the throat. We could also observe their ability to flex the tips of their long pink-based bills." (Auk, 1929, p. 321.) Julian Potter saw two on Brigantine and Charles Urner one on Newark marshes, on September 15, 1929, while in 1931 Urner saw one at Tuckerton on September 6 and one on Brigantine, on the 20th.

In 1932, Charles Urner has recorded the Marbled Godwit on Brigantine on August 20, 27 and September 3 (two) and on September 4, a single bird at Barnegat Inlet. In 1933 single birds were seen on Brigantine August 23 (Lester Walsh) and August 27 (Urner) while Joseph Tatum found three on the Absecon meadow on September 12. In 1934 Julian Potter found one on Brigantine July 28 and the same individual or another was seen by various observers on August 5, 21 and 28. One was also present there in 1935 on August 15 (Lehrman), September 1 and 29 (Tatum), and November 10 (Potter) the last being our latest date for the species.

So while we have no further Cape May records the numerous observations on Brigantine Island and the recent conversion of that spot into a bird sanctuary bid fair to restore this fine bird as a regular autumnal migrant along our coast.

# HUDSONIAN GODWIT

### Limosa heamastica (Linnaeus)

While this species, the Ring-tailed Marlin of the gunners at Cape May, must have been present in the time of Wilson and Audubon neither mention a New Jersey specimen and the former was entirely unacquainted with the bird. The first mention of its occurrence in the state is by J. Doughty in his quaint "Cabinet of Natural History" (1832) in which he describes and figures an adult specimen in full nuptial plumage which "was shot in May 1828, by Mr. Titian R. Peale at Cape May and preserved in the Philadelphia Museum [Peale's Museum]." He was aware of its occurrence occasionally in autumn in a different plumage but whether in New Jersey he does not say.

Turnbull (1869) knew the bird and regarded it as "rather scarce arriving late in September."

There are several old specimens in the collection of the Philadelphia Academy—obtained in the Philadelphia market by A. Galbraith in 1855, and another from the Delaware River, from Dr. S. W. Woodhouse, while there is a record of one shot by C. D. Wood, the noted taxidermist, on the Schuylkill River below the city in September, 1878.

Norris DeHaven told me that when he gunned on the Atlantic City meadows in the eighties this Marlin occurred with the Willet usually two or three in a flock of the latter species. Henry Hazelhurst showed me a specimen that he had secured at Cape May in September 1900 and had had mounted but he had never seen another. H. W. Wenzel shot two on the upper end of Five Mile Beach on August 26, 1901, one of which is in the Philadelphia Academy collection.

On Long Island between 1881 and 1893 Ludlow Griscom considers that there were about twenty-five definite records and since then they have occurred on five occasions with quite a flight on August 28, 1922. In 1929, Charles Urner has recorded four observations of this bird on the Newark Marshes—August 31, September 29 and 30 and October 13, two on each occasion, probably six in all. On Barnegat Bay, he was informed by Capt. Chadwick that he had seen three of these birds in the fall of 1924 and at Elizabeth he himself saw an individual in full breeding plumage flying north over the Newark marshes on July 3, 1925. At Barnegat, again, on July 17, 1927, he was told by the guides that "there were a few 'Marlin' in the big flight of Curlew" that was passing at the time and upon locating one of the lines of flight on August 31 he saw "two birds somewhat smaller than the Curlew, with apparently straight bills, darker, not brown, upper parts, a wing pattern, and dark tails with a conspicuous white band at the base. Under the wing the feathers seemed dark but the breasts relatively lighter." Later five others passed at a greater distance but seemed to be the same. I saw two flying with Curlew in the same manner back of Seven Mile Beach on May 9, 1931. One was seen by John Kuerzi on August 31, 1931, at Beach Haven, one by Charles Urner at Tuckerton on May 15, 1932, and another by Lester Walsh on August 23, 1933, on Brigantine Island. Additional records for 1933 were Brigantine, September 10 (Tatum); Newark Meadows, September 17, 18, 20, 23, 24, 27 and 30 (Urner or Kuerzi). In 1934, Urner saw one at Absecon on May 16. He regards both of the Godwits as "rare" species in his list of comparative abundance of our shore birds (see p. 385).

All of the specimens of this Godwit that I have seen have been taken in summer or early autumn and were molting, presenting a very mottled appearance; a mixture of the nuptial and winter plumages.

## *RUFF

### Philomachus pugnax (Linnaeus)

There have been casual records of this European bird all along the Atlantic coast and more, apparently, on the island of Barbados than at any other single spot. Just how or why it crosses the ocean we do not know but doubtless storms have something to do with it.

On the coast of New Jersey we have a record of a specimen in the American Museum of Natural History labelled Barnegat (Chapman, Birds within Fifty Miles of New York City) and a statement by Turnbull which may well refer to the same specimen, while there are three records for Long Island.

No others were observed on our coast until October 2, 1932, when Charles Urner saw two near Tuckerton, N. J. which he identified first by sight and later by a careful examination of skins. He states that "the birds were seen first at a distance of fully one hundred yards, walking about on the salt meadow in search of food. They appeared at that distance, with the rising sun striking them, quite light colored, the under parts of one being especially light, the other definitely tinted with and finely streaked with buffy across the breast. They were not as long-legged as the Greater Yellow-legs of which many were present, but their bodies were fully equal in size. They were decidedly larger than the Stilt Sandpipers which were close by. The bodies were rather chunky and when the birds stood at attention they reminded one very much, in general proportions and profile, of overgrown Buff-breasted Sandpipers.

"The length of bill in relation to head conformed to that of the Ruff skins examined. The upper parts, while considerably darker than the breasts seemed, when the birds took flight (they circled twice and lit again), a bit lighter and buffier in color tone than the Greater Yellow-legs. The span in flight was somewhat less than in that species. The outstretched wings showed a narrow white line contrasting, when the birds were near at hand, with the darker wing. The rump and tail showed two conspicuous white areas on the sides, divided by a darker medial line, broadening out at the tip of the tail. I got very satisfactory views at forty to fifty yards." (Auk, 1933, p. 101.)

# SANDERLING

Crocethia alba (Pallas)

PLATE 44, 46, pp. 449, 496

The Sanderling is preëminently the sandpiper of the sea beach and I have almost never seen it elsewhere. It is unknown on the sounds or on the grassy edged ponds, on the borders of the upland, where Yellow-legs often congregate. On the beach its favorite place is down on the edge of the water as close to the waves as it can get with safety and when it retires to rest it seldom goes farther than the high beach where the sand is dry, or perhaps back on some extensive sand flat that the storms have formed by breaking through the dunes and spreading them out over the salt marsh.

In general appearance, as well as in habits, the Sanderling closely resembles the Semipalmated Sandpiper of which, indeed, it is in many respects a larger and paler, edition. It is half again as big and the head seems larger in proportion to the body while the tail tapers off so rapidly that the whole bird seems to have "run to head" or become top heavy. While its style of coloration is the same as that of the little sandpipers it is very much whiter, with little brown in the plumage, so that the general effect is distinctly lighter. In spring, however, some of the Sanderlings have assumed the rusty red-brown breeding plumage, with bright ruddy breasts, and the first arrivals from the north in July are still in this plumage, while most of the adults of July and August are in various stages of molt, to the gray and white dress of winter. While the adult winter plumage is plain gray above and white below, the young of the year are white above heavily streaked with dusky on crown and back. The Sanderling's frequent associate is the Semipalmated Sandpiper and flocks of the two often intermingle on the beach. The former occupy the outer zone closest to the water, next the Semipalmateds while beyond them may be some scattered Ring-necks which take wing with the others when disturbed, though the three species usually hold together in separate bunches within the flock.

It can hardly be said that the Sanderlings seek the company of any other species. They usually occur in large or small flocks, rarely singly, and are sufficient unto themselves. Scattered individuals of other species however will join the Sanderlings and we thus frequently find one or two Turnstones or a few of the two species above mentioned intimately associated with them.

There are no more nervously active shore birds than these Sanderlings of the strand. Almost any day in late summer or early fall we find them running rapidly, close to the edge of a receding wave, or actually through the shallow water, probing here and there as they go. All the while they manage to keep an eye on the incoming wave and just in time they will turn and scamper back, going only far enough to avoid a wetting. Then they once again face the sea and rush back with the outflowing water picking up such food as is being carried along with it, or such small animals as are burying themselves in the soft wet sand. As a bird slows up before turning for the rush, its humped up attitude gives one the impression of shrugging the shoulders. The sallies through the receding water and the dashes back again to safety are usually made on diagonal lines so that the birds are always making progress along the beach, while if anyone follows them they run directly parallel to the shore line, temporarily abandoning their feeding. When convinced that no harm is intended they begin again to follow the waves, glancing once in a while over the shoulder to see that their confidence is not abused. If pressed too closely they take wing and wheel out over the surf coming in to the beach a little farther on. As they fly there is a great show of white, the bands on the wings being especially conspicuous. The body seems heavy and the head and neck are bowed over as if straining every muscle to increase their speed, when they alight one might suppose that the bill touched the sand as soon as the feet so quickly is it in action again, pushing along through water and wet sand for several short steps without being withdrawn. Then the head is raised, the bird runs rapidly a few steps, probes once, and is off again, or else it slows down and pushes the bill along for a few steps as at first. Coming up to spots where the birds have been feeding thus, in wet places on the beach, I have found strings of little double holes as if the mandibles had been separated when the probing was done and in some spots the whole surface of the sand was fairly plowed up for an area of ten feet square. Sometimes, too, I have seen them at close range digging small Hippa crabs from the sand, plunging the bill again and again into the same hole until the entire face was covered.

Frequently one feeding bird will fluff up its feathers until he appears very much humpbacked and like a chicken will charge another one, pursuing him until he takes wing. Sometimes a third individual assumes the offensive and drives the first aggressor to flight, the latter relaxing his plumage the moment he is attacked. Sometimes, the attacked bird resents the onslaught and they jump at one another in true game cock style.

The Sanderlings bathe in pools along the beach which have formed around old pilings, squatting down and ducking their heads under with a great fluffing of the plumage.

When resting, usually at high tide, they retire to the higher sands of the back beach and collect closely together. A roosting flock observed on Two Mile Beach on August 2, 1920, contained over a hundred birds which were huddled closely together, looking at a distance like a mass of sand and shell fragments. Some were squatting on their bellies, others standing with their heads turned over on their backs and their bills buried in the feathers, and some of the latter resting on one leg with the other drawn up under the body. When approached, instead of taking wing, they scuttled away towards the water like a host of fiddler crabs retreating from an intruder, and their bodies glide so smoothly over the sand that it gives one the curious impression that they are impelled by some other force and are not connected with the rapidly moving legs. Many of the birds on one leg refused for some time to put the other one to the ground, stumping along like cripples over the sand, and I have seen feeding birds do the same thing until I was almost convinced that they actually had but one leg.

When standing in groups on the higher beach or the dry sand flats, they seem always to select the highest spots and blend so perfectly with the sand that one often fails to detect them until they begin to scatter and scuttle away.

Once or twice I have found two or three Sanderlings feeding along the line of trash marking the last high tide, fully forty feet from the water and once on October 17, 1920, two of them came to rest on a sand spit in the shallow pond above the Lighthouse just back of the beach, but this was a very exceptional occurrence and even in flight they prefer to follow the beach line or the surf. As in the case of the gulls, light materially affects the appearance of shore birds under certain circumstances. Once early in the morning, September 1, 1921, when the sun's rays were still not far from horizontal, a group of Sanderlings far down the beach were illuminated so that their white breasts shown like spots of glistening silver and again, September 15, when the sun was shining brilliantly on the beach I waded out into the water and approached a large flock of feeding Sanderlings from the ocean side, and in this direct light they appeared to splendid advantage, their breasts gleaming like snow.

Rarely Sanderlings are blown from the beach by storms and I so regard several seen on the shallow pond east of the Lighthouse and one observed flying over the sounds back of Two Mile Beach. At the time of the famous hurricane of August 23–25, 1933, Sanderlings were found along the turnpike leading to Cape May Point, but this at the time was practically the beach line as everything between it and the sea, with the exception of a few of the highest sand dunes, was under water.

My records for the arrival of the Sanderlings at Cape May on their southward flight are:

| | | | | | |
|---|---|---|---|---|---|
| 1916. | August 7. | 1920. | August 1. | 1923. | July 21. |
| 1917. | July 28. | 1921. | July 22 | 1924. | July 22. |
| 1918. | August 8. | 1922. | July 27. | 1925. | July 22. |

| 1926. | July 24. | 1929. | July 27. | 1933. | July 26. |
| 1927. | July 24. | 1930. | July 24. | 1934. | August 1. |
| 1928. | July 18. | 1931. | July 17. | 1935. | July 21. |
|       |          | 1932. | July 19. |       |          |

The August dates may be rejected as late, since it has not been possible to watch the beach continuously, and small bunches of early migrants may easily have escaped notice. The flocks of summer number usually from six to thirty but in September and October they become much larger, often from one to five hundred. The constant annoyance occasioned by people strolling on the beach in summer doubtless tends to break up the flocks, although the birds are really not afraid and continue their search for food close up to where persons are bathing. The tendency, moreover, is to congregate at the entrances to the inlets as the season advances and our largest flocks have been seen at the ends of Seven and Five Mile Beaches, four hundred on the former, October 18, 1931; one hundred and fifty, October 14, 1928; five hundred, September 14, 1916. On the first occasion they lined the shore for a long distance, running along the water's edge and now and then turning head-on to the tide to feed. Sometimes a portion of the assemblage would take wing and the flock would be broken into several units and later united again.

While always to be seen at such places, and less frequently on the sea beaches, in October, the Sanderlings seem to decrease in numbers in November, although a few are to be seen on almost every trip to the Cape during this month. The Delaware Valley Club always finds Sanderlings at the time of its Christmas census as the record will show:

| December 26, 1927, one (Potter) | December 26, 1932, sixty |
| December 23, 1928, twenty | December 24, 1933, 195 |
| December 22, 1929, twenty-five | December 23, 1934, eighty-six |
| December 28, 1930, twenty-eight | December 22, 1935, 136 |
| December 27, 1931, fifty | December 27, 1936, 211 |

Doubtless some of the large flocks remain at one or other of the inlets all winter, or smaller scattered groups somewhere along the shore, since we have records of eight at Stone Harbor January 23, 1927; four at the same place, February 22, 1928; four hundred on Gull Bar, March 26, 1932; and one at Corson's Inlet, April 8, 1928. Absence of observations through late April and May leave the actual arrival dates for the northward flight somewhat in doubt but the following will give some idea of their first appearance:

| 1909. | May 4 | 1925. | May 10. | 1928. | May 10. |
| 1924. | May 10. | 1927. | May 16. | 1929. | May 10. |
|       |       |       |         | 1931. | May 9. |

They remain usually until May 30, and there are several June records: Five Mile Beach, June 13, 1879, June 20, 1923; Seven Mile, June 16, 1918, June 18, 1922, June 12, 1927, and June 19, 1926; Ludlam's Beach, June 10, 1928.

These like other June shore bird records may probably have been non-breeding birds which never completed the northward migration, two seen at Anglesea on July 8, 1922, were certainly of this nature as they were in the gray plumage of winter, while the June birds were more or less ruddy.

Charles Urner's records for the upper beaches from Brigantine north showing extreme dates, period of regular or common occurrence, and maximum count for one day at a single locality, are:

Northward migration:

    1929.  March 10–May 30 (May 11–30).   50 on May 11.
    1930.  April 13–June 22 (April 13–May 23).   50 on May 23.
    1931.  to May 31 (May 12–31).   300 on May 31.
    1932.  wintered to May 25 (May 8–25).   160 on May 8.
    1933.  wintered to June 4 (May 7–28).   400 on May 14.
    1934.  wintered to May 27 (April 8–May 27).   50 on April 8.

Southward migration:

    1928.  July 1–January 13 (July 15–December 9).   500 on July 29 and Sept. 8.
    1929.  July 4–December 8 (July 19–November 10).   600 on August 31.
    1930.  July 6 through winter (July 16–December 20).   600 on July 26.
    1931.  July 11–January 17 (July 18–December 27).   1100 on July 25.
    1932.  July 10 through winter (July 17–Dec. 26).   1000 on July 29 and Oct. 30.
    1933.  July 2 through winter (July 22–December 24).   500 on July 30.
    1934.  July 8 through winter (July 15–October 14).   500 on August 25.

He regards the Sanderling as one of the six "abundant" species of shore birds on our coast today, in his comparative list (see p. 358).

The note of the Sanderling is a continuous twitter, a sociable conversational sound, fitting for birds of such eminently gregarious habits. Just as each bird brings to mind some scene, some particular environment, with which it is inseparably associated, so to me the thought of the Sanderling brings up recollections of a day late in summer, a glittering wind-swept ocean with bright sunlight reflected from every wave cap. The white surf booming and breaking on the beach and the sheets of shallow frothy water rushing up the strand, slower and slower until the turning point is reached, when they slip back to meet another wave advancing. And in their wake go the white and gray Sanderlings. A whole line of them push forward as the water retreats down, down, dabbing right and left as they run, on to the last moment of safety and then scampering back out of harm's way, the roaring of the breakers and the rush of water ever in their ears. Then as something disturbs them they take wing and away they go with rapid mutterings, wheeling out over the surf. They gleam white in the sun as their snowy breasts are turned toward the light, away in mad flight to new feeding grounds farther down the beach. Wild, hardy birds of the sea!

## AVOCET

### Recurvirostra americana Gmelin

PLATE 40, p. 353

Alexander Wilson found Avocets and Black-necked Stilts associated on the salt marshes of Cape May County on the 20th of May about 1810. "They were then breeding. Individuals of the present species were few in respect to the other. They flew around the shallow pools, exactly in the manner of the Long-legs [Stilts], uttering the like sharp note of *click click click*, alighting on the marsh, or in the water, indiscriminately, fluttering their loose wings, and shaking their half bent legs, as if ready to tumble over, keeping up a continual yelping note. They were, however, rather more shy, and kept at a greater distance. One which I wounded, attempted repeatedly to dive; but the water was too shallow to permit him to do this with facility. The nest was built among the thick tufts of grass, at a small distance from one of these pools. It was composed of small twigs, of a seaside shrub, dry grass, sea weed, &c. raised to the height of several inches. The eggs were four, of a dull olive color, marked with large irregular blotches of black, and with others of a fainter tint.

"The species arrives on the coast of Cape May late in April; rears its young, and departs again to the south early in October. While here it almost constantly frequents the shallow pools in the salt marshes; wading about, often to the belly, in search of food, viz., marine worms, snails and various insects that abound among the soft muddy bottoms of the pools." (American Ornithology, Vol. VII.)

Audubon visited Great Egg Harbor in May, 1829, and saw but three Avocets and found no nests. Perhaps they had, even then, all but disappeared as breeding birds, while they seem never to have been plentiful.

The older ornithologists have left us no further records, although Turnbull (1869) states that it is "rather rare." As his dates of occurrence are evidently taken from Wilson he may have had no personal experience with the bird. There is also an old specimen in the Philadelphia Academy collection received from Samuel Ashmead of Beasley's Point, which is opposite Peck's Beach, where Wilson found his Avocets.

Later records follow.

Long Beach, May 20, 1877 one seen by W. E. D. Scott (Bull. Nutt. Orn. Club, 1879, p. 224). Barnegat, May 31, 1880, one shot by John Fonda (Auk, 1905, p. 78). Tuckerton, one shot by I. Norris DeHaven, last of of August, 1886 (Stone, Birds of E. Penn. and N. J., p. 70). Seven Mile Beach (Avalon), middle of September, 1908, one seen by I .W. Griscom. Krider (Forty Years' Notes) states that both the Avocet and Stilt nested on Egg Island in Delaware Bay but many of his statements must be taken with reservations.

Then after a lapse of twenty-four years Charles Urner had the good fortune to find three Avocets "on September 15, 1932, on what was formerly a salt marsh near the Newark, N. J., airport, at a point where the high tide still partly floods the fill with a mixture of salt water and sewage. They were among flocks of hundreds of assorted shore birds. There were two black and white and one dark brown and white bird. The heads and necks showed no color tint. The legs appeared clay-colored. One old bird called occasionally when disturbed though they were very tame. Its notes reminded one of the Lesser Yellow-legs, but louder and fuller, at times with a shade of hoarseness. The individual notes, when uttered in sequence, were often spaced with an appreciable interval between. The birds fed both by side-swiping the surface of the water, as does the Lesser Yellow-legs, and by probing.

"They remained until October and were seen to swim on October 1; when pursued by a Duck Hawk they took to deep water where their profile afloat with stern carried high, seemed distinctive and a good field mark at a distance." (Auk, 1933, p. 100.)

In publishing his account of the lone Avocet seen by him on the beach near Avalon (Seven Mile Beach) I. W. Griscom writes "It seems that these singular birds with their long, slender, up-turned bills were at one time quite abundant on this part of the Atlantic Coast but are now very rare east of the Alleghanies. It came across from the meadows to the beach and flew so close by me that identification was certain and its discordant clamor indicated that the bird had lost none of its lawyer-like qualities. It opened up its boisterous address upon seeing me in the distance and did not change its course in the least to avoid me" (Forest and Stream, January 31, 1909)

## BLACK-NECKED STILT

### Himantopus mexicanus (Müller)

Alexander Wilson presents an interesting account of this species which has long departed from the Cape May meadows where he found it of regular occurrence, in 1810. He writes:

"This species arrives on the sea coast of New Jersey about the twenty-fifth of April, in small detached flocks, of twenty or thirty together. These sometimes again subdivide into lesser parties; but it rarely happens that a pair is found solitary, as during the breeding season they usually associate in small companies. On their first arrival, and indeed during the whole of their residence, they inhabit those particular parts of the salt marshes pretty high up towards the land, that are broken into numerous shallow pools, but are not usually overflowed by the tides during the summer. These pools, or ponds, are generally so shallow, that with their long legs the Avocets [i. e. Stilts—Wilson called them Long-legged as opposed to the Red-necked Avocet] can easily wade them in every direction. . . . In the vicinity of these bald places as they are called by the country people, and at the distance of forty or fifty yards off, among the thick tufts of grass, one of these small associations, consisting perhaps of six or eight pair, takes up its residence during the breeding season. About the first week in May they begin to construct their nests, which are at first slightly formed of a small quantity of old grass, scarcely sufficient to keep the eggs from the wet marsh. As they lay and sit, however, either dreading the rise of the tides, or from some other purpose, the nest is increased in height, with dry twigs of a shrub very common in the marshes, roots of the salt grass, seaweed, and various other substances, the whole weighing between two and three pounds. This habit of adding materials to the nest, after the female begins sitting, is common to almost all other birds that breed in the marshes. The eggs are four in number, of dark yellowish clay color, thickly marked with large blotches of black. These nests are often placed within fifteen or twenty yards of each other, but the greatest harmony seems to prevail among the proprietors.

"While the females are sitting, the males are either wading through the ponds, or roaming over the adjoining marshes; but should a person make his appearance, the whole collect together in the air, flying with their long legs extended behind them, keeping up a continual yelping note of *click click click*. Their flight is steady, and not in short sudden jerks like that of the plover. As they frequently alight on the bare marsh, they drop their wings, stand with their legs half bent, and tremble as if unable to sustain the burden of their bodies. In this ridiculous posture they will sometimes stand for several minutes, uttering a purring sound, while from the corresponding quivering of their wings and long legs, they seem to balance themselves with great difficulty. This singular manoeuvre is, no doubt, intended to induce a belief that they may be easily caught, and so turn the attention of the person from the pursuit of their nests and young to themselves.

"The Red-necked Avocet, practises the very same deception, in the same ludicrous manner, and both alight indiscriminately on the ground, or in the water. Both will also occasionally swim for a few feet, when they chance in wading to lose their depth, as I have had several times an opportunity of observing.

"The name by which this bird is known on the seacoast is the Stilt, or Tilt, or Longshanks. They are but sparingly dispersed over the marshes, having, as has already been observed, their particular favorite spots; while in large intermediate tracts, there are few or none to be found.

"They occasionally visit the shore, wading about in the water, and in the mud, in search of food, which they scoop up very dexterously with their delicately formed bills. On being wounded while in the water, they attempt to escape by diving, at which they are by no means expert. In autumn, their flesh is tender, and well tasted. They seldom raise more than one brood in a season, and depart for the south early in September." (American Ornithology, Vol. VII.)

Audubon has nothing to say of their occurrence in New Jersey except that he never noticed them raising the height of their nests as described by Wilson.

William M. Baird wrote to his brother Spencer from Cape May, July 16, 1843, that there were still some of them present and later, on July 21, that he had secured a specimen, at Cape May Court House. Wilson seems to have gotten the local names of this and the preceding bird confused as he calls the Avocet the "Lawyer" whereas that name belonged to the Stilt, the Avocet being known as the "Blue Stocking." Turnbull (1869) says that the Stilt is "rather scarce, I have found its nest on Egg Island, Delaware Bay." Doubtless the extensive marshes where the Willet has recently been found breeding abundantly, were the last stand of the Stilt.

From Turnbull's time to date I have been unable to find a single reference to this bird in New Jersey except the specimen mounted by Charles A. Voelker which was said to have been shot on Seven Mile Beach on April 27, 1894, and concerning which I have no further information.

## NORTHERN PHALAROPE
### Lobipes lobatus (Linnaeus)

Phalaropes are essentially seagoing sandpipers, and so far as New Jersey is concerned, are distinctly birds of the ocean like the Kittiwake, the jaegers and the petrels, and only on exceptional occasions are they found along the coast or farther inland, driven by severe storms from their true habitat on the open sea. During their spring and autumn migrations between their winter home in the southern hemisphere and their breeding grounds in the Far North, both the Northern and Red Phalaropes are seen by passengers on ocean steamships floating in great rafts on the waves. We have several records of such observations off the coast of New Jersey. Dr. Frank M. Chapman has recorded both this species and the Red Phalarope off the Delaware coast on May 9, 1897, and Dr. James P. Chapin and others saw phalaropes, probably the Red, off New Jersey, November 27, 1928. Occasional specimens of the Northern Phalarope have been shot, captured or picked up dead on the beaches of the New Jersey coast but usually by persons who have kept no record of the weather or of the behavior of the birds. On May 6, 1933, in company with Otway Brown, I was fortunate enough to be on the strand of Seven Mile Beach during one of the most notable occurrences of these birds of which we have record. There was a strong northeast wind and overcast skies with a fine misty rain and heavy surf. As soon as we came out on the beach from the dunes we noticed a number of small birds flying just beyond and among the breakers. They kept close to the water constantly alighting upon it and rising again to avoid the breaking waves. They appeared in the wind much as a flock of Tree Swallows under similar conditions, their bodies short and compact with neither head nor tail projecting as they beat into the gale. But they differed from swallows in showing a distinct flicker of white in the wings such as most shore birds do in flight. Approaching closer I could see them swimming with head more or less erect and turning to this side or that, ever alert for an approaching wave. Others that we found farther along the shore were swimming in shallow beach pools just beyond the reach of the tide, where they were not annoyed by the waves. They held the neck erect and apparently stretched upward to the limit, while the delicate head with its needle-like bill was turning constantly this way and that. When progressing straight ahead they swam rapidly but for the most part they kept twisting to right and left sometimes whirling entirely around in a circle. They floated buoyantly, like corks, and were evidently feeding as they would dab the bill to the surface of the water continually sometimes ducking the head completely under.

A number of those first seen came in and alighted on the wet sand where they also fed. They walked in a somewhat bowlegged fashion and progressed rather slowly, with many short steps. Some of them squatted on the beach holding the head stiffly erect and turning it as did those that were swimming in the pools. Others plumed themselves rapidly poking the bill over the shoulders and down into the breast feathers all the time seeming to rub the side of the head against the plumage.

There was a Semipalmated Sandpiper and several Ring-necks nearby on the strand and by comparison the Phalaropes seemed about the size of the latter but shaped more like the former, having the sandpiper build rather than the plumpness of the plover, but more delicately formed than either. In the dull light and the rainy mist they seemed quite black above, many showing clearly the longitudinal bands of brownish chestnut down each side of the back and a white stripe on the wing, some also showed a white tuft at the shoulder. Below they appeared black across the breast and down the sides of the body mixed with white toward the belly which was pure white. There was also a white throat spot spreading on each side so as to form more or less of a collar and below it a band of chestnut.

They were very tame, or perhaps exhausted, and allowed us to approach to within fifteen feet without taking wing. There were twenty on the sand at one time and about one hundred over the surf at this point with other similar flocks farther along. At one spot there was a large band of Barn Swallows sitting on the beach and they appeared slightly larger than the Phalaropes which were resting close to them. Some of the Northern Phalaropes that were feeding on the beach ran right into an oncoming wave and floated back on it but took wing when threatened by a curling crest.

The next day Joseph Tatum found a similar flock of these birds at Ship Bottom, on Long Beach, some distance up the coast and I quote from his account of his experience. He says: "I saw a bird out on the water just inside the first line of breakers which looked like a Semipalmated Sandpiper. A few yards away was another and still others to the number of perhaps a dozen. They were quite active swinging from side to side or turning completely around with incredible rapidity. They were constantly picking something from the surface of the water with their needle-like bills making twenty-five dabs per minute. None were seen to dive but they would frequently arise from the water with no apparent effort and fly a few yards dropping back again onto the water where they at once resumed their feeding.

"In flight they looked like sandpipers but with a little more sweep and grace to the wing stroke. The head seemed rather large in proportion and distinctly round, while the neck was held very erect, at right angles to the plane of the body. As they bobbed around in their feeding the head would swing back and forth, like a pigeon's head when walking. In fact the whole impression of the bird's progress in the water is of walking rather than swimming. They are the most buoyant birds I have ever seen, riding the crest of a breaker with the easy nonchalance of an empty bottle. I could hear them utter no sound except an occasional peep as they flew. At no time did I see any of them on the beach. They were found at different points along the coast during the day, probably more than one hundred in all.

"On the jetty at 4:00 p. m. I had a dozen of them within fifty feet of me. I could look almost vertically down upon them and noticed a flange of feathers projecting from the body onto the water like the overhanging decks of a ferryboat, which apparently could be extended or withdrawn at will thus keeping the bird always in perfect balance. This may account for their remarkable buoyancy. As they float they seem to use the feet for wheeling and for maintaining equilibrium, the action being a down stroke like treading water rather than a backward pushing stroke.

"Their outstanding markings were the white chin and upper throat; white eye ring and rich chestnut red patches on the sides of the neck."

Storms occasionally carry phalaropes far inland and Earl Poole has four records of this species at Reading, Pa.—September 14, 1909; October 3, 1923 (two); August 28, 1932; August 24, 1933. Julian Potter also found a pair on an overflowed meadow near Camden, N. J., on August 13, 1916. He writes me that they seemed to be feeding on small insects on the surface of the water and swam very swiftly and easily against the strong wind, while they twirled in the water at times turning completely around. The larger bird continually sought the company of the smaller; they uttered a sharp *peet, peet*, when on the wing. He watched them for half an hour at distance of from fifteen to forty feet and they were still dashing about when he left. There had been a northeast storm the day before.

Additional records for the New Jersey coast are:

1894. May 23, Peck's Beach, F. L. Burns.
1895. September 13, Barnegat Bay, A. P. Willets.
1903. September 4, Seven Mile Beach, David McCadden.
1909. May 4, Cape May, Walker Hand.
1911. May 16, Cape May, Walker Hand.
1928. Barnegat Bay, August 12, September 15, Charles Urner.
1931. August 30, Brigantine Island, Charles Urner.
1932. May 12, Beach Haven, Charles Urner.
1932. September 8, Newark Meadows, Charles Urner.
1933. May 7, Long Beach, Joseph Tatum.
1933. Newark Meadows, August 23 (2), September 9, 10, 13 (Charles Urner).
1934. August 4, Cape May, J. L. Edwards.
1934. September 18, Newark Meadows, J. L. Edwards.

# RED PHALAROPE

### Phalaropus fulicarius (Linnaeus)

   This larger and heavier species has precisely the same status and habits as the Northern Phalarope although it appears to be less frequently blown inshore, or perhaps through force of circumstance, has been less frequently observed or recorded.  Dr. Frank Chapman has seen it off the Delaware coast as he returned by sea from a sojourn in Mexico and others aboard ship have noticed these little birds disporting themselves on the ocean.

   Capt. Horace O. Hillman of the Cape Cod mackerel fleet, which puts in to Cape May every spring, reported immense numbers of them resting in great rafts out on the open ocean where the fishermen were casting their nets sixty-five miles south-southeast of the Cape and at the request of Walker Hand secured eleven specimens for the Academy of Natural Sciences of Philadelphia, on April 28, 1929.  These were all in mottled plumage in various stages of the molt from the gray and white dress of winter to the rusty red of summer.  The fishermen of the fleet were all familiar with the phalaropes and called them "Bull-birds," "Sea Geese" and "Sea Plover," names which they apparently applied as well to the small species.

   While the occurrence of this bird offshore was well known from early times I had but two definite records for Cape May County up to 1910—one obtained by William H. Werner on Peck's Beach, May 6, 1907, and another secured by Walker Hand at Cape May, May 3, 1909, and so far as I am aware there were no records from the northern beaches of the state.  While living in a little fisherman's cabin on the meadows back of Two Mile Beach on May 18, 1924, I found a Red Phalarope's foot close to a stake which had been driven into the ground and which served as a feeding perch for visiting hawks and Ospreys.  Although the scattered remains of fish and bird skeletons were carefully examined no other phalarope bones could be found. This is my only personal record of the species at the Cape!

In December, 1918, there seems to have been a flight of Red Phalaropes extending inland to Pennsylvania where two were picked up dead, or dying, one at George School, Bucks Co., on December 15 (Cocks), and the other near Lenape, Chester Co. in mid-December (Ehinger). Both of these birds were in the gray plumage of winter. While these captures were entirely outside the limits of our study they are of interest as evidence that the species must winter to some extent at least on the north Atlantic. Further interest attaches to these records because the specimen figured by Alexander Wilson was of similar occurrence, one of three obtained near Philadelphia in May 1812, evidently blown in by a storm. On May 26, 1931, Laidlaw Williams and others saw a female in full summer plumage on Barnegat Bay (Auk, 1931, p. 597), and Charles Urner has a record for that year in the same region.

On May 12, 1932, during a northeast storm, occurred the greatest invasion of Red Phalaropes that has ever been recorded on the New Jersey coast, and fortunately it was witnessed by several observers who realized the importance of what they saw and made a satisfactory record. Charles Urner and J. L. Edwards have published the most detailed account of the flight (Auk, 1932, p. 475). They saw a few of the birds on the Tuckerton meadows fighting against a strong wind and the first one observed appeared, in the poor light, absolutely black like a Black Tern, with a white stripe in the extended wing. "As we crossed Barnegat Bay" writes Mr. Urner "over the Manahawkin Bridge to Long Beach another individual was seen. Driving south toward Beach Haven we found others in the bay and one swimming in a puddle by the roadside. Soon we became conscious of the fact that all the shore birds that were passing over the dunes making slow headway against a heavy wind and rain, were of this species.

"When we reached Beach Haven Inlet, a rare sight greeted us. The place fairly teemed with Red Phalaropes. We stood on a small spit of sand, while in a sheltered bit of water, literally right at out feet, a large flock of these striking and agile birds fed over a mass of seaweed and garbage. We collected two and picked up another dead on the road.

"The birds were in every degree of plumage change, about forty percent fully colored. A few were in almost complete winter plumage except that the forehead, white in the winter birds, was dark. The darkening of the forehead is probably one of the first noticeable changes toward the summer attire. A good many birds were fully red but showed little or no definite white area on the side of the head (not even as much as the male bird shows in summer). The white face is thus probably the last feature of the breeding plumage to be acquired. We saw fully three hundred birds and probably more."

Mr. Urner further comments on the resemblance of this species to the Northern Phalarope saying that "those still in winter dress could easily have been mistaken for Northerns but for the yellow on the base of the bill, visible only at short distances. Seen alone, without contrast, the bills of the

Reds did not seem particularly heavy." In the case of a single Northern Phalarope riding the waves with the Reds its thinner bill and the absence of yellow could be noticed.

Stuart Cramer who was at Brigantine Beach three days later saw two Red Phalaropes swimming on one of the channels about one hundred yards apart in fairly deep water. They were picking up food of some sort from the surface of the water holding the bill vertically, point down, and when a morsel would float past they would spin about to secure it. The white bar on the wing was very evident. Natives informed him that the water was full of these birds a few days before, especially farther back on the meadows. Rainy, stormy weather prevailed during the week prior to his visit which doubtless drove the birds inshore.

On May 14 members of the West Chester, Pa., Bird Club found a flock of twenty-five Red Phalaropes on the point of the island below Beach Haven and picked up another exhausted individual (Isaac G. Roberts *in lit.*).

On May 7, 1933, on Long Beach, Joseph Tatum observed a few of these birds in the flight of Northern Phalaropes which he has described as quoted above. Their habits were identical but they could easily be distinguished from the latter species by their reddish breasts, being in nearly full summer plumage, and by the white patches on the sides of the head and the lighter bills. The amount of red on the breasts, however, varied in different individuals. Oscar Eayre also saw several in June of that year at sea sixteen miles off the same beach and on September 6, 1935, F. W. Loetscher saw a single Red Phalarope on Brigantine Island. Charles Urner has given me three additional records: May 7, 1933, and August 18, 1934, both at Beach Haven and May 12, 1934, Absecon.

## WILSON'S PHALAROPE
### Steganopus tricolor Vieillot

Unlike the other two phalaropes this species instead of summering in the far north, breeds in the middle western United States and southern Canada and its occurrence on the North Atlantic, or on our eastern sea coast, would seem to be entirely abnormal. Nevertheless I am convinced that such occasional individuals as have been recorded from New Jersey have come in from the sea as in the case of the other species. They may very likely have accompanied flocks of shore birds with which they always seem to associate, and have travelled with them in a southeasterly direction from their breeding grounds in the interior.

Our earliest records are very indefinite. George Ord records a specimen shot near Philadelphia on May 7, 1818, and prepared for Peale's Museum; Audubon was shown two that his informant told him were shot in July near Cape May "close to their nest which contained four eggs," a statement that tends to discredit the entire record, while Dr. C. C. Abbott records two captures without dates or authority—one taken at Deal Beach and the other at Atlantic City—but they may have been referable to one of the other species.

The first Wilson's Phalarope to come to my personal attention on the New Jersey Coast was one shot by Gilbert H. Moore on Peck's Beach, on May 19, 1898, and now in the collection of the Academy of Natural Sciences. On May 4, 1909, two were shot at Cape May one of which was procured by Walker Hand and presented to the Academy. I have no information as to the circumstances of the capture of either of these specimens nor as to their habits or actions.

On September 2, 1929, a single individual in the dull plumage of winter, or of immaturity, was found by Julian Potter on a tidal mud flat on Newton Creek in West Collingswood, Camden Co., N. J.  It was feeding with a group of Lesser Yellow-legs and its thin neck, small head and light coloration were in marked contrast to its associates.  It was very active, swimming about in a small pool, darting its slender dark bill from side to side and sometimes turning its body half way around as it fed.  Once it came out on the bare mud to plume and arrange its feathers, showing its pale yellow legs, white rump and pale wings.  During the half hour that the bird was under observation it confined its activities to a space of a few square yards.

On September 15, what was apparently the same bird was present in almost the same spot and was studied by four members of the Delaware Valley Ornithological Club and on the 18th it was found again.  On each occasion it was feeding with the Yellow-legs (Auk, 1930, p. 76).  In 1930, two Wilson's Phalaropes were seen on Brigantine Island by John Gillespie on August 10, and two on September 1, by Charles Urner.  One was also observed at Secaucus by J. L. Edwards and others, on September 13.  On August 28, 1932, Julian Potter was fortunate enough to find another of these rare visitors on Brigantine, running about with a large flight of shore birds on a mud flat.  It presented a comical sight with tail held up at an angle and neck stretched out in front while it held the body in more or less of a crouching position.  On September 11 he saw another individual at the same place while Charles Urner saw single birds (or the same individual) on the Newark Meadows on September 18, October 1, 6 and 8 and two at Tuckerton on September 3.  In 1934, F. W. Loetscher found a Wilson's Phalarope on Brigantine Island on August 18 and again on the 25th, while Warren Eaton saw probably the same bird on the 20th, and Richard Pough saw one on Ludlam's Beach, Cape May County, on September 10.  There were a large number of observations of this phalarope on the Newark Meadows during this year, single birds on September 4, 8, 9, 10, 13, 16, 17, 18, 20, 23 (Urner, Edwards, Herbert, Kuerzi and Loetscher) while Urner saw three on the 24th, two on the 27th six on the 30th and four on October 1; a remarkable influx of these birds due undoubtedly to severe storms at sea.  In 1934, J. L. Edwards saw a Wilson's Phalarope on Peck's Beach, Cape May County, August 4, in company with a Northern Phalarope while Charles Urner found one at Tuckerton on August 5 and four on the Newark Meadows on August 8.  He has also records of one on the northern beaches on May 12 of the same year.

In 1936, Julian Potter found one of these birds on the Killcohook Wild Life Refuge on the Delaware River in Salem County, on October 11.

## PARASITIC JAEGER

*Stercorarius parasiticus* (Linnaeus)

Jaegers, like petrels, are birds of the open ocean so far as the New Jersey coast is concerned and their occurrence inshore is exceptional and usually due to storms. They are the "hawks of the sea," gulls modified into birds of prey, as it were, and their parasitic habit of forcing other sea birds to disgorge food for their benefit is unique. At Cape May nearly all of our records of jaegers have been during late September and October when on their southward migration from Arctic breeding grounds.

Julian Potter saw one on October 1, 1925, pursuing a Laughing Gull at the Point. It appeared quite dark in contrast with the gull and showed a distinct flicker of white in the wings and a rounded tail although the usually extended central tail-feathers were not noted. Next day he saw two Parasitic Jaegers harrassing the gulls and when one of the latter was hard-pressed "it spread the contents of its stomach on the waves and immediately both jaegers and gulls settled on the water to devour their ill-gotten gains."

On September 30, 1928, Potter saw another Parasitic Jaeger come flying in from the ocean and begin to hunt over the marsh back of South Cape May like a Marsh Hawk. It hovered and dived into the grass several times before a passing Pigeon Hawk gave chase, when it immediately put out to sea and rapidly disappeared from view. Philip Livingston saw one in the same place on October 5, 1930.

On September 27, 1931, one of these birds was repeatedly flushed from the ocean beach and seemed exhausted and unable to remain on the wing, possibly a victim of oil poisoning; and on August 24, 1933, following the great hurricane, I saw one fly in from the sea and cross the Fill to the Harbor, the white flashes in the wings showing conspicuously.

While jaegers seem to be very rare in spring and early summer, Walker Hand and Frank Dickinson evidently saw one on Delaware Bay off Town Bank on June 6, 1922. They were fishing from a skiff and their attention was attracted to the bird by the calls of a Laughing Gull which was dodging this way and that in its efforts to escape the persecutions of the strange dark bird which followed it relentlessly. Finally as it was passing down the beach the gull disgorged a mass of food which its pursuer caught up and swallowed and then put off down the Bay for the ocean. It appeared black above and white below, was not quite so large as the gull and flew differently with more rapid wing strokes. Frank Dickinson reports another instance when he saw a bird, similar to this one, pursue a Red-breasted Merganser on the sounds and force it to disgorge its food which was immediately eaten. He was closer to this individual and it appeared grayish brown above.

One or two jaegers, probably of this species, were seen off the coast below Cape May on October 25, 1929, when members of the American Ornithologists' Union visited the Cape. Audubon was apparently the first to record a jaeger on the New Jersey coast as he says, in his account of the Laughing Gull at Egg Harbor, in May, 1829, just one hundred years before our last mentioned record, "Like other Gulls the *Larus atricilla* disgorges its food when attacked by a Lestris." As the Parasitic Jaeger is the only one that he mentions as ranging this far south he must have referred to it, although he says that he never saw it here except in winter! We have additional records of three of these birds seen off Peck's Beach by William Baily on November 9, 1895; one collected by Capt. John Taylor on Five Mile Beach, on October 23, 1891 (in the Reading, Pa., Museum); and one seen off Seven Mile Beach by Charles Voelker, on May 27, 1901. Farnum Brown also examined one shot by a fisherman off Atlantic City, in March, 1892.

Farther north on the coast jaegers seem to be more frequent and occur on earlier dates, as Charles Urner and others have recorded them from Brigantine, Barnegat and Point Pleasant on July 6, 1927 (six); July 23, 1926; July 23–24, 1927 (six); August 22, 1925 (eleven); August 23, 1933; August 26, 1926; August 28, 1927 (eight); and on numerous occasions in the autumn. During September 1926, there was a great flight of these birds and at Point Pleasant they were recorded as follows: September 6 (seven); September 15 (fifteen); September 18 (forty); September 19 (seventy), and sometimes as many as six were seen pursuing a single gull. It would appear from observations elsewhere along the coast that jaegers remain on the North Atlantic in small numbers still later in the autumn, or early winter, although most of them pass on to the more southern seas. T. Donald Carter and Ralph Friedman have recorded eight at Barnegat on October 31, 1926, and Charles Urner one on November 29, 1924.

## POMERINE JAEGER

Stercorarius pomarinus (Temminck)

The Pomerine Jaeger is a larger and heavier bird than the Parasitic and is much rarer on the coast although well known to occur offshore during the autumn migration. We have no record for Cape May but Dr. James P. Chapin has recorded them at sea not far from our coast (Auk, 1929, p. 102), as he saw twenty following the wake of a vessel upon which he was a passenger somewhere between New Jersey and Virginia.

On the North Jersey coast Charles Urner and others have recorded Pomerine Jaegers as follows: Barnegat, August 26, 1926 (two) (Kuerzi); August 28, 1926 (Urner); August 28, 1927 (Urner); October 11, 1925 (two) (Weber); September 6, 1925 (Weber); Pt. Pleasant, September 18 and 19, 1926 (Urner).

W. E. D. Scott has an earlier record for Long Beach of two shot on Barnegat Bay in December, 1876 (Bull. Nuttall Orn. Club, 1879, p. 227), and I have seen a specimen mounted by Charles Voelker, which was said to have been shot on the Delaware River in October 1898.

Ludlow Griscom states that the Pomerine Jaeger is of regular occurrence from three to five miles offshore from Long Island, August 2 to October 30, and that adults may be distinguished from the Parasitic Jaeger by their square-ended not pointed, central tail feathers, although immature individuals are difficult to identify. (Birds of the New York Region.)

## * LONG-TAILED JAEGER

Stercorarius longicaudus Vieillot

While this jaeger undoubtedly occurs at sea off the New Jersey coast the only positive evidence that we have is Dr. Frank M. Chapman's statement that he saw one eighty miles off Barnegat, from an ocean steamer, on May 6, 1894. Griscom records three occurrences on the coast of Long Island. It would seem to be much rarer than the other two species.

## * GLAUCOUS GULL
### Larus hyperboreus Gunnerus

This visitor from the Far North has not yet been found at Cape May but is confidently looked for and considering the infrequent visits of ornithologists to the Cape during the severe snow and ice storms, of recent winters, it may easily have been present and gone unrecorded. A single individual was seen on the Delaware River at Philadelphia by Richard Erskine on January 1 and 4, 1918, and was reported by others in the interim, all observers commenting on the absence of black on the wings and the large size of the bird compared with the numerous Herring Gulls which frequent the river. This bird in all probability had come up from Delaware Bay and passed Cape May on its course.

This gull is stated by Griscom to be an uncommon, but regular, winter visitant to the coast of Long Island and New York Harbor, rarely seen much before Christmas but lingering into May. Charles Urner has a number of records for Barnegat Bay and on January 23, 1927, he and Ludlow Griscom counted five individuals. At Seaside Park John Emlen saw a single bird on February 26 of the same year accompanied by an Iceland Gull. On March 24, 1934, William Baily found a Glaucous Gull on Brigantine Beach feeding with a few Herring Gulls on the strand. "It was easily distinguished from the latter by the absence of black tips to the primaries, and was practically white all over but for a faint buffy edging to the feathers of the back. It was of noticeably heavier build than the Herring Gulls with a greater wing spread, and was easily 'cock of the walk' defending itself against all who would claim its freshly opened clams." It was still present on March 30, when it had been joined by an Iceland Gull. (Auk, 1934, p. 374.)

At Bridgeport in Gloucester County not far from the Delaware River Julian Potter found a single Glaucous Gull on March 2, 1935, with some five thousand Herring Gulls, feeding on frozen fish that had been exposed by a thaw. Other records of the Glaucous Gull have been published as follows:

Twenty miles off Long Branch, December 31, 1904, (Stackpole and Wiegman).
Barnegat Bay, May 22, 1926, (two), (Urner).
Barnegat Bay, April 30, 1927, (Urner).
Barnegat Bay, January 8, 1928, (Kuerzi).
Shark River, April 15, 1934, (Urner).

## * ICELAND GULL
### Larus leucopterus Vieillot

This smaller edition of the last is also a visitor from the Far North and like it has not yet been detected on Cape May waters, although there are records of straggling individuals much farther south on the coast and on the Delaware River, which doubtless passed the Cape.

In the New York region it is said by Griscom to be less common than the Glaucuous Gull but probably of annual occurrence. Charles Urner records it on Newark Bay from January to April 1, 1922, and April 10, 1927.

At Seaside Park John Emlen found a single bird on February 26, 1927, in company with a Glaucous Gull, while on Brigantine William Baily found one of each species on March 30, 1934. He noticed that the Iceland Gull was four or five inches shorter than the other and was white with a little more of the buff tint on the back and upper tail coverts, while its bill was shorter and its legs a darker shade of flesh. It stood most of the time with head drawn down on the shoulders, plover-like. Both birds were quite tame and were easily approached (Auk, 1934, p. 375).

On May 12, 1934, Stuart Cramer found a dead Iceland Gull, possibly this same individual, on Brigantine Beach, it was badly decomposed but he saved the skull and from the measurements thought that is must be the so-called Kumlien's Gull. (Auk, 1934, p. 375.) The skull was later sent to Dr. Alexander Wetmore who pronounced it an Iceland Gull. (Auk, 1935, p. 186.)

On the Delaware at Philadelphia Julian Potter and Joseph Tatum saw an Iceland Gull on January 15, 1934, and again on April 10, following.

Additional observations of the Iceland Gull in New Jersey are:

Barnegat Bay, December 10, 1926 (Griscom).
Barnegat Bay, February 22, 1925 (Griscom and Urner).
Seaside Park, March 28, 1926 (Yoder).
Shark River, April 15, 1934, in company with a Glaucous (Urner).

# GREAT BLACK-BACKED GULL

### Larus marinus Linnaeus

#### PLATE 47, p. 534

The Great Black-backed Gull, largest of our gulls, occurs regularly in small numbers as far south on the coast as Hereford Inlet, during the winter months.  It appears to be somewhat more common at Townsend's and Corson's Inlets and still more so on Brigantine Beach and along the coast to the north.  Like the Herring Gull and certain other water birds it seems to be particularly partial to the bars at the mouths of the inlets or to the points of beach on either side; indeed the Black-back is rarely seen at rest elsewhere.  Doubtless it may have occurred in the past at Turtle Gut Inlet and the closing of this channel and the lack of suitable bars at the entrance to Delaware Bay may account for the absence of the bird nearer to Cape May, while passing individuals, if such there be, doubtless travel too far out to sea in crossing to the Delaware coast to be seen from the shore.  Apparently the Black-backs never enter the Bay nor the sounds along the Cape May coast.

On January 1, 1926, a day of bitter cold wind from the north, the long sandy point which juts out on the southern side of Corson's Inlet was capped

and bordered with white ice while great floating blocks filled the thoroughfare and rushed out to sea on the swiftly ebbing tide.  The whole upper
portion of the spit was covered with gulls.  Some two hundred Herring Gulls,
in varied plumages, stood or squatted on the sand or hovered over the water.
There were a few of the smaller Ring-billed Gulls and, scattered through the
flock, four of the great Black-backs, distinctly taller and bulkier than the
others and distinguishable by their colors as far as they could be seen.  The
entire back and most of the wings appear jet black in strong contrast to the
snowy white of the head, rump, tail and under parts.  There is no suggestion
of gray in the plumage, although the "black" is found to be very dark slate
when we have a specimen in hand, and as we view the bird through the glass
it looks as if a vest of black velvet had been drawn over an otherwise white
gull.

On the wing these great gulls spread wider than the Herring Gulls and
their wingstrokes seem more powerful.  In flight they display a narrow
white border along the front of the expanded wing and another along the
posterior margin; the under side of the flight feathers appears dusky gray
but the under wing-coverts, as well as the ground color of the bill, are white.

These Corson's Inlet birds at intervals flew out over the surf at the
mouth of the inlet, circling about among the Herring Gulls which were there,
and later returned to the strand to roost.  They seemed to be more wary
than the Herring Gulls and ever on the alert for possible danger.

This inlet as I am informed by Wharton Huber has always been a winter
resort for these birds and both adults and immature individuals were to be
seen there on almost every visit.

Throughout the winter, on the sand bars that are exposed at low tide in
Townsend's and Herford Inlets, I have seldom failed to find, in the long
lines of Herring Gulls that resort there, from one to three Black-backs which
may easily be picked out even with the naked eye from the northern tips of
Seven and Five Mile Beaches respectively.

On February 6, 1932, I saw one on the ocean beach at Avalon, near to
Townsend's Inlet, which remained apart from the Herring Gulls that rested
at the same spot and I have occasionally seen individuals on the beach some
distance from Hereford Inlet, while on several occasions Black-backs have
been seen going from one inlet to the other along Seven Mile Beach out beyond the surf.

Usually one sees but one to three Black-backs together but we have
several records of four, five and six, while the number seen during a day has
reached much higher figures.  The Delaware Valley Club's counts on the
Christmas census are as follows:

December 23, 1928, six                December 24, 1933. seven
December 22, 1929, six                December 23, 1934, seven
December 28, 1930, five               December 22, 1935, eighteen
December 27, 1931, five               December 27, 1936, eleven
December 26, 1932, eight

John Emlen saw thirteen on Seven Mile Beach on January 23, 1927, while Charles Urner at Barnegat, on December 22, 1925, saw no less than twenty.

While the Black-backs do not occur regularly until November on the Cape May inlets we have earlier records—September 12 to 17, 1914, one in Townsend's Inlet (Mrs. Prince); September 20, 1931, at the same place (Brooke Worth); September 20, 1936, (John Hess); September 28, 1935, Hereford Inlet (four) (Stone); September 28, 1935, Peck's Beach (Clarence Cottam, Auk, 1936, p. 81). Our latest observations in spring are: March 12, 1922, and March 14, 1931, Townsend's Inlet; March 26, 1932, Hereford Inlet; April 9, 1922, Corson's Inlet. There are several late April records for the Brigantine and Barnegat areas farther up the coast and Charles Urner saw one on Barnegat during the period from June 21, to July 2, 1926, when making a survey of the bird life of Ocean County.

## * LESSER BLACK-BACKED GULL

### Larus fuscus graellsi Brehm

On September 9, 1934, James L. Edwards and Charles Urner saw a gull on the ocean strand of Long Beach, just south of Beach Haven, which they identified as this European species. It was associated with a single Great Black-backed Gull and a number of Herring Gulls and while distinctly smaller than the former did not seem to exceed the latter. It was of the same color above as the Great Black-back but its legs were yellow instead of pink as is the case with the other species. The opportunity for comparison with the other species, as Mr. Edwards says, makes this "sight record" worthy of consideration. (Auk, 1935, p. 85.)

The species had never been recorded from North America before, but on December 15, 1934, another very similar bird was seen by the Messrs. Kuerzi in the east Bronx, New York. (Auk, 1935, p. 185.)

While there is of course no Cape May record of this gull it may possibly occur there in the future and the records are presented in order to complete the list of gulls seen on the New Jersey coast.

## HERRING GULL

**Larus argentatus smithsonianus Coues**

PLATES 48, 49, p. 534

One associates the big silent Herring Gulls with wintertime, when they constitute the most noticeable feature of the bird life of the shore, just as we identify the smaller black-headed Laughing Gulls with midsummer. But while most of these large winter gulls go north to the coast of Maine or to the Great Lakes, to breed, not a few remain along our New Jersey shores throughout the summer—mainly dusky gray brown immatures or birds in which, for some reason, the migratory impulse has failed to develop. Thus there is not a month in the year—not a day indeed—that Herring Gulls cannot be seen about Cape May if one knows where to look for them.

They may be found at all seasons on the sounds and meadows back of the island beaches, all the way from Two Mile Beach to Barnegat Bay, resting on the higher sand flats or scattered over the meadows where their white and gray plumage makes them very conspicuous, especially against the brown winter grass, and groups of them huddled together glisten in the sunshine like patches of snow.    At this season they gather immediately back of the town where Cape Island Creek winds its way through the meadows and on its muddy banks they find an abundance of food.    We see them rising above the level of the meadow for a moment and settling again and finally resting in close ranks back on the edge of the upland where a border of trees and bushes shields them from the northwest gale.    No less than one hundred and fifty were counted here on February 12, 1921, while for a day or two in January 1932, after a high tide, they covered the meadows and the adjoining golf links right up to Lafayette St., which forms the edge of the town on this side.    Their number was estimated as more than a thousand.    Again on December 30, 1935, five hundred gathered there feeding along the edge of the flood.

On the great stretches of meadow lying north of the Harbor and back of Five Mile and Seven Mile Beaches they occur all through the winter but vary in abundance at any one spot, from day to day, as they are constantly shifting their position.    Now they will gather in numbers on some sand flat left by the dredges apparently to rest or to await the ebbing of the tide.    Again we see them scattered widely over the meadows after a spell of heavy rain or a high tide blown in by a winter gale, feeding like chickens upon stranded scraps of food as they walk about amongst the tufts of dead grass and sedge.    On March 6, 1932, just after sunset, they were advancing across the meadows in a dense column in the face of a terrific gale.    It was a weird sight as, with darkness fast settling down upon the marsh, thousands of the great birds passed us, now settling for a moment and then pushing on, those in the rear often flying forward and dropping down at the head of the column as if the mass were rolling over the ground.    Then as the water continued to rise and flood every resting place they all took wing and battling with the wind sought some other shelter probably in the lee of the outer beaches.

At all seasons Herring Gulls like to gather on the points of beach on either side of the inlets or on the bars or sandy islands which form at their mouths.    I have counted as many as five hundred on a bar in Hereford Inlet on February 1, 1931, at sunset, with more coming in every minute—a veritable migration of the meadow gulls to this spot to roost.    Whether they spent the night there I could not determine but I feel sure that they did on the larger extent of Gull Bar nearby, where hundreds can be found at almost any time.    Another favorite assembling point for winter Herring Gulls is the extreme southern point of Seven Mile Beach on the other side of the inlet.    When these stations are crowded with birds the meadows appear almost deserted, just as they do at ebb tide when all of the gulls are busy feeding down on the exposed bottoms of the creeks and thoroughfares, below the level of the marsh.

Gulls that have been feeding along the Bay shore often, if not always, resort to the meadows or inlets at night and we see them crossing the peninsula in the neighborhood of Cold Spring flying in close formation in regular V-shaped flocks of six to ten individuals. Other birds that have been feeding out at the "ripps" at the mouth of the Bay may be seen at evening winging their way back over the ocean in single file low over the waves. The "ripps" are a favorite feeding place for these gulls, just as they are for the Laughing Gulls, and they may be seen there at various times during the winter as well as in spring and autumn, mingling with the other species in the latter season. From the shore we see a maze of moving wings as they flap back and forth over the rough water constantly swooping to the surface and rising again as they pick up food of one sort or another. In the autumn besides the two species of gulls there will be Common Terns weaving in and out of the maze and diving precipitately into the sea and one or two dark colored Fish Hawks laboriously flapping about.

From the "ripps" Herring Gulls follow the Bay and the Delaware River to and beyond Philadelphia shifting up and down with the ebb and flow of the tide but the individuals that we see between that city and Camden probably remain all winter in that vicinity picking up their food from the refuse that floats on the river. They rest on the ice cakes that crunch against one another in midstream or roost on the river marshes below the cities.

Herring Gulls are common on the sea beach in winter usually scattered at intervals along the strand, busily feeding. Occasionally one of these birds will take a few running steps in pursuit of some floating object or will wade out into the water and breast the smaller waves as they come rolling in. When they take wing from the beach it is usually one after another so that the flying birds are stretched in a line along the shore and not in a compact flock. On such occasions they will usually come to rest on the water out beyond the surf and may remain there for some time riding the waves with heads drawn down on their shoulders.

Herring Gulls perch regularly on the tops of pilings on the edge of the Harbor or along the beach. They usually stand with the body held well up leaning slightly forward and with the head a trifle lowered. Sometimes their position is more erect and they plume the feathers of the breast and sides as they rest or they may crane the neck over forward and peck at their feet. Again they may settle down on the feet and breast and, turning the head backward over the shoulder, will bury the bill among the scapulars and assume an attitude of perfect rest. We realize the complete mastery of the air that a Herring Gull possesses when we watch one settle on a piling in the face of a strong wind. It hovers over the perch and arches its wings, closing them just enough to maintain a stationary position in the air. Then with feet dangling the wings are gradually drawn in so that the body slowly drops until the toes touch the perch. Occasionally a bird will hover over a post already occupied and descend directly upon the back of the perching gull forcing it to take flight and usurping its position, only to be itself displaced a few moments later by the former occupant or another. Now and then a gull will resent being crowded off its perch and will raise its head and open its bill and perhaps elevate the wings and utter its call *keé-ough, keé-ough, keé-ough, kaw, kaw, kaw.* Usually however, there is no protest and the bird slides gracefully off alighting on the water or circling in the air preparatory to taking another perch. A bird is often forced off even if there be vacant perches available and sometimes several gulls come in at once and there is a general shifting of positions.

In summer Herring Gulls occupy much the same localities as in winter but are everywhere less numerous. There are always some assembled at the inlets and at favorite roosting places on sand fills or they may be scattered about feeding on the meadows. On the beaches however they are scarce although one or two may be seen flying up or down the coast well offshore. In general they seem to prefer remote spots at this season where they will not be disturbed and keep farther away from the bathing beaches and the immediate vicinity of the town, except where there is a regular supply of food as about the fishing wharves on the Harbor. As the summer wanes and autumn approaches they increase in numbers and we see more adult birds in gray and white mingling with the dusky immature individuals which make up most of the summer population, and the proportion increases as the season advances.

One of the nearest summer assemblages of Herring Gulls has for years been on a sand flat on the meadows back of Two Mile Beach a little north of the Harbor and here on May 21–24, 1922, and May 16–19, 1924, I counted flocks of thirty-one and forty respectively. Since the fish dock was built near this spot the birds have increased greatly and there were over one hundred Herring Gulls assembled there on July 16, 1932, and about five hundred on the 29th. When I studied this gathering in 1922 and 1924 from a nearby fisherman's cabin we saw them collect in nearly the same numbers every evening. In the morning they would sit motionless most of the time, or walk slowly about, but when disturbed by a passing boat they would take to the air and flap and sail about making a great display of moving wings in the early sunlight. Then they would settle again or if the tide were ebbing they would scatter to feed on the exposed flats. On the meadows close to our cabin there were many dead fish thrown overboard by the fishing boats and washed up by the tides, quantities of sea-robins and several huge Lophius fishes with their great gaping mouths and curious tentacle standing up from the upper jaw. These were a great attraction to both Herring Gulls and Fish Crows, though the latter held aloof while the gulls feasted. There were eighteen gulls feeding here on the morning of May 19 and as we watched them we were reminded of Turkey Vultures as they rushed at one another with partly spread wings in their efforts to secure the choice bits from the feast, and now and then one bird would pursue another for some distance with wings raised high. Like the Vultures, too, they seemed to pick out the eyes of the large fishes before tearing them asunder.

The gulls when moving quietly about had a heavy waddling gait and now and then, for no apparent reason except perhaps to gain time, one of them would leap into the air and settle again a few yards away, dropping down slowly with wings held aloft for a moment after alighting. When one gull would settle near another the latter would often raise its head and with neck outstretched nearly vertically, and bill pointed upward, would utter its call *koo-lick, koo-lick, koo-lick, koo-lick,* followed by *keeer, keeer, keeer* the neck being gradually lowered as the call proceeds. Herring Gulls do not utter many sounds while here or else they become vocal only when far-removed from the haunts of man. I once heard one on the beach in mid-September call, with neck stretched out horizontally a little below the level of the shoulders, and once in March one passing overhead called *kee-law, kee-law,* followed by a goose-like "*goggle*" still another called from a piling on September 7, 1931. I have copied the calls as I wrote them at the time.

While lying out in a skiff on Jarvis Sound, on July 23, 1922, I had an excellent opportunity to watch the Herring Gulls feeding at low tide on the exposed flats. Two in immature plumage arrived when the water was still a few inches deep and the mussel bed was exposed for an area of only about sixty by ten feet, then came one in nearly adult plumage and another immature bird alighted on an adjoining shoal. They all stood for a while and then squatted on their bellies awaiting the slipping away of the water. Soon there were six on one flat and eleven on the other, and now all began to feed as the area of exposed mussel beds increased. They plucked the mussels from the shells and hastily devoured them and when passing from one bed to another they were often forced to swim. When a boat disturbed them they took to the water and later mounted in the air one flock after another until there were sixty-four of them sailing and flapping about overhead. One feeding bird would often pursue another which had secured some choice morsel, and now and then a bird would leap a foot or two off the ground for some reason that was not apparent, possibly the spouting of a buried clam nearby. Some individuals seemed much less aggressive than others and we noticed one that was feeding on a dead sea-robin desert his food, when approached by another apparently more powerful bird, and return to it only after the intruder had flown away.

On September 14, 1921, large numbers of Herring Gulls were scattered over the sound some of which were feeding on live blue crabs. They would lift the crab in the bill and cast it down again its legs and claws wriggling in the air. Another individual was eating dead conchs and would raise an entire shell in its beak in an effort to dislodge the animal. A flock of immature gulls feeding on the mud flats back of Five Mile Beach on July 21, 1930, were eating dead blue crabs which had been left there in numbers by the receding tide. As we looked at them from our skiff, almost on a level with them, they seemed distinctly bob-tailed and appeared very clumsy as they ran or walked quickly about with neck held erect. Occasionally they would run at one another with shoulders hunched and heads down. When

PLATE 47

*William Vogt*

*W. L. Baily*

1. DOVEKIE ON THE LONG ISLAND COAST.

2. GREAT BLACK-BACKED GULL, MAGDALEN ISLANDS, JUNE, 1911.

PLATE 48

*Wharton Huber*

1. HERRING GULLS ON PILINGS IN CAPE MAY HARBOR, AUGUST 14, 1923.
2. RING-BILLED GULLS TAKING TO THE AIR.

PLATE 49

*Courtesy of "Bird Lore"*                    *R F. Engle*

*Courtesy of "Bird-Lore"*                    *C. M. Beal*

1. DRIVEWAY OVER BARNEGAT BAY SHOWING CLAM SHELLS BROKEN BY HERRING
   GULLS WHICH DROPPED THEM FROM THE AIR.

2. HERRING GULLS RESTING ON THE WATER.

PLATE 50

*W. L. Baily*

*W. L. Baily*

TWO NESTS OF THE LAUGHING GULL ON THE MEADOWS BACK OF SEVEN MILE BEACH, CAPE MAY COUNTY, N. J., 1899.

the tern colony, back of Five Mile Beach was washed out, in 1931, the Herring Gulls resorted there and ate the broken eggs and the little downy tern chicks which had been drowned in the flood. From the way in which the terns pursue them, when they fly near a breeding colony, they may also appropriate fresh eggs and living young if opportunity offers, but I have never actually seen them do so.

At Corson's Inlet, on January 1, 1926, a day of bitter cold and howling north winds, a number of Herring Gulls were catching winter crabs (*Cancer irroratus*) in the shallow water of the channel at low tide. A gull would hover over the water and suddenly drop to the surface with head stretched down so that it was submerged in the act of seizing the crab, and failing in the attempt the bird would rise again for another plunge but never did it make a true dive or submerge more than the head and that for only an instant. Having secured a crab by the leg the gull would carry or drag it to an exposed sand bar near at hand and walk around it jabbing at it with the bill and deftly avoiding the widespread claws. Once these were broken off it was an easy matter to crush the shell and devour the soft parts of the animal. Sometimes another individual would drive off the successful fisherman, appropriate his catch, and proceed with the attack. I have once or twice seen Herring Gulls swimming on shallow pools on the meadows feeding on something on the bottom, plunging the head under the surface and keeping it there for several seconds at a time. When arising from mud flats after feeding they often shake the wings and wriggle in the air as if to dislodge sand or water from the plumage.

I saw an immature Herring Gull on December 27, 1931, plunging down to the water in an effort to secure food of some kind and once or twice it splashed pretty well in but did not make a regular dive and its action, such as it was, was quite exceptional. In my experience I have never seen these gulls make a regular dive and such action is very unusual in any of our gulls except the little Bonaparte's.

Herring Gulls occur regularly on the Harbor and about the fish wharves at all times of year but much more abundantly in the winter. Here they feed on all sorts of refuse that may be thrown out on the water and in late summer follow the fishing craft that are returning from the banks, snatching up the offal and rejected fish that the fishermen are throwing overboard.

One well known habit of the Herring Gull is to be observed frequently on our New Jersey coasts in winter—that of carrying up clams and dropping them on the beach in order to break them. Usually this is a solo performance, the gull carrying the clam up to a height of fifteen or twenty feet and following it in its fall to the beach to devour the contents. Where many clams are washed up on the strand, however, a number of gulls may gather and the one which carries the clam rarely gets back to the beach in time to share in the feast though he probably profits on the attempt of the next individual that mounts in the air. Frequently the beach is not hard enough to break the clams and several attempts result in failure. As a result, in some places, as at Beach Haven a few years ago, the birds left the beach for the deserted board walk with great success, and the walk was literally strewn with broken clam shell. I watched a lone gull carrying up clams on the Avalon beach on March 5, 1932, and upon recovering a large one that he had dropped found it to measure five and a half by three and three quarter inches and two inches in thickness. I have seen Herring Gulls on the meadows carrying up large mussels and dropping them on the ground with, of course, no result although they tried it over and over again, one individual swooping down and catching the shell in its bill on the rebound from the ground. Another one had secured a large natica snail and made repeated but vain efforts to break it on the muddy shore of the Harbor.

On March 4, 1934, there was a great deposit of clams on the Brigantine Beach and Herring Gulls seemed to come from considerable distances to partake of the feast. Julian Potter estimated that there must have been ten thousand present. I have seen similar gatherings on Seven Mile Beach when the beaches of the entire northern half of the island were thronged with the birds. Potter also tells me of the freezing of a lagoon at Bridgeport, Gloucester County, not far from the Delaware River during the exceedingly cold weather of January, 1935, which killed tons of catfish, carp etc., and that with the thawing of the ice the exposed mass of fish attracted some five thousand Herring Gulls along with several Ring-bills and a single Glaucous Gull. They were seen busily at work on this unexpected feast on March 2 and in one week's time had entirely disposed of it. The below zero weather of February 11, 1934, brought a similar assemblage of Herring Gulls to the Atlantic City garbage dump where they hovered overhead in an immense swarm (Potter).

The flight of the Herring Gull along the coast is a continuous easy flapping, once the bird gets under way, and the body slides ahead with no apparent effort. But there is much labor at the start as can readily be seen if we are close at hand. I came up with some gulls, in a motorboat, one day, just as they had arisen from the water and before they could develop their usual momentum. Side by side we progressed; the birds with head and neck stretched well forward and slightly downward, and the wings apparently beating clear over them as they swept forward, seemed the very picture of strain, until the steady restful gait had been attained. Under certain conditions Herring Gulls will sail in short arcs and, when the time comes for the northward migration, they will mount high in the air flying in wide circles as do the Laughing Gulls in their aërial evolutions.

When launching forth in flight these big Herring Gulls leave a clear record of their actions on the sands of the beach. The ordinary walking footsteps will be seen to pass into running steps in which the forepart of the foot is most strongly impressed and finally a print of the toes only, deeply dug into the sand, shows where the bird gave its final shove as it launched itself into the air. If we follow back to the other end of the trail we shall find two footprints deeply indented posteriorly where the bird, when first it touched the sand, "dug in its heels" to check its forward progress. When taking wing from the water the action is just the same and there are numerous vigorous strokes of the feet before the bird clears the surface.

At all times the Herring Gulls seem to prefer to keep to themselves and when they are associated with other birds it is apparently the latter that make the advances. On the beaches they prefer to be solitary and when roosting they gather by themselves, although Ring-bills, Laughing and Bonaparte's Gulls may join them. Occasionally immature dark-plumaged Herring Gulls do seem to join the large assemblages of Laughing Gulls but that is usually before the great autumn and winter flocks of the big gulls have arrived. A curious instance of association on the part of a Herring Gull was a single individual in adult plumage which joined a nesting colony of Laughing Gulls, at Little Beach on July 18, 1921, and circled about in the midst of the raucous assemblage that was violently protesting against the invasion of their domain. He seemed as much concerned as they although he certainly had no nest or young to defend and uttered no vocal protest!

I have seen Herring Gulls on the Harbor drive away Laughing Gulls which attempted to join them on the water and have also noticed one pursuing a Common Tern, endeavoring, but without success, to make him drop a fish which he was carrying. On the other hand the terns often attack a luckless Herring Gull which ventures too near their nesting grounds. On May 1, 1932, a Bald Eagle flying over the meadows passed near a gathering of Herring Gulls which were roosting along the edge of a creek and about fifty of them arose and pursued him. He was seen to drop a fish or some sort of food that he was carrying upon which they gave up the chase.

The large size of the Herring Gull readily distinguishes it from any of our other Cape May gulls although its adult plumage is so like that of the Ring-bill that solitary birds, seen when there is no opportunity for size comparison, may occasionally be confusing. The Herring Gull is longer necked and less graceful than the smaller species and its bill is noticeably longer, appearing almost curved or hooked, while in color it is yellowish or flesh color, usually with a reddish or dusky spot near the end of the lower mandible but without the vertical black bar so characteristic of the Ring-bill. In less mature individuals the dusky spot is more pronounced and often the entire terminal portion of the bill is dark.

The plumage varies considerably according to age but not at all as to sex or season. The adult has the mantle and wings pearl gray but is otherwise pure white, while the bird in its first breeding plumage has dusky or dark gray splotches here and there, and dusky lines on the head and on the sides and there is a conspicuous dark terminal band on the tail. The young birds of the year are entirely different being dark gray brown or chocolate throughout with darker centers to the feathers and buffy edges to some of them, there is a dusky band along the posterior edge of the spread wing and a dark blackish tail band. The bill is smaller than that of the adult and wholly dusky. A number of birds in this plumage and some in the one described just above fail to molt in the spring and likewise fail to acquire the migratory impulse and these are the birds that make up our summer colonies of Herring Gulls at Cape May. With their constant increase in numbers and the spread of the breeding range of the species southward we may yet see this great gull nesting on our New Jersey coast.

The autumnal migration of Herring Gulls seems to take place in September and October as it is usually about the middle of the former month before they are to be seen on the Delaware River at Philadelphia, but there would seem to be an earlier influx of birds from the north on the sea coast, for certain it is that the proportion of those in adult or semi-adult plumage is much greater in August than in May and June. In April most of the Herring Gulls move north and it is not uncommon to see them at this time circling high in the air, or sailing across to the Bay and back giving every indication of restlessness. The last of the migrants seem to have left us by the middle of May, leaving only the dusky-plumaged band which will remain throughout the summer.

The life and habits of these great silent scavengers of our winter sea coast offer a great field for study. Their very silence seems to increase their dignity and add to the impression of independence, self reliance and contempt for their lesser associates which characterize the Herring Gulls. In spite of their presence here in summer, I always associate them with winter and picture them in my mind's eye as accompanied by the angry roar of the surf and the rush of waters on some wild beach by the harbor's mouth, as they gather together for the night. Many times I have seen them on a narrow bar at sunset where they stand out silvery white and gray against the deep blue black of the darkening ocean, while every moment a long line of snowy surf boils up behind them as if to wash them from their narrow strand. Farther out other lines of surf appear successively and are lost again in the flood of waters. Every moment the pale yellow moon is growing brighter as the last rays of the sun die out in the west, and the night shadows creep closer and closer, while the great gulls stand there like a row of sentinels silhouetted against the sky until they are slowly and gradually swallowed up in the night.

## * THAYER'S GULL

### Larus argentatus thayeri Brooks

This slightly different subspecies of Herring Gull comes down to us in winter from far northern shores mingling with the individuals that breed on the New England and Canadian coasts. A specimen of this form, which probably cannot be distinguished in life, was secured by Samuel Rhoads near the Delaware River at Mt. Ephraim, N. J. on March 9, 1888, the only one to be recorded from the state so far as I know. In all probability it occurs occasionally with the ordinary Herring Gull about Cape May. It is slightly paler and has a different proportion of white on the primaries.

## RING-BILLED GULL

Larus delawarensis Ord

PLATE 48, p. 534

The Ring-billed Gulls arrive at Cape May each year during the first week of August, or earlier—August 3, 1921 and 1922; August 4, 1923; July 2, 1924; July 30, 1925; August 8, 1926; July 24, 1927; July 18, 1928. They take up their position on the strand, often close to the bathing beaches, and at intervals of about twenty-five yards, as if each bird had its own feeding station. This habit of feeding on the beaches during August and September is rather distinctive as the other gulls rarely do so, at this season at least, and do not exhibit the tameness of the Ring-bill. The latter when busy feeding will allow a close approach but if one comes too near will wheel out over the surf and land again a little farther down the strand.

The feeding Ring-bills walk about through the shallows, now and then running suddenly and rapidly after a receding wave to pick up some morsel from the sand or water, often one of the little Hippa crabs which come in by the thousand with the waves and scuttle down in the sand as the water retreats. At such times the gulls remind one, in their actions, of gigantic plovers. In the excitement of the chase the wings are often raised above the back and now and then a bird will run along with the wings half spread as if about to take flight and then change its mind and come to rest again. When they do launch into the air several strokes of the wings are given before the feet leave the ground and the bird gets fairly under way.

Sometimes when feeding before an incoming wave the water suddenly becomes deeper and the gull, in picking up its prey, completely submerges its head and, again, it will wade right into an oncoming wave and jump through it like a surf bather.  Sometimes, too, they will be carried off their feet by the sudden rush of water and swim off gracefully with breast well down and wing tips projecting above the tail.

When feeding out over the ocean, as they often do, they fly with steady rather quick wingbeats but all of them of equal length and regular, like those of the Herring Gull, and with none of the short half-beats of the Bonaparte's Gull.  Every now and then a bird will pause for a moment and then drop or "dive" usually striking the water with the feet and belly and, snatching up some floating scrap of food, will be on the wing again.  Sometimes the head will be bent far over and will be submerged as the bird strikes the water but there is never a true head-on dive and the body never goes under.

Ring-billed Gulls will often remain on the beaches throughout the winter but many retire at times to the more elevated dredgings and sand fills on the meadows and all probably go to such spots to spend the night.  In both places they associate more or less closely with the larger Herring Gulls and sometimes, in late summer or early fall, will be attracted to a gathering of terns on the sea beach but they usually stand off by themselves and do not mingle intimately with the terns as do the Laughing Gulls.  Occasionally I have seen them back on the sounds at low tide perched against the vertical mud banks much as they might rest on some rocky cliff in their summer home far to the north.

Ring-bills are not so abundant as the Herring or Laughing Gulls but while they frequently occur singly they also associate in moderate sized flocks; Julian Potter saw a flock of forty at Corson's Inlet on August 19, 1928, and counted a hundred birds on Seven Mile Beach on December 23, 1929, while I found nineteen gathered closely together on the ice of the Lighthouse Pond on February 14, 1925.  A flock of twenty was found on August 25, 1931, on Seven Mile Beach and on September 27 we found that it had increased in number to over fifty.  This flock remained until late October and then decreased in numbers, though six were still present on December 25.

The first birds to arrive on the sea beach in August are usually adults in beautifully fresh plumage, with snowy white head and breast and pale gray wings and mantle—slightly darker than in the Herring Gull but not nearly so dark as in the Laughing Gull.  When the wings are spread the gray is so pale that the white tips of the secondaries, which form such a conspicuous border to the wing of the Laughing Gull, are scarcely distinguishable, but the black terminal portion of the primaries and their white tips are strongly contrasted and conspicuous both in flight and at rest.

Generally speaking the Ring-bill has the plumage of the Herring Gull but approaches more nearly to the size of the Laughing Gull; unless one of these two is present, however, for comparison, it is by no means easy to judge its size or to distinguish it at a distance from the Herring Gull.  As further means of identification there are the yellow, instead of pink, toes and tarsi and the much shorter yellow bill with its dark vertical bar near the middle. The Herring Gull usually shows a red spot near the end of the lower mandible which is often more or less dusky but this is quite different from the vertical bar covering both mandibles of the Ring-bill, while the long, almost hooked, bill of the Herring Gull gives to its head a very different outline. The very dark upper surface of the Laughing Gull renders it easily separable from the other two at any season. While not so slender as the latter the Ring-bill is a more graceful, trimmer bird than the Herring Gull, especially as it stands on the beach with neck contracted and head drawn down on its shoulders in an almost dove-like pose.

Light plays curious tricks with the appearance of all gulls and two Ring-bills observed on the Bay off Cape May Point on March 29, 1936, appeared as dark as any Laughing Gulls and I was convinced that they were this species and could not account for the white heads so late in the spring. Suddenly, however, at a different angle their backs faded to pale gray!

Young Ring-bills resemble Herring Gulls in plumage, intermediate between the dark bird of the year and the gray and white adult. They are never so dark as young Herring Gulls and have more white in the plumage, but have a dark terminal tail band and dusky bill and feet. We are therefore dependent almost entirely upon size as a means of identification.

A few Ring-bills, as is so frequent in the case of the Herring Gull, do not migrate northward in the spring, evidently undeveloped non-breeding birds and they may be seen in the immature plumage all summer. One such was found with immature Herring Gulls on the meadows back of Ludlam's Beach on June 24, 1928.

During their winter sojourn at the Cape the Ring-bills ascend the Delaware River to Philadelphia, especially in spring, when, by March 12, they seem to reach their maximum number and gradually supplant the Herring Gulls until by April 15 Julian Potter has found only immature birds of the latter species on the river while the Ring-bills present were all adults. In the autumn John Carter has found them arriving at Chester on the Delaware in late August or early September, in advance of the Herring Gulls.

In Salem County along the upper Bay Julian Potter tells me of a flock of one hundred and fifty Ring-bills on April 6, 1935, foraging in plowed fields and of a small flock following a farmer who was plowing. In the same vicinity John Gillespie saw at least twelve hundred of these gulls in flocks of two hundred or more in several different pastures feeding on scattered earthworms which had been drowned out by encroaching water.

As spring approaches the Ring-bills at Cape May seem to increase in numbers and then decrease again as they leave for farther north. Most of them have left by April 1 but we usually have records of individuals or small flocks up to the last week of that month and last records as late as May 8, 1925, and May 19, 1924, while I saw a flock of twenty-five on May 10, 1925, flying steadily along over the surf following the flight line of scattered Loons and long ranks of Double-crested Cormorants which on the same day were winging their way to their breeding grounds in the Far North.

## LAUGHING GULL

**Larus atricilla Linnaeus**

PLATES 50–57, pp. 535, 550, 551

The most striking feature of summer bird life at Cape May, to one familiar only with the birds of the upland, is the presence of the graceful Laughing Gulls which all summer long pass and repass high overhead or beat their way up and down the coast low over the breakers. Looking at them from below one sees only the snow white under surface of the body and wings which now and then glistens like silver in the sunlight, and the black hood which envelops the head as far as the upper neck and throat. When skimming the ocean or wheeling in midair, however, the dark slaty mantle which spreads over the back and wings is conspicuous, contrasting with the white tail and hind neck and the white border which fringes the wings. When we find a bird at rest on the meadows and are able to approach closer we note that the head is not black but a darker shade of slate, darker than the mantle, and we distinguish the curious white crescent-shaped mark behind and around the eye which gives such an uncanny expression to the bird's face while we admire the dark carmine of the bill and feet. The delicate rosy flush which suffuses the breast is, however, usually visible only when the bird is in hand.

The manner of flight of the Laughing Gulls varies. Usually they go singly or in loose flocks, each bird for himself, with no attempt at concerted action.

The wings move with short easy beats as if there existed endless reserve power and the bird were not half exerting itself. In the face of a strong wind they take a few strokes and then a short sail, tilting up now on one wing, now on the other, and producing a rather erratic, zigzag flight. In their efforts to escape the force of the gale, too, they will come close down to the ground in crossing the Fill or the meadows and will skim the house tops as they pass over the town.

The Laughing Gulls have a regular line of flight from their nesting grounds on the marshy islands back of Seven Mile Beach to the "ripps" at the mouth of Delaware Bay, where the waters of the river meet the ocean swells and make a favorite fishing ground for various sea birds. The morning flight is usually southward, while at evening most of the birds are travelling northward again to roost in the vicinity of their nests. These evening flights, especially later in the summer, are much more business-like and direct, a dozen birds often traveling in close formation, sometimes in a more or less definite V, with steady even strokes of their long wings and no deviation whatever from their course.

Over the ocean their direction of flight is not always so definite and they may be seen traveling along both up and down the coast at almost any time of day. They fly about twenty feet above the water and every now and then one will sail down close to the waves on set wings, sometimes disappearing entirely in the trough of the sea. As the bird turns the white fan-shaped tail now full spread, catches the sunlight and flashes out conspicuously against the dark water. At other times, especially on days when the sky is overcast and the birds on steady flight, their slaty upper parts merge so perfectly into the steel-gray of the sea that it is difficult to distinguish them, and in the attempt to follow their course, even with the glass, one will lose them entirely for considerable distances, catching them again farther on.

The number of Laughing Gulls passing over Cape May increases steadily as the summer advances, from the few scattering individuals that venture so far from the breeding grounds in June, to the hundreds that make up the flights of late August and early September, after the young are able to shift for themselves. The factors that influence the flights and roosting habits of birds are not easy to discover and just as one imagines that he has all their movements reduced to a schedule they defy all the laws that careful observation seems to have established. These gulls are no exception.

In August, 1921, they drifted as usual down to the feeding grounds at the "ripps," every morning, and between six and seven in the evening passed north again in force, sometimes directly over the town and again in the lee of the woods which border the salt meadows on the west. On the 27th, however, contrary to all precedent, the northward flight took place in the morning in long straggling columns with gaps between, like Crows going to roost. At 8:30 I counted 160 birds and later on detachments of 130, 109 and forty all in half an hour, but I had undoubtedly missed many which passed before I was aware of the movement. On the next day the flight was also at this time.  On both days a strong east wind prevailed which doubtless induced the birds to spend the night on the Bay but why return north in the morning?  Again on August 23, 1924, under similar conditions they flew north in the morning in squads of 220, 240, 190 and seventy and on September 17, 1921, a similar northward flight took place at 3:00 p. m. this time out over the ocean; 210 in the first division and 108 a little later, each flock stretching out about two hundred yards in varying density.

Laughing Gulls have a peculiar aërial performance which I have not been able positively to explain.  They gather together in numbers at some point, usually over the meadows, and fly back and forth within a limited area forming a veritable maze of flapping, turning birds and reminding one of swallows feeding on a cloud of gnats.  In the case of the gulls, however, I have never been able to detect the presence of insects of any kind and rarely any movement of the bills of the birds, even though I have held the glass on them for many minutes at a time.  One of these assemblages on July 30, 1921, and others at the same spot on August 25, 1917, and August 29, 1922, consisted of upwards of one hundred birds which in the first instance kept low down over the meadows none of them rising more than twenty-five feet in the air while those of the later gatherings mounted higher, the last including both old and young birds in all stages of plumage.  On August 30, 1921, a somewhat similar gathering of fifty birds occurred high in the air, immediately over the town, but in this case the birds were, for the most part, sailing regularly in circles and mounting higher and higher until they appeared like small hawks and later even like martins.  A precisely similar soaring occurred at Schellenger's Landing on July 5, 1923, and another on August 3, 1921, over Cape May Point, the gulls in the latter instance mingling with several Fish Hawks which were engaged in the same sort of evolutions.  On one occasion I saw a lone Laughing Gull begin to circle over the town and watched him mount higher and higher until he became a mere speck and finally vanished in the sky.

A habit apparently peculiar to the Laughing Gulls, since I have never observed the other species practicing it, is their resorting to fresh water ponds for bathing.  When the water in Lake Lily is sufficiently deep and free from vegetation they gather there regularly during intervals in their feeding at the "ripps."  On July 29, 1920, I watched a number of them so engaged.  As they came sailing down to the water they threw the feet forward and drew the wings in gradually as they settled down.  Others observed on August 24, 1924, fairly threw themselves into the water from a height of several feet and did it repeatedly.  Once on the water they would duck the head under the surface and withdraw it again with a sudden jerk.  The plumage was then ruffled up and the closed wings, held a little way out from the body, were worked up and down, churning up the water all around.  Several birds usually bathed together getting as close to one another as possible during the operation.  Eventually they flew off, one at a time, while others came in to take their places.  Occasionally a newly arrived bird would dip its head to the water several times without submerging it, apparently drinking, and I have seen birds fly down and skim over the surface dipping the bill in to sip up water. Some individuals after bathing sat quietly on the water as if loath to depart and several times a bird about to alight would raise its foot and scratch its head while still in the air. In certain years Lake Lily has been almost entirely deserted by the gulls as a bathing spot, due apparently to the great accumulation of bladder-wort and other aquatic plants but the birds have other fresh water ponds to which they resort. One of these is an old sand hole pond surrounded by trees and bushes just east of Wildwood Junction and much nearer to their breeding grounds than Lake Lily. Here on July 8, 1923, gulls were continually coming and going in pairs or singly, flying from the meadows to the mainland. Another favorite pond is the Sea Isle Reservoir, a picturesque spot on the Shore Road, surrounded by white cedar woods against which background the gulls stand forth in beautiful relief. Still another resort is the Poor House Pond also close to the Shore Road and some miles farther south. Here on August 15, 1931, there were about one hundred birds crowded closely together, energetically churning the water and ducking their heads; some always springing up into the air and settling again, causing constant motion throughout the mass while they made much clamor with their calling. Why with such a wide expanse of water available they must crowd together in a compact mass covering only an area of a few square feet is hard to understand but such is their invariable habit. Temporary pools are quite as satisfactory as these regular resorts and when on July 16, 1926, and at other times, heavy rains had made extensive shallow pools on the fill back of South Cape May they were crowded with gulls so long as the water remained.

Laughing Gulls frequently rest on the ocean, on the Harbor, or on the thoroughfares, just as do the Herring Gulls, especially late in the season when they may be found in immense masses riding the waves off Cape May Point, but they are rarely seen to alight on pilings a habit which is very characteristic of the larger species. When they do so it is usually in company with terns and Bonaparte's Gulls and on some continuous perch rather than on single posts. On the ground they are much quicker and more active than the large Herring Gulls and their legs seem proportionately longer and more slender. While they often associate with the larger gulls I have on several occasions seen the Herring Gulls pursue them and drive them away. They occur regularly on the Delaware River ascending at least as far as Fish House above Camden. According to Julian Potter they are most abundant there in spring, arriving about April 12 and remaining until about the 20th, although some are to be seen until May.

The Laughing Gulls arrive at Cape May from the south by April 20 our earliest records being April 14, 1904; April 8, 1913; April 6, 1919; April 1, 1928; March 31, 1929; April 1, 1930; some of these were probably stragglers coming in advance of the main flight, the March record being of a single individual. On April 23, 1922, Julian Potter saw a flock of twenty, apparently just arrived, circling high in the air and calling.

Of late years the Gloucester mackerel fleet has been in the habit of putting in to Cape May Harbor in April to ship their catches and the boats attract large numbers of Laughing Gulls, the earliest arrivals being frequently seen there.   On April 29, 1923, over a hundred of the fishing boats were gathered close together about Schellenger's Landing, their slender masts looking like the trunks of a burned cedar swamp against the evening sky and all about them was a whirling mass of Laughing Gulls.   About two hundred were in the air at once with others resting in ranks on the meadows beyond. They were flying in every direction and swooping right and left from higher to lower positions, now flapping vigorously, now sailing on set wings and pitching downward to the surface of the water.   They displayed the whole upper surface of the body when, for the moment, they poised in air with one wing extended upward and the other down.   All the while they called continually as they contended for the scraps that were constantly being cast overboard by the fishermen.   I have seen similar flocks in late August following the fishermen's excursion boats into the Harbor and on August 29, 1922, over fifty were flying in the wake of one of these vessels swooping down and picking up scraps of bread that were thrown to them, without settling on the water.   Many of these birds were young in the dusky plumage.   I think that the early spring flocks on the Harbor may very likely be migrant birds on their way farther north for a large number, at least, of the local breeding gulls resort at once to their nesting grounds.

While anchored off Little Beach Island on May 18, 1927, not far from a breeding place of the Laughing Gulls, we could hear the calls of the birds floating across from the meadows and later encountered fifty-four of the birds feeding out over the water.   They would drop to the surface and plunge their heads under after their prey, checking further immersion by prompt wing action.   Later sixty-two of them gathered about the stern of our boat to pick up scraps of bread, calling all the while in harsh chorus.   They flew low and made a dab at the bread as it floated along on the tide and were often compelled to bend the head under the body in their efforts to secure the prize, so that it appeared as if they were making a backward lunge between their legs.

None of our gulls seem to dive in the true sense of the word as do the terns but are ever alert to seize upon any fish that the latter may drop and are constantly swooping to pick up morsels from the surface and now and then, in the excitement, plunge the head under.

Most of the feeding of the Laughing Gulls is apparently done from the water and they may be seen on the Harbor, ocean, sounds or thoroughfares collecting whatever food may be found or coursing along looking for such floating matter as may be to their liking.   One of their favorite feeding stations is at the "ripps" at the mouth of Delaware Bay.   Here at almost any time during the summer and autumn, large numbers of them may be seen associated with other gulls, terns and Fish Hawks, flapping back and forth in a veritable maze.   Occasionally the birds come in close to the shore when the wind changes the location of the rough water but usually we must resort to the glass to study them. Sometimes there will be only a few dozen present and at others, especially late in the season, there will be thousands.

Occasionally they feed on the beach under exceptional circumstances. On July 3, 1917, there were a number of fish stranded in the shallow water and a Laughing Gull coming winging its way along the shore spied them, hovered for a moment, and dropped with zigzag darts, its red feet widely spread and pendant. When close to the sand it swooped forward and upward picking up one of the fish in its beak. This was repeated several times and then alighting on the beach it ran quickly about greedily picking up the fish right and left and gulping them down. Back on the channels, too, I have seen them swoop down to the surface of the water to pick up morsels of food and once a gull that had secured something attached to a piece of sea weed, dropped it and recovered it again from the water in a vain effort to detach the objectionable appendage but finally flew off with the weed streaming from its beak.

On August 31, 1920, there was a great gathering of Laughing Gulls over a shallow pond and exposed mud flat that formerly existed near the Lighthouse, the birds diving and rising again continually behind the dense growth of Spartina grass which surrounded it. They appeared to be feeding and subsequent examination disclosed numbers of small fish stranded there or swimming in the shallow water. I again saw them feeding in this way along Mill Creek on September 10, 1924, and on May 18, 1927, I saw a number walking about like shore birds on the black mud of an exposed bar, all headed to the wind and busy picking right and left. On other occasions they may be seen out on the salt meadows walking about like chickens picking up food from amongst the roots of the grass and sedges. This sort of feeding is practiced especially after high tides have flooded the meadows and receding have left all sorts of crustaceans and other forms of animal life stranded there.

Laughing Gulls are always more interested in live food than in dead and are not scavengers like their larger cousins the Herring Gulls. Besides the life that swarms over the exposed flats at low tide I have found them catching fiddler crabs on the sloping banks and bottoms of the tide water creeks to which they resort at the proper time, running after the crustaceans, breaking off their large claws and crunching the bodies between their mandibles. Alexander Wilson, writing about 1810, says that at Great Egg Harbor the Laughing Gulls resort to the plowed ground about the farmers' houses to feed.

While living in a gunner's shack on the meadows back of Two Mile Beach, May 16–19, 1924, I had an excellent opportunity to study the habits of the Laughing Gulls prior to the nesting season. They put in an appearance soon after sunrise each morning and from then until dark were constantly in sight, flying over the meadows and waterways and uttering an interrogatory *tuk, tuk*, as they winged their way past our cabin. They usually went in pairs and now and then rested on the channel before our door, floating leisurely along with the tide, their dove-like beauty a delight to the

eye. Once during our sojourn here we experienced one of those phenome-
nally high tides which prove so disastrous to the nesting sea birds. The
water rose to the top of the channel banks and then spread gradually over
the meadows until only the tips of the tallest grasses remained in sight and
the waves, driven by stiff winds, rushed under our little cabin as if a miniature surf were breaking there. The gulls at such times became very active
and were constantly on the wing coursing back and forth over the flood attracted doubtless by the variety of food that must inevitably be washed up.
They flew about ten feet above the water, pausing every now and then to
drop to the surface and snatch up some floating morsel. At such times they
have a rapid hovering flight with head bent far over and feet dangling so
that head and feet strike the water simultaneously and the former goes
slightly under in grasping the prey. Often a bird will rest for a moment on
the meadow standing in water up to its belly and then takes wing again.
And so they feed until darkness shuts them from our view.

During May and also through the summer large numbers of Laughing
Gulls frequent the extensive flats of Jarvis Sound and other shallows which
are exposed at ebb tide. Against the broad expanse of black mud they appear like splotches of white scattered here and there as far as the eye can
reach. They stand often in pairs at the beginning of the season, or singly,
and now and then a dozen of the barren white-headed individuals will be
found in a group by themselves. Other gulls passing overhead are constantly
calling to those on the flats which answer them as they pause from their
search for food.

On these mud flats Laughing Gulls have been seen to pair and one curious
performance was witnessed by Walker Hand and me on May 23 and 24, 1922,
which probably is part of the courtship behavior of the species. A Laughing Gull came to rest on a mud flat near us and was joined by another which
seemed smaller and slightly paler. The first bird was very sluggish but the
new arrival was all activity walking back and forth close in front of the other
one and throwing its head upward and backward as it uttered a low *kah,
kah, kah, kah,* at short intervals while the first bird replied occasionally with
a low *krrooo.* Now and then the active bird attempted to force its bill between the mandibles of the other, which would gape slightly or bend over
and apparently sip water, the former action causing redoubled activity on
the part of the other individual. Presently about five minutes after the
performance began the sluggish bird gave a mighty convulsion and ejected
a yellowish mass of partly digested food about the size of a hen's egg, which
the other bird, ever alert, seized as it appeared and with several gulps swallowed it without allowing it to touch the ground. Both birds now seemed
relieved and walked about sipping water, or washing their bills and soon
after flew away. Precisely the same performance was observed at the same
spot on the following day.

The Laughing Gulls always nest back on the salt meadows usually on
a section that has been converted into more or less of an island by the in-

numerable narrow tidewater creeks which wind their way backward and forward and eventually join with the broader channels or thoroughfares. They are distinctly social birds and nest in colonies, all of the flock joining in their defense. The nests are placed reasonably close to one another and are usually located in the coarse growth of marsh grass that skirts the little creeks, sometimes built directly on the growing grass but more often on masses of trash—dried grass stems—that have been washed up on the meadows by the high tides of the previous autumn and winter. There seem to be only two colonies of the birds nesting on the New Jersey coast in recent years, at least. One is located back of Seven Mile Beach about twelve miles north of Cape May, which contained some fifteen hundred birds on July 20, 1919, and has fluctuated in numbers in later years. The other is in the neighborhood of Little Beach Island north of Brigantine, in Atlantic County.

A visit to the Cape May County colony in 1923 showed that the nests are often mere depressions in the dry "trash" which is supported and raised somewhat from the ground by the growing reeds and grass stems underneath. Other nests are more carefully constructed, largely of this same material. The trash is composed mainly of coarse dead stems of the tall Spartina grass, one eighth to a quarter of an inch in diameter with some finer grass stems and strips of dried eel grass (*Zostera*) intermingled. Some nests, however, are constructed wholly of the stems of the finer marsh grasses. The average external diameter of the nests is eighteen inches but some of the longer stems, forming the base, project at least a foot farther. Some nests are located out among the short grass away from the creeks but the material for these had evidently been carried from the trash which had accumulated in the latter localities. At the Little Beach colony, which I visited in 1921, the nests were all built along the course of a larger creek where the Spartina grass grew to a much greater height and had been bent and beaten down into a great loose bed into which one sank up to the waist.

The eggs usually number three and are olive-brown splotched with purple and dark brown. The earliest date we have for a full set is May 18, 1919. The later dates vary greatly since the gulls are seriously affected by the high tides which flood the meadows and often wash out all the nests. In such cases the birds lay again so that in certain years eggs may be found until late in the summer. In 1922, as early as May 30, great numbers of eggs were found washed up along the causeway leading across the meadows from near Cape May Court House, evidently the result of a storm and high tide, and second sets were found in most of the nests a little later. On June 18 there were twenty-seven nests with three eggs, five with two and three with one. In the next year a similar flooding occurred and the whole beach at Corson's Inlet was strewn with eggs of gulls, terns and Clapper Rails. In that year some of the Seven Mile Beach nests contained eggs as late as July 13. High tides in the springs of 1933 and 1934 were very hard on the gulls and August 1 of the latter year found scarcely any immature birds in evidence, indicating a total failure of the nesting.

Turner McMullen and Richard Miller have given me the following data on nests examined by them in the breeding colony back of Seven Mile Beach.

July 4, 1920, fourteen nests with eggs.

June 7, 1921, fifty-one nests with eggs.

June 19, 1922, twenty-five nests with three eggs; one with four; many with two or one.

May 30, 1922, colony washed out; fourteen eggs found in ditches.

June 21, 1925, one nest with four eggs; nine with three; two with two; two with one.

June 20, 1926, 236 nests with eggs or young.

June 19, 1927, fifty-one nests examined; ten with one egg; fourteen with two; five with three; and others with downy young.

June 9, 1928, 181 nests with eggs or young.

June 6, 1931, forty-one nests with eggs.

July 20, 1932, 680 nests with eggs or young.

The young seem to leave the nest as soon as they are hatched and seek shelter in the tangled mass of grass stems upon which the nests are built. Here their mottled brown and black down renders them inconspicuous and we may gaze directly at one of these youngsters without detecting it, so perfectly does it blend with the black mud, dead grass stems and the play of light and shadow through the vegetation. Usually the young remain near the nest, often half submerged in the shallow water, but often they force their way through the grass to the open creek and swim with ease, even at a very early age, sometimes completing the crossing of the water and disappearing in the grass on the opposite side. When caught and placed back in the nest they immediately jumped out and pushed on through the grass, invariably on the side where it was rankest and where the water was deepest. Some nests had a sloping platform of trash at the side, accidental in all probability, but down this the young always scrambled in making their escape.

It seems probable that the young birds return to the nests or to the adjoining patches of trash when danger has passed, and are there fed by the parents. At any rate the flattening of the nest into a mere platform as the summer advances, and the plentiful excrement and scattered feathers show that the adults, at least, use it as a roosting place while the young are being raised. If the little birds do climb back to the nests to be fed, it is certain that they must scatter to seek shelter as soon as the old ones give the alarm cry, for not a young bird will be found in the nests when we approach them after the down dries and they are able to use their legs. The cry of the downy young is a shrill call resembling that of a young Robin *chir-r-r-rup; chir-r-r-rup.*

The actions of the Laughing Gulls on the nesting grounds are interesting. At a distance one sees them scattered here and there about the meadow with many others in the air, some putting out for the feeding grounds; some just arriving with food; dropping down into the grass or hovering for a moment just above, evidently passing food to the young below them. As

PLATE 51

*B. C. Hiatt*

LAUGHING GULL AT NEST, SEVEN MILE BEACH, CAPE MAY COUNTY, N. J., JUNE 6, 1936.

PLATE 52

*Wharton Huber*

1. LAUGHING GULLS OVER NESTING GROUNDS ON MEADOWS BACK OF SEVEN MILE BEACH, N. J., AUGUST 14, 1923.

2. LAUGHING GULLS ON THE WING OVER WATER, BAY HEAD, N. J., AUGUST, 1924.

PLATE 53

*R. T. Peterson*

*Wharton Huber*

1. LAUGHING GULL AT NEST.

2. LAUGHING GULLS SWIMMING IN THOROUGHFARE NEAR NESTING GROUND, ON MEADOWS BACK OF SEVEN MILE BEACH, N. J., JULY 11, 1929.

PLATE 54

*Wharton Huber*

*Wharton Huber*

1. PAIR OF LAUGHING GULLS AT NEST.
2. INCUBATING GULL CALLING WHILE ON NEST, SEVEN MILE BEACH, N. J.,
   JUNE 30, 1926.

PLATE 55

*Wharton Huber*

*Wharton Huber*

1. YOUNG LAUGHING GULLS HIDING IN THE TALL GRASS.
2. YOUNG LAUGHING GULLS IN THE NEST, SEVEN MILE BEACH, N. J., AUGUST 14, 1923.

PLATE 56

*Wharton Huber*

*Wharton Huber*

LAUGHING GULLS AT THEIR NESTS ON THE MEADOWS BACK OF SEVEN MILE BEACH, CAPE MAY COUNTY, N. J., JUNE 30, 1926.

PLATE 57

*Wharton Huber*

*Wharton Huber*

NESTS OF LAUGHING GULL ON MEADOWS BACK OF SEVEN MILE BEACH, N. J., SHOWING EGGS AND YOUNG, JULY, 1924.

Wharton Huber and I landed from our skiff on the morning of August 14, 1923, and started across the level meadows back of Seven Mile Beach, it was high tide and about six inches of water covered the entire island, only the tips of the short grass and glasswort (*Salicornia*) showing above the surface while the winding lines of taller Spartina grass marked the course of the creeks. Most of the adult birds were evidently roosting on the patches of trash or on the flattened nests and they arose in several instalments as we approached, coming beating across the meadows to meet us, company front and all in full cry.

The most frequent call was *kek-kek* or *kek-kuh*, repeated continuously and rapidly, different individuals having slightly different expressions. Some also called in triplets—*kek-kek-kek; kek-kek-kek*, with more of the woody quality of the clarinet. Then some birds would begin to break through the chorus with a *kek-kek-kek-kek-keeeer, keeeer, keeeer*, or *haaaar, haaaar, haaaar*, like mocking laughter—the call that has given the bird its name of Laughing Gull.

The circling, soaring crowd of birds overhead, now numbering some two hundred individuals, looked beautiful in the sunlight. As seen from directly below the pure white of the breast and tail of the adults contrasted sharply with the apparently jet black head and wing tips. The sunlight moreover shown through the translucent posterior margin of the wings and tail producing a silvery white effect in contrast with the opaque white of the breast and belly. There were some white-headed birds with dusky ear patches which appeared to be individuals already in the molt since some of the white tail feathers were missing. There were also a number of birds of the year, uniformly dusky except for the lower abdomen and base of the tail which were white. Now the moving maze of birds drifts away as we turn to one side and some of them settle on the meadow, but as soon as we return toward the nesting ground they rise in a cloud and once more come toward us low over the ground. It is a striking picture. The tide has ebbed and the meadows stretch away in brilliant green. The little fiddler crabs have come out of their burrows and go scuttling and sideling away while the periwinkles are slowly climbing the grass stems where they hang by hundreds like great excrescences or curious seed pods. Beyond our meadow island are the sparkling waters of the sound and on the distant horizon the low-lying woods and shining sand dunes of Seven Mile Beach while high overhead the snowy white, dusky-winged birds pass and repass in intricate circles under the great blue vault of the sky.

Once in a while an intruder enters the gulls' domain—a Turkey Vulture innocently sailing out over the marsh to inspect some possible carrion or a Marsh Hawk beating the grass for meadow mice—and he is at once set upon by the angry gulls and made to twist and turn until he is glad to beat a hasty retreat. Similarly on Jarvis Sound I have seen feeding gulls, apparently forgetting that they are no longer on the nesting grounds, rise to attack a Bald Eagle which had started to cross the meadows to the sea. On May 22,

1922, a single gull routed this royal enemy while on July 23 of the same year three gulls joined in the pursuit. So also on September 4, four gulls pursued a Fish Hawk out over the surf at Cape May Point and made him pitch and toss and finally fall through the air for some distance, for he is not accustomed to rapid wing action and is no match for the gulls at twisting and turning. On August 12, 1929, I saw an adult Laughing Gull pursue a Common Tern which had caught a small fish and was carrying it in his bill. The gull kept close after him turning and twisting and following every movement of the smaller bird until the tern dropped his fish and the gull caught it, gulped it down and flew away. I do not however regard this as a common habit.

The Little Beach colony, which I have known since 1892, was visited last on July 18, 1921. It was then located on either side of a large salt creek which wound its way through the meadows and emptied into a thoroughfare directly opposite the cabins on the island. Some three hundred Laughing Gulls could be seen from a distance perching on the masses of trash and constantly jumping up into the air and settling again. Upon closer examination we found that there were only a few nests that still contained eggs but there were many broken egg shells from which young had recently hatched, and splashes of excrement covered the dead meadow trash on all sides. Search as we would not a single young bird could we find. The depth of the masses of trash made it exceedingly difficult to locate them in any case, and as we were, at the time, unaware of their habit of leaving the nest and remaining perfectly still amongst the grass, sometimes until almost trodden upon, we undoubtedly passed over many without detecting them. All night long from our cabin across the channel we could hear a continual clamor from the colony, evidence that the young were still there and that their parents had returned to watch over them.

When we had approached the nests during the day the birds arose *en masse* several hundred in number uttering their harsh *kek, kek, kek, kek, haaar, haaar, haaaar, haaar*, about four of the long calls in three seconds. When quite close to them it seemed that some of the calls had a "*k*" sound at the beginning and end and that they consisted of two slurred syllables— *kee-ahhk, kee-ahhk, kee-ahhk, kee-ahhk*. Some birds also omitted the short preliminary notes, *kek, kek, kek, kek*, at least at certain times. The birds formed an intricate maze as they wheeled and circled overhead or, catching a favorable wind, a number of them would sail off a little way together and return again to the fray. As they arose in the air they appeared smaller and smaller until one could scarcely realize that the large birds close overhead were of the same species as the little ones higher up. All the while the bedlam of noise continued. There were in the flock several white-headed, non-breeding birds, that had never molted, and one great adult Herring Gull which seemed to be just as much concerned as his lesser brethren, though we could discover no vocal effort on his part.

While in August, 1921, the gulls passing north over Cape May in the

evening had as their immediate objective the extensive sand flats left by
the dredges back of Two Mile Beach, where Turtle Gut Inlet then emptied into the sea, I think that this may have been only a temporary stop
or a roosting place for only a part of the colony. Certain it is that up until
close to the time of their departure for the south the greater part of the
colony remains in, or returns to, the meadows where they nested, or to the
adjoining meadows back of Five Mile Beach. On numerous trips across
from the mainland to the beach islands during August and September they
were present in abundance. On August 12 and 13, 1930, they were scattered
all over the meadows south of the Wildwood Road while on the 23d, there
were close to one thousand on the higher meadows near the mainland north
of the road to Stone Harbor. They were seeking safety and shelter during
a very high tide and a strong wind, and probably one thousand more occupied elevated spots on the meadows back of Five Mile Beach a few miles
farther south. As the water fell the birds scattered in every direction seeking food left stranded by the tide. On September 27 of the same year at
low tide there were six large assemblages of Laughing Gulls on the mud
flats in the thoroughfares or resting on the water back of Five Mile Beach,
and another gathering on the upper meadows; about three thousand birds
in all.

In 1931 there were large assemblages of adults and full-feathered young
on both stretches of meadow, on August 15, while on September 12 and 26,
at high tide, we estimated three thousand present north of the Wildwood and
Stone Harbor Roads. They were gathered in dense masses either on the
grass or on the salt ponds. Every little while an entire flock would shift
from one spot to another, arising section after section, and settling with
much confusion and flapping of wings. Some of the ponds seemed simply
paved with birds. There were no Herring Gulls mingled with them at this
time and all of the adults seemed to have acquired their white heads. On
the former date a long straggling flight was coming in from the south shortly
before sunset; doubtless birds that had spent the day at the "ripps."

From the time of their first arrival there will be found some Laughing
Gulls with white or mottled heads, birds which have never acquired the
full nuptial plumage and which seem to be non-breeders. They are often
seen standing solitary along the beach or on the mud flats at low tide, where,
however, they frequently flock together, and a bunch of twelve with no full-
plumaged individuals among them was seen on May 23, 1922. Some of these
barren birds however frequent the nesting grounds and join the colony in
protesting the presence of intruders.

During the latter weeks of July the first dusky-plumaged young are seen
on the wing and they become increasingly plentiful in August. These birds
in their brown-drab plumage contrast strongly with the gray and white
adults. They show white only on the rump and at the base of the tail, the
latter having also a very distinct black terminal border, a character shared
by the barren birds but absent in the adult at all seasons.

As early as July 23 and August 8, in different years, I have seen adults which had begun to lose the dark hood and by mid-August most of them show white mottlings on the head while others lack some of the tail feathers, or are in other phases of molt. On July 30, 1927, the shallow pools and the sand fill back of South Cape May were covered with scattered feathers, the result of this annual molt of the adult gulls. Some black-headed individuals, however, are still to be seen as late as August 30, but by early September the molt is practically over and a flock seen on the 16th, 1927, and another on September 12, 1931, were all white-headed. The brown birds of the year do not change their plumage until later and on September 27 and 28, 1924, I found them in full molt. There was a flock of about fifteen hundred Laughing Gulls gathered on the shallow pond north of the Lighthouse, and so closely were they crowded together that the pond seemed literally paved with them, while their varied plumages produced a remarkable color effect. Close study of the brown immature birds showed that each body feather had a darker dusky border while the wings were edged behind with buffy white and the tail, dull white at the base, was mottled with darker and had a distinct dark terminal band. The adults which had, of course, completed the molt were clear dark slate on the back and wings with white breast, tail and head, the latter with a clearly marked dusky ear patch. The primary feathers, as always, were black. These two plumages were to be seen all through the flock while many young birds showed all sorts of intermediate conditions. Some had white feathers on the head and large white patches on the breast while blue gray areas were appearing on the back and all over the pond could be seen the cast-off feathers.

The whole flock was busy bathing and preening, the birds rising a few feet in the air and dropping back again with dangling legs. On alighting they would often hold their wings aloft for a few seconds and would now and then stretch out one wing and leg horizontally as if for exercise. Finally all took wing with much clamor, their call at this season being a short *keek*, *keek*, somewhat like the short note of the Common Tern.

During October the Laughing Gulls rapidly decrease in numbers on the meadows but increase correspondingly at the "ripps" and about Cape May Point, where they repair to rest on the beach or formerly on the shallow pond which for many years existed just east of the Lighthouse. In 1921, I noticed the first of these gatherings on August 2 and on the 5th there were thirty gulls on the beach associated with Common Terns which also habitually gather there. They lined up just back of the terns and after August 8 separated from them entirely. When at rest on the beach the gulls stand at the very edge of the water with heads all pointed toward the wind as is customary with resting water birds. Some individuals now and then walk rapidly about in the shallow water, apparently picking up food, while others are busy preening themselves, with head bent down on the breast or twisted around over the shoulder in order to reach the feathers of the back. Occasionally, too, a bird will rise in the air, give a half dozen wingbeats and alight farther along the line.  On August 11, 1922, over three hundred Laughing Gulls were gathered on a sandy spit on the pond near the Lighthouse and the next day were resting on the strand where they resorted several times during September.  On August 23, 1923, six hundred assembled here with many Common Terns.  On September 16, 1921, there was a flock of fifty-eight on a wet spot on the beach near South Cape May which I was able to approach and study, creeping up under shelter of the sand dunes and bayberries.  Many were standing on one leg with the head bent over on the back while others in similar position had both feet on the ground.  After watching the birds for some time I suddenly arose and the attitude of the group changed instantly.  Every bird was alert and ready to take wing in strong contrast to the easy positions of rest of but a moment before.  Soon they spread their wings and heading out to sea settled on the water in a long irregular line, several birds deep, just beyond the surf.

This habit of resting on the ocean seems more characteristic of the end of the season and is doubtless preparatory to migration.  A flock on the beach, on September 15, 1921, settled on the sea when flushed and then arose in a cloud on the approach of a chugging power boat.  On September 17, 1923, the ocean just off the Point, was fairly strewn with Laughing Gulls, all adults in full winter plumage, and on October 1 of the same year and October 11, 1930, there were approximately five thousand feeding at the "ripps" and three hundred more resting on the beach.

On October 24, 1921, I found some three thousand on the water just off the Point.  They rode the waves very prettily all facing to windward, their heads drawn well down on their shoulders with the tips of the wings standing out clear above the rump.  On November 7 there remained about one thousand, while in 1921 there were several hundred feeding offshore on October 31, some of which remained until November 10, and in 1923 five hundred were present at the same spot on October 21.  The Laughing Gulls linger during the first few days of November—five hundred on November 7, 1922, four hundred on November 4, 1923, and one hundred and fifty on November 7, 1931, but by the middle of the month they have passed south, my latest dates being November 12, 1922; November 14, 1926; November 16, 1929; a few individuals each day.  My only winter record is a single bird seen feeding on the bed of the channel near Stone Harbor at low tide, December 25, 1931, and another in a similar situation at Avalon on the same day.

They occur on the Delaware River in autumn as well as spring and Julian Potter has seen them as early as August 27, 1927, and September 30, 1924, when many were blown in by heavy storms on the coast.  They often occur through October in flocks of ten or more and single birds have been seen as late as November 13, 1924; November 10, 1921; November 8, 1928.

On September 9, 1924, many Laughing Gulls were seen about Cape May which seemed peculiarly restless, coursing back from Two Mile Beach to the Point in numbers.  Their flight was very different from that of the summer birds, lacking in directness and definiteness of purpose.  Many flew over the golf links and another flight passed along the ocean front, all converging at the Point where at least two thousand birds were soon assembled on the beach facing a southwest gale.  These were perhaps birds from farther north, the first southbound migrants of fall, or local individuals stimulated by the change in the weather.

The Laughing Gulls of Cape May seem to be the last of the summer sojourners to leave the coast and in our studies of them we have, year after year seen the airy light-winged Black-heads of spring time, birds of green meadows and azure skies, change to these white-headed, leaden-backed denizens of the steel-gray November ocean; ready at any moment to start on their southward journey, leaving our shores to the great gaunt Herring Gulls and the dainty dove-like Bonaparte's Gulls which constitute the winter gull population of the Cape.

## BONAPARTE'S GULL

### Larus philadelphia (Ord)

At the first approach of cold weather there arrive at Cape May flocks of the beautiful little Bonaparte's Gull and all through the winter it is a characteristic bird of the sea coast. It is distinctly smaller than our other gulls and in its plump build and general proportions calls to mind a white Domestic Pigeon, while its restless activity and its habit of frequently holding its bill point down as it flies reminds one of a tern. Indeed George Ord, who originally discovered it on the Delaware River at Philadelphia, described it as a tern.

While typically a winter bird we have sporadic occurrences in late summer and early autumn—August 5, 1920; August 3, 1921; September 12, 1926; September 27, 1928; all single individuals and all in immature plumage; also several immature birds at Corson's Inlet on June 27, 1925 (Miller). The regular time of arrival at Cape May seems to be late October—October 25, 1929; October 30, 1921; etc., though they do not become common until November and from then until mid-March we are likely to find them present on any visit to the coast. Our latest records are April 2, 1921; April 4, 1924; April 18, 1926; April 1, 1928; April 7, 1929; April 12, 1930; with several exceptional dates—May 9, 1925; May 10, 1931; May 27, 1931. This little gull has been reported in large numbers ten miles off Long Branch on the upper New Jersey coast, in Christmas week, and we wonder if it may not always be more common out at sea, and if the earliest and latest occurrences at Cape May may not be stragglers from offshore flocks. Farther up the coast Charles Urner has seen them on Barnegat Bay in June on several occasions and in 1925 immature birds remained there throughout the month, while at Perth Amboy thirty were present on July 25, 1923.

The occurrence of Bonaparte's Gull at Cape May is somewhat erratic. It usually associates in flocks of from half a dozen to fifty, and these drift about from place to place so that on some days we may miss them entirely on a winter's walk. At other times the sea may be covered with them as flocks of one and two thousand individuals suddenly arrive from somewhere to be gone again the following day. The shallow pond near the Lighthouse used to be a favorite resort for them and even when it was largely covered with ice the birds would gather over whatever water remained. On other days they may all fly over to the Bay or perhaps put out to sea beyond the breakers. They are often found, too, about Schellenger's Landing and at other points on the Harbor while flocks may be seen coursing over the meadows back of Five Mile and Seven Mile Beaches, or gathering about the shallow salt ponds.

The actions of Bonaparte's Gull in the air are varied. When gathered together at some feeding station they wheel and quarter over the water with remarkable grace and dexterity, darting to the surface with all the agility of a tern to pick up some morsel of food while a hundred or more observed on the Bay shore on December 30, 1920, were performing intricate evolutions while every moment one or another of them would wheel suddenly and swoop to the surface. Their wingbeats on a straight away flight are more rapid than those of the larger gulls and less regular, while sometimes the wings appear as if their tips were pointing backward; they frequently flutter, too, in true tern style as they pause momentarily in their flight.

On March 13, 1921, I found three flying over a salt pond on the meadows and every moment others were arriving until there were twenty-six in the flock. A careful analysis of their flight showed that they give several rapid wingbeats and then sail softly down, pausing suddenly over a likely spot with quick short beats—often a distinct flutter, and then, just as they seem about to alight, and just as the dangling feet touch the water, they are up in the air again bouncing along in buoyant flight. With individual birds in all stages of this performance the result is a veritable maze of white wings. They will go crisscrossing through the air, swooping down and flapping up again and then suddenly, stirred by a common impulse, away they go all together like a flight of shore birds, out to sea beyond the surf line where they come to rest on the water.

On March 24, 1923, a small flock was observed over the meadows flying with short, quick wing strokes followed by a short sail. Sometimes they halted instantly with backward strokes, almost turning somersaults, and then hovered, for a moment, the actions being very like those of the Black Terns on the same spot in August. On February 14, 1925, a flock was seen putting directly out to sea in bullet-like flight.

On November 12, 1922, Julian Potter saw a flock, possibly on migration, which he estimated to number 2000 birds and which was performing wonderful evolutions off Cape May Point. The birds would rise from the water in close formation and fly up the coast a short distance, where they would suddenly settle in one large assemblage, pitching and diving through the air in every direction, before coming to rest on the surface. Then, after a few minutes rest, they would rise again *en masse* and fly back down the coast to repeat the whole performance.

Six birds watched on January 7, 1922, were wheeling about one another in a small area over a patch of open water in the ice-covered pond by the Lighthouse. They flew about twenty feet in the air and one after another pitched downward, actually plunging into the water, an unusual action for any gull. They kept their wings half spread and never submerged entirely though the head went under at every plunge. They would rise again almost instantly, flapping their wings which had never been closed and dangling their feet, all the while uttering a tern-like cry. A flock of ten watched on the Harbor on December 27, 1929, dived repeatedly and went entirely under in the deeper water but only for a second or two. Several Bonaparte's Gulls studied at very close range from the bridge at Schellenger's Landing (February 11, 1921) were beating against a strong wind. Their flight was very light and buoyant and many times they recalled pigeons as they turned against the wind with head and neck outstretched and slightly raised. Their bodies bounced up and down in the air as if the wings were fairly pounding it and causing the rebound.

On the water they float lightly and often revolve, whirling around suddenly like a phalarope. When swimming vigorously the neck is stretched forward and slightly elevated and the wings held clear of the water and crossed above the tail. One bird in this position suddenly plunged its head completely under the surface while another bent its head over and scratched the side of its face with its foot. When at rest they ride the waves like ducks. With heads drawn well down on their shoulders and all pointing to the wind, they bob up and down like corks when the water is rough. Even the most restful assemblage, however, is liable to take sudden flight and a flock floating peacefully on the Lighthouse Pond took wildly to wing and was out over the Bay in a few moments. The advent of a Cooper's Hawk proved to be the cause of their alarm although he made no apparent effort to attack them. On another occasion a Duck Hawk managed to isolate a gull from the flock but in the dodging that ensued the hawk was outmastered at every turn and eventually flew off.

Sometimes we see Bonaparte's Gulls resting on the ground, most frequently on the strand, and twenty gathered on April 2, 1922, near the Coast Guard Station at the Point, close to some Herring Gulls which seemed like perfect giants in comparison. I have also seen them standing close together in a line on a narrow sand spit in a salt pond on the meadows. These birds later swam about on the pond tilting and plunging their heads under for a moment with the tails held erect like surface-feeding ducks.

On November 7, 1931, there were eight Bonaparte's Gulls along with twenty Common Terns and a few immature Laughing Gulls all perched on a row of close set pilings at Cape May Point, the only ones I have noticed in such a situation, as they seem to prefer to rest on the water or the beach.

In his study of the great flock that assembled on the Delaware in April and May, 1922, Julian Potter writes me that they fed sometimes on small minnows which they caught by diving and swallowed while skittering over the waves like petrels. Sometimes a bird would drop its fish and was unable to recover it and once one went completely under and emerged with a fish only to be attacked by many others with the result that the catch was lost to all. Again they seemed to be picking some sort of insect food from the surface of the water dipping down with the utmost grace and barely touching the water with bill and feet. On one day the flock was spread out in a long line three-quarters of a mile in length, all of the birds headed into the breeze, and as they neared the shore the leaders would swing back to the rear so that the flock remained in the same position. They floated high on the water with tail and wings elevated so that the body seemed tilted forward. When facing a heavy wind, or resting, the head was drawn close to the shoulders and at a distance the birds seemed to be headless. The great majority were immature, or at least white-headed, birds with only a sprinkling of black-headed ones. They had an explosive call somewhat like the *haaa* of the Laughing Gull and a call that might best be imitated by a whistled *cheer* while there was also a succession of rapid notes recalling the spring "song" of the hop toad. One morning a flock of forty sailed high overhead apparently catching insects in the air as the Laughing Gulls seem to do and continually rising disappeared entirely from sight. They were first seen on April 12, had increased to five hundred by April 27, and were last seen on May 6, a mere half dozen.

During the time that they are with us the Bonaparte's Gulls exhibit much variety of plumage. The winter adults are delicate pearly gray above with white head, breast and tail, and an always conspicuous character is the white outer border to the front of the wing caused by several pure white primary feathers which contrast with the rest of the pearl gray upper parts. There is also a black area on the posterior wing border formed by the tips of the other primaries. Young birds are quite different having a dusky stripe immediately over the bones of the wing and a dark terminal band on the tail. There are also dusky patches on the head and back which vary in individuals and produce a strongly mottled appearance. There is a dusky spot on the side of the head in both plumages while the bill is always black and the feet pink. The adult bird in breeding plumage has a dark gray hood like the Laughing Gull, which seems almost black at a distance, this is apparently rarely assumed before the birds leave Cape May on spring migration. One individual seen on the Harbor at Schellenger's Landing, on April 27 and again May 10, 1931, had the black head and several seen on the Delaware River some miles above the Bay, on April 15, 1927, had partly completed the molt. No others in this plumage were recorded at the Cape, and one seen at Stone Harbor, May 9, 1925, still had the head white. A similar specimen was secured by Norris DeHaven at Atlantic City on April 4, 1896, and another at Gloucester on the Delaware River on April 10, 1890. Another Gloucester bird on the same date had only a slight dusky tinge on the top of the head while a similar bird was seen on the river below Philadelphia on March 3, 1890, and another was picked up dead at Cape May Point on April 4, 1924. These are perhaps just beginning the molt.

Light conditions affect the appearance of these gulls as they do other species. When resting on the water their snowy breasts are often concealed or turned away from the observer and their backs seem darker, so that they appear as slaty gray birds with white heads, and when flying low over the waves they often seem unnaturally dark. Their full beauty is best displayed in the brilliant winter sunshine against dull brown meadows or blue sky.

All in all they are delightful birds with more vigor and action than most of our winter sojourners, and with an apparent enjoyment of flight for flight's sake not appreciable in the sluggish, business-like actions of the Herring Gulls.

## * LITTLE GULL

### Larus minutus Pallas

This European bird has never been seen on Cape May waters but it has occurred at the northern extremity of the state's coast line.

One was seen by Warren F. Eaton in company with James L. Edwards and John Thompson on the Newark meadows on May 12, 1929. He writes: "In a mixed flock of about 200 Bonaparte's Gulls, fifty Ring-bills and a dozen Herring Gulls we picked out two birds with black heads. One of these showed black under the wings and the other was an adult Bonaparte's Gull. The former fluttered its wings like a tern and was several times an object of attack by the many Bonaparte's Gulls. In size it was about two inches shorter than the latter and markedly smaller when they were seen side by side. The color of the under surface of the wings looked absolutely black and the upper side was apparently not marked at all, the body, tail and back were white; head and neck black" (Auk, 1929, p. 376). On May 6, previous, James P. Chapin saw what he felt sure was one of these little gulls under particularly favorable circumstances in upper New York Bay (Auk, 1929, p. 377) and on August 11, 1929, James L. Edwards, with Charles Urner and others, saw still another, in the white-headed plumage, but with the black under surface of the wings very evident, with a flock of Common Terns on the Manasquan River, at Point Pleasant, N. J. (Auk, 1929, p. 532). The upper side of the wings was seen to be pale gray with no white area as in the Bonaparte's Gull, except for a white posterior margin.

## * KITTIWAKE

### Rissa tridactyla tridactyla (Linnaeus)

This little gull is a pelagic species which is occasionally blown to our beaches by severe storms.

William H. Werner told me that he secured quite a number of specimens from fishermen who went out to the banks off Atlantic City, in the winter of 1894–95, and that they were reported as present there every winter up to 1900, and doubtless later. They were especially plentiful in 1898.

From the lists of those who went to sea for their Christmas bird lists for "Bird-Lore" we get some interesting data. On December 31, 1904, Robert E. Stackpole and William H. Wiegmann, counted seventy-four adult and fifty-seven immature Kittiwakes while cruising from ten to twenty-five miles off Long Branch, N. J., but did not begin to see them until they had "almost lost sight of land." On December 27, 1908, Robert E. Stackpole and Charles H. Rogers saw fifteen off Seabright, N. J.; December 18, 1910, Noemi Pernessin and Charles Rogers saw twenty off Seabright; December 28, 1912, Wiegmann, Rogers and Waldron Miller, saw fifteen in the same region; and on December 19, 1913, the same with John T. Nichols, saw forty. On all of these trips the Bonaparte's Gulls outnumbered the Kittiwakes ten, or sometimes fifty, to one. On December 27, 1925, five were seen at Barnegat Bay, and Charles Urner has other records from that region for October 11, 1925; October 31, 1926; November 12, 1921.

Two Christmas census trips on fishing boats out of Cold Spring Inlet, Cape May, to the fishing banks failed to yield any Kittiwakes although conditions of weather may have had something to do with this. The bird is more frequently seen from the shores of Long Island than farther down the coast and there are records from November 4 to February 27 (Braislin). In size the Kittiwake is comparable only with Bonaparte's Gull which is a little smaller; in plumage the adult is of almost the same pattern as the much larger Ring-bill but the black at the tip of the wing cuts straight across at right angles and the feet are black; the immature bird is distinguished from the winter adult and young Bonaparte's by the black feet, the absence of white on the primaries, and a black bar across the back of the neck, instead of a spot behind the eye; both have a narrow black tail band (cf. Peterson). Other Kittiwakes have been recorded off Barnegat by Charles Urner on October 11, 1925; November 29, 1926 (six); November 12, 1927 (twelve); and by Carter and Friedmann on October 31, 1926 (two).

## GULL-BILLED TERN

### Gelochelidon nilotica aranea (Wilson)

Alexander Wilson discovered this tern on one of his several trips to Cape May probably in 1811 and announced the fact as follows: "This new species I first met with on the shores of Cape May, particularly over the salt marshes, and darting down after a kind of large black spider, plenty in such places. This spider can travel under water as well as above, and, during summer at least, seems to constitute the principal food of the present tern. In several which I opened, the stomach was crammed with a mass of these spiders alone; these they frequently pick up from the pools as well as from the grass, dashing down on them in the manner of their tribe. Their voice is sharper and stronger than that of the Common Tern; the bill is differently formed, being shorter, more rounded above, and thicker; the tail is also much shorter, and less forked. They do not associate with the others; but keep in small parties by themselves." "This species breeds in the salt marshes, the female drops her eggs, generally three or four in number, on the dry drift grass, without the slightest appearance of a nest."

By 1869 Turnbull regarded it as rare. In 1886 Harry G. Parker reported it as nesting at the lower end of Seven Mile Beach, but this spot is a sandy beach frequented by the Common Tern and it seems unlikely that this species could have nested there. Charles S. Shick, however, speaks of it as still present in 1890 and nesting at this same point "on the meadows and sand flats." These men were primarily egg collectors and whether they could distinguish the bird from the Common Tern is open to question. Turner McMullen has reported a nest and two eggs found on June 20, 1926, in the Laughing Gull colony on the meadows back of Seven Mile Beach. But the fact that I have found nests of the Common Tern on the meadows back of Atlantic City built on "trash" would indicate that location alone is not conclusive and none of the expert students of our coastal birds has been able to find a single individual of this species. We seem to have no records of the occurrence of the Gull-billed Tern in New Jersey, since Wilson's time, not even as a straggler, that seem convincing. While it is a southern species there are three records for Long Island—July 4, 1882; July 8, 1884; July 1, 1885. (Griscom, Birds of the New York City Region.)

# COMMON TERN

Sterna hirundo hirundo Linnaeus

PLATES 58–69, pp. 566–567

While Common Terns do not nest on the beaches immediately about Cape May a colony was established some years ago on Gull Bar, in Hereford Inlet, and on the points of beach on either side of the entrance and since then the birds are to be found somewhere about the Cape from the time of their arrival in May until their departure in October.   They were abundant all along the coast in early times down to the eighties when the slaughter for millinery purposes bid fair to exterminate them.   Detailed history since that time is lacking but they have increased greatly since 1890 when my acquaintance with the bird life of the Cape began.   Scattered individuals may now be seen at low tide on Jarvis Sound resting on the exposed mussel beds or perched on channel stakes along the thoroughfares while others will be flying back and forth over the waters of the Harbor.

More regularly we see small bunches of terns travelling up and down the coast flying low over the waves out beyond the surf line or wheeling in over the bathing beaches.   In certain lights they appear dull gray and blend so perfectly with the color of the sea that it is difficult to distinguish them, while in others they show silvery white against the dark waters, the apparent change in color being remarkable.   Occasionally too we see detachments of twelve to twenty-five travelling at a higher elevation, dropping to the waves and rising again in irregular undulating flight, the picture of grace and agility. These birds come in to the strand now and then, especially in stormy weather when the sea is rough and the sky leaden gray with a spit of rain in the air, and not infrequently give voice to their harsh cries.

These passing birds are traveling from their fishing grounds on the "ripps" at the mouth of the Bay, to their nesting grounds or vice versa and there is a spot on the beach near the Lighthouse where they used to congregate in considerable numbers to rest from their vigorous fishing or later in the season to pause on their migrations, While they still gather here there are fewer of them and the increasing numbers of pedestrians on the beach causes them constant alarm. From late July until September this spot was a regular roosting place for terns although as the summer advanced part of them, at least, seemed to shift to a sand flat at the upper end of Two Mile Beach, a spot to which roosting gulls resort. Large numbers of terns *en route* for this later roosting place pass over the town at dusk on August evenings in compact flocks of twelve to fifty individuals, flying steadily with much more regular wingbeats than usual.

In May and June, also, some terns assemble on the beach opposite the "ripps" but not in such numbers nor so regularly as later in the season. The earliest of these are, I think, transients bound for farther north while some are immature non-breeding birds, from colonies not far distant, which come here to feed. Of some two hundred birds assembled there on June 21–22, 1923, nearly half were in the immature plumage with white foreheads. On May 20, 1927, there were fifty-one adults busily engaged in fishing close to the beach and twenty-five more resting on pilings a little west of their usual gathering place, while on July 11, 1922, there were two hundred on the beach, on June 1, 1923, ninety-five, and ninety-seven on June 27, 1925.

It is August, however, when the southbound migrants collect on this strip of beach, that the Common Terns become a leading feature in the bird life of the Cape. The first large assemblages from 1920 to 1931 were on:

| | | | |
|---|---|---|---|
| 1920. | August 2. | 1923. July 28. | 1927. July 27. |
| 1921. | July 29. | 1924. July 22. | 1929. July 30. |
| 1922. | July 11. | 1925. July 27. | 1931. August 1. |

There seem always to be some Black Terns mingled with the larger birds and since they do not nest south of the Great Lakes their presence suggests that the Common Terns in these early southbound flocks may also come from far north and not from the New Jersey nesting colonies. The fact that the New Jersey birds still had downy young and hatching eggs as late as July 18, 1821, and unhatched eggs on July 9, 1923, lends weight to this theory. The Black Terns that come with the others seem gradually to leave the flock and disappear, at least in most seasons, and the stray Laughing Gulls that associate with them at first leave later to roost elsewhere with their own kind. The gathering of the terns on the beach at the Point was for many years a characteristic sight to those who follow the shore line during August but of late years they have sadly dwindled. The number of birds fluctuated from day to day, ranging from fifty to one thousand, but the variation was perhaps more apparent than real since a large part of the flock was often out at the "ripps" feeding. The frequent pedestrians passing along the beach constantly disturbed the terns and finally forced them to seek a resting place back of the dunes, on sand flats which formed there as result of winter storms and high tides, or on the borders and mud bars of the shallow pond east of the Lighthouse.    In still later years dogs ranging over the beach have well nigh driven the flocks away while the beach itself has suffered erosion until its width is sadly reduced.

Usually when disturbed the birds simply fly up the beach a little way and settle again or else, especially after being flushed several times in succession, they scatter over the ocean and begin feeding.    There is usually much excitement and the angry birds protest vigorously at the intruders. The racket begins as soon as they take wing which they sometimes do *en masse* or sometimes rank after rank, in regular order down the beach.    There is a great flapping of the long narrow wings but not in unison, as every bird beats the air independently.    The first birds to take wing wheel, and come back, meet the next installment going forward, so that ere long birds are flying in every direction; an intricate maze of moving wings ensues and there seems to be wild confusion.    Now as the sunlight strikes them the Common Terns look snowy white and the Black Terns that are mingled with them blacker than ever, then the angle of light changes and they appear in varied shades of gray and pearl.    One flock of about one hundred flying with exceptional regularity came toward me head-on and the wings, with only the forward edge visible, appeared white with a dusky border above and below, while the jet black heads of the birds showed prominently against their snowy breasts, a truly beautiful sight.

The volume of sound produced by a flock of terns in full cry can hardly be appreciated by one who has not heard them and, although these beach flocks hardly equal a nesting colony in vocal ability, they are not far behind, and their calling is really but a continuance of the clamor of the breeding grounds, which they have maintained on occasion every since their arrival there in May.

Terns have several notes.    The most characteristic is the long drawn, grating *keer-r'eer; keeee-te'arrr;* or *teeee-a'rrr* as I have written it at various times.    It consists of two equally accented long drawn out syllables with much of the harsh "*rr*" sound especially at the end.    This is repeated over and over; and with a hundred or more birds all crying simultaneously the bedlam of noise can be imagined and will continue to ring in one's ears long after the birds have been left behind.    There is another quite different call, short and emphatic but lacking the volume of the last.    It resembles closely the call of the Robin in defense of its nest or young but is not so loud and I have written it on several occasions *sheep'; chip'* or *quip'*.    I have heard this cry from birds gathered at Cape May Point in spring (May 20) and it is frequent on the nesting grounds.    The common cry is given both on the wing and while resting on the beach—at least in the spring, but the short cry is always uttered by a flying bird.    A third cry is usually restricted to the breeding grounds but on rare occasions has been heard in the August gather-

PLATE 58

*John Bartram*

COMMON TERN ON NEST, LOWER END OF SEVEN MILE BEACH, CAPE MAY COUNTY, N. J., ON PILE OF "BEACH TRASH."

PLATE 59

*J. F. Street*

*Wharton Huber*

1. COMMON AND BLACK TERNS ON THE BEACH AT SOUTH CAPE MAY, AUGUST, 1920
2. COMMON TERNS ON THE BEACH NEAR CAPE MAY POINT, AUGUST 23, 1923.

PLATE 60

*Wharton Huber*

*John Bartram*

1. COMMON TERNS ON THEIR NESTS IN COLONY ON EPHRAIM'S ISLAND, FIVE MILE BEACH, N. J., WITH A BLACK SKIMMER IN THE FOREGROUND.

2. COMMON TERN ON NEST, LOWER END OF SEVEN MILE BEACH, N. J.

PLATE 61

*B. C. Hiatt*

COMMON TERN ON NEST, SOUTHERN END OF SEVEN MILE BEACH, N. J., JUNE 21, 1936.

PLATE 62

*B. C. Hiatt*

COMMON TERN ALIGHTING ON NEST, SEVEN MILE BEACH, N. J., JUNE 21, 1936.

PLATE 63

*Wharton Huber*

*Wharton Huber*

FOUR VIEWS OF COMMON TERNS AT NESTS ON GULL BAR, HEREFORD INLET, N. J.,
JULY 9, 1925.

PLATE 64

*W. L. Baily*

*Wharton Huber*

1. COMMON TERN AND YOUNG, PECK'S BEACH, N. J.
2. COMMON TERN WITH NEST AND EGGS, GULL BAR, HEREFORD INLET, N. J., JULY 9, 1925.

PLATE 65

*Wharton Huber*

*W. L. Baily*

YOUNG OF COMMON TERN: UPPER, GULL BAR, HEREFORD INLET, N. J.; LOWER, SEVEN
MILE BEACH, N. J., JULY 9, 1923.

PLATE 66

*Wharton Huber*

*Wharton Huber*

THREE NESTS OF COMMON TERN, MERE HOLLOWS IN THE SAND WITH LITTLE OR NO
ADDED MATERIAL, SEVEN MILE BEACH, N. J.

PLATE 67

*Wharton Huber*

*Wharton Huber*

1. YOUNG COMMON TERNS AND EGG IN NEST SURROUNDED BY RAZOR SHELLS, EPHRAIM'S ISLAND, FIVE MILE BEACH, N. J., JULY 10, 1929.

2. COMMON TERNS GATHERING ON THE BEACH AT SOUTH CAPE MAY, AUGUST 23, 1923.

PLATE 68

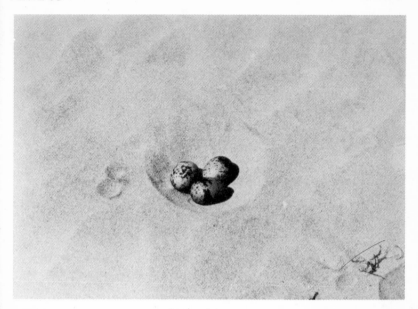

*W. L. Baily*

*Wharton Huber*

COMMON TERN EGGS ON BARE SAND, PECK'S BEACH, N. J.

COMMON TERN'S NEST IN A DEPOSIT OF RAZOR SHELLS, EPHRAIM'S ISLAND, FIVE
MILE BEACH, N. J., JULY 10, 1928.

PLATE 69

*Wharton Huber*

*J. K. Potter*

1. ELABORATE NEST OF COMMON TERN, SEVEN MILE BEACH, N. J., 1925.

2. NEST AND EGG OF ROSEATE TERN, GULL BAR, HEREFORD INLET, N. J., JULY 15, 1923, CAPE MAY COUNTY, N. J.

ings on the beach. It is uttered by an enraged bird as it dashes down at the head of an intruder and is a rasping *kek-kek-kek-kek-kek-kek-ke'eeeer* the last syllable delivered just as the bird veers off without actually striking its enemy and sounds like the tearing of cloth. Then there is the cry of the young bird as it runs to meet its parent bringing food; a low tremulous call *kruuuuurr* or *chuuuuuurr* the note usually repeated four times. The clamor incident to the flushing of one of the beach gatherings continues until the birds begin to alight again or scatter widely over the ocean when silence is once more established.

When reassembling on the sand the terns come directly into the wind and settle in long lines with their heads all pointing one way. With the prevailing south wind they always face the sea but on several occasions when strong northwest winds were blowing they faced landward. On August 2, 1920, the first assemblage of the season, probably unacquainted with the spot and naturally nervous, arose at once upon being disturbed and circled around, higher and higher, until they had reached a considerable altitude and looked no larger than swallows, and then drifted with the wind out to sea and disappeared. Whether the same birds returned or whether this was a continuance of their migratory flight I could not determine. The same restlessness sometimes prevails in the spring and a flock observed on May 26, 1923, flushed and returned to the beach many times with no apparent disturbing cause. One day when the terns had shifted their roosting place to the sand flat they were completely enveloped in a dense fog which for some days spread over the coast for a quarter of a mile inland. The effect as they arose was weird. The air was at first full of the cries of birds that were invisible and then, as they advanced, their white tails and under surface of the wings would catch the light and gleam for a moment like silvery sheen from polished metal and then disappear again, swallowed up in the gray blanket of the fog. By the time the air had cleared somewhat the birds had settled on the sand flat, covered with its scattered shells and pebbles, and the resemblance of the resting terns to this background was remarkable. The white and gray of the adult plumage and the black caps being duplicated by the shells in various stages of bleaching and decay, while the mottled brown and gray of the young birds was matched by the various colors of the sand.

As the terns gather normally on the strand they remain standing for a time on their short red legs, many of them preening their feathers, bending over and arching the back so that the plumage of the under parts may be reached, or twisting the head over the shoulders to reach the feathers of the back. All the while the tail is partly erected and is spread out for a moment, first on one side, then on the other. Occasionally the preening bird will ruffle up its entire plumage and stretch out its wings like a man stretching his arms after a sleep. At other times they are raised vertically but only for a moment or two, as we often see them do when alighting on the beach. Some of the birds walk about in a rather clumsy manner, others bathe in the shallow pools and one individual scratched its head with its foot. Eventually, however, all settled down, squatting directly on the sand. Now and then one would raise its head and open its bill as if calling to another in the air above, and when a screaming tern does fly over head, or a Fish Hawk sails past on his way to the sea, there is much commotion in the flock and it is amusing to see the heads turned over on the side so that one eye looks straight up at the intruder.

There is a curious habit that seems to belong in part to the courtship behavior of the terns although it is to be seen also in these late summer gatherings. A bird will fly into the assemblage with a small fish in its bill and immediately another bird, sometimes an adult, sometimes a young of the year, will beg for it with open bill, doubtless a relic of the feeding period. Then another adult will strut past with neck elevated, bill pointed skyward and wings drooping, a most ludicrous pose. This took place on the beach on August 3, 1922, but I have witnessed precisely the same performance in a spring beach flock (May 28, 1923) when two individuals strutted past the one holding the fish, evidently a courtship performance. On the mussel beds of Jarvis Sound (May 21–22, 1922) I saw one of a pair—presumably the male—come in and feed the fish to the other but when apparently the same individual returned with another fish a second male was already there. The first bird paraded past the female in the attitude described above holding the fish aloft but being driven away he swallowed it himself, as he did on another occasion when he found no terns at all on the spot. This bird moreover ducked his head under the water several times and churned it up with his wings before taking flight. During August I have repeatedly seen terns flying along the shore with a small fish crossways between their mandibles and supposed that they had been so harrassed by other birds that they were unable to swallow their prey when caught, but later I saw one alight on the beach entirely free from molestation and instead of eating his fish he carried it around and eventually flew away without making any effort to swallow it. As late as July 30, 1923, I saw an adult come in with a fish and join a flock resting on the beach. A full plumaged bird of the year came running up to it and was fed the fish while it uttered the peculiar *kruuuurr* cry of the nesting grounds.

Terns feed on small fish that have been stranded on the beach, swooping down to pick them up, and they also dive into pools and ponds on the salt meadows as well as into the Harbor and the Bay. Their favorite feeding ground, however, is the "ripps" at the mouth of Delaware Bay, to which large flocks resort daily and viewed from the shore through the glass the assembled birds make a lively scene. I watched them thus for a long time on August 26, 1920. It was a day of approaching storm and the water looked gray and dull but the light was ever changing, there were bright flashes as the sun broke through the clouds, followed by bands of shadow. The wind had roughened the water and where the currents from the Bay and ocean met there was a broad stretch of whitecaps. Over these hovered the birds, flying in every direction, the terns pitching head foremost into the water, the gulls skimming the surface or swooping down and alighting on the waves, and the dark heavy-winged Fish Hawks passing and repassing higher in the air than the lighter birds. Now and then one of them dropped like a plummet into the water and emerged with a fish in his claws and was off to his nest back in the country. The terns appear gray at one angle and snow white at another and the white wings are constantly flashing as they catch the sunlight, now here, now there, in the misty distance, like gigantic fireflies in the dusk of evening. It is a wonderfully animated scene and food evidently abounds.

On August 26, 1931 I found two adult terns and three young practically full fledged and able to fly, resting on Seven Mile Beach. The old birds were constantly feeding the young and flying back and forth in search of prey. There was a flock of Sanderlings also feeding on the beach, catching small Hippa crabs or shrimps, and every time a Sanderling made a successful catch a tern would dart after him and pursue him relentlessly out over the surf and back over the beach but I did not in any instance see him relinquish his prey. While the Sanderlings were frequently taking wing or running up and down the beach the tern never pursued one of them unless he carried a shrimp. While I have seen terns pursue one another I never again saw them try to seize prey from other birds. Terns dive from the air, usually from a considerable height, plunging into the water with a splash, beak first, and usually go entirely under though they sometimes suddenly shear off and deftly pick up some scrap of food from the surface. When they do go in they seem to fairly throw the body so forcibly does it strike the water. A flock feeding close in along the Bay shore on August 26, 1921. was diving continually and every five seconds one or more birds would strike the water. They would pause suddenly in their flight and turning tail up and bill straight down would go under with a splash, the wings still partly spread, and in two or three seconds would emerge again usually with a fish held firmly between the mandibles. Sometimes they would pause and hover like a Marsh Hawk without making a plunge.

Terns flying offshore and traveling low over the water have also been seen to dive but in their case there was not sufficient altitude for a vertical plunge and they went splashing in at a low angle with the momentum of their flight. Several were seen August 29, 1920, diving in shallow pools on the meadows and one drove his bill well into the muddy bottom, clouding up the water. Back on the thoroughfares above the Harbor they seem to dive mainly near some point of land where two currents of water meet and where fish no doubt congregate. One bird watched for some time (May 26, 1929) at close quarters, as it hovered over a partly submerged islet in Jarvis Sound, was diving repeatedly. It held the same position in the air all the time, about four feet from the water with wings beating rapidly and tail fully spread, the long feather tips constantly fluttering so that it was only now and then that their dark outer webs could be distinguished. The body seemed to rise and fall with the motion of the wings as if floating buoyantly on the waves of air.   The head was held a little below the horizontal and was turned constantly from side to side, sometimes twisted far around.   The bird usually splashed in at a slight angle, often among the grass tips, but seldom made a catch.   Occasionally it would rest on the water and plunge the head and neck under while it churned the wings, evidently bathing.   So far as I am aware the terns do not resort to fresh water to bathe as do the Laughing Gulls.

Straggling terns are seen flying over the meadows or more frequently over the thoroughfares and often come to rest on the stakes which mark the location of oyster beds on the sounds, or on the channel markers on the thoroughfares, and one bird will sometimes alight on the back of another which is already in possession of a stake and force it from its perch, just as the Herring Gulls do on the Harbor pilings.

The beach flocks near the Lighthouse, which used to be a permanent feature during August, seemed to diminish in September and I have no record of more than fifty in that month, while most of them usually leave by October 1.   My latest records are October 13, 1929, thirty, and October 12, 1930, fifty, with two exceptional occurrences—nine seen by Ludlow Griscom on November 11, 1921, and twenty that I saw roosting on pilings a little farther on, on the Bay shore, in company with some Laughing and Bonaparte's Gulls on November 7, 1931.   Julian Potter saw a flock of some fifteen hundred Common Terns arise from the beach at the Point on October 1, 1925, and after attaining a great height disappear to the southward, doubtless on migration.   Owing to my inability to be on the nesting grounds of the terns regularly during the spring my dates of arrival are not entirely satisfactory.   The earliest occurrences at Cape May are May 9, 1925; May 10, 1924; May 14, 1928; May 9, 1931, while on May 11, 1929, they were present in numbers at a nesting colony established that year on Ephraim's Island, back of Five Mile Beach.

Julian Potter saw Common Terns on the Delaware River at Philadelphia on April 22, 1922, and Richard Miller on the same date in 1929.   As an illustration of where our terns go to in winter a bird banded as a downy young in the colony back of Five Mile Beach by John Gillespie on August 23, 1925, was recovered on the island of Trinidad on May 16, 1926.   The favorite nesting grounds of the Common Tern seem to be beaches at the entrances to inlets or harbors or the low sand bars formed at the mouths of the inlets. Most spots of this sort have in recent years been rendered unsatisfactory for the birds by "improvements" of various sorts while the development of summer resorts all along the coast has also tended to drive the birds away. On the other hand the dredging of the channels to form the so-called inland water way has resulted in extensive sand flats where the sand and shells from the dredges have been spread upon the meadows and these have proved very acceptable nesting grounds for the terns in lieu of the beaches.   Various factors however have operated to cause the birds to shift their breeding places from one year to the next and many former nesting sites have been deserted.

A visit to a breeding place on Brigantine Island, while well beyond the limits of Cape May County, gave me a good idea of the activities of the bird at this season which were later found to be the same on nesting sites nearer home. Our visit was on July 17–18, 1921, and the scene was one of wild activity. About three hundred birds arose at our approach and as long as we remained the air was rent with their harsh chorus. The excited birds hovered and wheeled over our heads in layers, as it were, those highest up appearing no larger than swallows. The call of the individual tern was *keeer, keeer, teeeeé ark', teeeeé ark'*, but with dozens of them calling at once the din was indescribable. There were young birds already on the wing, too, full-fledged except for the bobbed tail which was their chief characteristic, but their more labored flight was noticeable as also their straightaway course, in contrast to the more erratic and wheeling flight of the adults. Their wings and bill were seen to be shorter and when they came to rest they somewhat resembled heavy-billed shore birds, standing high with practically no tail in evidence. The details of their plumage are discussed beyond.

On the ground on every side were other young birds, some just hatching with down still wet, others like mottled pieces of fur, the youngest browner and the older ones more gray, in each case so closely resembling the sand and bare ground that they were easily passed by, especially as they lay flat on their bellies, with the head and neck stretched forward to the fullest extent. Other young had pin feathers appearing among the down while others, still, had the wings nearly half-grown. These heavy-headed, top-heavy little fellows waddled away in a curious fashion and sought shelter in the marsh grass nearby or under the scattered tufts of sea rocket and goldenrod. The nests were usually mere hollows in the sand, sometimes with a few pieces of dry reeds or small sticks laid about the edge, but others were fairly well lined with the same material and some built on patches of trash that had been stranded on the meadow by the high tides. The eggs were never more than three in number and varied in color from pale green to deep olive brown with large and small splotches of brown and purple. We counted thirty-nine nests still occupied, containing eggs or young. All the time we were examining the nests the pandemonium overhead continued, there was a *chip, chip*, Robin-like call mingled with the usual cries and now and then some particularly aggressive bird would come swooping down directly at my head with glaring eyes and wide open red mouth from which came the rattling *kek-kek-kek-kek* cry ending with the tearing *keeeeeeeer'* as the bird checked itself just at my hat brim and veered off without actually striking me—the picture of rage and defiance.

Hereford Inlet with its numerous sand bars, and the wild stretches of lower Seven Mile Beach were favorite breeding places for Common Terns for many years, the latter constituting the last beach colony in Cape May County.

I first visited the inlet colony on June 20, 1923, when it was divided into two or more sections. One of these on Gull Bar at the mouth of the inlet consisted of about three hundred birds and another of two hundred was located on the sand point on the northern extremity of Five Mile Beach. On the date of our visit we counted in the former forty-six nests with eggs and two with small downy young. Another visit on July 8 found the colony largely washed away by the high tides which had swept over the bar, but the terns, undaunted, had begun to nest again and we counted twenty-nine nests with a single egg each, sixty-seven with two eggs, and fourteen with three. There were also probably fifty downy young on the higher part of the bar which had survived the flood.

On July 11, 1926, one section of this Gull Bar community numbered seventy-two nests, eighteen with one egg, thirty-eight with two, and fifteen with three, while thirty-five downy young were counted. Later in this year a high tide again swept over the bar and on August 10 no nests were to be seen and we found only three young. These were as yet unable to fly and ran fearlessly down the strand when we attempted to catch them and even out into the surf ten feet from the shore, where they swam the waves while their parents hovered anxiously over our heads. There were several hundred adult terns on the bar which arose as we approached with all the clamor of a nesting colony and later arranged themselves in ranks on the beach.

It is surprising that these high tides which nearly every year, and sometimes twice in a season, sweep over the low bars and beaches which the terns select as their nesting grounds, do not discourage the birds and drive them elsewhere, but they return year after year and when they do desert an old breeding ground it is usually for some other reason.

The other portion of the colony located on the northern point of Five Mile Beach apparently escaped the tides of 1923 and on July 8, while there were but few nests with eggs, we found a large number of young birds in the short grass of the adjacent meadow where they had taken refuge and were being fed by their parents. In 1924 this section of the colony was much reduced and not more than fifteen pairs of birds were seen. As late as July 21 of that year there were four nests with eggs and one with downy young while many fledged young were on the wing. In 1925 and 1926 it was deserted but a few pairs returned in 1927 and 1928.

On the lower point of Seven Mile Beach a third section of the Hereford Inlet tern colony was located. This, according to Richard Miller, consisted, on June 26, 1921, of fifteen pairs of birds and twelve nests were found four with three eggs, four with two and four with one. On July 10 it was reported washed out but by July 17 six new nests had been made in which laying had just begun. On June 25, 1922, Miller reported sixty pairs of terns present with many full sets of eggs and fifty on July 17, but on June 17, 1923, only five pairs were in evidence. I visited the spot on May 9, 1925, and found some birds already there but while they showed some resentment at my intrusion there was no indication of nesting, nor was there in 1926.

In 1927 Gull Bar being entirely under water except at high tide the birds that had nested there, or at least a part of them, moved over to this spot and on July 9 there were about fifty pairs present with young running about and many nests with two eggs each. The colony had evidently been washed out earlier in the season as numbers of eggs were found buried in the wet sand and only the nests located on several isolated sand dunes had survived. On July 24 of the same year Julian Potter counted five hundred terns here, and they have continued to nest here in varying numbers ever since.

In 1928 while a few pairs still continued to nest here the majority moved over to a sand flat on Ephraim's Island, back of the southern part of Five Mile Beach, where the Black Skimmers that had nested on Gull Bar had already repaired. This is a low meadow island, which has been partly covered by dredgings of sand from the channel, and is protected from approach from the mainland by broad thoroughfares. I first discovered the presence of terns and Skimmers here on July 28 by noticing a great concourse of birds in the air as I crossed in a boat from Cape May to Wildwood. Visiting it on August 4, Walker Hand and I found from eight hundred to one thousand terns present and many Black Skimmers. There were young terns in all stages of development and many eggs. The nests frequently had little strips or stems of straw or grass laid around their edges but in many cases the shells of razor clams, which were strewn in great abundance over the sand, were used instead, making a remarkable appearance.

The young downy birds showed much variation in color apparently independent of age; some were buff with scarcely any spots while others ranged from vivid buff to chocolate and light gray with definite blackish spots or irregular blotches. The eggs likewise showed a wide range of color usually some shade of olive brown or chocolate with dark brown or purplish spots or blotches; once or twice we have found sets that were plain bluish green with practically no spotting and one found on this visit consisted of two eggs, one dark chocolate color and the other Robin's egg blue without spots.

The parent birds were brooding the downy young, sitting over them breast down on the sand with wing tips slightly elevated. They scratched in the sand as if to deepen the nest cavity and also revolved. Those that were out seeking food would bring in small fishes about an inch in length and the well-fledged young would run up to them to be fed. The downy young when offered a fish did not seem to respond but I did not see them fed in any other way.

On August 14, after a heavy northeast storm (August 11–12) this colony was visited again and I found that most of the island had been submerged and the higher spots subjected to a pelting rain. Most of the little terns were drowned and were lying all about attracting swarms of flies while the eggs that had not hatched were broken or buried in the wet sand. One young bird was discovered that had just hatched and it would seem that the parent must have weathered the storm and saved its young by sitting on the nest. There were many old birds in the air but not a quarter as many as on the previous visit.

In 1929 this colony was visited on May 11 and two hundred and fifty terns were found with twenty-five Black Skimmers. The former were sitting on the sand, some strutting about in the absurd courting poses and many in the air, but no sign of nests. There was much calling but quite irrespective of my presence, and the Robin-like note was frequently heard. The flying birds were usually in groups of three, sometimes four and occasionally two, one bird always carrying a small fish, the others in pursuit. So far as I could see the pursuers never secured the prey although they turned and twisted most adroitly. The whole performance was perhaps part of the mating behavior. The tail feathers of the flying bird were always held tightly together forming a single slender whisp. One solitary bird on the strand had a small fish which he swallowed and then seemed to gag, holding the mouth open and taking water several times before closing it. The birds flying overhead were at all levels and as one looked up through the maze of wings those in the uppermost strata seemed no larger than swallows while in the brilliant sunlight all seemed rose-tinted below and their wings curiously translucent.

The Crows and Turkey Vultures that occasionally passed over were promptly attacked and forced to beat a hasty retreat, with redoubled flapping of their wings.

On June 30 there were young of all sizes in the nests and about two hundred adults. Rats were discovered on the island on this occasion with burrows in the hard sand hills and they seemed to have made some inroads on the eggs and young. On July 17, no fledged young were seen among the adults in the air and there were no downy young on the ground and only one set of eggs. Possibly another high tide had destroyed the early broods.

On May 16, 1930, only fifty terns were present at the nesting site with no sign as yet of eggs or young. On July 4 it was found that a tide had again swept the island and only a few water-soaked eggs and four young birds could be found. Some of the birds persisted, however, and on July 21, there were twenty pairs present but only a few eggs or young and on July 25 several birds were still setting. They were much less timid than the Black Skimmers, some of which also remained, and when I erected a blind near a nest the parents returned the moment I disappeared inside. One parent, probably the male, stood nearby while the other was incubating the eggs and when a Skimmer approached too near it was promptly pursued. When a nest contained young the parent returned at once and stood over them to shelter them from the sun. On August 4 the tides had again covered the spot and no young birds were in evidence although two adults were seen carrying small fish.

On July 6, 1931, the colony had been again entirely washed out and the stranded and broken eggs were being devoured by Herring Gulls. Only four terns were seen and they were flying high in the air and showed no concern at our visit. We learned later that they had followed the Skimmers to a new location on a similar dredging on the meadows a mile farther north toward Grassy Sound. The move being attributed to the rats which had been increasing in numbers. In 1932 this new spot was occupied by the birds and on a visit to it on July 13, we found approximately two hundred terns and sixty Skimmers. There had evidently been a high tide some time previously as eggs lay scattered all about and in rift rows against stranded patches of meadow trash. The terns, however, had begun to nest again and there were over fifty nests nearly all with full sets of eggs. Only one downy young could be found, a possible survivor from the flood. Conrad Roland and I studied the birds for some time from our boat nearby in the channel thus avoiding the disturbance that our presence on the island would occasion. When forced to leave their nests by the passing of an occasional Turkey Vulture, or other cause, the incubating birds returned at once and settled immediately upon the eggs. Sometimes a male bird stood close to his mate but in other cases he seemed to spend most of his time fishing, returning now and then with a small fish which he fed to her; sometimes she sat on the nest while receiving it, at others she walked a few steps to meet him and then resumed her position. All the time we were there there was an assemblage of terns on the adjoining mud flats which were exposed at low tide, sometimes as many as seventy. These birds remained perfectly still or were engaged in pluming themselves and in bathing in the shallow water and took flight only when the colony was disturbed. Whether this assemblage consisted of males whose mates were incubating or of birds that had not begun to make new nests I could not determine.

The innocent trespass of an occasional Turkey Vulture had amusing results as the entire colony arose and attacked him, from six to twenty continuing the pursuit far over the meadows. The great bird flapped his wings laboriously and twisted and turned to avoid the annoying assaults of the agile terns and in nearly every instance he disgorged part of his food although the terns paid no attention to this tribute. Curiously enough a tern coming back from the chase would dart after any Skimmer that chanced to be awing apparently mistaking him for another enemy.

We found the nests on this island very attractive many of them built in the middle of a mass of reed stems which formed the meadow trash, or lined with the same material, while others had dry grass, reed stems and bleached razor shells in their make-up.

At various times the Common Terns nested on the southern extremity of Seven Mile Beach sometimes with Skimmers and Least Terns usually occupying several elevated sand hills. On May 16, 1936, Benjamin Hiatt found ten pairs present but no eggs had been deposited. On June 7 there were fifteen pairs with eggs and on the 20th fifty nests with well incubated eggs and a few young birds. A storm had swept over the point and washed out almost all of the Least Terns' nests as these birds built on the lowest stretches of the beach.

From the records of nests examined by Richard Miller and Turner Mc-Mullen I have compiled the following data: Earliest date for eggs, one nest containing a single egg at the southern end of Seven Mile Beach on May 27, 1928, all other egg dates are in June or July, as follows, all being at the above locality unless otherwise stated:

June 26, 1921, four nests with two eggs and four with three.

July 3, 1921, three nests with one egg; two with two and three with three.

July 10, 1921, four nests with one egg; two with two.

July 17, 1921, two nests with one egg; one with two.

June 18, 1922, forty-six nests with three eggs; one with two.

June 25, 1922, fifty nests with two or three eggs.

June 17, 1923, only five pairs of birds present; two nests with two eggs.

July 8, 1923, several pairs but only one nest containing three eggs.

June 22, 1924, twenty nests with a single egg; ten with two and seven with three; some hatching; seventy-five pairs of birds present.

June 29, 1924, ten nests with a single egg; ten with two and thirty with three; four downy young.

July 4, 1924, forty-three nests with two or three eggs.

June 7, 1925, only a few pairs present; four nests with two eggs.

June 21, 1926, colony deserted, but thirty-one nests with two or three eggs on the northern point of Five Mile Beach.

June 19, 1927, eleven nests with one egg; nine with two; twenty-one with three; fifty pairs of birds present.

July 3, 1927, twenty-three nests with one egg; fifty-nine with two; twenty-one with three and a few downy young.

June 24, 1928, two nests with one egg; two with two; one with three and many young.

July 4, 1931, fifty birds present; eight nests with one egg; six with two; two with three and many young.

June 26, 1932, only four pairs present; one nest with three eggs.

The spring plumage of the Common Tern is pearly gray above while the lower parts are washed with a paler tint of the same. The crown as far as the back of the neck is glossy black and the bill and feet red, the former dusky at the tip. Individuals in this plumage may be seen as late as the last week of August and some perhaps leave for the south before undergoing any change. In the autumn and winter they are whiter below, and the forepart of the head is white, and the bill and feet black, the molt usually taking place in August or September. Some birds fail to change plumage in the spring and, returning north in this dress, remain so throughout the summer. These are non-breeding individuals in which neither the sexual impulse nor the molt have developed. While they sometimes participate in the excitement of the nesting colony they also may be found flocking by themselves on the beach. In the flocks of late summer, besides the adults in both summer and winter plumage, there will be found many young of the year which have white heads bordered with dusky and with dusky patches on the wings and back. They also lack the long outer tail feathers of the adults, as do the latter when undergoing the molt, and appear somewhat bobtailed, while the bill is largely dusk.

Besides the Brigantine colony, already mentioned, there are several flourishing nesting colonies on islands in Barnegat Bay. On practically all of their nesting places they associate with the Black Skimmers.

The reëstablishment of nesting colonies, of Common Terns within the bounds of Cape May County, precarious and temporary as they seem to be, is interesting as illustrating conditions which formerly prevailed on the Cape May beaches themselves, and it is encouraging to those of us who have claimed that proper protection would bring about such results. Were it extended and maintained we might hope for still further restoration of former conditions. At present, however, the August gatherings of terns near the Lighthouse constitute the most striking feature of tern life immediately about Cape May and add greatly to the beauty and interest of the strand—even though sadly depleted by the inroads and activities of the human species.

No matter what the weather this assemblage of Common Terns seems always in place. On bright sunny days, when the sky is deep blue and the ocean pale green, the snowy breasts and glossy black caps of these graceful birds make a brilliant array against the shimmering sands as they rest in long rows facing the gentle south wind. Then there are days when the sea is roughened and the whole flock is out over the "ripps" in pursuit of their prey making a maze of white wings over the water. Again there are lowering days when the sky is dull and leaden with rain presaging in the east and the ocean steely gray with but little surf. The strand at ebb tide stretches away like a broad plain upon which are scattered bunches of Sanderlings, ever on the move and so pale that they almost escape notice, and solitary Ring-neck Plovers which appear jet black in the uncertain light. Still closer stands our long line of terns, rank upon rank, in varied plumage, awaiting the storm which they seem to know is coming. Every now and then they give voice with their grating, raucous calls so in keeping with the threatening squall and the only sound to reach our ears save the swish of the waves running up the beach.

## FORSTER'S TERN

### Sterna forsteri Nuttall

Forster's Tern is a bird of the interior of North America ranging south to the Gulf but like several other western birds it occurs as an irregular transient on the Atlantic coast and what is more remarkable it bred, for a time at least, on the Virginia shore and possibly in southern New Jersey. Turnbull (1869) states that he had found it breeding on Brigantine and Dr. William L. Abbott obtained specimens on Five Mile Beach on May 15, 1877, April 26–May 17, 1878, June 3, 1879, May 6, 1880, May 20, 1881 and May 22, 1882, all of which are in the collection of the Philadelphia Academy. Common Terns were taken at the same time and it looks as if they might have been nesting there together. W. E. D. Scott shot a pair on Long Beach on May 14, 1877, but regarded the species as rare. Charles S. Shick reports it as breeding on Seven Mile Beach in 1890, but I am not inclined to place much reliance upon this statement.

By 1923 Ludlow Griscom had relegated Forster's Tern to the extinct list, so far as the New York City Region was concerned, but John T. Nichols saw one in early September of that year and in 1925 there were many records extending from Long Island down the New Jersey coast, beginning with August 9, and no less than seventy-five were seen at Point Pleasant on August 30, sixty-two at Elizabeth on September 19 and fifty the next day with a final record on October 25.

In 1927 they were present on Barnegat Bay on various days between July 30 and September 10 with a single record for October 1, and in the same year Julian Potter found one on Ludlam's Beach on October 9.

In 1928 one was identified at Barnegat on September 2 and at Cape May on September 1 to 3.

1929 brought another influx and many were seen on Long Island from July 16 to October 16. In 1930 there were four records for the upper coast, one from Barnegat as late as November 9 (Urner). In 1931 two records for the Newark marshes, and in 1933, three records for Long Island with many records all along the coast in 1935, extending through September, with several at Cape May on September 7 (Eaton and Pough). In 1936 four immature birds were present on Barnegat Bay, June 21 to July 2 (Urner).

The "disappearance" of Forster's Tern may be due in part to the cessation of collecting which became prevalent about the time that the bird was supposed to be lost and its remarkable return to the better knowledge of field identification which developed later. In the autumn the adults in winter plumage may easily be distinguished from the Common Terns by the absence of the black band which extends around the back of the crown from eye to eye in that species, this being replaced by a black spot on either side of the white head.

In spring it is difficult to distinguish the two species except by voice. The color difference rests mainly in the fact that the outer web of the long tail feathers in Forster's Tern is lighter than the inner and vice versa in the Common Tern. I have tried in vain to ascertain this point in adult terns at Cape May in spring and summer and it may well be that Forster's Terns have occurred here in recent years at these seasons as they did in the years of Dr. Abbott's collecting and have gone unrecognized.

## * ARCTIC TERN

### Sterna paradisaea Brünnich

Bonaparte, Audubon and Turnbull all mention the Arctic Tern as rare on the New Jersey coast but without a definite record. Indeed it would seem that the two latter were simply quoting Bonaparte and as immature and winter tern plumages were very imperfectly known in early days they were probably all in error. There are no recent records and only one, I believe, for Long Island, and no new Jersey specimens are extant. As the bird breeds from the Arctic Regions south to Massachusetts and winters in the Antarctic seas it must pass our coast well off shore but like other pelagic birds it might occasionally be blown in by storms.

## ROSEATE TERN

### Sterna dougalli dougalli Montagu

PLATE 69, p. 569

This beautiful and graceful tern was stated to be a summer resident on the New Jersey coast by Turnbull (1869) while Harry G. Parker and Charles S. Shick have reported it as an abundant breeder on Seven Mile Beach up to 1885 but their identification, apparently based upon eggs, is not convincing.

We have no further record until a pair was detected by Julian Potter breeding in a colony of Common Terns on Gull Bar in Hereford Inlet on June 20, 1923. He described them as beautiful birds with black bills and red feet and longer outer tail feathers than the Common Tern. Their note was quite different too, resembling the "blink" of the Baltimore Oriole, although when charging they had a harsh tern-like cry. On July 8 when I visited this colony they were seen again, and on July 20, 1924, a brood of young about ready to fly was found by Julian Potter and banded by John Gillespie. In 1925 the breeding pair was not located.

On June 5, 1925, however, I came upon four terns resting on the beach at the entrance to Corson's Inlet, which seemed restless and particularly wary. They did not act exactly like Common Terns and when I obtained a good view of them I could see their slender black bills, with a slight reddish tinge at the base, the long outer tail feathers and the very white appearance of the rump and tail.

Once or twice I have seen other individuals in flocks of Common Terns on the Cape May beach that seemed to have the characteristics of this species but could not secure satisfactory studies of them.

Julian Potter saw two on Seven Mile Beach on June 12 and July 24, 1927, and William Yoder saw one feeding at sea off the end of the jetty on the mouth of the Harbor on July 18, 1926. On September 2, 1928, Julian Potter saw two at Cape May Point and another was seen resting on a piling there with Common Terns on May 30, 1931 (Parry).

On July 13, 1932, in company with Conrad Roland, I visited the tern colony which that year was located on a filled piece of meadow back of the northern part of Five Mile Beach and found a pair of Roseate Terns evidently nesting there. One of them rested for some time with a number of Common Terns on a mud flat close by and allowing our skiff to drift slowly down toward the flat we had an excellent view of the bird. We could distinguish its black bill with a slight red suffusion at the base, and note that it was slightly longer than that of the Common Terns which stood close by. We could not always pick it out when they were on the wing because they were above us, but when the upper parts came into view we could recognize the whiter appearance of the Roseate. As it sat upon the black mud the breast seemed slightly rosy but this was probably imagination, as this is usually only discernible when the bird is in hand.

There have been a number of records from farther north on the coast and one or more pairs have been reported breeding in the tern colony on an island in Barnegat Bay. One was seen there on August 9, 1925, and in June, 1928, there were twelve present (Potter) while John Gillespie found two pairs on July 15, 1934. In 1935 it was estimated that ten pairs bred on the New Jersey coast.

1936
CR

## LEAST TERN

*Sterna antillarum antillarum* (Lesson)

PLATES 70–74, pp. 582–583, 598

This, the smallest of our terns, was for many years very rare on the New Jersey coast. Time was when it was one of the most plentiful inhabitants of the strand, nesting in the sand just above high water mark, but it was sacrificed and all but exterminated to satisfy a passing whim of fashion which demanded its use as a millinery adornment. The birds that we see today are the descendents of the few that survived the slaughter or of others that pushed north from more southern shores and reoccupied the old breeding grounds.

Alexander Wilson says that when visiting the nesting places of the Least Tern about 1810, probably on Peck's Beach, "the birds flew in clouds around me, and often within a few yards of my head, squeaking like so many young pigs." W. E. D. Scott refers to them as "abundant" at Long Beach, in 1879, "breeding exclusively on the ocean beach." George Morris, writing to me in 1909, of conditions at the same spot in 1881, says: "It is difficult to give an estimate of numbers, but I can remember standing in one spot and seeing five or six nests within a radius of fifteen or twenty feet, but my recollections are that these conditions only pertained to an acre or so of the beach. In July 1884, I could no longer find Least Tern's eggs, and natives told me they no longer found eggs on the beach. During the period, 1881–1886, I saw a good deal of the slaughter of the birds in this region. I remember coming upon two professional millinery gunners, I think in the summer of 1885, who had two piles about knee high of Least and Common Terns, which they said they were sending to New York, my recollection being that they got twelve cents apiece for the birds."

Dr. B. H. Warren describes the same thing on Brigantine in the summer of 1883; he says: "The Least Terns were breeding in considerable numbers, laying their eggs in slight depressions in the dry sand and among the shells on the sand hills along the beach. I obtained the bodies of over 75 of these Terns from two taxidermists, who were collecting the skins for New York and Philadelphia dealers to be used for ladies' hats. These birds were all killed in one day."

On Seven Mile Beach, Charles S. Schick writes in 1890 (Auk, 1890, p. 326) that the Least Tern is a common breeder; "I must state, however, that all of the Terns are gradually forsaking their former breeding grounds on account of the new seaside resorts that are being started on all the islands. Formerly many hundred pairs occupied a small sand flat near Sea Isle City, but they are now all gone, not one pair breeding where a few years ago hundreds raised their young." Harry G. Parker estimated that there were thirty pairs nesting on Seven Mile Beach in 1888 and Philip Laurent said that there were still a few nesting in 1892. William Baily saw two birds on this beach in 1899 which he felt sure had nested and recorded individual birds on Five Mile Beach, June 1, 1893; Seven Mile Beach, August 28, 1896; Cape May, August 22, 1897.

On the beaches immediately around Cape May the Least Tern is today a transient visitor on its way to and from nesting places established a little farther up the coast and we see it most frequently during the month of August, always on the sea beach. The birds may be resting on the strand or flying out over the waves but seldom far from the shore. They are very light and active on the wing, bouncing up and down in the air in a distinctly erratic flight. The wings appear very narrow and seem to curve backward more than in the Common Tern, while the beats are about twice as frequent. The action is continuous and every now and then there is a distinct flutter as the bird pauses over some likely feeding spot, the body rising slightly the while. At other times a bird will suddenly dive, pitching headlong into the water. The bill is always pointed downward in flight as is customary with terns.

While the Least Terns associate with Common Terns as they rest on the beach, they do not mingle intimately with them but usually keep by themselves a few feet from the other assemblage. Indeed while seeking company itself this little tern seems to resent the approach of other species and when some passing Common Terns came in to join a group of Leasts the latter took wing. On one occasion a Least joined company with a single Ring-necked Plover, and several times I have found them with Sanderlings, but usually their association is with other species of terns.

The length of the Least Tern is about half that of the Common Tern and about equals that of the Sanderling although of course not nearly so bulky in body. They usually sit scattered along the beach and not in a close flock like the other terns. The head, held low on the shoulders, projects slightly forward, the wing and tail tips stand up above the line of the back. One bird busily engaged in pluming its feathers, shook both wings and tail vigorously, moving the wings back and forward so that the tips crossed and recrossed over the rump, while the tail was jerked from one side to the other.

PLATE 70

*Courtesy of "Bird Lore."*          *C. M. Beal*

*Courtesy of "Bird Lore."*          *C. M. Beal*

LEAST TERN AT NEST, LUDLAM'S BEACH, N  J.

PLATE 71

*Wharton Huber*

*Wharton Huber*

LEAST TERN ON NEST; LOWER WITH TELEPHOTO LENSE.   CORSON'S INLET, N. J.

PLATE 72

*Wharton Huber*

*Wharton Huber*

1. LEAST TERN WITH YOUNG AND EGGS.

2. YOUNG LEAST TERN, CORSON'S INLET, N. J., JULY.

PLATE 73

*Wharton Huber*

*Wharton Huber*

NESTS AND EGGS OF LEAST TERN, CORSON'S INLET, MAY 30, 1928, AMONG THE SURF CLAMS.

On another occasion several birds that were engaged in pluming themselves bent the head over forwards in order to reach the breast, and back over each shoulder to the rump, while the long primary feathers were carefully drawn between the mandibles one at a time.

Two plumages are distinguishable among the birds that occur on our beaches in August. The breeding adult has a black cap and narrow white frontlet and line over the eye, black outer primaries, a yellow bill slightly tipped with dusky, and orange feet. The young of the year has much more white on the head, the black being restricted to the occipital region while the fore part of the spread wing is dusky and the bill black. The snowy white under parts and pale gray mantle are common to both.

I have several times seen Least Terns run on the beach for a few steps and they move more rapidly and easily than the Common Terns, although the extremely short legs of all terns make their movements on land somewhat grotesque.

The migrant birds have two calls to which they occasionally give voice one a high-pitched shrill, *pts-sek, pts-sek;* the other *chĭlik, chick, chick,* a double note followed by two short ones.

On one occasion two of the birds resting on the strand suddenly took up a fighting attitude like miniature game cocks bill to bill and heads stretched out close to the sand. They flew at one another once and then parted.

To illustrate the gradual increase in the number of migrant Least Terns on the beach at Cape May we saw single birds three times and two on one occasion during August, 1920. In 1921, none were seen although the strand was visited with about the same frequency. In 1922 there were two on July 25, fifteen on July 31, twenty on August 3, ten on August 4, one on the 7th, nine on the 9th, two on the 13th and four on the 19th.

In 1923, the first one came on July 21, another on the 24th and four on the 26th. On August 4 seven came in from the sea in single file and alighted on the beach, beginning at once to preen their plumage vigorously. Later another joined them making five adults and three birds of the year.

In 1924 only two were seen and in 1925 they were observed four times. Subsequently they have been more abundant and as many as twenty-six were seen together on August 27, 1926.

In the summer of 1924 a breeding colony of about twenty pairs of Least Terns was found established at Corson's Inlet, by Norman MacDonald and Horace Rolston. One or more pairs had nested on Brigantine Island farther up the coast in 1920, and probably had never been entirely exterminated from this or the nearby Little Beach Island, but this was our first knowledge of the return of the birds to Cape May County as breeders. On May 29, 1925, a visit to the Corson's Inlet colony showed several nests with two and three eggs each and on June 4 and 5 of the same year I found four nests with one, two, two, and three eggs respectively, none of them the same as those found previously, while from the actions of the birds there were many others that I failed to locate.

The nesting spot was on a narrow flat sand spit forming the northernmost point of Ludlam's Island and stretched up into Corson's Inlet.  It is about two hundred yards wide and on the eastern side the ocean surf rolls in on a shelving beach while at low tide there is a series of short lines of rollers one behind another, marking the many bars and shoals with which the entrance to the inlet is filled.  On the other side lie the smooth glassy waters of the thoroughfare.  Several low sand hills covered with dune grass occupy the center of the flat while the sandy stretches all about are covered with shells of all sorts—clams of several kinds, scallops, naticas, young conchs, razors etc., some stained with iron and others dark blue gray from the blue mud banks off the shore, making a great mixture of colors as the sun shown down upon them.  Here the terns had deposited their eggs in little hollows scooped in the sand, about four inches in diameter.  They are cream colored often tinted with pale purple and spotted with purple and brown, a coloration that almost defied detection against the myriads of varicolored shell fragments with which the sand was strewn.

An examination of the nest hollows earlier in the season (May 19) indicated that they are deliberately scooped out by the birds as many were found all ready for the eggs which had not at that time been deposited, while the marks made by the birds' feet were evident.  About half of the nests were in little oases of pure sand and not immediately among the shells, while telltale tracks leading to the nests from half a dozen directions, and extending for six to ten feet away, aided in locating them.  Nests placed among the shells often had, apparently by chance, pieces of broken razor shells or clams as a flooring but others had none.

The tracks forming the approaches to the nests consisted of hundreds of little footprints made by the birds in going and coming; they were roughly diamond-shaped with a little scratch behind each, probably made by the toes as the foot was drawn forward with each step.  When the birds were watched they were seen to run with a rather clumsy gait, waddling a little from side to side.

As one approaches the colony the terns may be seen in the air, even at a considerable distance.  Their wings catch the light of the sun and flash out silvery white for a moment and disappear as quickly, like will-o'-the-wisps, as the bird turns in its course.  Approaching closer we see many of them flying back and forth over the nesting ground and with the first cry of alarm those that have been resting on the sand or incubating their eggs arise to join those already on the wing.  The flying bird seems to have a very short neck and the wings have the appearance of springing directly from behind the head and to be always pointed diagonally backward, in graceful curves.  The beats, however, are strong and the body seems at times to bound up and down in the air.  When flying about undisturbed the birds have a rather clear call, though none of their vocal efforts are of much volume.  *Tsíp; tsíp*, they cry or, as we get closer, *chísek, chísek*.  Almost immediately upon the discovery of an intruder a harsher cry is substituted *zhweét, zhweét,* and for a few moments it may alternate with the other: *tsíp; zhweét; tsíp; zhweét* etc.   Soon all are uttering the harsh cry, which recalls some of the notes of the Purple Martin and there is a perfect bedlam of harsh *zhweéts* all about, and as different individuals have slightly different accents the effect is much like a chorus of harsh voiced tree toads.   Occasionally a bird comes diving headlong at me, his black crown, yellow bill and gleaming eye making a striking appearance and in wild rage he cries, still more harshly, *zkeeék* as he turns abruptly upward just before striking my face, or perhaps he may be hovering above my head and drops precipitately before making the upward swoop, but always with that harsh *zkeeék*. This note and the clear calls of other birds not yet alarmed vary the chorus.

Upon my retirement the excitement soon dies down and the nesting birds drop back again to the sand alighting a few yards from their nests and running to them by short stages, soon settling upon the eggs, with neck held erect and wing tips crossed over the base of the tail.   They run rather rapidly and pause and then run on again much like a plover, holding the neck high all the while and ever alert.

At low tide the Least Terns of this colony resorted to the beach and perched on the wet strand where I counted thirty in sight at once.   From here they went fishing among the riffles and shallows of the harbor mouth. Hovering in the air like a Fish Hawk, their wings beat so fast that they appear like a double pair, and effect often seen in rapid flying ducks.   The bird will then turn suddenly tail up and, with wings partly closed and bill pointed straight down, will plunge into the water.   It is gone for the moment and then emerges and is again on the wing.   Sometimes it will have a small fish in its bill, and with a wriggle and shake of its plumage it is off to its mate with its plunder.   Only one in several trials actually results in a plunge for more often than not the prospective prey disappears and the tern spreads its wings just before reaching the water and rights itself, swooping up again to the required height for diving.   Near shore, in very shallow water, they often make a diagonal dive and swerve up again barely touching the water and apparently seizing something on the surface.   One bird settled on the water as if to swim but instead began churning its wings violently up and down, splashing the spray over its back; it then arose from the surface and settled again repeating the process several times.   It was apparently bathing.

When alighting on the beach the birds often hold their wings aloft, stretching them up to their fullest extent for a moment before folding them. The male, which has captured a fish, takes it to the female and struts with it in front of her in a grotesque manner and then offers it to her, evidently a part of the courtship behaviour.   On May 20, 1927, before any eggs had been laid, I saw a male with a small fish approach a female on the sand and take up a position behind her with his body nearly upright, then, after mating, he presented the fish.   On other occasions the male fed the female while she was incubating.

The yellow bill with slight black tip, the black cap with white frontlet, and the orange feet, are the most conspicuous color markings of the breeding bird, together with the black on the outer primaries which forms a dusky border to the wing. I saw one individual in the colony with a whitish head and somewhat mottled back, evidently a non-breeding bird which had not completed the molt.

Another visit to this colony on July 16 of the same year, found many young already on the wing, not such strong fliers as the adults and all with shorter and much less forked tails, the back browner and a brown band over the bones of the wing. They came to rest now and then on the wet sand near the inlet and were fed there by their parents. The bedlam of sound continued, as on my previous visit, whenever the nesting ground was approached but the harsh *zhweét* cry was now the only one used. Downy young, almost exactly the color of the sand, were found scattered about here and there on the upper beach or among the grass on the low sand hills. While some nests still held eggs, I found none with young. When the downy birds were picked up the parents became frantic and a new note was introduced, a rapidly repeated *chip-chip-chip-chip*. Wharton Huber noticed on the earlier visit that if we lay down flat on the sand the anxiety of the birds always lessened and the harsh cries gave way to the softer *tstp*, or *chísek* notes or to shorter repetitions of the *chip-chip* note just described. When we stood upright the excitement began again.

In 1926, a visit to the Corson's Inlet colony on July 31 found only a half dozen birds present and these showed no excitement upon our visiting the nesting ground. Evidently all of the young were on the wing and had drifted away along the beaches to the southward.

On May 20, 1927, there were thirty-four birds sitting about on the sand and while freshly scooped nest hollows were found only one contained an egg. In 1928, most of the colony removed to a recent fill back of Sea Isle City several miles to the south where a dredge had spread fresh sand over the meadows. On May 20 nests had been scooped out here and on June 9 Fletcher Street counted thirty birds present. There were fewer birds to be seen on June 24 but several downy young were found which lay flat on their bellies, quite invisible at a little distance when on the white sand, but most conspicuous whenever they strayed onto the patches of black mud. Two nests were found with eggs—one and two respectively. Many Least Terns have continued to nest on this sand flat up to the present time, the Corson's Inlet locality having been rendered unavailable by building operations.

On July 17, 1925, four birds, adults and young were found at the upper extremity of Five Mile Beach where the Common Terns used to breed and they flew about calling as if they had nested somewhere in the vicinity.

Least terns have bred also in the Common Tern colony at the southern extremity of Seven Mile Beach since 1925, in some years, and on June 7, 1936, Benjamin Hiatt found twenty-five pairs present some with full sets of eggs others just beginning to build their "nests." By June 20, the point had been swept by a high tide and almost all of the Least Terns' nests washed over. Later in the summer I failed to find a single bird there.

In June, 1937, Otway Brown found a colony of Least Terns on the extensive sand flats back of the fish docks on what was formerly Two Mile Beach, and birds seen later in the season about Schellenger's Landing doubtless came from there. In July of this year I also found a number of the birds both old and young on the beach near Bidwell's Ditch on the Bay shore and while the latter were still being fed by their parents, they were perfectly able to fly and I do not think that they had been raised there, although they may have been.

Lists of nests examined by Turner McMullen, Richard Miller and Fletcher Street follow:

Corson's Inlet

June 14, 1925, sixteen with a single egg; fifteen with two.

June 28, 1925, four with one egg; eight with two; and one with three.

July 11, 1925, three nests with two eggs and several young running about (Street).

June 27, 1926, eleven with one egg; six with two; one with three; several young; thirty pairs present.

May 21, 1927, five with two eggs.

June 12, 1927, two with one; twenty-four with two; one with three; several young; fifty pairs present.

June 18, 1927, thirteen nests with two eggs not counted on the 12th.

July 3, 1927, one with two eggs and others just hatched (Street).

July 10, 1927, four nests with eggs.

May 26, 1928, twenty-five nests with eggs.

June 4, 1932, fifty-two nests with eggs.

Peck's Beach (Turner McMullen).

May 30, 1926, eleven nests with eggs.

June 7, 1931, seventy-one nests with eggs.

Lower end of Seven Mile Beach

July 5, 1925, one with two eggs; one with young (Miller).

June 16, 1935, nine nests with eggs (McMullen).

Brigantine Beach

June 7, 1921, twelve nests with eggs (McMullen).

June 25, 1922, eleven nests with eggs (Street).

June 24, 1926, fifteen nests with eggs (McMullen).

June 11, 1933, ninety nests with eggs (McMullen).

In June, 1925, Julian Potter had located five nesting colonies from Brigantine southward containing respectively thirty, ten, fifteen, four and two pairs. On July 17, 1927, the largest still maintained a population of thirty to forty and in 1928 the two Ludlam's Beach colonies contained one hundred birds, with twenty-five nests and eggs in the larger.

In June, 1933, Charles Urner found a few pairs beginning to nest on a gravel road across the meadows near Barnegat Bay and Potter estimated that there were two hundred Least Terns nesting on the coast in that year.

With the reëstablishment of this delightful little bird as a summer resident species in Cape May County it has increased as a transient on the Cape May beach. Thirty gathered at South Cape May on August 7, 1929 and a dozen were seen by Otway Brown at Cape May Point on June 12, 1932.

On the meadow ponds back of both Five and Seven Mile Beaches the Least Tern has also become of frequent occurrence throughout the summer and has been recorded there from July 9 to September 1 sometimes in flocks of twelve to forty-five, and on Price's Pond several were seen fishing during July and August, 1936. We have one record for Camden, on the Delaware River, August 26, 1933, (Potter) doubtless blown inland during the great hurricane a few days before.

Unfortunately the status of the Least Tern is rather precarious since the beaches which are its true home are almost entirely taken over by building operations and resort developments, while people and dogs constantly disturb the birds during the early summer, when they should be free from persecution. Were it not for the recent sand flats left by the dredges in deepening the inland waterway they would probably ere now have again taken their departure. Whether they will permanently establish themselves on these more or less artificial nesting grounds remains to be seen.

## SOOTY TERN

### Sterna fuscata fuscata Linnaeus

This southern tern has several times been blown by tropical storms to the New Jersey coast. The first record, so far as I am aware, is a specimen, since destroyed, which I have seen and identified, shot by Amos P. Brown, Sr., on Long Beach in the "seventies," doubtless 1876 or 1878, when several of these birds reached Long Island and New England. It was an adult in full plumage.

On September 7, 1916, Wharton Huber collected an adult female at Corson's Inlet. "It was resting in the long grass in the sand dunes, a very short distance back from the beach. It was very tame and allowed a close approach before flushing" (Auk, 1917, p. 206).

Another record is a dead and largely decomposed specimen found by William C. Doak and others on the salt meadows of Seven Mile Beach, about a quarter of a mile back of the Stone Harbor Coast Guard Station, on January 13, 1929 (Auk, 1929, p. 224). The bird had probably been blown north by the storm of September 19, 1928, which was responsible for seven birds of this species on Long Island, dead or alive, September 21–23.

The original specimen of Trudeau's Tern (*Sterna trudeaui* Audubon) which was supposed to have come from Great Egg Harbor seems to have been obtained in Chile.

## ROYAL TERN

### Thalasseus maximus maximus (Boddaert)

There seems to be no record of the occurrence of the Royal Tern on the coast of New Jersey until Turnbull listed it in his "Birds of East Pennsylvania and New Jersey," in 1869, as "very rare" and after that no records until quite recently. There are, it is true, several statements of its occurrence in the meantime but owing to the confusion on the part of most observers, between this and the Caspian Tern, it is not possible to say to which they refer and it seems more likely that they belong to the latter, since it has proven to be the more common on our coast in recent years.

The first "rediscovery" of this tern on the New Jersey coast was on September 17, 1933, when Julian Potter and Joseph Tatum found a flock of nine on Brigantine Beach following a heavy storm of September 14–16. All had "white foreheads extending back over the crown, bills more slender than those of the Caspian Terns and orange in color, the birds more buoyant in flight and more slender; cries less harsh and not so low." On June 30, 1935, Potter encountered four more of these birds at the lower extremity of Seven Mile Beach; they took wing as he approached and flew out to sea. "They were all adults with yellow bills but very little black on their heads, note not so low as that of the Caspian and less harsh." (Bird-Lore, 1933 and 1935—"The Season".)

On September 15, 1935, Joseph Tatum had the good fortune to find the two species together at the lower end of Brigantine Beach. There were two Caspians and one Royal. "The Royal was distinctly smaller with more white on top of the head and a more slender bill, which was orange color in contrast to the strong red of the Caspian.   There was an apparent difference, too, in the legs, those of the Caspian being longer and black, while the Royal's seemed to be greenish yellow or brownish.   In flight the Royal was more graceful with darker wing mantle and with less black at the wing tips." (Auk, 1936, p. 95.)

### CABOT'S TERN

Thalasseus sandvicensis acuflavidus (Cabot)

Turnbull states that "a specimen of this straggler from the Gulf States was shot on Grassy Bay (back of Five Mile Beach) in August, 1861."   There is no other New Jersey record, nor has it been taken on Long Island where so many unusual birds have occurred.   It was doubtless the victim of one of the tropical storms that have blown many southern birds to the lower New Jersey coast.

## CASPIAN TERN

### Hydroprogne caspia imperator (Coues)

The splendid Caspian Tern is but a casual visitor to Cape May and seems disinclined to pause in its passing flight along our coast. Doubtless if one were constantly on the watch, especially at some of the more remote inlets, more would be recorded but when we consider the short space of time that a bird flying along the beach is in sight, at any given point, it is not surprising that records of such stragglers as this are infrequent.

On August 30, 1930, I saw the only Caspian Terns that I have been fortunate enough to observe here. They passed me at South Cape May as I was walking down the beach and flew about thirty feet above the water just beyond the surf line. The atmosphere was somewhat hazy and as the two big birds approached I at first took them for gulls but was at once struck by the light color of the upper parts passing into pure white on the lower back and tail. The wings seemed relatively longer and narrower than gull's wings and the tail shorter. The great red bills and solid black caps, however, were their unmistakable and conspicuous characters. They kept calling as they pased along and I could see the bills open and shut but the calls were almost completely drowned in the noise of wind and surf. They pointed their bills downward in true tern manner and every now and then one of them would swoop down, turning tail up as if to dive but always caught itself a couple of feet from the water, sheared off and, rising again, continued on its way. The birds were in sight only about two minutes and were soon only specks in the distance as they headed across the mouth of the Bay for the Delaware coast.

On August 29, 1926, Julian Potter and William Yoder came upon three Caspian Terns on the strand at the southern extremity of Seven Mile Beach associated with a flock of Common Terns and Laughing Gulls; there were two adults and a bird of the year. The former were distinguished by their large red bills, dark feet and slightly forked tails and as they sat on the sand the wing tips seemed to extend slightly beyond the end of the tail. "Their call was a pitiful *kr-r-r-r-r-r*."

On Ludlam's Beach on August 21, 1927, William Yoder saw two Caspian Terns, and Richard Pough thirteen on Seven Mile Beach on September 10, 1933, while several were seen by the Audubon Society Wardens at Cape May Point in 1935 and 1936. Of these two were reported on August 28 and two on September 7, 1935 by William Rusling, the latter birds seen also by Warren Eaton and Richard Pough, and three were observed on September 19 and one on October 15, 1936, by James Tanner, one of the former also seen by John Hess on September 20.

There are two early records of large terns which, in all probability, refer to this species; one seen by William Baily at Avalon, on Seven Mile Beach, on August 26 and 27, 1896, which remained about the pier for several hours all told; and two recorded by W. E. D. Scott (Bull. Nutt. Orn. Club, 1897 p. 227) an adult and bird of the year seen on Long Beach on August 23, 1879.

Caspian Terns occur rarely on the Delaware River and three were seen by John Emlen and others near Palmyra on April 21, 1929, flying about with a flock of Herring Gulls during a drizzling rain. The whiter plumage of the terns was easily distinguished as well as the black cap, large red bill and the relatively short distinctly forked tail (Auk, 1929, p. 534). At Fish House near the same spot, on August 20, 1932, Julian Potter and John Gillespie saw two of these birds and following the great storm which swept the coast in 1933, John Gillespie saw two on the river opposite Camden on September 4, and Julian Potter five on September 13. Clifford Marburger saw four Caspian Terns at Delaware City farther down the river on May 3, 1931.

On the northern part of the New Jersey coast these birds seem more frequent than on the Cape May coast and many records have been published in Potter's "The Season" in "Bird-Lore" as follows:

1925, November 29, Barnegat Bay region, Charles Urner.
1926, August 18, Brigantine Beach, Herbert Beck and Clifford Marburger.
1926, September 12 (2), Seaside Park, Lester Walsh.
1926, September 19, Point Pleasant, Charles Urner.
1927, July 22, Barnegat Bay region, Charles Urner.
1927, September 18, Barnegat Bay region, Charles Urner.
1928, May 20, Manasquan, Charles Urner.
1928, July 1, (five) Point Pleasant, Charles Urner.
1929. May 1, (three), Manasquan, Charles Urner.
1929, September 7, Barnegat Bay region, Charles Urner.
1931. August 30, Brigantine, Julian Potter.
1932, May 1, Metedeconk River, Charles Urner.
1933, August 23, Brigantine, Lester Walsh.
1933, August 27, (two), Brigantine, Berkheimer.
1933, September 3, Brigantine, Julian Potter.
1933, September 10, (two), Joseph Tatum, Brigantine.
1933, September 19, (five), Brigantine, Charles Urner.
1934, September 9, (five) Brigantine, Brooke Worth.
1935, Charles Urner reported twenty records between July 22 and September 18.

It will be noticed that the greatest number of these big terns occurred after the famous hurricane of late August 1933.

I am of the opinion that, like many other species, they put out to sea after leaving Barnegat and therefore are not so often observed on the more southern beaches. Breeding as they do at many places in Canada and the Far North the Caspian Terns that we see are undoubtedly on regular migration, but the Royal Tern with which it may be confused is distinctly a southern species and the few individuals that have been recorded in New Jersey are accidental stragglers blown north by storms.

J. F. S.

# BLACK TERN

### Chlidonias nigra surinamensis (Gmelin)

PLATE 59, p. 566

The first large assemblage of migrant terns which formerly gathered on the beach during the last week of July usually included a few Black Terns and the same is true of the smaller flocks of today. There are often only one or two at first but their number increases later so that there used to be as many as one hundred in some years. Over the great meadows north of the Harbor during August there are often many times that number coursing about.

The dates of arrival at Cape May are as follows:

| | | | | | |
|---|---|---|---|---|---|
| 1921. | July 29. | 1925. | July 31. | 1931. | August 1. |
| 1922. | July 23. | 1926. | August 1. | 1932. | July 13. |
| 1923. | July 28. | 1927. | July 24. | 1933. | August 5. |
| 1924. | July 21. | 1928. | July 14. | 1934. | July 19. |
| | | 1930. | July 31. | | |

Late August is the time of their greatest abundance and by the middle of September they have usually all passed on; our latest records are September 20, 1925; September 19, 1926; September 30, 1928. They are however very irregular migrants; very abundant in some years and all but absent in others. Fletcher Street found them abundant far offshore when fishing on September 15, 1936, doubtless on migration.

The Black Tern visits us normally only in the autumn, its return flight in spring being confined to the Mississippi Valley. Nevertheless we have a few spring records, birds which probably have been wintering with Common Terns and have followed them in their northward flight rather than the main body of their own kind. These were all in full breeding plumage of black and gray and were always associated with Common Terns.

One was seen at Cape May Point, May 30, 1924, two at the same spot,

( 594 )

May 14, 1928, and another May 30 of the same year.  Turner McMullen saw one at Corson's Inlet on May 21, 1927, and another on June 4, 1933. They occur also occasionally on the Delaware River in spring as well as autumn and Julian Potter saw four at Camden on May 10 and 11, 1919.

On July 17, 1921, on a visit to one of the nesting colonies of Common Terns located on Brigantine Island, fifty miles north of the Cape May beaches, we found a lone Black Tern in perfect nuptial plumage which seemed just as much concerned over the welfare of the eggs and young of the other species as were the rightful owners.  It followed me about from place to place poising in the air only a few feet above my head on beating wings and calling continually in great alarm, *sheep, sheep, sheep, sheep; sheep, sheep, sheep, sheep*, the notes always in blocks of four and uttered rapidly and emphatically in sharp contrast to the long drawn *keeé-àrr* of the Common Terns.  In spite of its apparent concern this bird was either an unmated and belated spring migrant, separated from its fellows, or possibly a very early southbound migrant.  At all events, attracted by the assemblage of Common Terns, it was evidently influenced by the excitement of the nesting activities which recalled similar experiences of its own and renewed its parental anxiety.  A precisely similar occurrence was observed by Julian Potter at the Common Tern colony on the northern end of Five Mile Beach, on July 7, 1929, when two of the Black Terns were present, and at the Ephraim's Island colony on August 10, 1926, I found two individuals greatly excited, and a single bird at the more northern colony on July 13, 1932.

When resting on the beach, where we see them most commonly at Cape May, they mingle intimately with the Common Terns but can always be distinguished by their smaller size and darker color.  A single individual one day joined a flock of Semipalmated Sandpipers, in the absence of any tern companions, for they always seem to desire company.  While they may outnumber the Common Terns in a composite flock I never have seen a beach flock composed wholly of Blacks.  On August 22, 1923, a flock fishing off Cape May Point was composed of six hundred Black Terns, three hundred Common Terns and a few Laughing Gulls; all quite close to the shore and busily diving and hovering over the water.

Black Terns rest facing the wind as do all birds on the beach or water. They preen their plumage and often raise their wings high up above the body and hold them so for a moment or two.  In flight their wings are at once seen to be distinctly shorter than those of the Common Terns, and relatively wider, while the strokes are not so full and powerful and cover a smaller arc. When a mixed flock of terns starts up the beach the Blacks are soon relegated to the rear, unable to keep pace with their larger stronger flying associates.  They often swoop down, as do the other terns, to pick up small minnows stranded in the shallow beach pools and I have on one or two occasions seen them preen their breast feathers while on the wing, bending the head back under the body.  The real feeding ground of the Black Terns, and their natural habitat when on the wing, is back on the green meadows where they secure insect food of one kind or another. They are widely scattered when thus feeding and course back and forth with easy turns quartering low down over the wide expanse of grass and sedge.

Theirs is an easy flapping flight, the body rising and falling without apparent effort, with now and then a short sail of a foot or two or a slight rise as the bird pauses and flutters for a moment when sighting some prey. There are usually several rapid wingbeats followed by one or two slow ones, producing a rather irregular flight, while their actual progress is slow on account of the frequent changes in direction. Every now and then a bird dives, bill foremost, into the grass or down to the surface of some shallow pool, but never, apparently, do the feet touch, so quickly is the recovery effected. The prey is snatched up and the tern, flapping rapidly, rises and is off again on its course.

In late August of 1922 there were many Black Terns busily engaged in feeding on the meadows back of South Cape May and mingled with them were numerous Barn Swallows; while the object and general activities of the two species were similar their method of feeding, and doubtless their food as well, differed materially. The swallows would glide or "stream" along close down over the tips of the grass at lightning speed, in marked contrast to the diving and the hovering, halting, and relatively slow flight of the terns. Over Lake Lily Black Terns act in the same way as on the meadows and doubtless there, too, they are feeding on insects of some kind. They swoop repeatedly down to the water and graze the surface without actually touching it.

On August 31 of this same year, a year of great abundance for these terns, one could see them with the glass scattered widely over the meadows from the Harbor away north beyond the Wildwood Road. There must have been hundreds of them in sight at once, and all through the first week of September they were to be seen quartering the meadows in their characteristic easy flight, rising and falling with little apparent effort.

The summer of 1928 was another great season for the Black Terns, like those of 1922 and 1926. There were many on the meadows back of Five Mile Beach on August 14 and hundreds back of Seven Mile Beach on August 31, while on September 5 they were hawking about on Pond Creek Meadows. On September 4 a flock was seen out over the ocean now flying in a close pack now scattering over the waves and once more gathering together. 1934 was another year of abundance and they occurred from August 26 to September 16.

On September 1, 1924, several of these terns apparently tired of the chase came to rest on oyster stakes on Jarvis Sound where they perched for some time and exactly the same thing occurred on September 7, back of Schellenger's Landing where twelve stakes each had an occupant.

During August, 1926, the Black Terns frequented the Lighthouse Pond, hawking about over the surface of the water, from three to fourteen gathering there almost every day. On August 27, while watching them, I was impressed by the similarity of their flight and general wing action to those of the Nighthawk, and to my astonishment I presently realized that one of the birds actually was a Nighthawk. These terns seem interested in almost any body of water and on August 25, 1931, a number were found feeding over a rain water pool which formed on the flat back of South Cape May and which also proved attractive to a variety of shore birds. While rarely actually diving, Black Terns do sometimes strike the water in swooping down to the surface for food. On August 26, 1926, I found a number of them on the water just below the bathing beach in company with Common and Least Terns. The latter were diving repeatedly with their usual abandon, the smaller birds fairly flinging themselves into the water. While the Black Terns did not dive so frequently they did strike the water on several occasions. Just what they were securing I could not determine.

As the season advances and cool northwest winds begin to blow one often sees compact groups of Black Terns come suddenly coursing straight over the meadows like a pack of hounds following the scent. They travel fast and keep close together and are soon past and disappearing in the distance. Flights of this sort seem to be for the sole pleasure of exercise, possibly preliminary to migration, as the birds certainly never pause to feed, nor do they appear to have any definite destination.

The first Black Terns to arrive in late July or early August are usually adults in full breeding plumage, dark slate gray above with black head, breast and belly. Later arrivals, from August 5 to September 12, are in all stages of molt tending to the white-crowned, white-breasted dress of winter. There come too, mostly in the later flocks, large numbers of immature birds of the year, much like winter adults but with brownish patches above. In 1926, however, young birds accompanied the first adults. In any plumage the very dark upper surface of the Black Tern will distinguish it from any other of our common New Jersey terns in which the gray of the back is so pale as often to appear actually white in certain lights.

Warren Eaton and Richard Pough saw a pure albino Black Tern at Cape May Point on September 5, 1935.

The only call note that I have heard from these late summer migrants is a weak *seep*, *seep*, but the birds seen in the summer nesting colonies of the Common Tern were more vocal.

## BLACK SKIMMER

Rynchops nigra nigra Linnaeus

PLATES 75-85, pp. 598-599

This grotesque bird forms one of the prominent features of the wild life of any coast that it favors with its presence. Although reported as common years ago on the beaches of Cape May County it is now a long time since it has been anything but a rare and casual visitor in the immediate vicinity of the town, if indeed it ever bred there. On the beach islands a few miles north, however, it has returned of late years to nest to the delight of all who are interested in wild bird life. In upwards of forty years of more or less intensive study of the Cape May avifauna we have but seven records of Skim-

PLATE 74

*B. C. Hiatt*

*B. C. Hiatt*

LEAST TERN ON NEST AT SOUTHERN END OF SEVEN MILE BEACH, N. J., JUNE 21, 1936.

PLATE 75

*Courtesy of "Bird-Lore."*                    *H. R. Carey*

BLACK SKIMMERS OVER GULL BAR, HEREFORD INLET, N. J., JULY 9, 1925.

PLATE 76

*John Bartram*

*Wharton Huber*

1. BLACK SKIMMERS ON SEVEN MILE BEACH.
2. BLACK SKIMMERS RISING FROM NESTS ON GULL BAR, HEREFORD INLET, N. J.,
   JULY 9, 1925.

PLATE 77

*J. K. Potter*

*Wharton Huber*

1. GULL BAR, HEREFORD INLET, N. J.
2. NEST AND EGGS OF BLACK SKIMMER, GULL BAR.

PLATE 78

*William Vogt*

*J. F. Street*

1. BLACK SKIMMERS OFF LONG ISLAND, N. Y.
2. NEST AND EGGS OF BLACK SKIMMER, BRIGANTINE ISLAND, N. J.

PLATE 79

*J. F. Street*

*Wharton Huber*

1. EGGS AND YOUNG OF BLACK SKIMMER, BRIGANTINE ISLAND, N. J., JULY 18, 1921.
2. YOUNG BLACK SKIMMERS ON GULL BAR, N. J., JULY 25, 1924.

PLATE 80

*Wharton Huber*

*Wharton Huber*

1. BLACK SKIMMERS ON NESTING GROUND, EPHRAIM'S ISLAND, FIVE MILE BEACH, N. J., JULY 10, 1929; FEEDING YOUNG IN FOREGROUND.

2. BLACK SKIMMER AT NEST, GULL BAR, HEREFORD INLET, N. J., JULY 9, 1925.

PLATE 81

*Harry Parker*

*Wharton Huber*

1. YOUNG BLACK SKIMMER, BRIGANTINE ISLAND, N. J., JULY 18, 1921.

2. YOUNG BLACK SKIMMER, GULL BAR, HEREFORD INLET, N. J., JULY 28, 1926.

PLATE 82

*J. F. Street*

*Wharton Huber*

1. NEST WITH EGGS AND YOUNG OF THE BLACK SKIMMER, BRIGANTINE ISLAND, N. J., JULY 18, 1921.

2. YOUNG BLACK SKIMMER, GULL BAR, HEREFORD INLET, N. J., JULY 28, 1926.

PLATE 83

*B. C. Hiatt*

*Wharton Huber*

1. BLACK SKIMMER AT NEST, SEVEN MILE BEACH, N. J., JUNE 21, 1936.

2. BLACK SKIMMER CALLING FROM THE GROUND, EPHRAIM'S ISLAND, FIVE MILE BEACH, N. J., JULY 10, 1929.

PLATE 84

*Wharton Huber*

*John Bartram*

1. BLACK SKIMMERS ON NESTING GROUNDS, EPHRAIM'S ISLAND, FIVE MILE BEACH, N. J., JULY 10, 1929.
2. BLACK SKIMMER FLAPPING ALONG THE GROUND AWAY FROM THE NEST.

PLATE 85

*R. T. Peterson*

*Wharton Huber*

1. BLACK SKIMMER CALLING FROM NESTING GROUNDS.
2. BLACK SKIMMER INCUBATING, GULL BAR, HEREFORD INLET, N. J., JULY 9, 1925.

mers on the Cape Island beach or between there and Cape May Point. Fletcher Street saw one skimming over the shallow pond near the Lighthouse in the summer of 1919 and Ludlow Griscom noted one off the Point on July 26, 1920, while a single bird came flying in over the bathing beach on July 10, 1921, about the middle of the afternoon, and another appeared near the same spot on September 25, 1927. William Yoder saw one flying past the end of the jetty at the entrance to the Harbor on September 27, 1925, and in 1924, Skimmers were found twice at the shallow pool near the Lighthouse. A single bird on August 27, 1924, associated with a flock of Common Terns, was obviously one of a flight of Skimmers which was in that year carried north by a severe storm and stranded all along the coast as far as Maine, while on September 27, of the same year, three were mingled with a great flock of Laughing Gulls which had gathered at the pond.

Alexander Wilson who, with George Ord, explored the beaches of Cape May County about 1810, says of the Skimmer: "Its favorite haunts are low sand bars raised above the reach of the summer tides, and also dry flat sands on the beach in front of the ocean. It lays in June. Half a bushel and more of its eggs has sometimes been collected from one sand bar within the compass of half an acre," but he is not explicit as to how many colonies he found. John Krider writing in 1879 states that they bred on all the beaches of the county, but his work, written from memory, is not very reliable. We know that they still bred on Seven Mile Beach (probably the southernmost extremity) as late as 1885 and 1886, when C. S. Shick counted seventy-five nests there, but by 1890 he tells us that while still present they had become very rare. On the other beaches we have no definite records.

Subsequent knowledge of the birds on our New Jersey coast shows them to be very local during the nesting period and seldom seen any distance from their breeding grounds, resting on the sand during most of the day and active mainly at night. These facts taken in connection with the bird's habit of selecting the more remote bars and sand flats for nesting purposes would make it seem very easy for small colonies to have been overlooked and we are therefore in some doubt whether the Skimmers really disappeared as breeding birds on the lower New Jersey coast, from 1895 to 1915, or were simply not observed by those who would realize the importance of making a record of their occurrence. Certain it is that there is a blank in their history on our coast during these years. While comparatively few ornithologists were interested in exploring the Cape May beaches during this time we know that William Baily failed to find Skimmers on Five Mile Beach during visits in 1896, 1897 and 1898 nor did Philip Laurent find them there in 1892, while Dr. William E. Hughes and David McCadden saw none during the summers of 1898–1900 on Seven Mile Beach. This is, however, not proof that small colonies did not exist.

The return or the increase of Skimmers on our coast began about 1920. Richard Miller found a single pair nesting at the southern extremity of Seven Mile Beach on June 26, 1921, while in 1922 there were three pairs present and two nests were found on June 25 not over six feet apart. In 1923 there was but a single pair and no nests were found. It was discovered later, however, that a colony of about forty birds had been established on Gull Bar at the entrance to Hereford Inlet not far away. Whether the birds had located there during the immediately preceding years I could not determine. This colony had doubled in size by 1926 but was apparently deserted in 1927 or 1928 as the bar decreased in size and was nearly washed away. In the latter year the birds moved to a sand fill on Ephraim's Island, a section of meadow back of the southern part of Five Mile Beach, and in 1931 they moved again to a sand flat about a mile farther north. In 1934, after being washed out several times the birds returned to Gull Bar but the same fate met them there and in 1936 they were back at the southern point of Seven Mile Beach. In this year they numbered about forty individuals. In 1927 when Gull Bar was deserted one pair of birds reared two young on a narrow spit of sand jutting out into the inlet from the south side, the northernmost point of Five Mile Beach, and several were seen at the southern extremity of Seven Mile Beach but apparently did not nest there, although they did so later, 1931 to 1936, and sporadically in earlier years.

It seems probable that these birds all belonged to a single colony which, as is usual with Skimmers, shifted its location from year to year just as the low bars and sand points which they select for their homes change in shape or disappear entirely at the mercy of the waves and storms. The population of the colony, or its several sections, changes too, one of them boasting the largest number in one year and another in the next. In every instance our New Jersey Skimmers have been associated with Common Terns on their nesting grounds and while the two species join in the defense of the colony they seem to nest, for the most part, in separate assemblages and do not intermingle promiscuously.

The history of the birds breeding on the more northern section of our coast is no more satisfactory than that of the Cape May Skimmers. W. E. D. Scott records them as abundant on Brigantine Island in 1877 and rare on Long Beach, a little farther north. We know that they still bred on Little Beach Island, between the two, in 1910 and immediately succeeding years when Richard Harlow found two pairs nesting, and in August 1915, I also found two pairs breeding there. We heard of their presence there from 1915 to 1920 and on July 17 and 18, 1921, in company with Fletcher Street and other members of the Delaware Valley Ornithological Club I visited this colony and one which had that year been established back of Brigantine, on a recently formed sand flat on the meadows, as a result of dredging out the channel. Charles Urner writes me that the first pair of Skimmers that he found "nesting north of Little Beach Island was at Brant Beach a few miles north of Beach Haven on June 30, 1925, on a high sand island created by the dredging of the channel. This colony grew rapidly and by July 25, 1926, there were six pairs. The following year there were thirty pairs and they have been present ever since with a maximum of about seventy-five pairs.

About 1930 Skimmers became established on another sand island created by dredging in the bay west of Beach Haven called Goose Bar Island and in 1931, there were Skimmer colonies on Brant Beach, Goose Bar, Little Island Beach, Brigantine, Shad Island in Little Bay, and Sandy Island west of lower Brigantine."

On our 1921 trip we approached by boat from Atlantic City but saw no Skimmers until within about a mile of the Brigantine breeding grounds, when one flew rapidly past us. A little farther on we found nine sitting all in a row facing us. Their legs were very short, which brought the body close down to the sand, and the wing tips were slightly elevated over the base of the tail. They looked jet black from a distance and very conspicuous on the little spit of sand and mud. From the side they appeared all black and their ample wings folded up against the body resembled a black overcoat. In front, the bulging white breast and the white lower part of the face were conspicuous, as was the remarkable red bill, the mandibles compressed like knife-blades set on edge one above the other, the lower one decidedly the longer. Farther on we encountered two birds wading or standing in the shallow water, poking their bills down in an apparent search for food. Another passed rapidly by, flying close in to the grass-capped mud banks of the channel, and not thirty-five feet from our boat. When just opposite he dropped the long lower mandible into the water, snapped up a fish about three inches in length and flew off with it. His red feet showed clearly, stretched back against the under side of his tail, as he passed directly over our heads.

In contrast to the "overcoated" appearance of the resting bird, as if its clothes were too large for it, nothing could be more graceful and pleasing to the eye than the flying Skimmer. Three passed us in tandem formation, their long wings beating in extended arcs apparently almost touching tips above the bird's neck which is stretched forward and downward, the remarkable bill suggesting a long nose or snout. Now they seem partly to sail and the wing beats are shorter, as if gently patting the air to keep their proper poise. Above, with the exception of a white posterior border to the wings, the plumage is jet black, contrasting with the snowy white lower parts, the line of demarkation passing along the side of the face just below the eye. Now dropping close to the water they proceed with the long lower mandible just touching the surface or immediately above it. The appearance is as if a string attached to the bill were being pulled rapidly forward by some unseen force beneath the water. In reality the bird flies in precisely the same position when some distance above the water as when "skimming," the apparent tilting of the body being more noticeable in the latter case. When skimming, the lower mandible is sometimes immersed, supposedly scooping up some sort of minute prey, but this theory has been questioned and in my experience it is always small fish that the bird catches in this way.

On July 28, 1929, I watched several Skimmers fishing on the thoroughfare just above the Wildwood Road flying back and forth over an area which evidently swarmed with small fish. Every now and then a bird would pause and elevating the tail slightly would stab its bill into the water; failing to catch a fish it would continue on its way but when the mandibles closed on one the bird made off instantly for the nesting grounds with its prey held crosswise. Three were seen on August 23, 1930, skimming over the shallow water off Seven Mile Beach and occasionally the lower mandible of one of them would strike the sand and the bird would almost turn a somersault.

When we visited the Little Beach colony, in 1921, we found five pairs located there. As we landed and approached the nesting ground several birds came flying down the beach like a whirlwind, as if to carry us off our feet, but just as they reached us they sheared off to the right and left, turning up their snowy bellies and under wing surfaces which glistened in the sunlight with dazzling brilliancy. All the while the peculiar reedy calls echoed all about us—*aaar, aaar, aaar, aaar*, or as it sometimes seemed to our ears—*kaup, kaup, kaup*, with an angry *aaar*, at the end uttered as the bird passed close to my head, when his red eye was clearly seen and the brilliant red bill shading into black at the tip. They seemed unnatural—like painted birds, so striking were their colors and so sharply defined.

In the main colony on Brigantine there were twenty-five pairs nesting and we counted forty birds in sight at once. Thirteen nests were located containing in all thirty-three eggs while sixteen young were found. The eggs, usually four in a set, are cream color with large blotches of brown and purple. The nests are round depressions scooped out of the sand varying in diameter from eight to twelve inches and three inches deep with no lining of any kind. Some of them, where the parent had been incubating, showed radiating lines all around the edge apparently made by the long bill of the setting bird. The youngest birds were lying in the nests flat on their bellies with head and neck outstretched, the pale gray down exactly matching the color of the sand, and with similar black specks scattered through it. One could easily have stepped on them without seeing them. To one who has been on the western deserts they recalled the horned toads or similar flattened lizards. The older nestlings ran clumsily about calling vigorously to their parents. They had feathers sprouting out all over the body which carried on their tips little tufts of the down. The old birds arose in a great flock as we approached, and with them rank upon rank of silvery terns took wing, while shoals of little sandpipers skimmed the surface of the flat to settle farther on, early migrants from the north. The air was a moving maze of birds and their united cries produced a veritable bedlam; the harsh *keeé-arr', keeé-arrr'* of hundreds of terns and the woodwind *aaar', aaar',* of the Skimmers mingling in a confusion that is difficult to describe.

The parent Skimmers wheeled about over the sand, maddened at our presence and by the cries of their young as the latter scuttled away to take refuge in the coarse grass of the marsh edge, or even in shallow pools of water. The old birds traveled in parties of six to eight, or in pairs, and frequently charged us in company front, dashing past at apparently increased speed and uttering the climax note, *aaar'*, just as they turned aside to avoid striking us.

Just before sunset after we had withdrawn from the first colony and quiet reigned again, we saw from the water a pair of Skimmers performing evolutions near the nests and apparently about to mate. One pursued the other relentlessly; they wheeled and twisted right and left, now the snowy under parts gleaming in the horizontal rays of the sun, now the dead black of the back showing quite as conspicuously against the blue gray haze in the east. They rise one above the other alternately until they are some two hundred feet above the beach and then on set, curved wings they pitch to earth and settle on the bar. In a few minutes the pursuit begins anew but this time they go skimming over the smooth waters of a little inlet, between the bar and the beach, one close behind the other as if following a marked course. I saw this same action later in colonies on the Cape May beaches notably on July 8, 1923, on Gull Bar, and July 21, 1930, on Ephraim's Island, and on the adjacent colony on July 13, 1932.

I first visited the Gull Bar colony, in Hereford Inlet, on July 8, 1923, in company with Julian Potter who had been there on June 20. We found forty birds in the colony but egg laying had only just begun, earlier sets having apparently been washed away by the high tides. The birds flew in squads of from two to six and sometimes the entire flock took wing together charging us like a pack of hounds in full cry as they gave vent to their throaty barking calls. They did not however seem as much excited as did those of the other colony which had young to care for. Two birds arose high in the air attacking one another and fencing with their long bills. We also saw one individual flying about with a fish about three inches in length held crosswise in its bill, though there were no young to feed. Perhaps this is part of the mating behavior as in the case of the terns.

We were impressed with the way in which the birds remained close to their nesting grounds; we saw two in Grassy Sound about a mile away and several flew over to a narrow harbor at Anglesea, on the south side of the inlet, to fish. None seemed to stray more than two miles away, at least in the daytime, and they invariably followed the thoroughfares and other waterways, never crossing over land except on the nesting bar.

Viewing the bar from the point of beach at Anglesea on July 21, 1924, and July 17, 1925, we could see the birds sitting in rows on the strand and every now and then one would come over and fish in the shallow water at the end of the harbor. They skimmed back and forth with the lower mandible immersed and on each visit a bird caught a fish two or three inches in length and flew with it back to the bar. Sometimes they called as they passed me. Julian Potter visited the colony again on August 17, 1924, and found forty adults and twenty young.

In 1926 Horace McCann visited the Gull Bar colony on July 11 and found seventy-five birds present and all nests with eggs, but a subsequent visit on July 25, found the entire colony washed out by the tides. On August

10 when I visited it in company with Alexander Wetmore we found but six birds of the year in the flock of seventy-five assembled on the beach, and four others not yet able to fly, showing how completely had been the destruction of the first broods. Even at this late date some of the birds were nesting again and we found eight nests with from one to three eggs each. Five of these were seen again on the 17th but I was unable to learn whether any young were raised.

The young on the beach would run very rapidly and then stand stock still with legs rigid and head held forward in line with the body the heavy bill looking ridiculously out of proportion. Their action when running, and their pose when standing, reminded one strongly of the Killdeer. Their plumage was grayish lead color with buff edgings to the feathers. Those in the air were similar but showed more or less black on the under side of the wings their bills dusky with just a trace of red, while the mandibles were equal in length. They called occasionally as they flew about but not continously as did the adults and their note was shriller and more highly pitched. The adults had in many cases lost some of their flight feathers, apparently the beginning of the molt. They would settle themselves along the strand, facing the wind, and take wing when approached, yelping at a great rate. Sometimes one would "skim" over the sand its body almost dragging on the ground. They were still on the bar on August 28.

On August 13, 1927, we were surprised to see two Skimmers on a sand spit a little to the south of the lower end of Ephraim's Island back of Five Mile Beach. On September 3 David Baird saw a number in the same place, as he stood on the boat landing at Wildwood Crest, and on the 7th I counted one hundred and fifty gathered there, adults and young of the year, associated with many Laughing Gulls. I thought that these were birds making a temporary stop while on migration from the Little Beach colony or that on Gull Bar. Next year, however, passing Ephraim's Island on a boat I found a great throng of Common Terns and eighty Skimmers evidently nesting there and, having meanwhile learned of the desertion of Gull Bar, I realized that the colony had moved to this spot. Some birds in immature plumage were in the flock but whether young of the year or possibly birds that had not molted I could not determine although subsequent investigations would suggest the latter.

I visited this colony in company with Walker Hand on August 4 and again on the 10th. We counted eighty adult Skimmers and many downy young scattered about on the sand, the youngest were nearly white and the older ones pinkish gray. They lay prostrate the head and neck stretched out in front, the younger birds in the shallow saucer-like hollows which constitute the nests, the larger ones in depressions in the sand which they apparently make themselves in the process of digging in, for the marks of their feet are plainly evident in the rear. The sand seems to drift in all around them and makes their protective resemblance all the more perfect and the danger of treading on them more imminent!

Some of the larger young which are able to run about follow their parents when they arrive with a fish and are fed by them just as in the case of the terns. Some of them run ahead of the flying parent and take short experimental flights of a foot or two; the parent flies over and alights in advance waiting for them to catch up. Others ran down to the grass on the edge of the green meadow and even into the shallow water. The same thing was noticed on July 17, 1929, when they ran in droves down to the wet meadow and many holes in the sand were found which had evidently been occupied by young that had scampered off to take refuge in the grass at our approach.

Upon our first arrival on every visit the old birds came charging at us flying close to the sand and stretched out in a long line barking their alarm and almost striking us before they veered off. Later if we concealed ourselves among the marsh elder bushes, on a higher part of the island, they settled down and we could see through the glass that they lay prostrate just as the young do, with neck stretched out in front and throat appressed to the sand, the shoulders forming a sort of hump, and the bill slightly elevated at the tip. When studied from this shelter, on our first arrival, we found many standing in rows with their heads turned back and tucked under their wings. Possibly they were asleep in both positions. On August 14, 1928, the date of my third visit, I found the birds on the wing to number one hundred and fifty. There were some well-grown young in the grass but no downy birds and no eggs; the adults seemed just as solicitous as on the previous occasions.

On June 30, 1929, there were many eggs and downy young but on July 7 many of the latter seemed to have been destroyed and the presence of a number of rats on the island perhaps explained their disappearance, there were about fifty pairs of adults. On July 17, the young in mottled gray down were just beginning to develop pin feathers and were all active and running about, sometimes when pursued the tip of the bill would catch in the sand and the bird would be tilted over almost turning a somersault. There were no eggs or small downy young. On August 12 there was not a Skimmer in sight either on the sand or in the air; a high tide about a week before and a heavy rain storm the previous day, had apparently driven them elsewhere.

In 1930 there were about forty pairs present. On July 4 the colony was visited by Horace McCann who found that while the terns, which occupied the lower part of the flat, had been completely washed out, the Skimmers, whose nests were located on a slightly more elevated belt which supported some clumps of grass and sea rocket, had escaped the flood. He found forty-three young and twenty-five more nests with eggs. On the 21st and 25th when I visited the island there were eggs and young birds of all ages but most of the latter able to run about. On August 4 McCann reported it again submerged by high tides, in fact the sand was still wet. The young Skimmers were all on the wing and he estimated the flock to contain nearly two hundred birds.

On July 25, 1930, I spent some time in a shelter tent in the colony. After I was out of sight the birds settled down and most of them paid no attention to the tent but two pairs, with young buried in the sand close to me, flew by several times calling.  There was no evidence of either feeding or seeking food while I was there and so far as I could detect the two young birds did not move or change their position a particle for three quarters of an hour, except for an occasional gape and a slight sideways movement of the head, but within five minutes after I left I found that they had disappeared.  I noticed that the old birds, when apparently trying to lure you away from a nest or young, would "taxi" along over the sand getting closer and closer to it until the feet would touch and the bird would almost pitch over forward, seeming to be in distress.  This action is perhaps a form of the "broken wing ruse."  When really alighting on the ground they act quite differently fluttering down like a gull.  The bridge tender on the Wildwood Road, who has paid considerable attention to these birds, tells me that when coming out to Grassy Sound to fish they always cross over the bridge never under, and that they are much more in evidence about dusk than during the middle of the day, while he hears them calling as they fly all through the night.  Curiously enough, with this colony established within four miles of Cape May Harbor, we never saw a bird there nor did they occur on Jarvis Sound which is still nearer to their nesting place.  They seemed always to go north to Grassy Sound to feed, but perhaps they journeyed farther afield at night.

On July 6, 1931, when I again visited the island I found that all the nests of both Common Terns and Black Skimmers had been washed out by high tides and the broken eggs were being eaten by Herring Gulls.  There were only four Skimmers present and they several times flew across the sand and called feebly but showed no real interest in my presence.  I ascertained later that the birds had moved to a new location about a mile north on another sand fill on the meadows.  Horace McCann visited this spot on July 29 and found forty pairs of Skimmers and banded ninety young; there were about one hundred terns present.

In 1934 they nested on the southern extremity of Seven Mile Beach and Julian Potter saw sixty adults and three young there on August 1, and there were twelve pairs in 1936.

While the nesting date of the Black Skimmer may be seriously affected by high tides and wash-outs the following additional egg dates are presented to show the variation:

Lower end of Seven Mile Beach (Miller and McMullen):

> June 26, 1921, four eggs.
> July 10, 1921, three eggs.
> June 25, 1922, three and four eggs.
> July 4, 1931, two with one egg; one with two; two with three and two with four.
> June 6, 1931, eleven nests with eggs.
> June 16, 1935, seven nests with eggs.
> June 20, 1936, six nests with eggs.

Gull Bar, Hereford Inlet:

> June 21, 1925, eight nests with eggs (McMullen).

Little Beach Island:

> June 15, 1915, three and four eggs (R. C. Harlow).
> June 17, 1916, three eggs (R. C. Harlow).
> July 15, 1925, many nests with eggs (Street).
> June 16, 1931, one hundred and thirty-two nests with eggs (McMullen).

Brigantine Beach (Fletcher Street):

> June 18, 1921, three nests with one egg; two with four; six with three; two with four and twenty young birds.
> June 25, 1922, one nest with three eggs; four with two; six with four; six with five; and five not yet laid in.

I visited the Ephraim Island colony several times in May before nesting had begun. In 1929, on May 11, there were twenty-five birds present flying round in packs of five to nine close to the ground, barking like hounds. Now and then they would set their wings as if about to alight and then change their minds and start off again, there were several hollows in the sand apparently made by either Common Terns or Skimmers but no eggs had been deposited. The bridge tender said that the first Skimmers came on May 4. On May 16, 1930, there were thirty-two on the island; they were very restless and continually took wing and sped away to a bar north of the Wildwood Road where in each season the first arrivals seemed always to congregate. Then they would return in bunches of five, six, twenty etc. In 1931 there were six on this bar as early as May 9 and in 1927 they were present at Little Beach Island by May 17, but there were none at Seven Mile Beach on May 16, 1936, although nests had been scooped out by June 7 (Hiatt).

I have not been able to check the time of the Skimmers' departure in autumn but according to the bridge tender they go in early October. I have seen them present on September 2, 1930, and September 7, 1927, and individuals have been seen as late as September 25, 1927, and September 27, in 1924 and 1925, while there were thirty present on October 4, 1931, and a flock of 150 at Brigantine on the same date, apparently about to migrate.

The adult bird seen with terns at Cape May Point on August 27, 1924, rested with them on the beach bending its head back over the shoulder and burying its bill under the scapular feathers. A bird in immature plumage, at the same place, September 27, squatted in the water up to its breast and poked its head under repeatedly, first on one side then on the other, after which it sank forward submerging the breast, and, raising the wing tips a little, churned the water with the forward part of the wings. This bird was dull brownish above, very different from the adults, the feathers edged with white and the bill dusky but red at the base. This is apparently the full juvenal or bird of the year plumage and so far as my experience goes it is not changed to the adult plumage before the birds leave for the south.

The presence of the Black Skimmers furnishes an exotic touch to the more or less prosaic bird life of our Cape May coast and their breeding grounds constitute one of its most attractive ornithological features. On July 13, 1932, I was studying this Hereford Inlet colony and wrote: Picture a wide thoroughfare reaching north to a broad Sound with a gentle south wind ruffling the surface of its waters. It is ebb tide and broad black mud flats lie exposed on either side of the channel with tufts of sea cabbage and oyster shells scattered here and there. On the side opposite to our stranded boat are scores of great brown gray Herring Gulls searching for dead crabs or other food exposed by the receding water. Some heavy-winged Turkey Vultures perch on the edge of the meadow which stands three feet above the flat, its vertical banks honeycombed with the burrows of the fiddler crabs. Other Vultures sail high overhead against the deep blue of the sky and graceful black-headed Laughing Gulls go lilting past, while early flocks of Dowitchers, Yellow-legs and little "peeps" go wheeling away to feeding grounds in the sound. On our side of the channel stand rows of Common Terns resting on the mud or bathing in the shallow water and behind them rise the meadows covered here with white sand and bleached shells of clams, razors and oysters left by the dredges. There are tufts of glass-wort, salt-wort, sea rocket and coarse grasses with masses of trash stranded among them. On this, as well as out on the open sand, dainty terns are setting on their eggs with dozens of eggs of an earlier laying, washed out by the high tides, half buried in the sand. On a bare expanse of sand are the Skimmers, sixty of them in a single flock, standing close together some asleep others craning their heads up and strutting about among their fellows. Although all of their nests had been destroyed the undaunted birds are digging out new hollows in the sand and some already have eggs. An unsuspecting Turkey Vulture soars over the colony and the terns, to the last one, are awing and after him, their raucous cries filling the air as they drive the intruder from their domain. The Skimmers, too, responding to the alarm rise in a solid phalanx and circle a couple of times before alighting, adding their barking cries to the chorus and attracting the attention of a tern or two which for the moment take them for Vultures and give chase. Then once again silence settles on the community and before we realize it all the nesting birds are back on their precious eggs.

Only in the roosts of Grackles, Crows, Martins or herons are we of the Middle States privileged to see such examples of bird life *en masse* as are offered by these sea bird colonies of our Cape May coast and the fact that these are breeding communities where the life of both the individual and the species are at stake adds greatly to their interest.

## RAZOR-BILLED AUK

### Alca torda Linnaeus

Doubtless some Razor-bills are present off the coast of New Jersey every winter but our knowledge of them is mainly confined, as in the case of other pelagic birds, to individuals cast up on the beach in more or less decomposed condition, or to others blown into the sounds by storms. Those that have been shot have all been obtained by fishermen who have given us no details of the actions of the birds. The only detailed observation that has been recorded is of a bird seen by Ludlow Griscom at the mouth of the inlet near the lighthouse at Barnegat City in the midst of a cold wave on December 19, 1926, with the temperature at 5° F. "It flew in at moderate range the deep bill plainly noticeable; also the greater extension of white back of the eye and the clouded effect. Half an hour later another individual was seen at close range going out to sea."

Young birds in their first winter have the bill much less elevated and without the white band, so that they might easily be confused with Brunnich's Murre. The best distinguishing characters in this plumage are the lack of the white line along the base of the upper mandible and the elevated tail tip when swimming.

Cape May County records are as follows:

Grassy Sound, Anglesea, three observed on several occasions in February 1891, Philip Laurent.
Sea Isle City, one shot and others seen, January 23, 1909, Thomas Mitchell.
Five Mile Beach, one shot by coast guards, January 20, 1880, W. L. Abbott.
Ocean City, one shot, January 10, 1901.
Five Mile Beach, one found exhausted, on the beach, May, 1927, F. W. Cole. Gillespie, Auk 1928, p. 91.
Cape May Beach, one found dead, March 11, 1922, Walker Hand.
Cape May beach one found dead, April 27, 1932, Witmer Stone.
Seven Mile Beach, one found oiled, December 27, 1928, C. Brooke Worth.

Records for the upper part of the coast furnished by Charles Urner and others range from December 19 to March 13.

# *BRÜNNICH'S MURRE

### Uria lomvia lomvia (Linnaeus)

So closely does this bird resemble the Razor-bill that it is not easy to be sure to which records of occurrence belong without careful examination of specimens. The high white-banded bill of the adult Razor-bill is sufficiently diagnostic but the bill of the immature bird in its first winter is little larger than that of the Murre.

From Cape May County we have no definite observations of this species although there seems no doubt but that it occurs offshore perhaps every winter, though it is certainly not as abundant as the Razor-bill.

At Barnegat Light farther up the coast Ludlow Griscom states that he saw one flying into the bay in company with a Puffin, on December 19, 1926, during a spell of very cold weather. Although at long range he noted the slender bill and narrow white wing stripe (Auk, 1927, p. 535).

Records have been published as follows:

Brigantine Beach, January 7, 1933, R. F. Miller (found dead).
Barnegat, December 12, 1926, Watson (close approach on the beach).
Delaware Bay, December 24, 1896.
Delaware River at Byberry, January 11, 1901.
Middletown, Delaware, December 18, 1896, Charles Pennock.

Stuart Cramer has recorded an individual seen on January 23, 1932, at the end of the breakwater at the entrance to Cape May Harbor. It was studied at close range with a glass and the flesh colored stripe at the base of the mandible and a dusky band across the breast (oil stain?) were clearly seen. The bird was diving continually close at hand for several minutes and finally disappeared under water (Auk 1932, p. 219).

( 610 )

## DOVEKIE

Alle alle (Linnaeus)

PLATE 47, P. 534

The Little Auk or Dovekie seems to be the most frequent of the Alcidae to visit the New Jersey coast and it probably occurs on the ocean off Cape May in greater or less abundance every winter. It is only when severe storms drive them into the bays or harbors, or when their dead bodies injured or oiled are washed up on the beaches that we see anything of these little sea birds. We have definite records of one or more individuals in eight out of the fourteen winters from 1921 to 1934 during which reasonably careful observations were made, and scattered occurrences prior to those years; back even to December, 1811, when the specimen figured by Alexander Wilson in his "Ornithology" was killed at Great Egg Harbor and sent to him "as a great curiosity."

I have never had the good fortune to see a live Dovekie nor even to find a dead one on the beach and those who have shot them have furnished no particulars as to their actions. One individual was blown in to Cape May on February 14, 1932, and was found dead in a garden on Washington Street and in the great invasion of Dovekies which occurred in November of that year along nearly the entire Atlantic coast a number of the birds were seen alive (cf. Murphy and Vogt, Auk 1933, p. 325, and Nichols, p. 448). Several were captured on the main streets of Cape May and others were seen on the Harbor where Otway Brown watched them swimming and diving in the deep water near the fish dock at Schellenger's Landing. They came within six feet of him and dived repeatedly, swimming under the water "like frogs," using their wings to propel themselves.

Oscar Eayre, cruising sixteen miles off Long Beach farther up the coast in January, 1933, counted eighty Dovekies from his boat.

A list of specimens obtained or observed in Cape May County is as follows:

December 17, 1878, Five Mile Beach.  W. L. Abbott.
Early in 1898, Grassy Sound.
November, 1904, Grassy Sound.  Walker Hand.
December 23, 1912, Peck's Beach.  W. B. Davis.
December, 1921, Corson's Inlet.  Wharton Huber.
December 31, 1922, Cape May.
January 7, 1924, Corson's Inlet.  Wharton Huber.
November 21, 1930, Cape May.  Walker Hand.
December 6, 1930.  Wilbur McPherson.
December 8, 1930, Cape May.  Walker Hand.  (2).
January 25, 1931, Cape May.  Schmidt.
January 31, 1931, Seven Mile Beach.  Brooke Worth.
February 14, 1932, Cape May.  Walker Hand.
November 20, 1932, Cape May.  J. W. Mecray.
November 21, 1932, Cape May.  Caught alive.
November 21, 1932, Five Mile Beach.  Otway Brown.
November 24, 1932, East Cape May.  Otway Brown.  (Two dead.)
November 24, 1932, Schellenger's Landing.  Otway Brown, several swimming.
November 27, 1932, Cape May.  Charles C. Page.  (Two dead).

There were other 1932 records from Seven Mile, Ludlam's and Peck's Beaches but we were unable to obtain details, and many from the Barnegat and Brigantine areas farther up the coast.  Most of the birds recorded above were picked up dead but one was shot on Barnegat Bay by William McCall on January 9, 1930.

While the great flight of Little Auks in 1932 was unusual it is probable that there were somewhat similar occurrences in the past when winter storms drove numbers of these little birds in shore but absence of ornithologists was responsible for our lack of information.  Lack of offshore records, where the birds are in their normal winter quarters, prevents the tabulation of dates of arrival from their summer home in Greenland in autumn or of their return in spring.

## BLACK GUILLEMOT

### Cephus grylle grylle (Linnaeus)

This rare winter visitor from the north has twice been recorded at Cape May, both times from the extreme end of the jetty, known as the "Stone pile" at the entrance to the harbor. The Guillemot like the Purple Sandpiper and the lobster prefers rocky coasts and like them, it seems to be attracted by the artificial rocky conditions offered by this rough stone jetty projecting out for a mile from an otherwise flat sandy shore.

Eliot Underdown reported the first Black Guillemot on December 10, 1929, an individual which flew from the northeast to comparative calm water on the lee side of the long jetty, which extends out from the entrance to Cold Spring Harbor, and remained within twenty feet of him for some fifteen minutes. The bird dived twice within this period and seemed to use its wings in submerging. It was in mottled winter plumage and seemed very light colored when in flight. The white wing markings were very conspicuous both in flight and when at rest, while the red feet at once attracted attention. (Auk, 1930, p. 242.)

On December 24, 1933, William Yoder saw two of these birds at the same spot, which was his post of observation during the Christmas census of the Delaware Valley Club. They flew across the channel and their light color and prominent white areas on the wings easily identified them.

A specimen mounted by Charles Voelker was said to have been taken on the Delaware River in December 1898, but we have no definite information concerning it. Charles Urner tells me of one picked up dead in the Barnegat region some years ago and Turnbull quotes John Krider as authority for two secured at Egg Harbor at some time prior to 1869 but we know of no other records for New Jersey.

( 613 )

## PUFFIN
### Fratercula arctica arctica (Linnaeus)

Of this very rare winter visitor to the New Jersey coast we have only Griscom's record of one flying into Barnegat Bay past the lighthouse on December 19, 1926, two reported by Oscar Eayre sixteen miles off of Long Beach Island in January 1933, in a flock of Dovekies, and one seen by Fletcher Street on Jarvis Sound during the Christmas census of the Delaware Valley Club on December 24, 1933. It has doubtless occurred in other years as far south as Cape May, but well out on the ocean.

Ludlow Griscom has given us an account of the occurrence of Puffins and other Auks in a remarkable flight at Barnegat Light on December 19, 1926: The bay was frozen and was crowded with grebes and gulls, as the tide was racing in from the sea. Brant, Scaup, Mergansers and Old-squaws were passing every moment. "Five minutes after my arrival, at dawn, a Brünnich's Murre followed by a Puffin flew in at long range, some Grebes just ahead, some Old-squaws just behind. The slender bill of the Murre and the narrow white wing stripe were plainly visible. The much smaller size of the Puffin and the absence of a wing stripe, the large head and buzzing flight were noticed. A little later a Razor-billed Auk flew in at a moderate range, the deep bill plainly noticeable, also the greater extension of white back of the eye, and the clouded effect. A lull of half an hour then ensued. Two Brünnich's Murres then flew out to sea; about five minutes later a Razor-billed Auk at close range came by tagging a flock of Old-squaws, also going out. This bird was near enough to be identified with the naked eye. Another five minutes passed and than a solitary Puffin came right past the light. This bird was also picked up and instantly recognized with the naked eye. It was buzzing in very rapidly, flying with the wind and was past me by the time I got my glasses on it, so that it was too late to make out the color of the bill-tip. The great depth was plainly seen, and of course all the other characters of the species." (Auk, 1927, p. 535.)

## DOMESTIC PIGEON
### Columba livia livia Gmelin

While the Domestic Pigeon, descendant of the Rock Dove of Europe, does not occur exactly as a wild bird in New Jersey, it would seem to merit mention as much as the English Pheasant, the Starling and the English Sparrow.

While Pigeons, so far as I know, nest entirely about houses and barns, so do the Sparrows, and in their feeding habits they are similar. The Pigeons gather on grain fields after the crops are cut, as well as on pastures, and frequently associate not only with Starlings and Sparrows but with Mourning Doves, blackbirds, and other native species. We also see Pigeons flying far away from man's habitations, over open ground, ocean beaches and the edge of the meadows. Occasionally, too, they may be seen alighting on trees.

PLATE 86

*W. L. Baily*

*W. L. Baily*

1. YOUNG MOURNING DOVES NEARLY FULL FLEDGED.

2. NEST AND EGGS OF RUFFED GROUSE, MANUMUSKIN, CUMBERLAND COUNTY, N. J.
   MAY 30, 1898.

PLATE 87

A. B. Miller

W. L. Baily

1. BLACK-BILLED CUCKOO ON NEST CLOSE TO CATERPILLAR WEB, SPRINGS, PA.
2. YOUNG YELLOW-BILLED CUCKOO IN NEST IN "PIN FEATHER" STAGE, ARDMORE, PA.

# MOURNING DOVE

Zenaidura macroura carolinensis (Linnaeus)

PLATE 86, p. 614

Doves occur about Cape May throughout the year but, as in the case of all resident species, it is a question whether the individuals that nest here are the same as those which pass the winter; certainly there is a considerable migratory movement, as the large flocks seen in late summer and autumn do not occur throughout the winter and can hardly be made up of the local breeding birds and their offspring, while in spring there are obvious arrivals from the south.

From November to March one may see single Doves or small groups, from one to ten on a day's walk, while the Christmas census of the Delaware Valley Ornithological Club has totalled as many as twenty. Late March and April bring additional birds from farther south and from now through May they are engaged in nesting and usually occur in pairs. While the breeding season continues throughout the summer we begin to find Doves collecting in small flocks as early as June, possibly largely young of the year, although flocks of ten and twelve flushed from the edge of the salt meadows on May 25 and 27, 1923, can hardly have been young, unless from very early nestings.

In millet fields, or in any fields where the crops have been cut, Doves gather in considerable numbers sometimes associated with scattered Flickers and Meadowlarks. On July 7, 1922, I counted thirty in a field just back of the town which took wing successively as I approached, while on July 5, 1921, and July 18, 1927, there were similar gatherings in exactly the same spot. When these feeding birds took wing they usually resolved themselves into pairs and often circled about and returned to the feast, quite unlike their usual straightaway flight.    September and October seem to be the months of greatest abundance and flocks of one hundred or more are sometimes seen.    These flocks are apparently not assembled for feeding but are gathered together for the winter and, for the most part, migrate farther south, although occasionally such large flocks remain in the Cape May district.    One gathering of ninety birds was seen by Walker Hand on January 12, 1919, and another large flock on November 29, 1909.

One of the greatest Dove flights of which I have record was observed by Walker Hand passing over open truck fields opposite Bennett Station on September 6, 1924.    For several hours they continued to pass in groups of from three to one hundred, stopping here and there to feed and then passing on again.    They followed a comparatively narrow course and he estimated that at least 1200 Doves passed while he watched them.    The next day at the same spot only one or two pairs could be found.    The flight was to the northwest in the face of a strong wind, corresponding in this respect to the Flicker and Woodcock flights and the autumn migration of passerine birds. Such Dove flights apparently were of common occurrence in the past when Doves were game birds and I am told that the gunners took advantage of their definite courses and, hiding behind corn shocks on the line of flight, killed great numbers of the birds.

Sometimes we see Doves flying high up in a direct course probably on normal migration.    Such were twenty seen crossing the Harbor on September 4, 1921, which kept on steadily southward over the town while a similar flock of nine flew over Cape May Point but when directly above the Bay shore turned backward, evidently in doubt about crossing the wide expanse of water.

We usually see Doves in pairs, or often in threes, passing overhead in rapid flight and in most cases they disappear in the distance without alighting.    The group of three is of too frequent occurrence to be attributed to mere accident and may represent a pair and single young; the fact that I have seen groups of three more frequently in the late summer and autumn would support this theory.

The flight of the Mourning Dove is rapid and direct with strong short wingbeats, giving the impression of much reserved strength and with the body once in motion the wing action, though continuous, seems as if it were merely guiding a body hurtling through space of its own initiative.    Occasionally, though rarely, Doves will sail for some distance when approaching a resting place, especially if they are compelled to descend from a higher level.    One observed at Cape May Point on May 10, 1924, sailed on set wings, like a hawk, for at least two hundred yards in a gentle curve finally coming to rest in a tree.    Another seen on March 22, 1935, flying in the usual manner suddenly set its wings and gave a remarkable exhibition of volplaning, jerking to the right and left in a zigzag glide.    The tail was kept tightly closed during the glide but was opened suddenly with much display of white as the bird came to rest. This soaring performance is apparently a mating display as the male bird descends to the vicinity of the nest. I have seen it only in the spring.

When we flush Doves from the ground it is obvious that they have seen us first and they take wing, as a rule, while we are still at a safe distance and do not alight again within range of our vision. Occasionally, however, their action is different. On July 31, 1925, I came upon four on a shady wood road, which alighted on a nearby pine tree and peered out right and left poking the head forward and at intervals jerking it back and forth spasmodically like a shore bird. Possibly these birds were a pair of young and their parents. Again I had a Dove flush from almost under my feet as I walked along a wood road, an occurrence so unusual that I thought the bird might have been asleep.

I have frequently seen Doves arising from sandy spots on the Fill, north of the town, and by watching for their arrival in such places have been able to study them through the glass. Sometimes they would lie flat on their breasts at others stand with head bent back over the shoulder and in both cases would hold the position rigidly until disturbed by someone passing on a nearby path. They did not feed and seemed to be merely basking in the sun. Other individuals were flushed from sandy patches in open pine woods where from the appearance of the ground they may have been dusting themselves. There are many sand pits and hollows in the dunes on the Bay shore of Cape May Point where one may flush pairs of Doves at almost any time during the summer. I had supposed that the birds frequented these places for the purpose of obtaining gravel for their gizzards but they seem to occur there too regularly to be so engaged.

It is very difficult to stalk Doves so as to see just what they are doing in such places but when busy feeding they seem much tamer and more easily approached. I have come upon them in stubble fields where they were walking about like Domestic Pigeons, and several times in millet fields they were so busy picking up the seeds that they were apparently unaware of my approach. I have seen Doves close at hand on lawns, on Washington Street or in the Physick grounds, when they evidently had nests nearby and were naturally not so wary as are birds in the open.

Although it would seem that the natural habitat of the Dove when at rest is on the ground, except in the vicinity of the nest, they now and then alight in trees, temporarily at least, spreading the tail and thrusting it forward to check the momentum as the bird settles on its perch, and then swinging it up and down until a stable balance has been attained. The spreading of the tail displays the striking gray and white pattern which crosses the ends of the feathers and, with the rapid beating of the wings, makes the alighting Dove a conspicuous object. On several occasions I have found Doves resting on telegraph wires, quite a feat for so large a bird, and the descent from such a perch to the road involves another notable display of plumage.

A Dove is very wary when perching in a tree.  Usually the neck is held high when the bird alights, as if to take its bearings; then it peers to right and left for possible danger and finally relaxes when all appears safe.  One that came to rest in a pine tree directly over where I was standing looked down at me with head turned over sideways and immediately departed in precipitous flight.  Another watching me from the top of a dead tree turned its head as I walked and kept me constantly in view, while two resting in a willow bush twisted their necks until they were looking at me over their backs.  Both departed the moment they realized that they were detected. Doves nest in the trees of the town especially in the Physick grounds where they are to be found at almost any time both summer and winter and where familiarity with human beings seems to make them much less wary.  They also build in the pines and small trees of Cape May Point and in orchards and other locations farther up in the peninsula.

I found a nest in a wild plum bush at the Point which contained two eggs as early as April 24, 1921, while two young were found in an old Robin's nest in a pine tree on May 30, 1924.  The latest nesting of which I have record was in the Physick grounds on September 6, 1924, the nest being located on the horizontal limb of an oak tree twelve feet from the ground.  It contained a single squab which flew out as I climbed the tree and one of the parents immediately flopped to the ground and went through the so-called broken wing ruse.

Turner McMullen examined a nest at Cape May Court House on June 20, 1920, which contained two eggs and in Salem County has found the following nests all with two eggs except one:

| | | |
|---|---|---|
| May 13, 1917. | April 15, 1923. | April 13, 1929, two nests. |
| April 15, 1922. | April 29, 1923, one egg. | April 13, 1930. |
| April 16, 1922. | April 20, 1924. | April 16, 1932. |
| April 22, 1922. | April 7, 1928, two nests. | April 23, 1932. |
| April 29, 1922. | April 14, 1928. | April 30, 1932. |
| | April 22, 1928. | |

There are certain locations where Mourning Doves may always be looked for in winter when the stubble fields have lost their lure.  Open sandy areas as already described are attractive at all seasons and thickets where the upland and salt meadow meet.  A thicket of marsh elder just above Schellenger's Landing, in such a situation, seems to harbor from three to five Doves on every winter visit.

While a familiar species, inasmuch as it appears on almost every daily bird list that we make at Cape May, the Mourning Dove, as we know it here, is not a bird with which one feels on intimate terms.  Its mournful call is not a pleasing sound and seems to speak of solitude and far off places and although it comes to our shade trees and orchards to nest it does so in a rather surreptitious manner.  After long experience the only picture of the Dove that has made a lasting impression on my mind is a momentary glimpse of two dark-colored pointed-tailed birds hurtling across the sky, gone almost as soon as they are noted, leaving us in ignorance as to whence they came and whither they are going.

## PASSENGER PIGEON

Ectopistes migratorius (Linnaeus)

While the Passenger Pigeon, now a thing of the past throughout its once extended range, formerly occurred in abundance in South Jersey it was regarded as rare by Thomas Beesley as early as 1856.

Our earliest record of the bird is by David Pieterson deVries who says in his journal that "an immense flight of wild pigeons in April obscured the sky" this was in 1633 apparently when he visited his colony near Cape Henlopen.

Then we have the account of the bird by Peter Kalm, who spent some time at the Swedish colony on the Delaware and probably his observations refer to the vicinity of Swedesboro. He speaks of the marked increase in the numbers of the birds in February and March and states that "in the spring of 1740, on the 11th, 12th, 15th, 16th, 17th, 18th, and 22d of March (old style), but more especially on the 11th, there came from the north [i. e. south] an incredible multitude of these pigeons to Pennsylvania and New Jersey. Their number, while in flight, extended three or four English miles in length, and more than one such mile in breadth, and they flew so closely together that the sky and the sun were obscured by them, the daylight becoming sensibly diminished by their shadow.

"In the beginning of February about the year 1729, according to the stories told by older men, an equally countless multitude of these pigeons as the one just mentioned, if not a still larger number, arrived in Pennsylvania and New Jersey. Even extremely aged men stated that on three, four, five, or several more occasions in their lifetime they had seen such overwhelming multitudes in these places." It was the opinion that eleven, twelve or more years elapsed between the unusual visitations. The birds roosted in such numbers that they broke the limbs of the trees. "The Swedes and others not only killed a great number with shot-guns, but they also slew a great quantity with sticks, without any particular difficulty." (Kongl. Vetenskaps-Akademiens Handlingar Vol. 20, 1759, translation by S. M. Grönberger, Auk, 1911.)

In Bergen County, John T. Waterhouse described the Pigeon flight in a letter to his parents in London dated March 23, 1838, as follows: "For the last fortnight the air has been almost black with Wild Pigeons emigrating from the Carolina swamps to more northerly latitudes. Within ten miles square during the first fortnight I suppose they have shot or netted at least twenty thousand. They fix up a kind of hut in a field made of limbs of trees and buckwheat stubble. They have one or two fliers which they throw out every time a flock passes; the fliers are of the Wild Pigeon breed usually wintered over or sometimes they take them directly from the flocks, tie their legs to a small piece of twine and throw them up. There is a floor cleared on the ground and buckwheat spread for a bait and they have a pigeon on the floor and also a stool pigeon which they move at pleasure by a rope fixed to it in the hut. There is then a net so fixed having a rope that fastens it to a stake in the ground at one end and soon as ever the Pigeons fly down the man in the hut pulls another rope fastened to the net and jerks it over them. They will sometimes net in this way at one haul three or four hundred. Whilst I am writing they are in the adjoining room picking seven Pigeons for our breakfast. They were shot this morning at one fire of the gun." (Condor, 1927, p. 273.)

Unfortunately there seem to be but very few later notes on the bird in New Jersey. Charles Westcott (Homo) mentions that he had shot Passenger Pigeons out on the beach but nothing further and beyond that we have only the records of last occurrences.

1878. Two recorded by F. M. Chapman, shot at Englewood, in September (Auk, 1889 p. 302).

1879. One shot by Dr. W. L. Abbott at Haddonfield, March 22 (Cassinia, 1907, p. 84).

1885. One seen by Thurber, shot at Morris Plains, September 16 (Morristown Democratic Banner, Nov. 1887).

1893. One shot by A. B. Frost from a flock of ten at Morristown, on October 7 (Cassinia, 1907, p. 84).

1896. One shot by C. Irving Wood, at Englewood, June 23, 1896 (Auk, 1896, p. 241).

## GROUND DOVE

### Columbigallina passerina passerina (Linnaeus)

This distinctly southern bird, which does not normally range north of South Carolina, has on one or two occasions been found in New Jersey doubtless carried by tropical storms which have been responsible for the occasional appearance of other stragglers from the south.

Turnbull (1869) states that John Krider, the noted Philadelphia taxidermist and gunsmith, shot one near Camden in 1858 and Krider himself in his "Field Notes" says: "I shot one specimen in the pine woods of New Jersey, which I suppose was a straggler. I had been out hunting quail in November, and on my return through a thick pine woods toward the ferry, this bird flew up from the ground."

Our only other record was a bird observed in the Physick garden by Otway Brown in October, 1935. He wrote me to ask whether there was more than one species of dove in this region stating that he had noticed a small dove feeding on the ground and thinking that it was a young bird and that the date was unusually late he approached it when it flew and he noticed that the tail was square and that it looked quite different from the ordinary Mourning Dove. This was the year of the severe August storm which may have been responsible for the presence of this waif from the south.

## YELLOW-BILLED CUCKOO

Coccyzus americanus americanus (Linnaeus)

PLATE 87. p. 615

While I have not sufficient data to be sure, I am of the opinion that at Cape May the Yellow-bill is the more common cuckoo back in the farming country but that the Black-bill is equally abundant in the gardens and among the shade trees of the town itself. The habits of the two are essentially alike and their general appearance identical. They have a swooping flight from tree to tree in which the tail seems very long and somewhat curved upward by air pressure from below, especially when a bird descends from a considerable altitude as I have several times seen them do.

When moving about among the foliage of a tree a cuckoo makes clumsy jumps from limb to limb and often fluffs up its plumage or partly spreads its wings making quite a disturbance, but when it remains still it is exceedingly difficult to detect. I saw one fly into a tree at Cold Spring one day but failed to locate it and only after twenty minutes search with the binoculars was it discovered. Meanwhile I felt sure that it had flown away but my companion assured me that no bird had left the tree.

When perching the Yellow-billed Cuckoo has a curious way of craning its long neck to one side or the other often twisting the head at the same time, all of these actions being very slow and deliberate. It also has a way of raising the tail and letting it fall slowly to its former position and only occasionally do we see the tail feathers spread.

Like the Black-bill this cuckoo seeks caterpillars on the catalpa and buttonwood trees along the sidewalks and I have also flushed it from dense growths of grass and herbs in swampy spots where it must have been clinging to the stems close to the ground or resting on the ground itself, and one was seen to bathe in an open drain in a garden at Cold Spring on August 19, 1923.

The characteristic retarded call notes of the Yellow-bill—*kakakakakak-ka-ka-kow, kow, kow, kow, kow*—are often heard in the town and one bird was heard calling as late as August 18, 1931, while another, one evening, added his cries to the hubbub of the Martin roost on the Physick place.

Our earliest dates of arrival are May 8, 1912, and May 4, 1915, while cuckoos are present regularly until mid-September with exceptional records for October 5, 1930, and October 6, 1929. A nest found by Turner McMullen at Rio Grande on June 3, 1923, contained three eggs while another in Salem County on May 30, 1934, held two eggs and a young bird. A single egg was found on a lawn at Cold Spring on August 25, 1931.

Both of the cuckoos seem to have two broods in a season or else are very erratic in their nesting habits as young birds are found on exceptionally late dates. On September 5, 1914, Julian Potter found a nest full of well-feathered young birds near Camden which left the nest and were able to fly on the 9th. Another nest in the same vicinity on July 15, 1916, contained three eggs and one young just hatched, the others came out on the 16th and 17th. The skin of the young was black with a few hair-like down filaments.

# BLACK-BILLED CUCKOO

*Coccyzus erythropthalmus* (Wilson)

PLATE 87, p. 615

When I began to study the birds of Cape May I was of the opinion that the Black-billed Cuckoo was a transient only. Strength was given to this view by the appearance of individuals about the middle of August along with the earliest south-bound migrants, which seemed to be lost and unfamiliar with their surroundings and obviously not local summer residents. These birds were found in the low dune thickets close to the ocean front from which one individual was seen to fly out over the surf and back again. They were also seen in the pine woods at the Point and in other places not usually frequented by cuckoos. Arrival dates for such birds were:

| | | |
|---|---|---|
| 1921. August 15. | 1923. August 30. | 1929. August 5. |
| 1922. August 9. | 1927. August 25. | |

Later I discovered that the Black-billed Cuckoo was quite as common as the Yellow-bill if not more so in the shade trees of the town throughout the summer, where it was a persistent hunter of caterpillars, while a young bird scarcely able to fly was found early in July; and Turner McMullen reported a nest with young at Rio Grande on June 8, 1924. These facts established the species as a summer resident although they did not affect the transient status of the dune thicket birds.

( 622 )

The caterpillar eating habits of the Black-bill are interesting. On July 19 and 20, 1934, the catalpa trees of the town were infested by a smooth yellow and black striped caterpillar (*Ceratomia catalpae*), about three inches in length, which threatened entirely to defoliate them. This cuckoo with some help from the other species, practically destroyed the pests on nearly all of the shade trees. Two birds were watched for some time at close range. One, evidently a bird of the year, had the white breast plumage rough and apparently in molt, while its eye ring was gray; the other, an adult, had the breast smooth and silky and the bare space around the eye red. They would seize the caterpillar just behind the head and switch it violently back and forth until it became perfectly limp and would wrap around the bill like a piece of string when the head of the bird was jerked sideways. The cuckoo would then raise its head and gulp the insect down sitting perfectly still for some minutes after. The adult bird sometimes jerked the caterpillar around for fifteen minutes before swallowing it but the young one would draw its victim through its bill from one end to the other and then back again, crushing it thoroughly between the mandibles and not wasting so much time switching it back and forth. Both birds would invariably wipe the bill on the twig upon which they stood after swallowing, but never beat the live caterpillar against it.

On September 7, 1927, the Black-billed Cuckoos were feeding upon a hairy caterpillar which infested the plane trees along the sidewalks. After jerking one of them about until dead they would deftly strip all of the hairs from the body before swallowing. Little tufts of whitish down were continually floating off from the feeding birds and helped to locate them. When a caterpillar was dropped the bird would fly to the ground and pick it up again, and Otway Brown tells me that he saw them repeatedly fly down to the ground and pick caterpillars from a fallen web-worm nest.

We have arrival dates for the Black-billed Cuckoo from May 10 to the middle of the month and while most of them have gone by the end of September there are several October records one as late as October 18, 1931.

Julian Potter has found two young birds apparently just out of the nest on September 14, 1919, which illustrate the late nesting of this species already alluded to in the case of the Yellow-bill.

The names given to our two cuckoos are unfortunate as they indicate the color of the bill as the best distinguishing mark whereas it is the color of the lower mandible only that is different while the rufous color of the inner portion of the wing feathers and conspicuous white tips to the tail feathers in the Yellow-bill, as contrasted with the uniform brown of the Black-bill's wings and its narrow grayish tail tips, are far better diagnostic characters.

# BARN OWL

### Tyto alba pratincola (Bonaparte)

#### PLATES 88, 89, p, 630

The Barn Owl is a regular autumn transient in the pine woods at Cape May Point occurring most frequently during October; some remain through the winter and a few doubtless nest in the vicinity. Usually we see only a single bird but, as they are very secretive during the day, others may often be present that we do not discover. Our dates of occurrence run from October 11 to November 11 during the years 1923 to 1931. These were merely the result of scattered trips covering only single days, but in 1935, William Rusling, who was present throughout the autumn until early November watching the hawk flight, counted twenty-six Barn Owls, some of which of course may have been duplications and on some occasions he saw as many as five or six in the course of a day, which probably gives a fair idea of their maximum abundance. He saw none until September 16 and his last record was November 3. He tells me that they roosted quietly in the pine groves during the day and flew over the houses at night uttering their harsh whistling gasp *eeeeee séeek*.

One Barn Owl that I found in this vicinity on October 18, 1925, flushed repeatedly, flying from one pine tree to another as I tried to approach it. A number of these owls were found dead all about the Point during the hawk shooting season, victims of the "sportsmen" who were either ignorant of the wholly beneficial nature of these birds or bent on shooting anything that flew. Fortunately since the sanctuary has been established this indiscriminate slaughter has been largely abated. The old practice of shooting hawks and owls and nailing them on barns still persists through the farming country of South Jersey and Turner McMullen tells me of one barn near Pennsgrove which was ornamented by the carcasses of six Barn Owls, eleven Long-eared Owls, four Screech Owls, one Short-eared Owl, one Great Blue Heron, four Red-shouldered Hawks and one Cooper's Hawk!

In Cape May single Barn Owls have often been found in the safe retreat offered by the Physick place with its numerous shade trees and other vegetation, and with a thicket of red cedars flanking it in the rear. One was present here from August 1 to October 6, 1929, and probably earlier. Its pellets were found regularly and four of them examined on September 3 contained remains of thirteen meadow mice, and one long-tailed shrew, while another on September 5, contained three meadow mice and one shrew. Another Barn Owl seen on July 4, 1930, left the trees in great haste when fireworks were discharged in the street nearby, and as pellets were found later he was doubtless established there. Still another entered these grounds on July 19, 1923, at dusk causing great consternation among the Grackles that were roosting there and on March 19, 1932, one flew from a hollow tree that was being cut down and which may have harbored more than one of these interesting birds, at any rate, individuals had been seen there on December 2, 1923, and December 28, 1930.

One that I saw on August 20, 1921, could hardly have been a migrant and from his tameness I thought that he was probably a young bird hatched somewhere in the vicinity. He was perched in a clump of willow bushes on the Fill clasping the slender branches of a fork, one in each foot. His wings were drawn in closely against the tarsi and he stood very erect with head well up. As I walked around the bushes he turned his head in an effort to follow me but could not twist it for more than three quarters of the circle. He did not flush although I was within ten feet of him.

When the old Stockton Hotel, a great frame barn-like structure close to the ocean front, was closed, a pair of Barn Owls nested there and when it was later pulled down a brood of young was discovered in one of the lofts.

Farther north in the peninsula the Barn Owl is a more regular breeder and perhaps a permanent resident as more old hollow trees and old buildings are available, but like most other owls it seems more partial to the Delaware Bay side of New Jersey beyond the pine lands and Turner McMullen has found a number of nests there, in Salem County, as follows:

| | |
|---|---|
| April 8, 1922, two eggs. | April 26, 1925, four eggs. |
| April 17, 1927, six eggs. | April 27, 1924, two eggs (four |
| April 23, 1932, three eggs. | by May 14). |
| | May 30, 1923, five eggs. |

These six nests were mostly in cavities in old sour gum trees, one in a sweet gum in swampy woodland, and ranged from eighteen to thirty feet from the ground.  The largest cavity was nearly three feet in diameter and in one of them both birds were present when the nest was examined and at once flew out and away.

The notebook of W. B. Crispin shows that he had found eight nests of this owl in Salem County from 1904 to 1913, April 10 and 11, four eggs; April 7, 9, 13 and 25 six eggs; April 13 and 27 seven eggs.  In two instances the same pair had two sets of eggs in the season.  A set of six was taken from a nest on April 9, 1910, and another set of five was found there on May 5.  Similarly another pair losing a set of six eggs on April 7, 1913, had another set of six on May 3.

A nest found in a hollow tree at Mount Holly, Burlington County, held six young on May 30, 1932, but at Glenolden, Pa., across the Delaware, not many miles away, John Gillespie found young just able to fly on November 22, 1927, and another nest with young on December 7, 1929, two of which still remained in the nest on January 16, 1929.

He also found a family of five downy young Barn Owls in an old building on October 31, 1925, and shortly after John Emlen found three young at Riverton.  Other families were found in Gloucester County on May 13, 1924 (seven young) and on June 21, 1925, while a female banded on the former date was found in the same place on November 15 indicating that this individual, at least, was resident.  However another banded at the same time was shot at Somers Point fifty miles away, while one banded at Riverton on May 20, 1925, was shot at Wilmington, N. C., November 16, following, and another banded on November 18, 1925, was killed at Trappe, Md., on April 5, 1926, which are equally conclusive of an extensive migration (Gillespie)!  Other nests have been found as far north in the state as Princeton, Plainfield and Summit and stragglers have occurred at Englewood, Chatham etc.

I have no spring Barn Owl records at the Cape that would indicate a northward migration but Julian Potter heard one flying overhead and uttering its characteristic screech on March 21, 1926, at Collingswood, Camden County, and at about the same time John Gillespie flushed one from near the ground at Glenolden, Pa., which evidently had no permanent retreat so that it appeared as if a migration might be under way.

The Barn Owl is a southern bird characteristic of the Carolinian Fauna and does not range much farther north than New Jersey.  While usually of irregular occurrence in the northern parts of the state it has bred in Union and Essex Counties (Urner and Eaton).  It is one of the species that give to the bird life of the Cape the southern character that renders it so interesting.

## SCREECH OWL

Otus asio naevius (Gmelin)

PLATE 90, p. 630

Except for an occasional Barn Owl the little Screech Owl is the only owl to be found in Cape May in the summer and even it is by no means abundant or regular in its occurrence.   While it is supposed to be resident almost all of my records are during the summer.

I have heard it hooting from shade trees along the sidewalks in the town in July 1918 and 1922 and again on August 28 of the latter year; also on July 20 and August 12, 1928, July 16, 1929, and August 29, 1931, while Otway Brown found one on June 17, 1932, in a bush on the Physick property on Washington Street with a pair of Cardinals and other nesting birds surrounding it and protesting in much excitement.   A pair was reported to have wintered there in the season of 1907–1908.

At Cape May Point they do not seem to be any more plentiful and the only recent record that I have is of one in the red phase of plumage flushed by Warren Eaton on September 7, 1935, when watching the hawk flight.

Farther up in the peninsula in the farming district Screech Owls seem to be more numerous and Otway Brown has heard them hooting about his place at Cold Spring from May 7 to November 19 in different years.

In Salem County, west of the pine lands, they breed more plentifully and Turner McMullen tells me of nests that he examined on:

| | |
|---|---|
| March 23, 1924, two eggs. | April 15, 1922, three eggs. |
| April 7, 1929, four eggs. | April 17, 1921, four eggs, and |
| April 8, 1923, three eggs. | another with three young. |
| April 10, 1927, one egg. | April 18, 1931, four eggs. |
| April 13, 1925, three eggs. | April 28, 1935, two eggs. |
| April 14, 1928, four eggs. | |

These nests were in cavities in trees usually in apple trees but sometimes in red maples or oaks; often in old Flicker holes.

There seems to be no evidence of migration as practically no Screech Owls were noted by the hawk observers at the Point.

## GREAT HORNED OWL

Bubo virginianus virginianus (Gmelin)

PLATES 91, 92, p. 630

The Great Horned Owl is rarely seen today in the immediate vicinity of Cape May but wherever primeval woodland existed in the southern part of the county it was formerly to be found.   Today, however, with the destruction of much of the old forest the Horned Owls have disappeared to a great extent although a few still remain.   The big woods skirting the meadows opposite Rio Grande, from the Wildwood Road to Bennett, was one of their last strongholds and there Walker Hand and I came upon one of them on July 26, 1920. When flushed he flew to a nearby tree and stood there looking down at us and raising and lowering his ear-tufts. When he flew again a party of Crows gave chase and made a great disturbance. Before we saw him we heard him call once or twice which seemed unusual as it was only about midday but on September 12, 1920, Walker Hand heard another calling in the daytime in Rutherford's woods near Pond Creek. I have seen a number of mounted specimens that were shot in the Rio Grande woods and gunners shoot them on every occasion, deliberately hunting them out when their roosting places are known.

On August 17, 1891, I flushed a Horned Owl from the woods at Cape May Point north of the turnpike; the nearest approach of which I have record. John Gillespie flushed another from the grove where the Night Herons nest, back of Seven Mile Beach, and upon its taking wing all the Crows that were gathered in the neighborhood at once started in pursuit. This was the only one of which I have record on the island beaches except for a single one seen on Five Mile Beach by Philip Laurent when that island was covered with tall woodland.

Walker Hand tells me of one that used to come out in the early evening when it was still quite light and perch on a dead pine stub near Bennett Station where it was a very conspicuous object. In the same vicinity he once heard three Horned Owls calling to one another from trees and fence posts one of which swooped down close to a flock of Killdeers which had gathered there causing great consternation.

On November 21, 1934, and November 19, 1933, Otway Brown heard two calling at Cold Spring and on December 26, 1932, and December 24, 1933, Julian Potter heard one hooting near Cape May Court House.

Turner McMullen found a nest of the Great Horned Owl not far from Cape May on March 4, 1923; which was situated about twenty feet up in a walnut tree in an open field; it was an old Fish Hawk's nest which had been appropriated by the owls and contained the usual two eggs as in all other nests that he has seen. The same nest was found on the ground on March 2, 1924, having been blown down by a storm and held two broken eggs. In Salem County he has found a number of nests as listed below with several reported by William B. Crispin:

| | |
|---|---|
| February 11, 1934. | March 23, 1924. |
| February 15, 1925. | April 8, 1922. |
| February 17, 1927. | April 13, 1935 (young birds). |
| February 17, 1935. | April 18, 1931 (young birds). |
| February 21, 1932 (two nests). | April 21, 1929 (young birds). |
| February 23, 1913 (Crispin). | April 23, 1933 (young birds). |
| February 27, 1910 (Crispin). | |

The February 27 nests was robbed and held a second set on April 15. These nests, mostly old Fish Hawks' or Crows' nests, were in tall trees from twelve to eighty feet from the ground, usually forty to fifty, and situated either in swampy or dry woodland.  The old bird was often found on the nest but generally flew away before a close approach was possible, sometimes coming back to within fifty yards of the nest but showing no inclination to attack the visitor.  In one instance the old bird raised from the nest and spreading her wings plunged straight down to within ten feet of the ground when she checked herself and flew off.  In another case both birds perched fifty feet away and remained there while the nest was being examined.  Crispin has also recorded a pair of Great Horned Owls occupying an old nest of the Great Blue Heron and another pair took possession of a Bald Eagle's nest in the spring of 1928.

A nest described to me by Brooke Worth was found on April 7, 1928. It was in a grove of pitch pines on the mainland, opposite Avalon, between the meadows and the shore road.  The pines were some fifty feet in height and bordered by dense growths of greenbrier and holly trees.  The nest was in a tree taller than the others and had the appearance of being an old Fish Hawk's nest; it was thirty feet from the ground and was saddled on a large dead limb.  There were two young and while they were being examined one of the parents remained in the vicinity but kept well hidden and only a few fluttering glimpses of it were obtained.  It made no attack at any time. In the nest were the remains of a rabbit and the wing of a Black Duck.

On visiting the nest again on April 21, many pellets were found in the woods and one or both of the parents were hooting in low tones recalling the distant baying of hounds.  About the base of the tree the ground was profusely littered with pellets and as the trunk was scaled one of the young flopped down to the ground, although the other remained crouched in the nest, its great yellow eyes glaring and its beak snapping with the rapidity of a machine gun.  Every feather on the body was elevated to the fullest extent and the wings puffed out as the bird backed away.  The one that had fallen went hopping and scrambling away with half-raised wings and when approached too closely would face about and go through the same performance as the one in the nest with the addition of a hissing sound made by the breath.  The parents were some distance away in the wood, their position being indicated by the ravings of half a dozen taunting Crows.

Stirling Cole tells me of the capture of a young Horned Owl early in 1904, at a nest in a timber swamp a mile from his home near Seaville.  It was kept in a large cage in the yard for over a month when it was liberated. One of the parents visited it every night bringing food—Doves, Flickers, Robins and sometimes mice.  She came regularly at dusk hooting every few yards as she came and the young bird would answer with a most peculiar call.  Her final flight was over an open field and she came along the ground apparently stopping every few yards.  She spent the whole night with her offspring except when off for food.  Finally she discovered the hen roost and thereafter took a young chicken every night although she had never molested them before.  After a loss of about two dozen chickens it became necessary to shoot the old bird which proved a difficult matter as it was very hard to see her although she could be heard all night. The young owl resisted every attempt to tame him. A pet Crow seemed to be a natural enemy; it would stand in front of the owl's cage and seemed to taunt him while he hissed continually and endeavored to get at his tormentor.

The Great Horned Owl is resident throughout the state where woodland suitable for its nesting remains.

## SNOWY OWL

Nyctea nyctea (Linnaeus)

The great Snowy Owl is apparently of very rare occurrence at the Cape as it seldom comes so far south on its periodic migrations from its home on the Arctic tundra. I have seen several mounted specimens which were shot in the vicinity of Cape May but never have seen a living individual.

Walker Hand tells me of one shot at Rio Grande, December 30, 1897, and two that arrived on the Fill during the late autumn of 1905 one of which was captured on November 26, the other remaining well into the winter.

Another was shot during the great flight of 1926–1927 and Prof. Gross in his report on this flight records twelve that reached the Jersey coast between Elizabeth and Atlantic City. (Auk, 1927, pp. 479–493.) During the flight of 1930–1931, while none was recorded from Cape May, one was seen on Long Beach by Earl Higgons and David Leas on December 22, and again on February 15, 1931, by T. Donald Carter. The former observers stated that the bird was sitting on the beach and allowed a close approach moving for a short distance rather reluctantly. After several such performances it flew out low over the water to an island in Barnegat Bay with very slow wingbeats and frequent soarings (Auk, 1931, p. 267). In the next flight, 1934–1935, one was found on Brigantine Island, on December 9, 1834, January 7, and February 12, 1935, by various observers. On one occasion it was feeding on the carcass of a Herring Gull which it carried with it when it was disturbed.

In earlier years W. E. D. Scott reports them "very abundant during the winter of 1876–77" on Long Beach (Bull. Nuttall Orn. Club, 1879, p. 223) while E. Carleton Thurber states that "four or five were shot near Morristown during the winter of 1886–87" (True Democratic Banner, Morristown, November 1887) and L. S. Foster writes of a number in northern New Jersey in November, 1889; one at Morriches on November 16 and another at Sea Isle City on November 20. (Forest and Stream, November 28, 1889.) On December 20, 1890, Philip Laurent saw one on Five Mile Beach (O. and O., April, 1892, p. 54). There are other northern records.

Albert Linton writes me of one seen near Riverton along the Delaware River above Camden on January 13, 1918, after a severe spell of weather when the river was completely frozen over. The bird was seen at a distance

PLATE 88

*W. L. Baily*

*J. A. Gillespie*

1. BARN OWL LEAVING NEST HOLE IN TREE TRUNK, SALEM, N. J., APRIL 1, 1899.

2. FLASH-LIGHT PICTURE OF BARN OWL RETURNING TO YOUNG IN OLD RAILROAD
   TOWER WITH FOOD.

PLATE 89

*J. K. Potter*

*Wharton Huber*

1. YOUNG BARN OWLS SHOWING VARIATION IN SIZE IN BROOD FROM A SINGLE NEST, CAMDEN CO., N. J.

2. YOUNG BARN OWL AT A LATER STAGE OF GROWTH.

PLATE 90

*J. K. Potter*

*Wharton Huber*

YOUNG SCREECH OWLS

PLATE 91

*B. C. Hiatt*

GREAT HORNED OWL AT NEST IN HERONRY AT DELAWARE CITY, DEL., MARCH 28, 1929.

PLATE 92

*Courtesy of "Bird Lore"*          *C. Brooke Worth*

*J. K. Potter*

1. YOUNG GREAT HORNED OWL ON NEST, MAINLAND OPPOSITE SEVEN MILE BEACH.
   N. J., APRIL 21, 1928.

2. YOUNG GREAT HORNED OWLS, CAMDEN CO., N. J.

PLATE 93

*Wharton Huber*

*Wharton Huber*

1. SAW-WHET OWL.

2. BARRED OWL.   BOTH CAPTIVE BIRDS.

PLATE 94

*J. K. Potter*

*W. L. Baily*

1. LONG-EARED OWL, CAMDEN CO., N. J.
2. NIGHTHAWK WITH DOWNY YOUNG AT LEFT OF BREAST.

PLATE 95

*W. L. Baily*

*W. L. Baily*

1. WHIP-POOR-WILL'S "NEST" AND EGGS.

2. YOUNG WHIP-POOR-WILL.

of 300 yards flying low over the marshy meadow. As he approached to get a better view the owl continued to fly over the frozen meadow remaining poised, now and then, in one spot on the lookout for prey. Suddenly he turned and came "directly toward me and his identity became evident. The owl face, the snowy plumage and great size marked him unmistakably as the Snowy Owl. I awaited his approach, not understanding the apparent lack of fear. About fifty feet away he poised and dropped down on the meadow with a distinct thud. As he dropped his back became visible and there were distinct bars of brown particularly on the wings. Apparently the pursuit had been successful, as the owl remained down for several seconds. He was completely hidden by the tall brown grass and I attempted to steal up on him. He was too alert, however, and in an instant was up and away, flying far out of sight up the river."

## *HAWK OWL

### Surnia ulula caparoch (Müller)

The Hawk Owl is a straggler from the Far North and is extremely rare in New Jersey. Dr. C. C. Abbott mentions two specimens shot in Mercer County in 1858 and Middlesex County in 1861, but with no authority or details. Eaton (Linn. Soc. Proc., 47) mentions one recorded from Essex Co. in 1904. These are the only records until December 19, 1926, when S. C. Brooks saw one near New Brunswick. It was "seen several times in the forenoon flying over open fields between scattered groups of trees, and later was observed perched in a small tree alongside a cattail-filled slough over which it made several short flights. There was ample opportunity for observation with 8 × glasses at about 150 feet; the long indistinctly barred tail, striking white spotting of the back, general light color of the top of the head, and the plain gray facial disc were noted" (Auk, 1927, p. 251). We have no record from Cape May County.

## BARRED OWL

### Strix varia varia Barton

PLATE 93, p. 631

The Barred Owl doubtless breeds in dense woodland of the middle or upper parts of Cape May County especially along the Bay shore but in the immediate vicinity of the Cape it is of irregular occurrence.

Walker Hand tells me that in the past the woods on either side of Pond Creek Meadows were always a favorite resort for them and that a number have been shot there. All of our recent records are from the same region.

On May 22, 1921, Richard Miller saw one above the Point pursued by a flock of some sixty Crows and in the pine woods on the edge of the New England Creek Meadows I saw one, also pursued by Crows, during a notable autumn flight of Flickers, on September 27, 1926. On December 28, 1924,

Julian Potter saw one in the woods a quarter of a mile below Higbee's Beach and at the same spot, on January 25, following, Henry Gaede saw probably the same bird. William Yoder saw one on October 20, 1929, and Dr. W. L. Abbott secured a specimen on January 29, 1878.

These records indicate that the species is a resident and we have no evidence of autumn migration. Farther to the west it seems to be a regular breeder and is doubtless resident. Turner McMullen has examined two nests in Salem and Cumberland Counties. One found April 11, 1926, in the former county, contained two eggs and was in a cavity in a gum tree twenty feet from the ground, two and a half feet deep and a foot in diameter; it contained leaves evidently the remains of an old squirrel's nest; one bird was on the nest and the other was seen in the vicinity. The second nest was found in Cumberland County March 17, 1933, and also contained two eggs it was in a cavity thirty-five feet from the ground in an old white oak in a marshy tract on the Maurice River and one bird was flushed from the nest. George Stuart found another nest near Salem on March 23, 1918, in a cavity in a swamp maple, twelve feet up, which contained two eggs.

William B. Crispin has left records of a number of nests in Salem County, February 28, March 5, 9, 12, 13, 17 with three eggs and March 27 with two eggs. Pairs that had been robbed had second sets as follows, March 12, 1911, three eggs and April 9, two eggs; March 17, 1912, three eggs and April 12, three eggs. Charles S. Schick has reported a pair of Barred Owls on Seven Mile Beach on May 10, 1890, which were probably nesting although neither nest nor young were found.

In woodland farther north along the coast the Barred Owl is of regular occurrence and comes close to the farm houses in winter in search of food. A male and female were caught in a steel trap on January 13 and 14, 1918, on the farm of J. W. Holman at West Creek.

The Barred Owl breeds in suitable woodland throughout the state and an interesting account of a nesting at Schraalenburgh in the extreme northeastern corner of Bergen County by William C. Clarke appears in "Bird-Lore" for 1908, pp. 99–102. Waldron Miller has also described a nest at Plainfield in which the female bird was imprisoned by a sheet of ice that formed over the aperture of the nest hole (Bird-Lore, 1907, p. 173).

# *GREAT GRAY OWL

### Scotiaptex nebulosa nebulosa (Forster)

While we have no record of this northern owl from Cape May there are two old records from the state. One shot near Mendham, Morris County, in 1887 (Thurber, True Democratic Banner, Morristown, November, 1887), and one killed in Sussex County, in December, 1859 (Abbott, Birds of New Jersey, 1868). Details are lacking in both cases.

## LONG-EARED OWL

Asio wilsonianus (Lesson)

PLATE 94, p. 631

Immediately about Cape May the Long-eared Owl, like most of the other owls, is rather rare and most frequently seen in autumn and winter. Our records are few. On October 1, 1923, I came unexpectedly upon one of them sitting in the heart of a low thicket near Cape May Point through which passed a wood road. The bird was busily engaged in preening its feathers reaching its head far over to the base of the tail and drawing each tail feather carefully between its mandibles. Presently it saw me looking at it through the binoculars at a distance of about twenty feet and it immediately fluffed up its feathers, spread its wings out on each side and arched them over so as to make a fan-like circle with its head in the middle. It glared at me and slowly raised first one foot and then the other off of the perch like a cat working its toes when it is being stroked. Upon lowering my glasses the bird at once drew in its wings and flew to the other side of the thicket.

Julian Potter saw two Long-eared Owls in the nearby pine woods on November 11 of the same year and again on December 2, while Otway Brown saw a colony of several in the same vicinity on November 19, 1933. This winter roosting in considerable numbers has been observed in several localities farther north in the state; at Yardville, Miss Rachel Allinson had a colony in a Norway spruce tree in her yard from 1891 to 1906, every winter and the ground below their roost was strewn with pellets containing mouse hair and bones. Another colony was reported by W. A. Babson at Princeton, which persisted for a number of years (Birds of Princeton, p. 50, 1901). Philip Laurent found a few in winter in the cedars on Five Mile Beach when this island was wooded. Julian Potter found three Long-ears associated with four Barn Owls and a Saw-whet in a clump of pines in Gloucester County in February 1921. Only one has been recorded in the Delaware Valley Club's Christmas census at Cape May, i. e., on December 28, 1930.

Farther west, in Salem County near to the Delaware River, these owls seem to be much more common and doubtless they do not find the environment that they desire on the ocean side of the peninsula. Turner McMullen has examined the following nests in Salem County, April 10, 1921, and March 29, 1925, four eggs; April 17, 1921, April 10, 1927, and two on March 30, 1929, five eggs. One pair had made use of a squirrels' nest and in other cases doubtless old Crows' nests served as the basis for their own; they were from seven to twenty-two feet from the ground in oaks and pitch pines with one in a red cedar. W. B. Crispin has recorded two nests from the same region on March 21, 1898, and April, 1897, each with five eggs.

The Long-eared Owl is resident in suitable localities throughout the state but more common in winter.

## SHORT-EARED OWL

Asio flammeus flammeus (Pontoppidan)

The Short-eared Owl is a winter visitant in the Cape May region and our records run from September 5 to January 25. Many of the birds fall victims to thoughtless gunners during the shooting season and this doubtless has something to do with the lack of records for late winter and spring.

The Short-ear is distinctly an open ground bird being found exclusively on the meadows, the Fill and similar flat exposed situations.

I came upon one on October 1, 1923, on the marsh below South Cape May, which alighted successively on a pile of salt hay, a pile of dry mud left from ditching, and finally in a patch of dry grass. It stood with its body bent forward and the tail nearly touching the ground, giving it a crouching appearance. When it flew the wing strokes were long and somewhat irregular but so powerful that they gave the impression of bouncing the body up and down between them. The round bullet-like head projected immediately in front of the wings with no neck apparent.

Julian Potter saw one at about the same spot on November 14, 1920, which was pursued by a flock of Crows. When they abandoned the chase the owl alighted on a bare space from which the black-grass had been cut for hay and as Potter writes me: "by keeping the sun at my back and directly in the face of the owl I was able to approach to within three feet of him. He was really facing the other way but with his head twisted so that he gazed at me directly over his back. He was crouching somewhat like a Whip-poor-will but when I circled around him he took wing and alighted on the sand dunes where he stood erect for an instant and then relapsed into the crouching position. When flying he took heavy measured strokes, his wings almost meeting under the body."

Several times we have found Short-eared Owls resting on bare spots on the Fill or among short yellow grass and on December 28, 1921, Earl Poole saw one busily hunting there, flying close to the ground at about 1:00 p. m. on a perfectly clear day.

The Christmas census of the Delaware Valley Club showed these birds present as follows:

December 22, 1929, five.          December 23, 1933, two.
December 28, 1930, one.           December 22, 1935, one.
December 27, 1931, four.          December 27, 1936, one.

While the records of Short-eared Owls about Cape May are usually of single individuals, they have the same habit of roosting in winter communities that is characteristic of the Long-ear and Samuel Rhoads found such a roost on Barrel Island in Barnegat Bay in late February, 1894, the ground being covered with ejected pellets, scattered bones and a number of mouse skins which led him to think that the birds had, to some extent at least, skinned their prey before eating it (Proc. D. V. O. C., No. II, p. 12).    W. E.

D. Scott describes a roost of one hundred and fifty to two hundred Short-eared Owls near Princeton, in the winter of 1878–79, in a field of some forty acres covered with a heavy growth of long dead grass. They arrived about November 1 and naturally many were shot as they flew about in the morning and evening hunting for mice. He later learned of two similar roosting places in the same vicinity (Bull. Nuttall Orn. Club, 1879, p. 83).

On May 9, 1905, William B. Crispin found a nest with six eggs on the marshes of Salem County at the head of Delaware Bay and several others were found later in the same vicinity; on May 6, 1923, Richard Miller and others saw a well-fledged young here on June 4, 1922, and found four young birds unable to fly but which had left the nest and were crouching at the bases of Juncus tussocks on May 6, 1923 (Oölogist, 1924, p. 109). Turner McMullen, who was with this party, later found two nests, one on May 21, 1932, in Cumberland County, containing seven eggs and another near Fortesque, on May 2, 1936, with five eggs. The former was located in short grass under a tuft of taller vegetation, on the edge of the meadows; the other in a tuft of dry yellow grass four feet in height and at least ten yards from the marsh.

Farther north along the coast W. E. D. Scott found a nest of Short-eared Owls containing seven eggs on the meadows adjoining Long Beach on June 28, 1878, and another was found in the same vicinity by Thomas D. Drown, while Richard Harlow found one on an island in Barnegat Bay, containing five half-fledged young, on June 17, 1915.

On the marshes near Elizabeth Charles Urner has found a number of nests as follows:

May 14, 1921, eight young of various sizes. (Auk, 1921, p. 602.)
May 22, 1922, six eggs. (Auk, 1923, p. 30.)
July 4, 1922, one egg and two young.
April 28, 1923, six eggs. (Auk, 1925, p. 32.)
May 5, 1923, six eggs.
June 8, 1923, young had left.
June 8, 1923, three young and seven eggs.
June 8, 1923, five young.

## SAW-WHET OWL

Cryptoglaux acadica acadica (Gmelin)

PLATE 93, p. 631

This little owl is a rare winter visitant at the Cape and we have but three records of its occurrence here. Walker Hand found one dead in the town on December 1, 1904, and Otway Brown once found one at Cold Spring which had killed itself by flying into a wire netting, while Reynold Spaeth told me of finding one at Cape May Point about 1895.

The Saw-whet is doubtless more plentiful than these records would indicate as many have been reported in the central and northern parts of the state.  While not roosting in close communities, like some of the other owls, the little Saw-whets seem to concentrate in limited areas, in some seasons at least, and W. E. D. Scott states that they were unusually plentiful in cedar groves near Princeton in the winter of 1878–79.  He secured ten on December 10, 1878, and seven more the next day and many more through the winter.  He states that "they roost close to the trunk and can frequently be taken alive in the hand.  They seem to affect scattered groves where the trees do not grow too thickly.  Most of the birds taken are females."  (Bull. Nuttall Orn. Club, 1879, p. 85.)

It occurs as a casual winter resident throughout the state.

## CHUCK-WILL'S-WIDOW

Antrostomus carolinensis (Gmelin)

Some years ago Otway Brown told me of a Whip-poor-will heard for several nights near his home at Cold Spring which had a call quite different from any that he had heard and his description tallied exactly with the call of the Chuck-will's-widow.  Shortly afterward I learned from Dr. Harry Fox, who was quite familiar with both birds, that he had heard a Chuck-will's-widow calling in swampy woods at Cape May Point when he was out at night collecting orthoptera.

In June 22, 1930, Frank Dickinson heard a strange Whip-poor-will near his home at Erma and Walker Hand who was present identified it at once as a Chuck-will's-widow.  I visited the spot on July 15 and was fortunate enough to hear it calling *chuck!—woo—woo; chuck!—woo—woo* repeated a number of times.  The bird came from a swampy thicket into an oak clearing back of the Dickinson farm and although it was too dark to see it we could tell that it was moving about by the different directions from which the calls came to us.  This bird had been heard many times during June and the early part of July but not after the middle of that month.  It began to call just at dusk.

Early in this same summer a bird struck the headlight of an automobile and was identified by a local taxidermist as a Chuck-will's-widow and from the description that I received he was undoubtedly correct but I was unable to see the bird myself.  Charles Page who had heard Chuck-will's-widows frequently in the South heard one repeatedly near his cabin in the woods at Cape May Point during June 1932 and 1934, but was unable to see the bird. The call contrasted definitely with the ever present Whip-poor-will chorus.

# WHIP-POOR-WILL

Antrostomus vociferus vociferus (Wilson)

PLATE 95, p. 631

In the immediate vicinity of Cape May Whip-poor-wills are found only in the woods and thickets of the Point but farther up in the peninsula they are of regular occurrence in all swampy wooded localities, coming out into more open spots to call at dusk. They are particularly abundant at Higbee's Beach and other densely wooded localities along the Bay shore and take advantage of the cleared areas about houses, whether occupied or vacant, for calling grounds.

About Cape May Point on almost any evening from late April to early August their characteristic calls may be heard, sometimes from a single bird but more often from several and on the night of May 20, 1928, William Shryock was able to distinguish no less than eight performers and there were doubtless more.

Charles Page who for several seasons occupied a little cabin directly in the woods had an abundance of Whip-poor-wills immediately about his door and even on his roof. Their din seemed to reach its height on June 1 but they continued to call until August 22, 1932, and August 26, 1934, although the calls were not so long-continued and the repetitions less in number. His latest record of the call was September 13, 1932, but Conrad Roland heard a few calls as late as September 16, 1933, and September 20, 1934.

While heard more frequently than they are seen, about the Point, Whip-poor-wills can easily be flushed in the daytime from the huckleberry thickets if we search for them and are willing to brave the "chiggers" (red-bugs) which also abound in such places, and while gathering huckleberries I have frequently disturbed them. A bird will flush sometimes from almost under foot. There is a short, silent, bat-like flight of a few moments and it drops to the ground a few yards in advance shielded again by the bushes. Sometimes for a moment or two it will alight on a low branch of a tree in full sight coming to rest cross-wise on the limb but wheeling at once to a position parallel to it.   It will blink once of twice with half opened eyes and once again there is the silent flight as it vanishes in the thicket.   One that I flushed in the pine woods on October 10, 1927, alighted on the sloping trunk of a large bayberry bush and perched there for several minutes with its great eyes wide open.   Sometimes I have flushed three Whip-poor-wills in quick succession but have never tried to see how many could be roused from their midday siesta; doubtless many of them do not take wing unless almost stepped upon.

On May 9, 1924, I flushed two birds which were sitting close together in a dense thicket east of the pine woods which seemed loath to move far from the spot and I presumed that they had eggs in the immediate vicinity, and a pair was roused from the same spot on July 18 and 20, 1925.   Curiously enough close to the May birds there grew a cluster of the lovely pink orchids (*Cypripedium acaule*) often called Whip-poor-will's shoes, so that there may have been some close association in folklore or legend of bird and flower which led to the name.   Certainly their habitats are the same.

While I have not actually found a "nest" here Julian Potter did find a female Whip-poor-will and one egg on a bed of dead leaves in the same vicinity on June 9, 1929, with the other egg lying broken close by; Richard Miller found a pair of downy young about the size of Chipping Sparrows near Rio Grande on July 3, 1923, which were resting on a carpet of dead leaves on the woodland floor; and I found another pair of young at the Point, barely able to fly on July 20, 1929.   Turner McMullen has found two sets of eggs of the Whip-poor-will, one at Whitesboro on May 20, 1922, and the other at Rio Grande on May 31, 1924, both placed on dead leaves in second growth woodland.

Walker Hand's dates of arrival with a few others run as follows:

| 1903. | April 26. | 1913. | April 30. |
|-------|-----------|-------|-----------|
| 1904. | May 1. | 1914. | April 29. |
| 1905. | April 26. | 1915. | April 17. |
| 1906. | April 21. | 1916. | April 30. |
| 1908. | April 13. | 1920. | April 11. |
| 1909. | April 23. | 1927. | April 24 (Stone). |
| 1911. | April 27. | 1930. | May 1 (O. H. Brown). |
| 1912. | April 19. | 1933. | April 25 (O. H. Brown). |

In the autumn various observers have seen them as late as:

| 1925. | September 29. | 1932. | October 14. |
|-------|---------------|-------|-------------|
| 1927. | October 10. | 1935. | October 5. |
| 1930. | September 28. | | |

Whip-poor-wills are summer residents throughout New Jersey in wilder sections of the country and are especially abundant in the Pine Barrens.

# NIGHTHAWK

Chordeiles minor minor (Forster)

PLATE 94, p. 631

While it nests, casually at least, farther north in the peninsula, the Nighthawk is only a somewhat irregular late summer and autumn migrant about Cape May. Single birds have been seen on July 9, 1922; July 25, 1926; July 30, 1929; and at Fishing Creek, to the north, one was seen on July 5, 1923, and July 9, 1924. All of these may have nested in the vicinity but it is usually mid-August before Nighthawks are seen in any numbers or with any regularity at the Cape.

In the spring we have very few records of Nighthawks; one flying over the sand dunes at Cape May Point on May 24, 1892, and one over the farm land a few miles north of the town on May 20, 1927, and these birds could easily have been northbound migrants.

When Nighthawks occur in late August and September, we usually see them about dusk flying high over the town or at Cape May Point. Their flight is erratic, marked by a constant shifting this way and that. When progressing definitely forward there is a long sail followed by a series of rapid wingbeats, as the bird hovers or holds itself poised for a moment, and then one of the sudden dives downward or to the right or left which are so characteristic of the species. The wings of the bird impress one as being set very far forward, the neck being so short that the head is scarcely in evidence; the wings are also quite narrow, about the same width as the body and tail, so that the flying bird presents somewhat the outline of a tripod or a letter Y. But as the wings are bent or curved at the wrist two of the branches of the tripod are not quite straight. Sometimes the flying birds pass so high that they would not be noticed were it not for their erratic flight. On the

( 639 )

evening of August 31, 1921, I was watching some gulls soaring high above the town and among them detected a Fish Hawk and later about a dozen Nighthawks. Except for their manner of flight it was really difficult to distinguish the several species as it was almost impossible to gage their relative altitudes. I have noticed this on many other occasions when swallows have been momentarily taken for hawks and even the numerous migrant dragon-flies, which occur so abundantly in late summer, have been projected until they were taken for birds soaring at a high altitude.

While some of these migrant Nighthawk flocks pass on immediately, others may be seen for several nights in succession in the same place, and from August 14 to 21, 1925, a number were seen every evening hawking about over the waters of the Bay. While usually numbering about a dozen some of the flocks are much larger and Conrad Roland saw at least 200 flying into a southeast wind at the Point on the evening of September 6, 1934.

Our dates of arrival of August Nighthawks run as follows:

| | | | |
|---|---|---|---|
| 1921. | August 16. | 1926. | August 27. |
| 1922. | August 20. | 1930. | August 28. |
| 1923. | August 20. | 1931. | August 30. |
| 1924. | August 27. | 1932. | August 30. |
| 1925. | August 14. | | |

The dates of last occurrence are:

| | | | |
|---|---|---|---|
| 1921. | September 18. | 1929. | September 29. |
| 1924. | October 2. | 1932. | September 18. |
| 1925. | September 28. | 1935. | October 10. |

William Rusling, Audubon Society representative during the autumn of 1935, made a careful record of Nighthawks at the Point. He saw the first one on August 20, five on the 23d, and one on the 29th. Then came a great flight of 117 on September 7 and then from twelve to fifteen daily until the 25th, and after that one or two, now and then, until October 10. It would appear that if one happened to be away on the day of the maximum flight he would probably be unaware that a notable migration had taken place and my inability to be in the field continuously after early September has no doubt been responsible for my scanty records of the movements of this interesting bird. Large flights, too, seem to be more frequent somewhat farther north and Julian Potter has recorded seventy-two passing Collingswood on September 8, 1929, ninety-two on the 9th and sixty-four on the 24th.

It is quite possible that the Nighthawk migration passes along the Bay shore rather than on the seacoast and Philip Laurent's experience on Five Mile Beach, where he saw but two in his many years' observation, would support this view.

Twice, on September 8, 1928, and September 7, 1931, I have seen one or two Nighthawks flying wildly over the pine woods at Cape May Point, diving precipitately into the trees and than sailing up again. They appeared

as if intending to alight and then beat their way out again flapping wildly;
the triangle appearance was well illustrated on these occasions. In the face
of a strong wind I have seen a single bird hold almost the same position in
the air for quite some time.

On August 27, 1928, while watching a number of Black Terns in their
erratic flight over the deep pond at the Lighthouse I was struck with the resemblance of their actions to those of the Nighthawk when suddenly I
realized that one of the nine birds before me actually was a Nighthawk;
there was the same soft flapping, the same flutter and the same swoop to
the surface of the water and it was by no means easy always to distinguish
one species from the other. It was a very dull day, late in the afternoon, and
the white patch usually so conspicuous in the wing of a Nighthawk was not
easy to see.

I have several times detected Nighthawks resting during the daytime
but so closely do they resemble the surroundings of their perches that there
must be many more roosting about us than we realize. One was seen on
the short dead branch of a pine tree, some thirty feet from the ground, which
raised its head slightly displaying its white throat; another perched lengthwise on the limb, as is their custom, with its eyes nearly closed. One sat on
a dead cedar tree on the Bay shore and still another on an open sandy spot
at Cape May Point. On September 17, 1923, a Nighthawk sat for some
time crosswise on the insulator of a telegraph wire in the heart of the town
and at exactly the same spot and on the same date in 1932, one rested on the
top of the pole!

In the northern counties it is usually a common transient but local or
occasional as a breeder. Urner finds it a fairly regular but not common
migrant in Union Co.

While I have no record of a "nest" in Cape May County Turner Mc-
Mullen found two eggs on bare sandy ground at Malaga, Gloucester County,
on June 16, 1928.

## CHIMNEY SWIFT
### Chaetura pelagica (Linnaeus)
#### PLATE 98, p. 646

The Chimney Swift is a common town bird at Cape May and during the late spring and early summer it is largely confined to the immediate vicinity of the houses, passing back and forth overhead with its narrow wings in rapid vibration or set in a bow-like curve as it sails in long arcs across the sky. When both sexes are on the wing a pair will pass in close pursuit with wings elevated in a V-like position, one bird almost touching the other, and while I have regarded such flights as mating flights I have never seen actual copulation in the air, as has been observed by others. Possibly some of these pursuit flights are of old and young. While I could never take seriously the claim that Swifts beat their wings alternately it is, nevertheless, no easy matter to prove by ordinary observation that they do not. The eye is not able to follow the detailed movements of the wings and the flickering flight is very confusing. By careful observation with binocular glasses, however, I have satisfied myself that the wing action is as in other birds.

Often from flying Swifts we catch the long drawn trilling chatter which is the characteristic note of the bird and from the chimney nest, when the young are being fed, there is an abundance of similar chattering and hissing sounds.

Swifts are always social birds and several pairs occupy the same chimney in amicable association and about every old farm house, in the open country north of the town, there will be a flock of Swifts coursing through the evening sky as well as the flock over the town itself and as the season advances several flocks seem to combine during their foraging flights.

So completely is the Swift a bird of the air that it has lost the power of perching, which is still retained by the Hummingbird and Swallow, nor does it rest on the ground or on large limbs as do the Nighthawk and Whip-poor-will—all birds of similar aërial ability. The Swift rests only in the interior of the chimneys in which it nests, clinging vertically to the soot-covered bricks. It has long since abandoned the hollow trees on the inside walls of which it originally glued its basket-like nest and although it occasionally places its nest in some deserted building or shed I have never come upon such a site at Cape May. Samuel Rhoads, however, did find a nest in an old barn at Haddonfield.

Exercise and the search for food, both for themselves and their young, are carried on in the air and even the gathering of small twigs with which to construct their nests. This latter activity may easily be witnessed if we can find a tree with dead and brittle branches at its top for here we are almost certain to see Swifts during the nesting season flying through the bare branches and endeavoring to break off small twigs. A line of old wild cherry trees growing along the Harbor railroad is a favorite source of such material and I have watched the birds time and again come sailing in and, fluttering opposite a likely branch, endeavor to break off a small piece by grasping it in the bill; occasionally the effort will be successful but more often the attempt fails and more often still, for some reason or other, the bird will change its mind and sail away over the marsh to return in a few minutes and repeat the performance. I have seen birds engaged in twig hunting on various days from May 28 to July 3. I am well aware that others have stated positively that Swifts grasp the twigs for their nests in their feet but it has always seemed to me that they use the mouth and how they could possibly alight on the wall of the chimney with their feet grasping a twig I cannot imagine.

It is in the early evening that the Chimney Swifts appear to be most active and vociferous and often at this time of day they will descend close to the ground and skim over the golf links or other level ground passing at arm's length in their precipitous flight. They skim in the same way back and forth over fields of new mown hay and I have seen them scouring the grass-covered sand dunes which used to lie back of the bathing beach. They are at such times evidently feeding on minute insects but so rapid is their flight that it is impossible to see the actual capture of the prey. I have several times tried to follow them with the glass and see the action but without success.

Swifts may be awing at any hour of the day, early morning being almost as congenial to them as evening, and I have seen as many as one hundred high in the air as late as ten oclock in the morning on August 21, though as a rule they are less active during the middle of the day. They continue to feed until it is quite dark and I have seen them skimming close along the pavement of Washington Street until nearly 8:00 p. m. in early July, while on August 13, 1936, on Price's Pond I watched twenty-five Swifts feeding over the water and found that they left all together at 7:15 p. m. The variation in their numbers, on different days and at different hours, is very noticeable. There are times when we may scan the sky in every direction without detecting a Swift and some entire days when we shall be unable to add the species to our list. Doubtless this is to be explained by their local feeding and our failure to happen upon the spot where they are for the moment congregated. After the young are on the wing they scatter and stray much farther afield, returning to the shelter of the chimneys where they nested, only on the approach of darkness.

In late July Chimney Swifts often frequent the open pine woods at Cape May Point coursing back and forth over the tree tops as well as threading their way in and out among the branches and coursing up and down a favorite overgrown wood road which passes close by. In all such spots they evidently find insect food of various kinds. Sometimes they travel only a foot from the ground along the narrow wood road or again they skim past shoulder high and barely miss my face as I stand perfectly still in the middle of the path. In August, too, they will congregate over Lake Lily or other bodies of fresh water skimming back and forth just above the surface. Sometimes they apparently dip their bill for a drink while at others they strike the water with the body and not with the bill, probably taking a quick bath, which, like all of their activities, must perforce be done in flight.

Swifts are experts on the wing and their aërial evolutions are always interesting especially in the face of a strong wind. On August 4, 1920, with a northeaster blowing, they would sail up against the wind until almost stationary, beating their wings for a moment or two to maintain their balance and then veering off to one side or the other, they came like lightning, spreading and closing their short tails as they guided themselves, and so held their equilibrium in the gale. On July 22, 1917, six Swifts were seen poised absolutely stationary in the air over Congress Hall Hotel, on rigid wings, and evidently supported by the upward air currents deflected from the walls of the building. Martins and Turkey Vultures do the same thing, an action which so far as I can see is instigated purely by the joy of flight.

Cloudy weather does not deter the Swifts from taking to the air and while I have not seen them actually flying in the rain they are awing almost immediately after a shower stops.

After August 1 of each year Swifts are noticeably more abundant and about the 20th of the month reach their maximum. This is due, in part, to the appearance of the young birds on the wing but it would seem that there must also be a decided migratory movement with an influx of birds from farther north, or else a concentration of all the nearby colonies. My notes show such an increase on August 19, 1921; August 13, 1923; August 19, 1924; August 21, 1925, etc. On all of these dates, and on others later in the month, upwards of a hundred Swifts could be seen flying high over the town in an intricate maze. Then about August 30 they may disappear entirely to be replaced later by flocks apparently from the north. The same thing may be witnessed at Cape May Point, where on August 25, 1927, and August 30, 1932, I found the air literally full of Swifts while none were seen afterward up to the time of my departure about September 10. I presume that Swifts migrate in these comparatively large flocks, in daytime, and that these gatherings may actually have been on migration. On both occasions there was a strong northwest wind which always causes a congregation of migrant birds at the Point. Scattered Swifts seen following the beach line with south-bound Barn Swallows earlier in August may or may not have been migrating.

About the time of these late August gatherings the Swifts begin to roost together in large numbers making use of certain favorite chimneys in the town. On August 28, 1922, they selected an old house on Lafayette St., where they concentrated about 6:45 p. m. flying at first in wide circles and gradually contracting as darkness crept on until the south chimney became obviously the center of attraction. Now and then the flock would concentrate and pause for a moment just over the chimney on fluttering wings. Perhaps one would drop in, raising its wings high up over its back as it disappeared, or perhaps half a dozen would go down in quick succession. Then the whole mass would whirl away once more on their circuit only to congregate again in a few minutes. Occasionally one of those that had retired would emerge and once more join the flock influenced no doubt by flock attraction. The return of the circling flock to the chimney was more frequent as night approached and finally with rapidly narrowing orbits it formed a great funnel-shaped mass and poured steadily down into the chimney a few stragglers being crowded aside and forced to make another round before descending. Although I had not seen the beginning of the roosting flight, and may have missed some of the birds that went down first, I was able to count one hundred and sixty Swifts entering the chimney while I watched. The owner of the house told me that, while he had not noticed the Swifts previously that summer, they had used the chimney two years before. They continued to roost there in diminished numbers until September 2 and on the following year a flock of thirty went down on September 6.

In 1925 the Swifts made use of a chimney on Washington St., where on the evening of August 22 I saw upwards of 300 birds enter, the main body going down between 6:55 and 7:10 p. m. and they were still using this chimney up to August 31. The first time they were observed was an evening following a cold windy night and morning and it seemed that the aggregation may have consisted largely of migrants urged southward by the change in the temperature. How many chimneys may be in use in a single season or to what extent the birds change their roost from night to night I am unable to determine, but certainly the number of individuals using a given roosting chimney varies considerably. I have no reason, however, to infer that more than one or two chimneys are used for this mass roosting on a single night within the limits of the town.

My latest dates for Swifts at Cape May after the departure of the large flocks about August 25 to 30 are:

| | | | |
|---|---|---|---|
| 1914. | September 13. | 1925. | September 20. |
| 1916. | September 4. | 1928. | September 8. |
| 1921. | September 5. | 1929. | September 2. |
| 1923. | September 7. | 1930. | September 4. |

The earliest of these dates probably do not represent actual last appearances as I usually left Cape May early in September and subsequent data were not based on continuous observation. Doubtless September 18 or 20 is the usual time of final departure. Exceptional records are single birds seen on October 21, 1928, and October 25, 1929. Julian Potter made daily observations about Cape May and the Point from September 20 to October 2, 1925, and failed to find a single Swift but William Rusling saw thirty-one at the Point on September 10, 1935, and one each on September 20 and October 10.

Walker Hand's records of spring arrival for the Swift for a number of years supplemented by other observations after 1920 are:

| | | | | | |
|---|---|---|---|---|---|
| 1902. | April 27. | 1911. | April 27. | 1922. | April 23. |
| 1903. | April 19. | 1912. | April 25. | 1923. | April 22. |
| 1904. | April 20. | 1914. | April 23. | 1926. | April 25. |
| 1905. | April 23. | 1915. | April 20. | 1927. | April 30. |
| 1907. | April 30. | 1916. | April 21. | 1931. | April 25. |
| 1908. | April 26. | 1917. | April 19. | 1932. | April 23. |
| 1909. | April 29. | 1918. | April 29. | 1934. | April 23. |
| 1910. | May 2. | 1919. | April 27. | | |

Turner McMullen examined nests in a chimney at Ocean View on June 17, 1922, which contained one and two eggs respectively while nests at Lenola, Burlington County, June 20, 1915, and June 22, 1918, contained three and four eggs. Philip Laurant found them nesting on Five Mile Beach in the eighties.

Chimney Swifts are common summer residents throughout the state.

PLATE 96

*W. L. Baily*

*W. L. Baily*

1. ENTRANCE TO KINGFISHER'S TUNNEL, SHOWING RUTS MADE BY THE BIRD'S FEET.
2. END OF THE TUNNEL, WITH EGGS AND DISINTEGRATED PELLETS OF FISH SCALES
    AND BONES.

PLATE 97

*W. L. Baily*

*W. L. Baily*

1. YOUNG KINGFISHERS SOON AFTER HATCHING, WITHOUT FEATHERS AND EYES CLOSED.

2. YOUNG KINGFISHERS IN THE "PIN FEATHER" STAGE.

PLATE 98

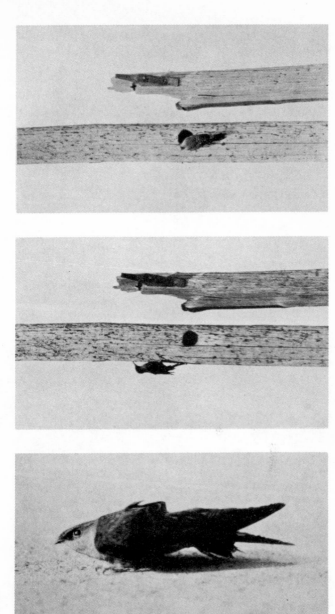

*Wharton Huber*

1. CHIMNEY SWIFT CLINGING TO WALL.    2. TWO VIEWS OF FLICKER AT NEST IN TELEGRAPH POLE. CORSON'S INLET, N. J.

PLATE 99

*Smith Studio*

*W. L. Baily*

1. HUMMINGBIRD ON NEST, CAPE MAY POINT.

2. YOUNG FLICKERS, SOON AFTER HATCHING, NO FEATHERS AND EYES CLOSED.

# RUBY-THROATED HUMMINGBIRD

Archilochus colubris (Linnaeus)

PLATE 99, p. 647

While we not infrequently catch a momentary glimpse of a Hummingbird passing like a bumble bee in straightaway flight, most of our observations are of individuals feeding among the flowers in the old gardens of the town. On rapidly vibrating wings they pass from one blossom to another probing with needle-like bill for nectar or possibly for minute insects which may be concealed in the corolla. They force the head within the larger tube-like flowers or into the flaring cups of the nasturtiums, and back out again, with partly spread tail swinging back and forth beneath the body.

The earliest spring arrivals frequent the scarlet flowers of the *Pyrus japonica* while larkspur, Weigelia and Japanese honeysuckle are favorites as well as many other blooms, both native and cultivated, as the season advances. Above all, however, they delight in the clustered red tubes of the trumpet creeper (*Tecoma radicans*) which abounds in thickets and along fence rows at Cape May Point and elsewhere in the lower part of the peninsula. While flowers of all colors seem to attract the Hummingbirds red is apparently their favorite hue although I doubt very much if color has much to do with their search for food. They doubtless find what they are looking for without such flaring advertisements.

Where flowers are massed Hummingbirds will occur in numbers especially after the nesting season is over. I have seen seven feeding at once on a small dense growth of Bouncing Bet (*Saponaria officinalis*) in mid-July and Otway Brown found at least twelve in a bed of gladiolus on the last day of that month. About clusters of the trumpet creeper six to twelve are frequently seen, but in Hummingbird gatherings it is always everyone for himself, there is no flocking.

While both sexes frequent our garden early in the season the males are seen there more consistently than the females. Indeed most of our observations of male Hummers are in such places. They seem to desert their mates as soon as the nests are completed and eggs laid and are seldom seen in midsummer at Cape May Point where females and young abound during July and August.

On May 20, 1927, doubtless at the height of the mating season, I saw a number of males at the Point perching frequently on the top sprays of climbing vines or small trees with tails partly spread and flirted up and down at intervals; a female was roosting in the same thicket. On July 6, 1925, I saw two other males perched in the same spot which displayed the white tuft of downy feathers just behind each foot, while the distinct fork of their tails could be clearly seen. Another male, studied on May 12, 1929, was perched on a dead twig in a more or less humpbacked position, with bill slightly elevated while he turned his head right and left in rapid succession. One would suppose that the brilliant metallic ruby red throat of the male would be most conspicuous but this is by no means always the case. This bird was perched in such a position that the throat was never facing the sun nor fully directed toward me and it seemed dull black during all the time that I watched the bird. The sunlight on the back however produced a brilliant metallic green. On other occasions a bird would alight on a twig facing me and the sun but even then the throat was illuminated only when the head was turned to exactly the proper angle. When this was effected there flashed out a gorgeous spot of orange crimson only to be lost again as the head was turned farther around.

The aërial flight of the male is performed in the spring in the presence of the female and once I witnessed it as late as July 14, 1923, the bird swinging back and forth a dozen times or more over a concave arc of about thirty feet, keeping as truly to the same path as if it had been definitely traced for it through the air. The female was doubtless perched in the trumpet vine over which the male performed; it seems likely that her first nest had been destroyed and that this was a second mating.

Of the trumpet creeper thickets at Cape May Point one situated at a sewer outlet is an especial favorite for the Hummingbirds. Even before the blossoms open the birds may be seen in the vicinity perched on the vines or adjacent bushes, drawn there perhaps by previous association, since the spot seems to be quite as much a gathering place as a feeding station. As the summer advances a number of the little birds may be seen there busily chasing one another through thicket. One will pause on whirring wings for a moment and then make off after another, only to be itself pursued a moment later. Every now and then one will alight on a slender twig and tilt its tail up and down several times as if making sure of its balance or in mere nervous excitement. On July 18, 1923, a female and young were in constant pursuit, possibly a seeking for food by the young and an avoidance on the part of the parent. Another bird had its crest feathers slightly erect and constantly turned its head from side to side, alert for the approach of others. The white spot behind the eye was very prominent and the dusky lores less so. It stretched its neck forward and upward in a peculiar manner and then pointed the bill vertically upward as another Hummer passed overhead. It also protruded its long tongue several times drawing it slowly back again and immediately flirted the tail in the characteristic nervous manner. On July 22, 1931, an adult male was present in the gathering at this thicket, a very unusual occurrence. He constantly pursued a female diving down into the foliage as she tried to escape. There was much chasing and perching for some minutes.

I have seen Hummers that were feeding in the trumpet blossoms fly directly into the corolla and cling there for a moment with only the tip of the wings and tail visible but usually, when feeding at the mouth of the tube, the bird continues the rapid buzzing of the wings. On several occasions I have seen feeding birds alight on the outside of the flower and sip nectar from the slits which large bees habitually cut near the base in their search for honey or pollen. When probing far into the blossoms many Hummingbirds cover the top of the head with pollen so that the crown appears quite white or buff and some individuals, doubtless young of the year, exhibit a whitish frosting on the feathers of the back due to lighter colored tips. On at least two occasions I have seen nesting Hummingbirds scratch the side of the head, bringing the foot up between the wing and the body. The wings were slightly drooping.

On a number of occasions from mid-July throughout August, Hummingbirds in the open pine woods at Cape May Point systematically examined the small dead twigs or the lower branches of the trees. They would hover close to the twigs but never alighted on them nor could I see them pick anything from the bark. So intent was one of these birds that it came within a foot of my face as I stood rigid by one of the trees. Once I saw one of them peck at the twig with its bill but could not see what it secured, if anything. All of the birds so engaged were females or young and only one was in the woods at a time. I saw the same thing at Cold Spring where the bird was exploring the dead branches of a red cedar.

While we are accustomed to think of Hummingbirds on the wing they perch much more often than we imagine and by watching a feeding bird constantly we shall often see it resort to some nearby perch for a few moments rest. They are continually perching in the thickets at the Point but I have frequently seen them come to rest in shade trees in the gardens, on telegraph wires along the roads, or on clothes lines in our yard.

Sometimes we see Hummingbirds far from their usual haunts. On August 30, 1920, at the very extremity of Cape May Point a Hummer came swiftly past me, headed for the Delaware coast and disappeared flying low over the water. Others seen during August flying down the beach close to the water's edge and one seen out in the middle of the salt meadows on May 18, 1927, flying north, were all probably on migration.

Walker Hand's dates of arrival of Hummingbirds at Cape May are:

| | | | |
|---|---|---|---|
| 1902. | May 2. | 1911. April 30. | 1926. April 29. |
| 1905. | May 4. | 1914. May 1. | 1932. April 27. |
| 1907. | May 1. | 1916. April 30. | 1933. April 23 |
| 1909. | May 2. | 1917. May 6. | (O. H. Brown). |

Our latest dates in the autumn are:

| | | |
|---|---|---|
| 1907. October 16. | 1925. September 24. | 1928. October 4. |
| 1917. October 1. | 1924. September 28. | 1935. September 29. |
| | 1921. October 9. | |

A nest found May 30, 1924, on a branch of a pine tree four feet from the ground, at Cape May Point, offered exceptional opportunities for study. It contained two eggs and the female, which appeared as soon as we assembled about the nest, immediately settled upon the eggs right before our eyes and remained there even though I stroked her back. On June 8 she acted in exactly the same way, going onto the nest each time that I approached although she was always off when I arrived. By June 22 when I again visited the nest the young had hatched and completely filled the cup. They were entirely covered with pin feathers, the sheaths of those on the back being black, those of the breast white, the wings banded white and black. There were some very minute rusty feathers on the body just above the wings and some long narrow filaments on the lower back somewhat curled together. The bills were short and were pointed up over the side of the nest, both birds facing the same way. Their eyes were open and their bodies pulsated with each breath. As I watched them, one bird wriggled and raised its body and voided a fine spray over the side of the cup.

There was no sign of the parent although I remained for half an hour nearby. Upon returning later she appeared and took up a position on a twig some fifteen feet from the nest where she remained stationary except that she once flew directly at my face and veered up over my head. Doubtless on the previous occasion she may have been perched on a nearby branch but escaped observation. The young were still in the nest on June 28, but had flown by July 5 having probably gone a few days earlier.

A nest with eggs was found in a similar situation on May 30, 1928, and another on May 30, 1923, ten feet up in a red cedar, while a third held small young on May 31, 1926.

Hummingbirds are regular summer residents throughout the state.

While we usually associate them with bright sunshine I have seen them awing on very dark cloudy days and one in our garden fed at the flowers between showers on a day of continual rains, taking refuge in the nearby trees, or on sheltered wires, at other times. They have also been noticed feeding at dusk as late as 7:30 p. m. when one would be more likely to see the sphinx moths which bear such a superficial resemblance to them. Indeed it is hard to convince many persons that the day-flying sphinx (*Haemorrhagia thysbe*) is not a hummingbird!

In spite of their small size Hummingbirds are very courageous and will drive intruders from their nests in a very determined manner. I have seen a female pursue a Crow and drive him entirely out of her territory while another on August 13, 1923, attacked an Olive-sided Flycatcher, darting at him again and again. The latter assault must have been shear pugnaciousness as the nesting season was well past by this time.

## BELTED KINGFISHER

Ceryle alcyon alcyon (Linnaeus)

PLATES 96, 97, p. 646

One or two Kingfishers may usually be found immediately about Cape May at any time of year, either in the vicinity of the Harbor, at Lake Lily or on the Lighthouse Pond, while in summer and autumn they extend their range to include any body of water that may contain small fishes or other prey. Before it was converted into a sewer they used to follow Cape Island Creek from South Cape May right into the town and they still come up the open creek from the Harbor to the edge of the golf links.

Kingfishers are most abundant in late summer and autumn after the young are on the wing, or when probable migrants come from farther north. In spring and early summer they resort to nesting places more or less remote and are of less regular occurrence while in winter their numbers reach the minimum. We can usually count on seeing one on a winter's walk and sometimes several, but there are times and indeed whole seasons when none can be found.

The Cape May Christmas census records are as follows:

December 24, 1922, one.          December 26, 1932, one.
December 23, 1923, one.          December 24, 1933, six.
December 27, 1926, one.          December 23, 1934, three.
December 28, 1930, two.          December 22, 1935, fifteen.
December 27, 1931, three.        December 27, 1936, six.

As a rule winter Kingfishers are solitary individuals which locate at some spot where open water is found and food may readily be obtained. They have been recorded in winter as far north as Plainfield (W. D. Miller) and Morristown (E. C. Thurber).

I have never seen a migration of Kingfishers and only on a few occasions have I come upon more than two birds on a day's walk. My records show six on July 6, and seven on August 25, 1927; six on September 23, 1928; five on April 20, 1924; four on September 17, 1922; September 11, 1926; September 30, 1923; while Julian Potter saw no less than twenty on September 30, 1928.

The flight of the Kingfisher is peculiar and easily recognized; there is a series of nervous flaps of the wings alternating with short sails which cause an undulatory movement somewhat like the flight of a Flicker, a resemblance which is emphasized by the bird's habit of occasionally turning the head from side to side while on the wing. Usually the head is held straight out which gives the bird the appearance of being unnaturally long. The flight is well sustained and direct and when passing from one point to another is often at a considerable altitude.

Strong wind may affect their flight and on one occasion a Kingfisher carried along with a northwest gale covered the entire length of Lake Lily on a continuous diagonal sail traveling at tremendous speed. A pair flying very low over the waters of the lake on April 2, 1922, and closely pursuing one another, held their heads well up while their wingbeats were short and spasmodic the effect being of a body bouncing up and down on an elastic surface. Another pair acted in the same way on June 28, 1928, and each bird in the course of the flight splashed once into the water, though evidently not in the pursuit of prey. Doubtless the whole performance was part of the mating behavior as was also the later mounting of one of the birds straight into the air to a height of a hundred feet or more.

When not passing rapidly on the wing we generally see Kingfishers resting or engaged in fishing. A favorite resting place for many years was an old wooden boat landing on the edge of the Lighthouse Pond where I could almost always count on seeing one of these birds apparently stretched out flat on its belly, the legs being so short that they do not raise the body perceptibly from a flat surface. I noted an individual on this perch on August 19, 1921, busily engaged in preening his plumage, probing straight down among the breast feathers with his massive bill and stabbing viciously under the wings while he ruffled up the entire plumage, shook himself and partly spread his tail. When through with this performance he assumed again the squatting posture with the head drawn well down on the shoulders.

Any sort of post or piling standing in the water is an attractive perch for a Kingfisher and may be used either for resting or as a vantage point for fishing operations. Sometimes I have seen stakes projecting only a foot above the water occupied by resting Kingfishers and range poles in the salt water far out on the edge of Jarvis Sound served a similar purpose.

A dead tree top on the Bay shore dunes, quite a distance from water, was a favorite roosting place and a signboard near the pool at the Point was another. Quite frequently Kingfishers will be seen balancing themselves on telegraph wires and the supporting poles are even more to their liking. Twice I have flushed Kingfishers from the pine woods at Cape May Point a hundred yards from the lake and was unable to determine what brought them there, and on the evening of August 15, 1921, and on several subsequent occasions a lone Kingfisher came into the Martin roost on the Physick property in the heart of Cape May, and could be heard uttering his rattling cry, apparently trying to find a suitable perch among the horde of noisy birds gathered there.

Kingfishers procure their food by diving either from a perch or from the air. The first method was well shown by two individuals which I watched on the shores of Lake Lily on July 29, 1921. They were perched on pine limbs overhanging the water, resting on dense masses of cones and needles rather than upon the dead branches. Each bird kept a constant watch on the water below and every now and then would give his tail an upward flirt allowing it to drop again slowly and then, suddenly, he would dive head first perpendicularly into the water but generally without success. After each plunge he would resume his perch, shake off the water by ruffling the plumage, and again take up his vigil. On August 17, 1921, and September 11, 1927, I saw a bird perched on a piling which stood just beyond the surf line on the beach from which he repeatedly dived directly into the ocean.

Diving from the air seems to be the more common method about Cape May, probably because of the lack of suitable perches near the fishing grounds. One can detect fishing Kingfishers at a considerable distance as they hover in the air poising twenty to thirty feet above the water on constantly vibrating wings. After several minutes of this hovering the bird will dive, not vertically, but at an angle; I have seen them do this in various ponds both shallow and deep and on one occasion a bird struck a fish at least twelve feet beyond the point over which he had been hovering. They usually make a great splash when they go into the water and sometimes disappear entirely beneath the surface. One that dived into the Lighthouse Pond flapped several times upon emerging before he was able to take wing. He had apparently either become entangled in the abundant aquatic vegetation, or was loath to let go a fish too large for him to lift from the water. He repaired immediately to a stake where he rested for several minutes flirting his tail nervously as he sat there. His plumage seemed very wet and his crest feathers were plastered flat on his head. Kingfishers usually seek some stake or post after making a dive, whether successful or not, and even after hovering and failing to dive at all they will often drop to some stake to rest. Occasionally, however, they will hover at several points in succession, flying a few yards from one to the next without resting.

One Kingfisher which I found perched on a stump in Lake Lily had secured a rather large sunfish which he proceeded to beat on the stump with vicious blows. Failing to break it or reduce it to a size suitable for swallowing he laid it down and pecked at it repeatedly with his bill but without result. Eventually he flew off carrying his prey with him.

The high bluff on the Bay shore of the Cape May Peninsula has long been a favorite nesting place for Kingfishers. For centuries the Bay has been cutting into the land and the vertical sandy wall is admirably suited for the tunneling of these birds, though of late years the development of small resorts all along this shore has sadly interfered with its bird life. A nest found here on May 24, 1925, contained five naked young. Elsewhere Kingfishers are forced to resort to artificial banks formed by digging away the soil or excavating sand. A nest found on May 23, 1920, near Rio Grande, about one foot from the top of a low sand bank, extended back for five feet with an enlarged chamber at the end which contained six eggs and was strewn with fish scales and bones from disintegrated pellets.

Another nest was located in a sand bank to the east of Lake Lily some fifty feet back from the water, and still another was found in a cut in a field south of Pond Creek Meadows where the surface soil had been cut away for filling, leaving a vertical bank on one side.

On the ocean side of the peninsula suitable nesting places are rare but on May 26, 1929, I found a nest hole in the side of a sand dune on Two Mile Beach about six feet above a shallow pool which had formed in a depression, The dune was a very old one and the sand had become hard enough to support the walls of the tunnel. On Seven Mile Beach Charles S. Shick found a pair of Kingfishers present all through the summer of 1886 and attributed to them a nest hole dug in a hollow stump (Auk, 1890, p. 328). Philip Laurent found them nesting on Five Mile Beach in the eighties.

Turner McMullen has furnished me with a list of Kingfisher nests examined by him in Camden and Burlington Counties which gives an idea of their nesting time here. They nest throughout the state.

| | |
|---|---|
| May 18, 1909, seven eggs. | May 4, 1919, seven eggs. |
| May 10, 1914, six eggs. | May 3, 1921, seven eggs. |
| May 22, 1915, seven young. | May 25, 1922, six eggs. |
| May 7, 1916, seven eggs. | May 23, 1925, six young. |
| May 13, 1918, seven eggs. | May 16, 1930, seven eggs. |

While young birds are on the wing about Cape May by June 1, I have seen a parent feeding a young one on a telegraph wire as late as July 5.

Kingfishers at Cape May are essentially solitary birds except at nesting time when pairs are seen and it would seem that the young must scatter soon after leaving the nest. This would be natural since, being lone fishermen, there would be nothing to gain and much to lose by close association which would inevitably involve trespass on a neighbor's preserve.

# FLICKER

Colaptes auratus luteus Bangs

PLATES 98. 99, 100, pp, 647. 662

Flickers are to be seen about the wooded areas of Cape May Point and in the farming country north of the town throughout the year. Well distributed in summer and nesting commonly in orchard and shade trees; they are reduced in winter to scattered individuals perched in the top of some tall tree or passing in undulating flight across the sky.

Immediately about the town Fickers may be flushed in winter from the edge of the salt meadows, where the black grass has been cut off for hay, or from sandy spots on the Fill and now and then one may be found resting in the trees of the Physick place where there is often a nest in summer. In spring and autumn, too, they may be seen feeding on the lawns.

It is difficult to determine which are migrants and which are winter resident birds as spring advances, but there are always days when the number of Flickers that are present has obviously increased and this we interpret as the arrival of birds from the south. Such dates are:

| | | |
|---|---|---|
| 1904. March 20. | 1911. March 27. | 1928. March 25. |
| 1905. March 21. | 1921. March 31. | 1929. March 31. |
| 1909. March 30. | 1923. March 25. | 1932. March 26. |
| 1910. March 26. | 1925. March 21. | 1933. March 18. |
| | 1927. March 17. | |

Even so it is usually early April before Flickers become common. On April 2, 1922, I counted twenty-five feeding on a burnt over area on the Fill and on April 4, 1924, the woods at the Point seemed full of Flickers. Most of these spring birds seem to pass on and in the nesting season Flickers are not much more abundant immediately about Cape May than in the winter. Back in the farming country, a few miles to the north, however, they are plentiful all summer.

In late summer and autumn Flickers become more frequent on the lawns along Washington St. and sometimes a portion of the great Flicker flights, mainly confined to the Bay shore, pass through the town. These flights usually occur from September 25 to October 8 and after they are over the Flicker population is reduced to its winter proportions. In an ordinary winter's walk one may see a single Flicker or perhaps two, while on some days none will be in evidence. On the Delaware Valley Club's Christmas census when the country from the Court House to the Point is systematically covered the observers' combined list shows Flickers present as follows:

| | |
|---|---|
| December 23, 1923, one. | December 27, 1931, twelve. |
| December 26, 1926, five. | December 26, 1932, twenty. |
| December 26, 1927, eleven. | December 24, 1933, thirteen. |
| December 23, 1928, three. | December 23, 1934, eighteen. |
| December 22, 1929, seven. | December 22, 1935, thirty-five. |
| December 28, 1930, eight. | December 27, 1936, eleven. |

In the open ground surrounding the town resting places for Flickers are rather scarce and I have frequently seen them on the tops of low bayberry bushes on the Fill while telegraph poles are favorite perches. A stake not over two feet in height placed in the middle of an open field was frequently occupied by a Flicker. He stood upright grasping the top of the stake and holding his tail close against the side, and remained rigid for many minutes.

In late summer or early autumn, at the Point or back in the farming country, they like to sit for long periods at the top of some dead tree or telegraph pole in this same frozen attitude, body hunched up, head low down on the shoulders, and bill pointed slightly upward as they gaze over the landscape turning the head occasionally to one side or the other.

The Flicker is our only ground-feeding woodpecker and this fact combined with the character of the country near the sea will explain why most of our Cape May Flickers are flushed from the ground.

When on the ground they can hop but they also progress for short distances at a surprisingly rapid gait by using the legs alternately in a sort of waddling shuffle and all the while the head is held aloft with the bill horizontal.

Flickers on the ground are usually feeding on ants and in one instance where I was able to locate the exact spot where the bird had been operating I found that he had dug out several small ant hills so that they were converted into funnels nearly two inches across and he was apparently picking up the ants as they appeared in them. This was along a shady wood road at the Point on August 9, 1920. Again, on August 1, 1921, I found a Flicker on the Fill, on a little sandy knoll covered with scant grass, where he had been probing into several ant nests, the entrances to which he had enlarged to about half an inch in diameter. A third bird on the edge of the meadows on May 1, 1926, was seen to bend far over forward apparently inserting his tongue into the burrow of an ant hill as there was no evidence of probing or digging into it with his bill as in the other cases.

A favorite nesting place in the town was a hole in a telegraph pole near Broadway, on the line of the abandoned trolley road, which was only three feet from the ground. Here on July 31, 1920, I flushed a male Flicker from a nearby sumac thicket and immediately a female appeared on the ground in front of me with tail spread out flat as she hopped along and looked back at me over her shoulder. Later I discovered two young birds clinging to a pole a little farther on and found the hole from which they had evidently just emerged.

On July 12, 1923, I found that the same hole contained a lively brood of pinfeather-covered young, which climbed excitedly up to the entrance when the pole was tapped. Those that gained the aperture called *choop, choop, choop-choop-choop-choop*, as they stretched out their necks while the others within made a peculiar buzzing sound like a swarm of bees. On July 17, the pinfeathers had burst open and the birds were fully clad in Flicker plumage but the swelling at the gape was still conspicuous. They did not now expose themselves as much as they did at first and by July 26 had all left the nest. The hole had become very offensive, due to the heat and the crowded condition of the brood. The parents always left the nest, if they happened to be within, while I was some distance away. This nest was not occupied in 1924, but was in use on May 8, 1925, and also in 1927. How many years the birds had used this hole I cannot say.

Another pair of Flickers dug a hole at the very top of a nearby pole and an old railroad tie, which had been stood upright when the Fill was being formed, offered a nest site for still another pair. A pair has bred nearly every year of late in a maple tree on the Physick place and had young still in the nest as late as June 30, 1931, while the ground was littered with chips for six feet around the tree. At Cape May Point Flickers nest in dead pines and on Seven Mile Beach Richard Miller found a nest in a dead holly, some fifteen feet from the ground, which contained five young on May 30, 1912. A nest at the Point contained seven eggs on May 25, 1919. Others are:

Seven Mile Beach, June 16, 1918, two nests containing seven and six young birds respectively, both in dead oak stubs (Turner McMullen).

Ludlam's Beach, June 9, 1933, five young, nest in a telegraph pole fifteen feet up (Fletcher Street).

During the mating season I have seen Flickers pursuing one another on telegraph poles and tree trunks and one pair rested in a bayberry bush the male raising and lowering his tail in a sort of display as he bent his body far over forward. A pair was observed copulating on a pole near the old nest site on May 25, 1922.

The alarm note of the Flicker as we hear it at Cape May is a *"kee-uke"* the same as is usually represented as *"yarrup"*; I have heared it from winter birds as they flushed from the ground and also in July and September. The familiar "spring song" *wick-wick-wick-wick-* etc., I have heard as late as July 15 and as late in the evening as 7:00 o'clock. I have several times counted the calls and have found a bird uttering as many as thirty *wicks* without a pause. The pairing birds utter a different call *whit-choo, whit-choo* as they dodge one another around a tree trunk, while a young bird of the year decoying to the excited calls of a Carolina Wren called *whée-o, whée-o.*

I have seen Flickers in the spring feeding on the ground with flocks of Purple Grackles while in the stubble fields, after the harvest, they associate with Red-wings and English Sparrows but these associations are always due simply to a common food attraction not to a social or flocking instinct. Indeed they do not form flocks of their own kind and even in the great fall migrations they travel in long scattered flights every bird for himself not in regular flocks as do the Grackles and Red-wings.

The autumnal migration at Cape May is one of the most striking ornithological sights of the region and one that I have not been able to explain to my entire satisfaction. It is exactly similar to the flights of Woodcock, Kingbirds and hawks, and the Flickers are usually accompanied by hosts of smaller birds, also on their way south.

The movement takes place mainly at night and what we see early in the morning is the closing of the flight as the birds settle down to feed and rest. While a few Flickers may be in evidence in the town at sunrise, drifting along to the southwest, we do not as a rule see many until after we cross the Bay Shore Road but from there to the Bay they abound, the thickest part of the flight being close to the shore itself. The curious thing about it is that the birds are all traveling north and the same is the case with the other migrant species which I have mentioned; moreover the flights always occur when there is a strong northwest wind and into this the birds fly.

It would seem that the normal flight is south along the sea coast, and that the birds are blown offshore by the wind and try to beat back to land or are in fear of such a catastrophe when they approach the Point, with the twenty mile stretch of Delaware Bay confronting them and the ocean on their left. Certain it is that I have seen hundreds of Robins and Bluebirds just above the Point beating their way in from the ocean in the early morning, appearing first as minute specks in the distance and looming larger until they make the shore, and flocks of warblers and scattered Woodcock have been observed coming in from the sea during the night. These birds do not stop but keep right on in the face of the wind following the long stretch of woodland that borders the Bay side of the peninsula. Probably the majority of the migrating column are not blown off of their course but slow up at the Point and cause the congestion there, while, by continuing to follow the shore line rather than launching out over the Bay, they are soon headed north as they round the point of the peninsula. The flights reach for twenty miles north of Cape May Point and so far as I have been able to ascertain they do not cross the Bay until the wind changes when they drift back to the Point and continue on their regular course. If there is no heavy northwest wind there is no flight; in other words everything progresses normally on nights when the wind is, as usual, from the south and hosts of birds may be heard passing south over the town and the Point. Philip Laurent states that when Five Mile Beach was covered with woodland Flickers were common in September but they did not nest; nor was there any concentrated flight.

To give a clearer picture of one of these Flicker flights we may select that of September 27, 1926. The 25th had been a mild autumn day with bird life at its lowest ebb. I had tramped nearly all day from 8:00 a. m. to 4:00 p. m. and besides the usual gulls and a few shore birds I was able to find only fifteen species—apparently the entire land bird population. It was cloudy with occasional showers and the next day was the same but by noon it had cleared and the temperature began to fall and by night the wind was coming strong from the northwest. At five o'clock the next morning there was a faint glimmer of light but sufficient to show an occasional Flicker passing overhead and it was evident that a flight was on. By sunrise Walker Hand and I were on the Bay Shore Road three miles above the Point. We had seen some thirty Flickers since leaving Cape May, scattered individuals passing steadily along overhead. As we skirted the northern edge of a dense woods stretching toward the Bay we saw Flickers constantly shooting out over the tree tops from the south and a hasty count showed twenty-five to thirty in sight at any moment within our range of vision. Occasionally one would alight on the top of some tree rising above the rest of the forest or perhaps standing alone in the open; others would decoy to him until there were six or more perched on the trunk or limbs then on they would go, leaving one at a time in close succession.

As we reached the head of New England Meadow we could see the Bay two-thirds of a mile away and the glistening white sand dunes with their dense black masses of prostrate cedars. Here we had a splendid view of the flight, Flickers were passing constantly, bursting out from the woods on the south, crossing the meadow and disappearing again over the northern woods barrier. Several counts showed that they were passing at the rate of thirty to fifty per minute.

Immediately over the dunes the flight was even more congested and, as we rested on the sand, the birds came close over head in a continuous stream, singly, then two together and now perhaps ten close together and then individual birds again, but there was no concerted action or semblance of flocking. The flight was strictly a stream, a follow-my-leader procession everyone for himself. In the bright sunlight which by now flooded both land and water we could see every detail of the Flicker's plumage; the pinkish gray of the under side with bold round spots of black; the black crescent on the breast; and the glorious golden lining of the wings and tail flashing at intervals as the birds spread and closed their wings. Now and then an individual would swing suddenly to the right or left, as he caught a glimpse of us, and would turn sufficiently to exhibit the pure white rump or more rarely the red crescent on the nape. The sexes could easily be distinguished by the black mustachial stripe of the male.

The tail was partly spread as they flew and there were rapid strokes of the wings—one, two or three, and then a glide through the air with wings folded closely to the body causing a slight loss of position and then the rapid beats as the bird regained its former level. This resulted in a somewhat undulatory flight but the birds were always going straight away in a definite direction as if they had no doubt as to where they were bound—head stretched out, and turning now to one side now to the other; the bill always slightly elevated; they appeared to be straining every muscle in some great effort. The impression was that some invisible but powerful force was impelling them on in their mad, uncanny flight.

As the sun came fairly up the flight slackened and the birds rested more frequently, flew in various directions, and began to feed. They were widely scattered over the country and most of them were resting quietly and all trace of the flight had disappeared. We estimated that at least five thousand Flickers had passed while we watched them, how many before sunrise we could not guess.

While the flight of the Flickers was the spectacle of the morning they were by no means alone. Thousands of smaller birds were passing continuously in a scattered stream or succession of waves. At first mere dusky spots against the sky but later, as the light grew stronger, identifiable as warblers, sparrows, flycatchers etc., though specific identification usually had to await their settling in the trees and shrubbery to rest and feed. We passed a little later down the Bay shore to the Point and the same woods and thickets which were practically bare of bird life two days before were now thronged with Catbirds, Thrashers, White-throated and Swamp Sparrows, Palm and Parula Warblers, Red-breasted Nuthatches, Red-eyed Vireos, Ruby-crowned Kinglets, etc., etc. Where on the 25th we had trouble in finding fifteen species of land birds we today listed fifty-five and some of them fairly swarmed. Impressive as this flight was to me Walker Hand considered that it fell far below some that he had seen in the past.

Not many years ago Flickers were lawful game in New Jersey and the Cape May gunners, well versed in the character and time of these flights, made regular preparation for them. Poles or fence rails were fastened to the tops of the low pines and cedars at the Point so that they projected upward above the topmost branches and formed resting places that the Flickers could not resist. The result was that the tired birds, stopping for a few moments on their wild flight, lined the poles so that at any moment six or more were clinging to the perches and a gunner concealed at the base of the tree "raked" them off with the greatest ease. Walker Hand informed me that two gunners of his acquaintance secured six peach baskets full of Flickers on a single morning and piles of dead birds as high as a man's knees were frequent sights. Another gunner got four hundred birds in an hour and a half and it was not unusual to get four at a shot. While this is now all a thing of the past it took constant effort in the face of the strongest kind of opposition before the State Legislature could be induced to make the practice illegal. Flickers are common summer residents throughout New Jersey and occur casually in winter in most localities.

Occasional Flickers have been found in New Jersey with a few red feathers in the mustachial stripe but I regard these as individual aberrations rather than indications of a strain of the western Red-shafted Flicker which has these stripes red.

## PILEATED WOODPECKER
### Ceophloeus pileatus abieticola Bangs

This splendid bird, the largest of our woodpeckers, was doubtless at one time common throughout the wooded parts of New Jersey but has long been extinct in most parts of the state. Today it is known as a resident of the wilder mountainous parts of Sussex and Passaic Counties in the extreme north—at Greenwood Lake, Newfoundland, Culver's Gap and perhaps elsewhere in the same region.

In Cape May County we have two records: birds shot by one of the Coast Guards at the Five Mile Beach station on November 8, 1878, and December 31, 1879, and now in the collection of the Academy of Natural Sciences of Philadelphia. They were presented to Dr. William L. Abbott, who was, at the age of eighteen, just beginning his collection of local birds and was accustomed to visit the station on what was then an almost uninhabited island with much virgin forest. Whether the birds were shot on the island or in the splendid tract of tall timber on the mainland opposite I have never been able to ascertain, but inasmuch as Schick mentions seeing one on Seven Mile Beach (Bay State Ornith., I, No. 2, p. 13) in June and Parker records one there in 1885 (Orn. & Oöl., 1886, p. 140), they may well have been shot on the island.

On June 4, 1983, Mark L. Wilde and J. Harris Reed saw one of these birds in Cumberland County just over the Cape May line on West Creek, and located its nest which contained five young birds (Bendire, Life Histories II, p. 107, and Atlantic Slope Naturalist, I, p. 27).

Our only subsequent record for southern New Jersey is a single bird seen by George Morris on the Egg Harbor River above May's Landing, on March 25, 1908.

The destruction of the primeval forest and the spread of civilization have been responsible for the disappearance of this fine bird not only in New Jersey but in all parts of the country. It is one of the species that cannot adapt itself to the presence of man and his activities.

PLATE 100

*W. L. Baily*

*W. L. Baily*

YOUNG FLICKERS AT LATER STAGES OF GROWTH, SHOWING THE PLUMAGE DEVELOPMENT; NOTE SWELLING AT BASE OF GAPE.

PLATE 101

*J. A. Moore*

*J. K. Potter*

1. ARKANSAS KINGBIRD, LONG ISLAND, N. Y.
2. YOUNG OF COMMON KINGBIRD, VINELAND, N. J.

## RED-BELLIED WOODPECKER

### Centurus carolinus (Linnaeus)

This southern woodpecker, which I have found, evidently resident and breeding, in southern Fulton County in Pennsylvania and along the Susquehanna River in Maryland, just below the Pennsylvania line, has been observed several times about Delaware City and has been recorded as breeding at Marydel, on the border between Delaware and Maryland, by Rhoads and Pennock (Auk, 1905, p. 200). In New Jersey it seems to be nowhere more than an accidental straggler. Charles Pennock shot a specimen at Cape May Point, near the head of Lake Lily, on April 11, 1903; Norman McDonald saw another on March 10, 1935, at Pennsville, Salem County; and Julian Potter saw one at Fish House on the Delaware, on October 11, 1908, which frequented the same grove for about two weeks; and another at Collingswood, Camden County, on November 27, 1927, while William B. Crispin shot one near Salem on December 20, 1912. There are also several records for the more northern counties.

Perhaps the fact that the Red-bellied Woodpecker is essentially resident in its breeding zone and not a migrant, is responsible for its not more frequently crossing Delaware Bay or River. Dr. C. C. Abbott records a nest and young in Ocean County, May 29, 1861, but without authority or details.

## RED-HEADED WOODPECKER

### Melanerpes erythrocephalus (Linnaeus)

The Red-headed Woodpecker is a rare autumn transient at Cape May with only one or two records each year and sometimes none at all; nearly all of the birds are young of the year.

Our autumn records arranged in monthly and daily sequence are as follows:

| | |
|---|---|
| August 26, 1920. | October 2, 1924. |
| August 31, 1926. | October 5, 1929 (2) |
| September 2 and 3, 1920. | October 13, 1913. |
| September 7 and 10 (2), 1935. | October 17, 1920. |
| September 9, 1916. | October 18, 1925. |
| September 14, 1924. | October 21, 1923. |
| September 20, 1929 (2). | October 21, 1928. |
| September 29, 1925. | |

In the winter of 1922–1923 one was resident at the Point frequenting an old frame church and storing acorns in holes in a large wooded cross on top of the building. It was recorded from December 24 to February 22 and doubtless had been there earlier. During the time that it was under observation the red feathers gradually appeared on the head.

I have but a few spring records of the bird at the Cape: one on May 13, 1923; another on May 10, 1928; a third near the junction of the Town

Bank road and the Bay Shore Road on May 29, 1921. This last bird flew from an orchard to a solitary tree standing in a field and it may have had a nest there. All were adults. Another single adult bird appeared at the Point on May 7, 1932, and remained until July 19, no mate appearing at any time, On May 20, it was busy digging a hole in an oak tree in the village while on June 23 it was watched for some time deliberately annoying a pair of Kingbirds which had a nest in the vicinity. It would fly close to the nest and both of the flycatchers would dart after it. After leading them away it would return and take up its position on a nearby house and call lustily after which the whole performance would be repeated. This occurred half a dozen times. I saw an adult north of Salem on May 7, 1896, and William Baily found another on Peck's Beach on May 5 of the same year.

While the Red-headed Woodpecker is, or was, a common summer resident through most of Pennsylvania it has always been rare and exceedingly erratic in its occurrence east of the Delaware and Hudson Rivers. I find but few breeding records for southern New Jersey and most of these are credited to Julian Potter and pertain to the vicinity of Camden. During Samuel Rhoads' many years residence at Haddonfield he never found the Red-headed Woodpecker nesting and had but few observations of the bird, but it seems to have increased of late years. Potter located one nest in a piece of woodland immediately on the Delaware at Fish House on May 19, 1910. It was located in a dead buttonwood tree forty feet from the ground and the birds were successful in raising their young which were seen out of the nest on July 9.

On November 27, 1910, a pair of the birds was located in another grove within the city limits of Camden and were seen continuously for the succeeding nine months. Their nest was located on May 21, 1911, in the dead top of a maple tree thirty feet from the ground and was found to contain young which left on June 25. On July 23, there was a second brood of young in the same nest which were able to climb up to the opening by August 6, while by the 16th they had left and a Starling had appropriated the nest. While the parents were attending to the second brood in the nest they persistently drove off the first brood and persecuted them to such an extent that they apparently left the locality by July 30. They fed the young in the nest at varying intervals sometimes every three or four minutes for half an hour and then failed to appear for twenty minutes or more. One parent spent the night in the nest and the other in an old hole in the same tree both entering about dusk. English Sparrows annoyed the woodpeckers to some extent but they were able to protect themselves and by the time the second brood was under way all the birds in the neighborhood seemed to have learned to leave them alone. (Bird-Lore, 1912, pp. 216–217.)

In May 29, 1916, a pair was located in a telegraph pole in Camden and two broods were raised there that year. This nest was an old Flicker cavity about twenty feet from the ground. Potter found the birds quite common at Camden in September 14 and saw individuals on October 6, 1912, and May

17, 1914, and one at South Vineland on June 19, 1914. On May 22, 1934, he located a nest in a public park in Collingswood which was apparently finished on June 2.

At Philadelphia there used to be regular flights of these birds in the autumn and the autumn records at Cape May are doubtless stragglers from such a movement. The Red-headed Woodpecker has always been a victim of the automobile, being apparently unable to adjust its movements so as to escape being struck. This may account for their scarcity in Pennsylvania in recent years and may have had some effect on their abundance in New Jersey as well.

## YELLOW-BELLIED SAPSUCKER

### Sphyrapicus varius varius (Linnaeus)

At Cape May, as in other parts of New Jersey, the Sapsucker is a regular autumn and rather rare spring transient. We seldom see more than one at a time usually in orchards or in rather open woodland. Unlike most other woodpeckers it is a real "sapsucker" puncturing the trunks of the trees for the sake of the sap which accumulates in the holes or for the cambium layer which underlies the outer bark. It doubtless feeds to some extent also upon small insects which are attracted to its borings. In spring I have several times found a Sapsucker in a little grove of hickory trees at the Point which it regularly girdled with holes. I watched one of these birds on April 4, 1924, which went from tree to tree probing into all of the holes which it had previously dug and sometimes waiting for them to fill up with the sap. At such times he hung against the trunk with belly and tail pressed close to the bark and legs widespread and directed a little upward. Now and then he would stab quickly at the bark on the side of the hole presumably at some visiting insect. A Myrtle Warbler followed the Sapsucker on his rounds seeking either sap or insects from the holes. The same trees were visited by the same of another Sapsucker on April 2 and 3, 1922, and once having made a chain of borings the bird will return for several days before continuing its migration.

In the autumn these birds exhibit quite a variety of plumage as the young start on their migration before the molt begins and change their dress *en route* as is the case with the Red-headed Woodpecker which often holds the juvenal plumage until well into the winter. William Rusling who was present at the Point throughout the autumn of 1935, watching the hawk flight, recorded his first Sapsucker on September 29, with eight on October 5, seven on the 7th, and one each on the 8th and 19th; this probably represents the normal autumn flight both in numbers and dates. Our records based upon scattered trips in autumn are as follows:

1913.  October 13.
1920.  October 3.

1923.  October 1, 7.
1924.  October 2.

| | | |
|---|---|---|
| 1925. September 29, October 11. | | 1931. September 28, October 18. |
| 1928. October 21. | | 1932. September 17, October 14. |
| 1929. October 5. | | 1934. September 19. |
| 1930. October 5. | | |

Spring records are as follows:

| | | | | | |
|---|---|---|---|---|---|
| 1908. April 6. | | 1924. April 4. | | | 1934. May 7. |
| 1922. April 2. | | 1928. April 1, May 16. | | | |

Philip Laurent found it common on Five Mile Beach in the eighties in early October but saw none in spring. One Sapsucker was found by the Delaware Valley Club on the Christmas census trip of December 28, 1930, and there are several records of wintering individuals farther north in the state, but it does not nest in New Jersey. Babson in his "Birds of Princeton" (p. 53) states that a specimen was taken there by W. E. D. Scott on October 21, 1876, which "approached" the western race *S. v. nuchalis*, doubtless having some red feathers in the nuchal stripe, but this is probably an individual variation which may arise independently in eastern birds, similar to the Flickers with a few red feathers in the mustachial stripe which are occasionally come upon in the East.

## HAIRY WOODPECKER

### Dryobates villosus villosus (Linnaeus)

The Hairy Woodpecker is a larger counterpart of the Downy, resembling it closely both in plumage and in habits. It is, however, a bird of more remote and secluded spots and usually approaches gardens and orchards only in winter, so that we are likely to see it more frequently during the cold months. The census taken at Christmas time by the Delaware Valley Ornithological Club covering the region between Cape May Court House and the Point shows it present as follows:

| | |
|---|---|
| December 23, 1923, one. | December 26, 1932, five. |
| December 26, 1927, one. | December 24, 1933, six. |
| December 23, 1928, two. | December 23, 1934, two. |
| December 22, 1929, two. | December 22, 1935, four. |
| December 28, 1930, five. | December 27, 1936, three. |
| December 27, 1931, one. | |

I have seen a pair near Green Creek on July 3, 1921, and another in the Bear Swamp west of Rio Grande on September 4, 1924, while Richard Miller found a nest in an oak stub only five and a half feet from the ground at Burleigh on May 25, 1912, which contained three fledglings. Turner McMullen found another nest at Mays Landing in the Pine Barrens, farther north, on May 1, 1920, which contained four eggs and two at Haddonfield, on May 9, 1921, and May 23, 1923, both of which contained young birds.

It is a resident species throughout New Jersey.

## DOWNY WOODPECKER

*Dryobates pubescens medianus* (Swainson)

Although not an abundant or conspicuous bird the Downy Woodpecker is to be found at Cape May in every month of the year. It is least common in June, when it probably seeks more remote spots for nesting, and most abundant in the late fall, winter and early spring, when it comes into the gardens and shade trees of the town and close about the farmhouses back in the country. A few were found in the woods of Five Mile Beach in the eighties by Philip Laurent.

Our observations are usually of single birds rarely two together, except at nesting time, and from one to four in the course of a day's walk although there are many days when none is seen. On the Christmas census of the Delaware Valley Club the record for the country from the Court House to the Point is:

December 26, 1927, three.        December 26, 1932, four.
December 23, 1928, three.        December 24, 1933, nine.
December 26, 1929, one.          December 23, 1932, twelve.
December 28, 1930, two.          December 22, 1935, fourteen.
December 27, 1931, seven.        December 27, 1936, twenty-four.

While they no doubt nest in the thicker woodland I have never found a nest, but a winter resident bird in an orchard at Cold Spring dug a hole in December in a broken tree stub perhaps for shelter but never occupied it.

Turner McMullen has examined nests in other counties as follows:

> Salem County, April 15, 1921, six eggs.
> Camden County, May 23, 1909, five eggs.
> Camden County, May 2, 1915, five eggs.
> Camden County, May 8, 1915, three eggs.
> Camden County, May 16, 1931, five eggs.

During August a single bird is usually to be found in the pine woods at Cape May Point, possibly a young of the year, evidently finding satisfactory food in this spot. I have also watched another individual visiting the holes made by a Sapsucker in hickories at the Point although it dug none itself, preferring to explore a rotten branch of a nearby oak.

We often see Downies quite low down in alder swamps and on August 24, 1928, I found one climbing up mullein stalks in an old field probing into the seed pods for insects of some sort.

While not associating with its own kind to any extent the Downy is often found in one of the winter assemblages of chickadees, nuthatches, kinglets etc., which often scour the woods and thickets at this season. It is resident throughout the state.

## *RED-COCKADED WOODPECKER

### Dryobates borealis (Vieillot)

This woodpecker, a native of the pine forests of the Southern States, has been recorded as a New Jersey bird on the basis of a specimen in the collection of George N. Lawrence labeled as taken at Hoboken and published by Mr. Lawrence (Ann. N. Y. Lyceum, 1867, p. 201). There is also a specimen marked near Philadelphia in the collection of the Academy of Natural Sciences which was shot by C. D. Wood, the noted taxidermist, in 1861, and the record of another presented by William Wood on August 6, 1850. Whether these were secured in Pennsylvania or New Jersey is not certain but they were probably the basis of Turnbull's statement (1869) that the bird occurred rarely in Eastern Pennsylvania and New Jersey. We know of no record for either Delaware or Maryland and it seems strange that this bird so characteristic of the southern pine forests should have occurred so far north, without intermediate records.

## *ARCTIC THREE-TOED WOODPECKER

### Picoides arcticus (Swainson)

There are so far as I know but two records of this woodpecker for the state —a specimen now in the collection of the American Museum of Natural History discovered near Englewood on November 29, 1923, by S. V. LaDow and shot shortly afterward, on the same day, by J. A. Weber (cf. Griscom, Auk, 1924, p. 343), and one seen by R. H. Howland at Upper Montclair, February 10 and 11, 1926 (Eaton).

## EASTERN KINGBIRD

Tyrannus tyrannus (Linnaeus)

PLATE 101, p. 663

From early May to early September Kingbirds are to be seen about Cape May perched upon tree tops or dead branches near to their nests, or on telegraph wires along the highways or railroads. Wherever found they are always in exposed positions and always conspicuous.

Nearly every summer a pair nests somewhere in the town and a pair or two at Cape May Point and along the turnpike connecting the two, while through the country to the north every farm has one or two breeding pairs. In 1920 a pair nested in the very top of a great silver poplar on the edge of the town and in 1921 an old pear tree on Lafayette Street harbored a family while in 1922 and 1923 a poplar along the sidewalk on Washington Street, in the very center of the town, furnished a building site. Kingbirds also nested on Five Mile Beach before the woods were cut down.

Sometimes the birds nest quite close to the ground and a nest in a wild cherry tree along the turnpike was less than six feet up while another in a scrub pine on the edge of Pond Creek was only three feet above the marsh. Other nests reported to me by Richard Miller were situated in oaks, cedars and apple trees at elevations ranging from eight to twenty-eight feet. Full sets of eggs have been found from June 1 to 23 and a set found on June 17 was just hatching. Full-fledged young were still in the nest on July 2, 1920, and July 10, 1921, but in the latter instance were beginning to climb out on the adjacent branches. Turner McMullen has given me data on the following nests which he had examined:

June 4, 1922, Cape May, three eggs.
June 8, 1919, Cape May Point, one egg.
June 15, 1924, Swain, four eggs.
June 18, 1922, Cape May Co., three eggs.
June 23, 1923, Seven Mile Beach, three eggs, and two eggs.
July 4, 1923, Seven Mile Beach, three eggs.
July 4, 1924, Seven Mile Beach, three eggs.
July 4, 1928, Seven Mile Beach, three young.

By July 7, 10, 11, and 12, in different years, the bobtailed young appeared on the telegraph wires where they were being fed by their parents and one youngster still unable to obtain food for himself was found on a bush on the Bay shore sand dunes as late as August 3.

The Kingbird is distinctly a bird of the air and high perches and most of his food consists of insects caught on the wing. He launches forth from his perch with head held high and wings rapidly beating and ascends at a steep diagonal toward his passing prey, seizes it, and returns in a long swoop to his perch to devour it. I have seen them catch monarch butterflies and many smaller insects and have noticed them fly straight as an arrow to meet some approaching victim when it was still a hundred feet away, and one Kingbird was seen in the middle of the Harbor with an insect in its bill which it had apparently pursued across the water. Sometimes an insect will turn and mount higher and higher in the air with the Kingbird in close pursuit on rapidly fluttering wings, while at other times the bird will descend to capture prey passing below the level of his perch and in one instance nearly turned a somersault in the operation and almost touched the ground.

I have seen Kingbirds dive down into hydrangea bushes apparently after some sort of insect and have also seen one hovering over fields of red-top grass, six or eight inches above the stalks, dart down at the heads of field garlic that were scattered through it, presumably after small insects which infested these blossoms. The bird would make eight or ten dives of this sort before coming to rest on a weed stalk and then would begin again after an interval of a minute or two. The wings moved continuously and very rapidly making a blur while the body was held in a partly upright position, the head held high and turning frequently from side to side. Other birds hovered in precisely the same way over a field of newly cut hay, apparently after grasshoppers, and I saw one dive repeatedly to the surface of a road finally flushing a "dusty-roads" grasshopper which he promptly seized and carried to his perch.

I have several times observed Kingbirds in the act of bathing. On July 14, 1920, one was seen hovering over the lily pond at the old race track. It was about a foot above the water and kept turning its head from side to side, as did the bird in the grass field, while it pecked at the surface of the water or at the lily pads. Finally it ducked its head into the water and retired to its perch. Almost immediately however it returned and plunged deliberately into the pond with quite a splash and was back again on its perch ruffling up its feathers and pluming itself. Another bird dived several times into the Lighthouse Pond retiring between dives to its perch nearby, and still another was seen to fly into the spray of a lawn sprinkler.

Kingbirds will occasionally alight on the ground which is rather unusual for such an aërial species. On May 27, 1929, I saw several of them in a plowed field with Robins, Grackles and Killdeers, and on July 3, 1922, one was sitting on the railroad track while another perched on a low weed nearby. On July 27, 1922, a Kingbird alighted on the beach of the Bay shore and on July 8, 1916, and July 21, 1917, one was seen sitting on the ocean beach picking up insects from the trash washed up at the high tide mark. Out on the Pond Creek Meadows I have seen them perching on reeds not two feet above shallow ponds where sandpipers were feeding and once I found one perched on a stake at least one hundred yards out on the salt meadows above Cold Spring. The early arrivals from the south seem to be more addicted to low perches and on May 18, 1928, I found no less than six resting on low weeds in an open field.

When on its perch the Kingbird's position is erect, the head is slightly bowed and every now and then is turned around sideways so that the bird seems to be looking over its shoulder—a peculiar and very characteristic attitude. When excited the crest is elevated which is always the case when one approaches the nest and it is then, or when he has driven away some intruder, that the Kingbird gives vent to his rapid, defiant call—*icky-icky-icky-icky-icky*. Kingbirds are valiant defenders of their nest and nearly every bird that passes near is likely to be attacked. I have seen one pursue a Bank Swallow and follow so closely upon a passing Chimney Swift that the latter bird was forced to the ground although apparently uninjured and able to take wing again shortly. Another Kingbird caused considerable annoyance to a Turkey Vulture which approached too close to its perch and a pair of the birds vigorously attacked two Meadowlarks which flushed from a grass field near to their nest tree. All four birds alighted on a telegraph wire each Kingbird close to his lark and when the latter again took wing the attack was renewed.

When pluming itself the Kingbird holds the tip of the wing away from the body with the bend, or wrist, close in to the shoulder just as the Swallows do, and probes below it.

The arrival dates for the Kingbird as recorded by Walker Hand are:

| 1902. April 30. | 1909. May 2. | 1916. April 30. |
| 1903. April 27. | 1910. May 1. | 1918. May 4. |
| 1904. April 23. | 1911. April 24. | 1919. April 27. |
| 1905. May 4. | 1912. April 22. | 1926. April 25. |
| 1906. May 5. | 1913. April 18. | 1927. April 24. |
| 1907. May 1. | 1914. April 27. | 1932. May 2. |
| 1908. April 28. | 1915. April 28. | |

The spring migration is not a conspicuous affair and it would seem that only the birds that nest in the vicinity or immediately to the north pass through Cape May, the main flight, perhaps, passing up the Delaware Valley as I think must be the case with a number of other species.

The return flight however is a very different matter and forms one of the ornithological features of the year and I am sure that anyone who sees it would be convinced that all the Kingbirds from a large part of the Eastern States must pass the Cape.

This migration first becomes noticeable in mid-August:

| 1921. August 13. | 1926. August 23. | 1931. August 13. |
| 1922. August 19. | 1927. August 16. | 1932. August 9. |
| 1923. August 13. | 1928. August 13. | 1933. August 13. |
| 1924. August 24. | 1929. August 16. | 1934. August 13. |
| 1925. August 11. | 1930. August 12. | |

First we see the Kingbird families of the neighborhood drifting about the country and perhaps uniting to a certain extent, but the August migrants from farther north are recognizably different. They usually come in high overhead at the Point in scattered bunches of from six to fifteeen and later in flocks of twenty-five to fifty or even more. One scattered flock follows another perhaps for several hours and fifty or more may be seen in the air at once. Their flight recalls that of a scattered flock of Robins and is different from the action during the breeding season. They stop to rest, as they arrive at the Point, on tree tops, wires and bayberry bushes, and a number will suddenly fly from a thicket as we approach. The birds seem lost and uncertain as to where to go next and when one individual takes wing others will follow, much like the Tree Swallows which a little later in the season will throng these same bushes. They will aimlessly chase one another about and when they take wing a number will go up to a considerable altitude in the diagonal lines that mark their pursuit of prey earlier in the summer. Even on the wires their attitude seems different from the birds that we knew in June and July. They perch stolidly with head bent over, somewhat in the pose of a Bluebird, with the tail slightly tilted up and the wings drooping a little below it. When first alighting, however, the head is held up and the wings tightly closed against the body.

While there may be several waves or flights of Kingbirds during the latter half of August the great migration occurs on or about the 30th of the month and after that only a few scattering individuals are to be seen and on many days none at all. The flights are mainly restricted to the vicinity of Cape May Point and northward along the Bay shore. We may have a veritable deluge of Kingbirds at the Point and practically none at Cape May only two miles to the east. It would seem that the birds come down the coast at a great height and when they sight the broad expanse of water where Delaware Bay joins the ocean they pause and descend forming the concentration that we find at Cape May Point. Or it may be that perhaps the birds which form the concentration may have been blown out to sea or in following the coast line lose it at the Point, and in either case, they beat in to land and follow the Bay shore into the wind as in the case of the Flickers. Kingbirds are supposed to migrate by day and my observations at the Cape bear out this theory. Certainly they are the most conspicuous birds that move in masses during the day with the possible exception of the Tree Swallows.

On August 27, 1920, I encountered my first notable migration of Kingbirds. Reaching the Point about nine o'clock in the morning I found the woods swarming with the birds; they were flying overhead in flocks, alighting and taking wing again continually. Many of them gathered about a sassafras tree on the edge of the pine woods and fed ravenously upon the berries. They would hover out at the ends of the slender branches or in the air and pick off the fruit, ten or twelve birds feeding at once, and then retire to perches in the nearby pines while others took their places.

As they came to rest there would be quite a tilt of the tail and then a bird would lean forward, lower the head and peer to this side and that in the manner of a cuckoo and then launch out once more into the sassafras tree, supporting himself on rapidly vibrating wings as he plucked off the berries. On September 11, 1927, a small belated flock was feeding in the same manner upon a cluster of pokeberry bushes, and on another occasion the migrants swooped down upon a patch of low huckleberry bushes and fed upon the fruit. This habit of an insectivorous bird feeding upon vegetable matter is characteristic of other species as well, when on migration, as I have noticed Tree Swallows and Myrtle Warblers devouring the berries of the bayberry and Red-eyed Vireos eating sassafras berries. On July 15, 1935, moreover I found a Kingbird, evidently not on migration, feeding on white mulberries in a tree on North Street.

When the great flight of 1920 took place, trees, bushes, and telegraph wires were literally teeming with Kingbirds all day. Flocks of fifty, forty or thirty-five would rise from trees on the Bay side and start out, widely scattered, across the water bound for the Delaware coast which, except for occasional views of the old Cape Henlopen lighthouse, at low tide, was entirely invisible. A few individuals which were kept in sight with the glass turned back and came to roost again but most of them kept on flapping their wings continually as they ascended at a very steep angle and attained a considerable height before advancing horizontally.

The birds that were thronging the tree-tops preparatory to making the crossing would pursue one another violently for short distances and then return to their perches. When I passed the Lighthouse on my return there were not more than twenty Kingbirds there and none at all at Cape May nor had there been all day. On August 30, 1930, there was the same mass movement in the face of a southeast wind.

On August 27, 1934, I happened to be at Cape May Point about 7:00 p. m. just before dusk and was surprised to find upwards of a thousand Kingbirds covering the bushes like Tree Swallows, their white breasts gleaming momentarily in the fading light as they arose in clouds and settled again in the same nervous manner characteristic of the swallows. They were still coming in, apparently from the north or down the ocean front, although it soon became impossible to distinguish them. They gave one the impression of settling for a night's rest and probably there are several distinct movements of Kingbirds during the day which are usually united at the Point where all pause, and that this was a delayed flock that had here reached the end of its day's journey.

When strong northwest winds are blowing at the time of the Kingbird migration the spectacle is somewhat different. There is the same congestion of birds at the Point but also a massed flight into the wind and north along the Bay. I was out on the sand dunes about a mile north of the Point on the morning of August 30, 1926, between 7:15 and 9:30 a. m. and witnessed the greatest Kingbird migration of my experience. The conditions were exactly those that would bring a Flicker flight later in the season, and the birds reacted precisely as do the Flickers.

There were always scattered Kingbirds in sight that morning flying along or perched on the tops of the gnarled and prostrate cedars which here dot the white sand hills. Then would come great straggling flocks of one hundred to five hundred birds spread out on a hundred yard front. They flapped their wings several times took a short sail, and then the wing beats again; some of them darted to right and left on short sallies and others passed low down close over my head. They seldom flew back but kept steadily on their way up the Bay. Every minute there were birds stopping to rest for a moment on the tops of the bushes or on leaning wind-blown trees, and others taking wing again. Sometimes a flock could be detected very high up coming in from the sea or from the ocean coast line I could not tell which, and apparently upon sighting the Bay they would drop down to the level of the tree tops. They seemed to come directly from the Lighthouse or a little farther east where I have seen ocean blown Robins beating their way back to land, and turn into the wind crossing the Pond Creek Meadows and on up the Bay shore. Some, however, seemed to come directly from Cape May Point having, perhaps, followed the coast line clear around the tip of the peninsula. On several counts I estimated that four hundred Kingbirds passed me within five minutes or about five thousand in an hour. This flight did not last more than two hours and there were an considerable gaps between the individual flocks. Doubtless there were other flights during the day. It is a difficult matter to study these flights as it is impossible to be at several different spots at the same time to see what is going on at each, which is a necessary requisite to a proper solution of the activities of these migrants, but by combining a number of observations in different years and of different species of birds I have arrived at the conclusions stated above.

In 1935 William Rusling made a careful study of the August Kingbird flight and writes that "after several days of southerly winds there was a shift to the northwest during the night of the 22d. Immediately after dawn the next day there was a great flight of Kingbirds estimated at two thousand birds. They flew low just over the tree tops heading north into the wind and following the Bay shore rather closely, some of them directly over the beach. They appeared to be very tired and flew quite heavily. Occasional groups would alight on the tops of dead trees for a few minutes. The flight lasted for an hour with groups passing at intervals. There were five distinct flights; five hundred passed on September 29–30, 105 on September 6, 625 on September 7, and 265 on September 10. After that five were seen on the 13th, two on the 16th, four on the 21st, and a last individual on the 29th."

The dates of the massed flights of Kingbirds are as follows:

| 1923. | August 27. | 1929. | August 31. | 1932. | August 29. |
| 1924. | August 29. | 1930. | August 30. | 1934. | August 27. |
| 1926. | August 30. | 1931. | September 1. | 1935. | August 23. |

Small groups of Kingbirds are to be seen during the first ten days of September, usually not over ten to twenty, and after that only scattering individuals. My latest records are:

| 1921. | September 13. | 1925. | September 22. | 1928. | September 23. |
| 1924. | October 2. | 1926. | September 12. | 1929. | October 5. |
| | | 1927. | September 12. | | |

These were all single birds except on two or three occasions when as many as three were seen.

Throughout New Jersey the Kingbird is a common summer resident.


## GRAY KINGBIRD

### Tyrannus dominicensis dominicensis (Gmelin)

This southern bird was seen and studied at Cape May Point on May 30, 1923, by several members of the Delaware Valley Ornithological Club including Julian Potter, John Gillespie and David Baird, all of whom identified it positively and independently from specimens a day or two later. It was perched on a low cedar on the Pond Creek Meadows near the outlet, a short distance from Delaware Bay, and was studied for some time with binoculars. It darted out after insects and perched in exactly the manner of the common Kingbird while its attitude and actions were identical. The larger size, absence of white tail tip, and lighter gray back at once attracted attention and then the dark line through the eye and the large bill were clearly noted.   The bird made no sound.   (Auk, 1923, pp. 536 and 694.)

I searched the entire neighborhood two days later but could find no trace of it.   This observation constitutes the only record of the species for New Jersey.

## ARKANSAS KINGBIRD

### Tyrannus verticalis Say

#### PLATE 101, p. 665

On September 17, 1923, I found one of these western birds perching on the posts of the fence surrounding the Coast Guard station at the Point.   It flew from one post to another and also launched up into the air after passing insects, returning each time to the fence.   As it perched it would turn the head, first to one side then to the other, looking diagonally upward.   It was so tame that I was able to approach to within six feet of it where every detail of color could be studied.

I am thoroughly acquainted with the species in the West and even at quite a distance I recognized the pale gray color of the upper parts and the even lighter shade of the head, which appeared almost white, and I could detect the pale lemon tint of the breast.   When close to it the light edgings of the tail feathers were plainly visible and the relatively small bill was noted.   It made no sound.

There are several other records for New Jersey but no previous or subsequent observation of the species in Cape May County.   Julian Potter saw one at Fort Mott on the Delaware, on October 6, 1929, and another on the same day at Oldman's Creek, Salem County; Charles Urner found one at Tuckerton on August 30, 1931; Joseph Tatum saw one at Barnegat on December 4, 1932; and another on Brigantine Island on October 13, 1935; Paff saw one at Barnegat Light on September 9, 1933.   I have suggested (Auk, 1933, p. 221) that Tatum's Barnegat record was a Great Crested Flycatcher inasmuch as Marc C. Rich had seen one of these birds at the same spot nine days before but his statement sent to me later shows that I was in error, "the bird was always in the open, head and neck very gray and crest not conspicuous and tail short and square at end."   A. H. Phillips secured an Arkansas Kingbird at Princeton on September 29, 1894, and there are I believe other records for the interior of the state.   It is rather curious that so many individuals of this western species have found their way to the Atlantic coast.

## *FORK-TAILED FLYCATCHER

### Muscivora tyrannus (Linnaeus)

This tropical bird, which does not normally come farther north than southern Mexico and the Lesser Antilles, has, strangely enough been recorded three times from the state of New Jersey.

Bridgeton, December, 1820 (circa) (Bonaparte, Amer. Ornith. I. p. 1).
Camden, June, 1832 (Audubon, Ornith. Biog., II, p. 387).
Trenton, autumn, 1900 (Babson, Birds of Princeton, p. 56).

While all three birds were killed none seems to have been preserved.  It would be idle to speculate as to how they found their way to New Jersey and whether man had anything to do with it.

## *SCISSOR-TAILED FLYCATCHER

### Muscivora forficata (Gmelin)

One specimen of this bird, which is a native of Texas and Mexico, was obtained by Dr. C. C. Abbott on the Delaware River at Crosswicks Meadow, five miles below Trenton on April 15, 1872, and is now in the museum at Salem, Mass.   (Amer. Nat., VI, p. 267.)

## GREET CRESTED FLYCATCHER

### Myiarchus crinitus boreus Bangs

Nearly every year one or two pairs of Great Crested Flycatchers nest in the town and a pair or more at Cape May Point while farther back in the country they are regularly distributed, a pair about almost every farmhouse. In the pine woods at the Point we can nearly always count on seeing one of these birds on a morning walk in summer and in August an entire family is often encountered there. As soon as the young are on the wing, however, they drift about and there are days when none can be found in their usual haunts.

I have noted Great Crests at the Point on visits to the shore on May 8, 1925, and May 2, 1932, but probably they arrive a few days earlier, My latest observations in autumn are on September 16, 1923; September 27, 1926; September 17, 1932; September 29, 1935; but they probably remain later as in 1926 on the date mentioned there was a great migration and two dozen of the birds were counted among the many migrants. Their harsh grating call has been heard as late as July 16 and 31 in different years and on June 22, 1924, two Great Crests were pursuing one another through the woods calling continuously, doubtless a mating pair.

Like all flycatchers this species seems top-heavy with its large head and erectile crest, broad shoulders and tapering body. Its rusty tail, long and conspicuous, especially when partly spread, is always diagnostic. When perching the head is often thrust forward as the bird leans over and the

PLATE 102

*W. L. Baily*

*W. L. Baily*

TWO NESTS OF THE WOOD PEWEE, WITH YOUNG AND EGGS.

PLATE 103

*Wharton Huber*

*Wharton Huber*

TREE SWALLOWS GATHERING ON THE RAILROAD TRACKS AND ON THE HIGHWAY,
LUDLAM'S BEACH, N. J.   MANY ARE KILLED HERE EVERY YEAR

crest feathers are elevated as it peers this way and that.  In flying from one perch to another it seems a little sluggish or deliberate but upon alighting there is the same shuffling of the wings as in the Wood Pewee.

For several years a pair of these handsome flycatchers nested in a bird box 6 x 6 x 10 ins., fastened lengthwise to a pole in Walker Hand's yard in the heart of the town.  The box was erected in 1923 with the hope of attracting a pair of House Wrens and to his astonishment a pair of Great Crests took possession about the middle of June and began to carry in building material.  The female seemed to do most of the carrying and also did most of the nest building although the male accompanied her to and from the nest with great regularity.  The sexes could be distinguished by the fact that the crest of the male was always elevated, while that of the female lay flat.  The eggs hatched on July 3 and one of the young was seen to leave the box on July 28, flying directly from the hole to a tree some distance away with perfect confidence, and with none of the preliminary short flights of the usual fledgling.  Its calls, too, were of exactly the same pitch as those of the parents.  How many young were raised I am not sure.

During incubation the male fed the female and would lean into the hole but about dusk he would invariably leave the vicinity of the nest and go elsewhere to roost.  After the young were hatched the female also apparently went away for the night.  Both birds fed the young, the female often entering the box and remaining for some minutes, standing in the entrance hole and looking about in all directions.  The male, however, departed at once after delivering the food.  When he came to the nest he held onto the edge of the hole and leaned over inside meanwhile flattening his tail against the outside of the box.  The parent birds caught many small moths and butterflies as well as other insects and an inspection of the nest after the young had left showed the hard shell of the abdomens of five cicadas.  Another individual was seen to swallow a good-sized sphinx moth head first, without tearing it apart.  Further inspection revealed the presence of ventral scutes and other fragments of the inevitable snake skins which the Great Crest places in its nest and which had been broken up evidently by the activities of the young.  The nesting material consisted mainly of pieces of dry grass, a quantity of cow hair and some chicken feathers, the whole forming a dense mat two or three inches thick covering the bottom of the box.

The nest was about eight feet from the ground close to a garden fence and members of the family were constantly passing close to it.  Hand was there most frequently and the birds showed perfect confidence in him, going to the nest to feed the young within a few feet of his head; they showed practically no alarm, however, at the presence of anyone in the garden.

In 1924 the male appeared about the box on May 15 and the female on May 29.  By July 10 they were busy feeding young.  The birds alighted, as the male had done in the previous year, leaning into the cavity and turning the flattened tail up so that the upper surface was close against the box above the opening.  Sometimes one of them, doubtless the female, would enter for a moment and appear again with a ball of excrement which she carried away. I saw one of the parents catch a dragonfly and a grasshopper, each of which was beaten against the wire upon which the bird perched before it was fed to the young. Once a beetle failed to go into the mouth for which it was intended and the parent promptly hopped inside and recovered it.

The young birds left the nest on July 12, flying directly to a tree some distance away, as before. A pair of these birds used the box in 1925 but had considerable trouble with a pair of House Wrens which occupied another box not far away and apparently as a result of this they did not return the next year although in 1927 a male visited the box sometime in May.

A nest found by Richard Miller at Swain was located in a hollow limb of an apple tree and contained five eggs on June 6, 1920, while Turner Mc-Mullen tells me of one at Ocean View, June 17, 1922, which contained five young. Walker Hand tells me of another nest built in an old wooden pump propped against a house, the birds entering and leaving through the hole where the handle operated. Still another nest I found at Goshen built in a cylindrical tin mail tube fastened to a post on the roadside opposite an unoccupied house. It held three well grown young on June 28, 1933, and while we watched it one of the parents appeared with a yellow Colias butterfly.

Marc C. Rich has recorded a single Great Crest found at Barnegat Light on the remarkable date of November 25, 1932 (Auk, 1933, p. 221). The bird is a common summer resident in most parts of the state.

## PHOEBE
### Sayornis phoebe (Latham)

The Phobe seems to be only a transient in Cape May County as I have been unable to find any record of its nesting southeast of the lower Delaware Valley and central Pine Barrens, in both of which localities it is rare. It is more abundant in autumn than in spring but even then we usually see only scattered individuals, perhaps half a dozen in a day's tramp, although there are days of massed migration when there may be a considerable flight. I found them very abundant on September 27, 1926, during a Flicker flight, and again on October 2, 1924, while on September 30, 1923, Julian Potter counted thirty individuals. We usually see Phoebes at Cape May Point and along the Bay shore to the north but they also occur regularly about orchards and fence rows back in the open farming country.

Arrival dates for the Phoebe in autumn are:

| | | |
|---|---|---|
| 1923. September 23. | 1928. September 27. | 1932. September 25. |
| 1925. September 22. | 1930. September 28. | 1935. September 29. |
| 1926. September 27. | 1931. September 28. | |

Latest dates are:

| | | |
|---|---|---|
| 1923. October 21. | 1930. November 9. | 1935. October 24. |
| 1928. October 27. | 1933. October 29. | |

We also have some midwinter records which indicate that an occasional Phoebe remains as a winter resident; Norman McDonald found four scattered individuals on December 26, 1927; William Yoder and Henry Gaede found one on January 25, 1925; while on December 27, 1936, Otway Brown and I found one at Price's Pond and Norman McDonald another at the Point. Our spring records are as follows:

| | | | |
|---|---|---|---|
| 1924. | April 4–20. | 1928. | April 1. |
| 1925. | March 21. | 1932. | March 25–26. |
| 1926. | April 6–18. | 1933. | April 1–17. |
| 1927. | March 18–April 24. | 1935. | March 23. |

The migrant Phoebes of Cape May do not seem to have the assurance of the nesting birds that we are familiar with farther north and appear rather lost in the absence of their favorite surroundings of running brooks, stone springhouses and old bridges. They are usually seen at the Cape on low bushes or on the lowest branches of small trees. The behavior of one studied on April 3, 1924, at the Point was typical. It flew from one twig to another now and then darting down and alighting on a perch only a few inches from the ground but I never saw it actually rest on the ground. The tail is wagged constantly at intervals of one or two seconds, a quick elevation and a slower return, and sometimes there is a double "flirt" the second one less pronounced. When perching the wings are slightly drooping and the head well down on the shoulders and after a flight there is a rapid flutter and shuffling of the wings. Spring birds occasionally gave the familiar call but autumnal migrants were silent. The nearest breeding records to Cape May are furnished by Turner McMullen as follows:

Houck's Bridge, Salem Co., a nest on a ledge over a doorway in a deserted house: May 16, 1920, one egg and one young; May 15, 1921, five eggs; April 29, 1922, four eggs. Another nest on a beam in an old barn: April 29, 1922, four eggs; May 24, 1924, four eggs; April 26, 1925, five eggs; May 2, 1933, five eggs.

Pennsville, Salem Co., nest on a beam in deserted house: May 4, 1924, four eggs; April 15, 1928, two eggs.

Course's Landing, Salem Co., a nest on beam of a plank bridge: April 16, 1922, three eggs.

In the Pine Barrens we know of but a single nesting at Fourway Lodge some miles above Mays Landing on the Egg Harbor River, where a pair has bred for several years. This nest, placed on a ledge over a window, held young on May 16, 1936. The Phoebe is a common summer resident in the northern half of the state.

## YELLOW-BELLIED FLYCATCHER

### Empidonax flaviventris (Baird and Baird)

A regular autumn transient, always present in the first notable wave of late August or early September. Usually seen first in the pine woods at the Point, or in bayberry bushes immediately back of the sand dunes at South Cape May but occurs later in the Physick garden and along the Bay shore in thickets and open woodland. In the great flight of September 1, 1920, they were common everywhere.

Autumn arrival dates:

| | | | | | |
|---|---|---|---|---|---|
| 1920. | September 1. | 1927. | August 25. | 1932. | August 22. |
| 1924. | August 27. | 1928. | September 1. | 1934. | August 27. |
| 1925. | August 22. | 1929. | August 29. | 1935. | |
| 1926. | August 28. | 1930. | September 2. | | |

They have been seen as late as September 28, 1925; September 27, 1926; September 17, 1932; September 10, 1935. We have no spring records whatever and infer that the northward flight passes up the Delaware River Valley. It is not known to nest in the state.

## ALDER FLYCATCHER

### Empidonax trailli trailli (Audubon)

A specimen of this little Flycatcher was taken on Five Mile Beach on September 12, 1896, by William Baily. I also saw one in a thicket west of the Rutherford farm in West Cape May, on September 5, 1928, and Conrad Roland observed another at the Point on September 18, 1932.

In the northern part of the state they occur through the summer and nest locally. Samuel Rhoads found them at Alpine in June 1901, at Lake Hopatcong in late May, and at Greenwood and Wawyanda Lakes in June 1909 while Waldron Miller established their breeding at Plainfield in 1899. They are nowhere abundant and doubtless occur more frequently in migration in the Delaware Valley than along the coast.

## ACADIAN FLYCATCHER

### Empidonax virescens (Vieillot)

The Acadian Flycatcher is the summer resident little green flycatcher of the Delaware Valley especially on the Pennsylvania side and formerly or locally across central New Jersey north of the Pine Barrens. It seems to have decreased in the northern counties which were close to its northern breeding limit and this may have had something to do with its scarcity at Cape May where I have never been able to find it even as a migrant. Fletcher Street, however, located a pair, apparently nesting, at Ocean View on June 7, 1936.

Doubtless they migrate along the western side of the Delaware Valley.

## LEAST FLYCATCHER

Empidonax minimus (Baird and Baird)

The Least Flycatcher is probably the commonest of the little green fly-catchers at Cape May. It occurs regularly as an autumnal transient at the same time as the Yellow-bellied Flycatcher and usually associated with it. I have records of occurrence as follows:

| 1920. September 1. | 1924. August 18. | 1931. August 25. |
| 1921. August 19. | 1925. August 28. | 1932. August 29. |
| 1922. August 20. | 1926. August 28. | 1934. August 27. |
| 1923. August 31. | 1927. August 25. | 1935. August 23. |
| | 1930. September 4. | |

They have been seen as late as September 14, 1921; September 17, 1932; September 5, 1928; September 7, 1935. We have no spring observations. The Least Flycatcher nests farther south in the state than does the Alder Flycatcher having been found in summer as far south as Haddonfield (Rhoads), Plainfield (Miller), Princeton (Babson), but its true summer home is in the northern counties, northward.

As we have only autumn records of any of the little flycatchers at the Cape they are of course not singing and one of the best means of identi-fication is therefore lacking.

## WOOD PEWEE

Myiochanes virens (Linnaeus)

PLATE 102. p. 678

One or two pairs of Wood Pewees are seen nearly every year at Cape May Point and in 1920 a pair bred in Cape May but this is unusual. To the north in the open farm land or along wood edges they are well distributed. They become more conspicuous in late summer when the young are on the wing and are then often quite abundant during the passing of the great flights of migrants from farther north.

Like all of the flycatchers the Wood Pewee spends most of its time on a perch on some dead limb or tree top from which it launches forth in pur-suit of passing insects returning at once to its stand. At rest on its perch the Pewee looks peculiarly top-heavy and when the crest is raised the head seems out of all proportion to the slender body which tapers rapidly to the tail. A bird perching on a telegraph wire had great difficulty in keeping its equilibrium in the face of a strong wind and it was interesting to watch it swing its tightly closed tail far forward under the wire while the head was stretched over from above. On July 13, 1920, a pair nesting in the pine woods was studied for some time. The more active individual, presumably the female, held its crest erect and flew from perch to perch, shuffling its wings immediately after alighting and then settling them closely to the body. While I was near it uttered continuously the characteristic call of the species *tsu—wee* or *tur—eee*, as it has sounded to me at different times, or *pee—wee* as usually written, with an interval of four seconds between calls.

The other bird, watched from a distance through binoculars, seemed to have lost all apprehension and assumed a perch on a dead pine twig from which it sallied forth every few minutes after its prey, returning at once after each effort, and if successful wiped its bill on the branch after swallowing the insect. Sometimes it dived off the perch to quite a distance and turned half over sideways until one wing pointed straight down and the other up, and it seemed that the bird would turn a somersault; at other times in pitched right through the foliage of the tree and once vaulted high in the air and came down fluttering for some twenty feet in a long spiral apparently following some small insect in its devious flight. When returning to its perch it always flew around the trunk of the tree from behind and if it happened to come to rest facing the wrong way it immediately turned about into its usual position. Upon alighting there was always the same flutter of the wings and the shuffling of the tips as they were folded. Young birds, easily distinguished by the very pronounced buffy wing bands, would sometimes perch for many minutes without moving, on the top of an upright stub which they resembled so closely in color that they appeared to be part of it.

A nest found at the Point on June 23, 1932, was located on a horizontal branch of an oak about fifteen feet from the ground, and contained eggs. On August 28, 1926, a female and full grown young were busily engaged in devouring a large brown moth.

Last dates of occurrence in autumn: September 29, 1917; October 3, 1920; September 25, 1927; September 28, 1930; September 25, 1932. I have spring arrival dates: May 26, 1923; May 20, 1927; May 20, 1928; May 26, 1929, but as I was not present regularly through the spring these are probably late.

While not a characteristic species of the coastal area the Wood Pewee is a more abundant summer resident in the Delaware Valley and throughout the state north of the Pine Barrens, as well as in the cedar swamps of the latter region.

## OLIVE-SIDED FLYCATCHER

Nuttallornis mesoleucus (Lichtenstein)

A rare but apparently regular autumn transient about Cape May Point where one or two have been seen every year. We have no spring records. I first saw one on the top of a dead cedar about fifty yards north of the turnpike, not far from the Bay, on August 13, 1923, and on September 4, 1924, collected one from the same perch. On August 25, 1927, this perch was again occupied by an Olive-sided Flycatcher and on August 14, 1932, one was located on the top of a tall dead tree in the sand dunes farther north on the Bay shore. This bird was quite restless and beside the usual sorties after passing insects it would make sustained flights to another dead tree top a quarter of a mile away and back again. The same, or another individual was found in the same place on August 29 and on August 9, 13, 26 and 30, 1934, one was perched on a dead pine at the head of Lake Lily.

The Olive-side is a glorified Wood Pewee with the head appearing still larger in proportion to the body; indeed with the crest erected the bird seems to be all head while the closed tail looks very short and inconspicuous. The blackish areas on the sides of the breast are very conspicuous, even at some distance, but the concealed white feathers at the sides of the rump when exposed are usually not visible from the ground. In the last individual mentioned, however, they were fluffed out and could easily be seen.

The habits of the Olive-sided Flycatcher are exactly like those of the Wood Pewee but there is a certain indescribable personality about it which, together with its size and habit of perching on the highest dead branches available, make it easy to identify. The first individual that I found was being harrassed by a Hummingbird, which may have had a nest or young in the vicinity, when it flew the Hummer was close after it and when the Olive-side rested the Hummingbird took its perch on a nearby twig.

The Olive-sided Flycatcher is a rather rare transient throughout New Jersey and so far as I know does not breed in the state.

## *SKYLARK

### Alauda arvensis arvensis Linnaeus

An article in the "Scientific American" for September 22, 1883, states that "eighty-four European Skylarks had been liberated on a farm in New Jersey and may now be seen apparently at home and quite happy." A subsequent note in the "Ornithologist and Oölogist" states that persons residing in the neighborhood of Winslow had seen Skylarks in a marshy scrub oak woods but there is no evidence that the observers knew the birds.

In the Patent Office Report for 1853 there is an article on the importation of Skylarks into Delaware by John Gorgas of Wilmington. He states that he imported from Liverpool two lots of these birds. The first twenty arrived on February 20, 1853, and were liberated on March 19. The second lot of twenty-two arrived on April 18 and were liberated next day. On July 24, following, the larks were ascending into the sky and singing "as cheerfully as they do in 'Merry England'."

In the vicinity of New York City Skylarks have been liberated from time to time and in 1887, according to Ludlow Griscom (Birds of the N. Y. City Region) a small colony became established near Flatbush, Long Island, but was destroyed by the advance of the city and none had been seen so far as he knew since 1913. So it appears that all of the introductions that might have established this bird in New Jersey have failed.

## NORTHERN HORNED LARK

*Otocoris alpestris alpestris* (Linnaeus)

The "Shore Larks," as they are appropriately called along the coast, are of frequent occurrence throughout the winter on the upper beaches and sand flats of Cape May as well as in the old fields immediately behind the town, while they also are to be found on the golf links and on the baseball field. Their dull colors make them difficult to distinguish against the brown earth and the short dead grass and it may not be until they take wing right before us that we are aware of their presence.

While a flock may remain in the same neighborhood for some days at a time, or may return to it through the winter, they are usually restless birds and drift hither and thither, seeming to take particular delight in strong winds and blinding snow flurries. In a storm on February 5, 1933, when a gale was blowing and fine snow was drifting deep on fields and roads, I came on a flock of Shore Larks near Cold Spring which had just alighted in a small bare spot, temporarily clear of snow, where they were running about finding food of some sort in the clumps of dead grass that the wind had exposed. Farther up the coast, at Brigantine Island, Brooke Worth tells me of finding hundreds of Horned Larks in a violent snow storm which raged there on February 21, 1929.

The Shore Larks are probably present every winter in one place or another, not only in Cape May County but all along the New Jersey coast, while we may find them in old fields in the interior when least expecting them.

As we see a flock of the birds working their way along the sea beach unalarmed, they impress one as being very short-legged and they seem to waddle a little as they scurry along at a quick walk—almost a run, for they are one of the few species of small birds that walk instead of hop when on the ground. They hold the head well up and forward as if they were straining to get along as fast as possible and it bobs forward and back as the bird advances. As the flock proceeds the birds keep pecking at the sand to the right and left and sometimes turn completely around before making a dab, apparently sighting some choice morsel, and then resume their advance after a few steps backward. They never stop to feed at any one spot but are ever on the go, foraging as they advance, and although they may scatter widely and follow their individual paths, the whole flock keeps moving in the same general direction and, with the peculiar uniformity of action that characterizes flocking birds, they will rise as a unit when something alarms them. They seem to find their food on the surface of the sand or earth and I have never seen them scratch.

Their "horns" are not elevated while they feed but may be erected at any moment in excitement or as they pause to look about. Sometimes they will rush madly at one another one bird apparently driving a trespasser from its own feeding territory. The tail is carried horizontally and the tips of the wings are on a level with the base of the tail or droop a trifle below it, the wings are noticeably long and pointed, as we see them when the birds occasionally leap into the air or when they take flight.

The flight is undulatory and, as each bird moves individually within the flock, some are always rising and others falling but they keep close together, now skimming the ground now rising a little, coming into clear view against the sky or when over the white sand, and vanishing from sight when they cross some old brown field or patch of winter marsh. Samuel Rhoads and I found a large flock in the bitter cold days of January, 1892, on old fields behind the town, where the waterworks now stand, and when we flushed them they would fly round in long ovals coming back eventually to almost the exact spot from which they had arisen, and this happened again and again so loath were they to leave the neighborhood. When they come to rest they usually stand directly on the sandy beach or on the ground but I once saw a number resting on old logs washed up by the tide and buried in the sand above high water mark.

While Shore Larks are excellent examples of protective coloration when feeding in open winter fields they are quite conspicuous against the white sand of the beaches and appear almost black when seen against the sun. In a good light, however, and in proper position, the pink tints of the back are brought out strongly and they seem to acquire a ruddy flush, while the yellow throat and black chest band stand out conspicuously as they face you. There is a perceptible difference in size between the sexes the female being the smaller, and usually more streaked.

Shore Larks are most frequently seen from November to February and are most abundant when a storm brings them from regions where the snow has recently covered the ground and they are seeking new feeding stations; though they are not averse to traveling with the snow. Our earliest Cape May date is October 9, 1921, and we have seen them October 17–18, 1931; October 25, 1929; October 27, 1928. We have only two March records March 6, 1927, and March 19, 1932.

While Snow Buntings are stated to associate with Horned Larks the only bird that I have seen in company with them is the Lapland Longspur, a number of which were feeding with them on the strand at the southern extremity of Seven Mile Beach on November 28, 1926.

## *PRAIRIE HORNED LARK

Otocoris alpestris praticola Henshaw

While the Common Horned Lake is strictly migratory and does not breed south of Labrador and Quebec the paler Prairie Horned Lark, a bird of the Mississippi Valley, breeds there and to a lesser extent on the Atlantic coast south at least to Long Island. It occurs in winter flocks in New Jersey either alone or mingled with the more northern race and seems to be extending its nesting range southward.

Nelson Pumyea has recorded many of them present on the golf links at Mount Holly, N. J., during the winter of 1932–33, which remained through the spring with some still present on May 14, six on June 23 and two on July 1. On July 4 he saw four one of which sought food and fed another, evidently a well grown young of the year. This seems pretty good evidence of their breeding at this locality. The birds were seen to soar high up in the air, in the "Skylark" habit of the species, and return to almost the exact spot from which they arose. Julian Potter found two singing at Bridgeport, Gloucester County, on May 31, 1936, one on June 6, 1937; and another at Auburn, Salem County. They were doubtless all breeding.

At Delaware City across the river John Gillespie and others found these birds singing on May 14, 1933, which suggests that they nested there as well. At Cape May, where they in all probability occur, at least in winter, no one has yet detected them.

Beside its paler coloration above, the Prairie Horned Lark can easily be recognized by the white throat and superciliary stripes in contrast to the distinctly yellow coloration of these parts in the other race. About Philadelphia and elsewhere the two races often associate in the same flock during their winter sojourn.

# TREE SWALLOW

Iridoprocne bicolor (Vieillot)

PLATE 103, p. 679

The Tree Swallow is the most characteristic swallow of the seacoast and has been observed about Cape May in every month of the year. It is scarcest, of course, in winter and reaches its maximum abundance with the enormous flocks of September and October, while as a breeding bird it is local and not very common. One or two pairs usually nest at Cape May Point and not infrequently we find a pair on the edge of the meadows just back of the golf links. Old Flicker holes in telegraph poles are their favorite nesting sites here, while one pair used a cavity in a piling on the edge of the Harbor, and another bred in a hole in a post far out on the meadow back of Two Mile Beach. This hole was not more than three feet from the ground and the female could be seen perched in the entrance while the male rested on a stake nearby. They paired on top of the nest post. On Seven Mile Beach there used to be an abundance of old dead cedar trees with wood-pecker nests or knot holes in their trunks and these harbored quite a number of Tree Swallows. Some still are to be found there. Richard Miller has visited this colony on Memorial Day (May 30) from 1911 to 1920 and has usually found eggs partly incubated although in 1933 and 1934 all nests contained young from one third to one half grown. As young were still in the nests on June 16, 17, and 19, in different years, it is quite probable that two broods are raised in a season, while a nest with eggs found here by Turner McMullen on July 1, 1923, and another on June 30, 1923, in Salem County, lend color to this theory. I have found young still being fed in the nest at Cape May as late as the first week of July while families of young have first appeared on the telegraph wires on July 9, 1923; July 16, 1924; July 4, 1927; June 30, 1932. The nests that I have examined are composed of grass and lined with feathers, the birds of Seven Mile Beach using Laughing Gull feathers, according to Richard Miller; the eggs number from four to six.

By the middle of July all of the young from local nests are on the wing and begin the formation of the great autumn flocks constantly augmented by arrivals from farther north. Throughout the Pine Barrens, especially along the Egg Harbor River and on flooded bogs and ponds, there are many dead trees of various sorts that have been killed by damming up the water and these furnish abundant nesting places for the Tree Swallows which in South Jersey always seem partial to the vicinity of water. While such areas produce a fair crop of swallows every year they constitute but a small part of the enormous autumn flocks, the bulk of which evidently come from much farther north. Instead of streaming steadily southward as do the Barn Swallows, in late August and September, the Tree Swallows form in large flocks and seem to remain more or less stationary for weeks at a time moving definitely southward only toward the end of the autumn.

A northwest wind in early August generally brings the first flock of migrants to Cape May Point, but even before this a considerable gathering may be seen on the Tuckahoe River from the passing train as it turns southward into the Cape May Peninsula, while an extensive sand pit at the western end of the Stone Harbor Road, where it enters upon the meadows, is another early gathering point. On August 1, 1921, several hundred Tree Swallows swarmed over a thicket of bayberry bushes, where none were to be seen the day before, and hovered close to the branches like monarch butterflies which often perform similar migrations later in the autumn.

Dates for the first of these migrant flocks are:

| | | | | | |
|---|---|---|---|---|---|
| 1920. | August 5. | 1927. | August 3. | 1932. | August 13. |
| 1922. | August 3. | 1928. | August 13. | 1933. | August 5. |
| 1923. | August 4. | 1929. | August 12. | 1934. | August 11. |
| 1924. | August 10. | 1930. | August 12. | 1935. | August 8. |
| 1925. | July 30. | 1931. | August 18. | 1937. | August 6. |

My notes of 1920 give a good idea of the character of the annual assemblages of Tree Swallows at the Point. On August 5, the flock that had gathered there was augmented by large numbers from the north, both old and young. They lined the wires and gathered in masses on a nearby cluster of bayberry bushes. Some clung to the telegraph poles like woodpeckers, looking for an opening on the wires where they might manage to squeeze in, and there was a constant sidling along the wires and wooden cross-trees as the birds packed ever closer together. Some adults were seen to feed full-fledged young and all were busy preening their plumage, holding the wings straight out from the shoulder, one at a time, in the stiff manner of the swallow tribe and reaching over the shoulder to preen the feathers of the lower back. They showed no alarm at my presence and I could walk past on the opposite side of the road without causing them to take wing. They swarmed over certain bayberry bushes which seemed to bear the most fruit but I do not think that they fed upon the berries at this time. If they did they must have simply scraped off the waxy coating from the surface as I found that the berries were difficult to detach from the branches. Furthermore on other occasions I have noticed Tree Swallows swarming in the same way over dead bushes which bore neither leaves nor fruit. Suddenly the whole assemblage of birds would take wing for no apparent reason, or several detachments would leave in succession, flying off a few yards and swarming back again. As I stood perfectly still, close to the bushes, I could feel the whir of the birds' wings as they passed within a foot of my face.

Flocks of Tree Swallows seem to pick some definite object upon which to swarm without any apparent reason, returning to it again and again only to desert it entirely the next day. On August 19, a small bayberry bush on the Fill, slightly taller than the surrounding vegetation, was selected and about thirty birds gathered upon it sitting so close together that it did not seem possible for them to move. On August 3, 1927, a spot at the base of the sand dunes near South Cape May struck their fancy and they crowded in great numbers onto sticks that were projecting from the sand and upon low bayberry bushes.

The 1920 flock at the Point had increased by August 17 to approximately 1200 individuals which thronged the wires and bushes the latter being simply loaded down with them. The long wires stretching across the meadows back of South Cape May were a favorite roost and the birds would line them so closely that at a distance they looked like heavy cables sagging down in the middle with the weight of birds. And so all through September they fluctuated in numbers and in location, some always passing southward along the beach, others gathering in larger or smaller flocks. Whether these were changing in their make-up from day to day or whether the same individuals remained throughout the month it was impossible to say.

On October 3, as I walked down the beach from Cape May, I found them as usual scudding back and forth over dunes and meadow, but arriving at the Point the air was suddenly charged with Tree Swallows. There were several thousand in a driving, swirling mass, quite definite in shape, like a great cloud. As quickly and mysteriously as they came they had gone again, alternately flapping and sailing, far off to the east. Then they were back again immediately overhead, the individual birds performing all sorts of evolutions within the prescribed limits of the flock. Then the cloud-like mass would rise steadily until nearly out of sight when it appeared like a swarm of minute gnats. At other times, as on September 13, 1921, the birds would suddenly scatter from the dense flock and pour over the country in all directions, as if belching forth from some enclosure of which the door had been suddenly opened, and then upon some common impulse they were all back in close formation. While never flying so habitually low as do the Barn Swallows, the Tree Swallows rarely ascend more than thirty to fifty feet until these great autumn swarms are formed when they may mount aloft clear to the limit of vision.

While Cape May Point seems to be the most favored place for these congregations of Tree Swallows they sometimes prefer to gather on the Fill.

On October 21, 1923, Walker Hand estimated that there were from ten to twelve thousand birds assembled there and again on September 26, 1926, I watched a flock of at least five thousand, a drifting maze of birds, now settling on the bayberry bushes, now shifting to the telegraph wires, and then spreading in a long procession far across the sky line like a gigantic swarm of bees. When at rest they covered all the wires on Madison Avenue as well as on some of the cross streets. On October 10 they occupied seventeen spans between the poles and with four wires to a span and two hundred birds to a wire there must have been close to 15,000 present.

They also like to gather over bodies of water and I saw one flock of about a thousand come down from very high in the air to the shallow pond at the Lighthouse skimming the surface in regular order. Then the van turned suddenly and flew through the ranks of their followers until all was confusion, then mounting in air again they circled several times and in three minutes had disappeared utterly. On October 23, 1927, at the same spot a flock was hovering or sailing over a small pool in the meadows, moving back and forth with great regularity, and every now and then a bird would touch the tip of its bill to the surface. Now and then one would advance by a short sail but usually all were flapping and hovering so that, at a little distance, they resembled a flock of butterflies. On November 8, 1930, a flock of one thousand clustered over this same pond in a dense mass, constantly dropping down, possibly to dip the bill, though it was usually the tail and belly that touched the water, and I wondered if this was a form of bathing. The birds that touched the water immediately arose again so that with some dropping and others rising there was a maze of motion, while every few minutes, with that remarkable uniformity of action, the entire mass would rise some ten feet in the air and then settle back to resume their performance. Finally they scattered widely over the meadow everyone for himself. While hovering over the water a Marsh Hawk several times passed close to them but made no attempt to molest them nor did they seem disturbed at his presence.

On some of these swarmings the birds appear to be catching minute gnats or other flying insects but there was no evidence of this on the above occasions. On July 23, 1934, however, a number of Barn and Tree Swallows were observed coursing back and forth over an old briery field catching strawberry flies which were there by the thousand and again on August 4, 1932, I watched both species of swallows as well as Chimney Swifts flying back and forth along a road catching flies of some sort.

Every year I have watched the Tree Swallow gathering on the Stone Harbor Road, and on August 14, 1923, I made a careful estimate of the birds on the wires which showed about ten thousand present, the crowded lines seemed to stretch across the meadows almost to Seven Mile Beach. There was a heavy wind blowing and many of the birds, as on several other occasions, sought shelter on the sides of the old sand pit nearby. On August 10, 1927, the sides of the pit were covered with them and they spread out over the level sandy floor, which was also out of the wind, and some fifteen hundred were ranged there in regular rows. On September 25 and 26, 1921, they assembled on the golf links, sitting close together and forming a great hour-glass some three hundred feet long by one hundred across the end. There is another spot where these swallows roost to their sorrow, on the shore road of Ludlam's Beach above Sea Isle City. Year after year they gather here on the concrete roadbed until they completely cover an area of some twenty-five feet square which appears as if covered by a glistening blue pavement. Why they should select this particular spot I have been quite unable to determine but it shows poor judgment for automobiles are constantly passing and serious slaughter of the birds ensues. John Emlen picked up ninety-six dead swallows on September 26, 1926, and on similar spots in the county Conrad Roland gathered up over one hundred from September 4 to 12, 1934. The killing is usually accidental as it is very difficult to avoid the birds but a few drivers deliberately increase their speed and plow through the flock with apparently no thought but to see how many they can hit.

On September 21, 1929, there was a veritible whirlwind of Tree Swallows on the Fill. With a strong north wind blowing they were beating their way against it, pyramiding high up into the sky, and then flattening down and spreading out into a sheet of birds a hundred yards wide. They flew low over the bushes and poured by close above my head until it seemed as if the whole sky was in motion and I felt dizzy. Then they would turn and drift slowly back again tacking and flapping against the gale and piling up gradually into another dense mass formation, shoulder to shoulder and layer upon layer, each bird holding his position by vigorous wing action. Once again they turn and going with the wind are fairly swept from the skies and we see them far to leeward like a swarm of gnats, gathering once more to face the gale.

Mass action such as this seems to be due primarily to the force of the wind. The swallows depend upon their wings to take them to water and to where insect food may be obtained in the air and a strong gale prevents them from reaching either objective. Their only hope is to keep beating to windward, as they would be blown to destruction if they travelled with the wind for any distance, and the strain would seem eventually to force them to the ground where without food or water they would perish. Walker Hand has described to me such an occurrence which forms a fitting climax to the account that I have just presented. "On October 25, 1930," he writes, "we had more Tree Swallows than I have ever seen before; the north wind was so strong that they were forced to the ground and were sitting on the open ground of the Fill by the acre and, the wind continuing, they were unable to obtain either food or water. On the 26th and 27th probably several thousand died. It was possible to stand in one spot and count over a hundred on the beach, on the Fill, or at the Point east of the Light. There are no ponds on the Fill and the gale prevented them from going to windward in search of water and there is no dew on the trees and bushes. The three days' struggle seemed to exhaust them. Myrtle Warblers and Robins which were in a similar plight flocked to a pan of water in our yard and I counted thirty birds there at one time. Being more or less terrestrial they were better able to cope with the situation than the aërial swallows." On September 16, 1903, a still more unusual incident occurred on the Physick property on Washington St., where the Martins were accustomed to roost, which was reported to me at the time by Walker Hand. The Martins had left and a host of flocking Tree Swallows took possession of the trees during a driving rain storm with very high wind, something that they never did before or since, except perhaps in the case of a few straggling individuals. In the morning the ground was literally covered with drenched, helpless swallows. Large numbers were gathered up in baskets and dried out and eventually all but about seventy-five recovered and flew off. The number on the ground as counted and estimated at the time was between six and seven thousand.

While the great October flocks decrease rapidly through November, some birds usually remain during the winter. In 1923 there were still 1500 present on November 17, 250 by November 24, and the same number on December 11, while from six to twenty were to be seen at intervals in January, February and March following. In 1926, another great Tree Swallow year, there were thirty-five present on November 13 and fifty on the 21st while twenty-three were seen on December 26. We have records of wintering Tree Swallows in 1900–1901; 1902–1903; 1923–1924; 1924–1925; 1925–1926; 1926–1927; 1927–1928; while in other winters no careful observations were made so that it is more than probable that some were present then also. The Christmas census of the Delaware Valley Club follows:

December 26, 1926, twenty-three.     December 24, 1933, eight.
December 26, 1927, two.              December 23, 1934, nine.
December 28, 1930, seven.            December 22, 1935, eleven.
December 26, 1932, fourteen.         December 27, 1936, eleven.

There is something inspiring about these supposedly delicate birds sailing over the frozen ponds in midwinter or rising from the brown bayberry bushes in the patches of yellow dune grass where they had sought shelter against the cold winds. Their food in winter is supposed to consist entirely of the bayberries which they glean from the bushes along the coast but an examination of the stomach of a midwinter specimen disclosed the remains of several large dipterous insects.

While the great autumn flocks of Tree Swallows contain no other species the earliest assemblages associate with Barn Swallows, stray Cliff and Bank Swallows and Rough-wings, and both Barn and Tree Swallows may join the Purple Martins in their roosting grove. Sometimes about the first of September one may be fortunate enough to find all six species resting on the wires at Cape May Point.

PLATE 104

*W. L. Baily*

*J. K. Potter*

TWO VIEWS OF BANK SWALLOW NESTING TUNNELS, ALONG THE DELAWARE RIVER
AT PENSAUKEN AND FISH HOUSE, N. J.

PLATE 105

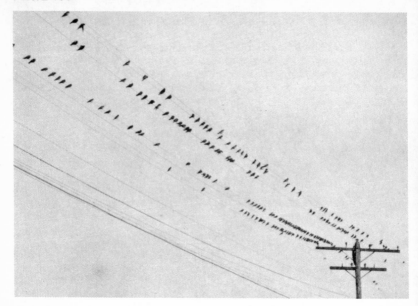

*Wharton Huber*

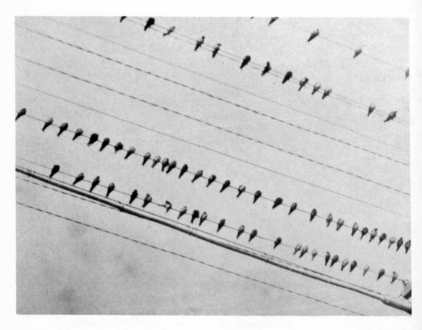

*Wharton Huber*

PURPLE MARTINS GATHERING ON WIRES, MADISON AVE., CAPE MAY; PREPARATORY
TO ENTERING THE ROOST; LOWER PHOTOGRAPH WITH TELEPHOTO LENSE.

It is difficult to ascertain the migration dates of a resident species but there seems no doubt but that there is a definite arrival of north-bound Tree Swallows at Cape May about April 24, and I have recorded such arrivals as follows:

| | | |
|---|---|---|
| 1921. April 24. | 1923. April 22. | 1931. April 25. |
| 1922. April 23. | 1926. April 24. | 1932. April 24. |
| | 1927. April 24. | |

No great northward flight of the birds has been seen in spring, however, and what becomes of the thousands that pass south in autumn is another of the mysteries of migration.

In the northern counties of the state, and especially along the coast, the Tree Swallow is an abundant autumn transient, less plentiful in spring, and a decidedly local summer resident. (Griscom, Birds of the New York City Region.) It would therefore appear that the autumn hosts that reach Cape May must come from much more northern regions.

On the first appearance of Tree Swallow families on the telegraph wires one notes the great contrast in color between the old and young, the former burnished greenish blue, the latter dull brown, but both alike in the silky whiteness of their breasts. By August 15, the adults are in all stages of molt and soon assume their new plumage with prominent white tips to the wing coverts which are lacking in the worn post-breeding individuals. Later on the brown young assume the plumage of the adults and by late autumn they are indistinguishable. The general resemblance of the young Tree Swallow to the young Rough-wing is rather striking but the whiter under surface of the former and the white, instead of rusty, edgings to the wing coverts will serve to distinguish them. Walker Hand observed a pure albino in one of the large autumn flights on October 10, 1926, and another was seen at Barnegat farther up the coast by William Loetscher on September 6, 1935.

The autumnal swarms of Tree Swallows—and swarm is the only word that will adequately describe their abundance—form one of the most striking features of Cape May ornithology. Only the roosting Martins, the breeding terns, or the feeding shore birds of the sounds, present such a concentrated mass of bird life, while the intricacy of the Tree Swallows' movements, the fluctuations in their numbers and the sudden appearance and disappearance of the great flocks, seemingly at a moment's notice, arouse our admiration and wonder and furnish a constant field for speculation.

## BANK SWALLOW

Riparia riparia riparia (Linnaeus)

PLATE 104, p. 694

So far as my observations go the Bank Swallow occurs about Cape May only as a south-bound migrant from late July to early September. While there are apparently no breeding spots to its liking in Cape May County there is no reason why it should not occur in spring on its northward flight, but we have seen very few at this season—four on May 13, 1928, with other swallows near the Lighthouse and one on Pond Creek Meadows. Bank Swallows usually occur in small numbers in flocks of Barn and Tree Swallows which rest at the Point on their southward flight, but sometimes there is a rather extensive migration of this species alone and for several days in August, 1920, numbers of them could be seen over the meadows and cat-tail swamps all the way from Broadway to Cape May Point. Their small size—the smallest of our Swallows—and the blackish breast band which in flight seems to be broken in the middle, are their most striking character-istics. When lined up on the wires with other species these features are very conspicuous and the breast band is seen to be complete although narrowed in the center. This character will distinguish them from the occasional Rough-wings and the young Tree Swallows, the other two swallows with brown backs and wings.

Bank Swallows are frequently seen, during August, sailing over the sur-face of Lake Lily, as many as fifty having been counted there on August 3, 1921, and sometimes they are intimately associated with Chimney Swifts which also resort to the lake at this time. While we see them mainly back over the meadows some of them travel down the beach with the Barn Swallows. They have one trait which seems peculiar to the species; when they settle to rest, as they often do, in the shelter of the sand dunes, several of them will be observed picking up small pieces of grass and sedge stems etc. in their bills, and then laying them down again as they waddle a few steps this way and that, over the sand. This habit does not seem to be a search for food as no attempt is made to swallow any of the pieces nor can it at this season (August 3) be a nest building impulse. A pure white swal-low seen over the meadows on September 2, 1920, was identified as a Bank Swallow on account of its small size and association with many individuals of this species. Arrival dates of Bank Swallows from the north are as follows:

| | | | | | |
|---|---|---|---|---|---|
| 1920. | August 3. | 1925. | July 30. | 1930. | August 12. |
| 1921. | August 3. | 1926. | July 23. | 1931. | August 1. |
| 1922. | July 27. | 1927. | August 3. | 1933. | August 5. |
| 1923. | July 22. | 1928. | July 18. | 1935. | August 7. |
| | | 1929. | August 2. | | |

Last dates of observation are:

| | | | | | |
|---|---|---|---|---|---|
| 1920. | September 2. | 1923. | August 27. | 1927. | August 25. |
| 1921. | September 3. | 1925. | August 22. | 1932. | August 29. |
| 1922. | August 28. | 1926. | August 24. | 1935. | September 6. |

The Bank Swallow nests at various localities in the state but owing to the necessity for vertical sand banks, in which to drill its holes, it is decidedly local. There are several breeding colonies along the Delaware River above

Camden in one of which, at Delair, full sets of eggs have been found from May 22 to June 6. The nearest colony to Cape May seems to be in a gravel pit about one mile south of Bridgeton in Cumberland County. In June 1936, Julian Potter found about one hundred birds breeding there while in 1937, there were but seventy-five. He tells me that when the sand holes are not worked the tops of the banks cave in and the sides become sloping and the birds desert. Twenty years ago he found Bank Swallows abundant in glass sand pits near Vineland about ten miles to the east.

Like many purely transient species the Bank Swallow is by no means a common or characteristic bird of the Cape. It would seem to vary considerably in abundance and in three of the last sixteen years it was missed entirely. This however may be due to lack of constant observation immediately along the coast, for such continuous observation is necessary if we are to make an accurate record of its activities; most of the individuals that occur here are on the wing travelling rapidly down the shore line to winter-quarters in the far south.

## ROUGH-WINGED SWALLOW

Stelgidopteryx ruficollis serripennis (Audubon)

A few pairs of Rough-winged Swallows have been found nesting in holes in the bluff along the Bay shore below Town Bank during May of several years and doubtless occur there every spring. Rotten roots of trees, that have been exposed by the action of high tides during winter, fall out from the face of the sandy cliff and leave satisfactory nesting holes for the birds. Doubtless the first July Rough-wings that we see about Lake Lily, at the Point, come from there and also the scattered individuals that are seen in the swallow flights of August. On June 15, 1937, Julian Potter saw a pair of Rough-wings entering the bilge holes of the wrecked concrete boat at the end of the Cape May Point turnpike and it seemed likely that they were nesting there. The bird is here very close to the northern limit of its range and there cannot be many to migrate from the country to the north.

Most of our observations of this little swallow have been of family groups perched on the wires or dead tree tops in July or skimming over the waters of Lake Lily. One flock (July 22, 1923) consisted of ten individuals, perhaps two families, which were foraging over the upper end of the lake, keeping within an area of sixty by sixty feet and skimming the water slowly, directly in the face of the wind, and then drifting back to begin the advance all over again. They rested, three or four at a time, on dead bushes on the bank, all the while calling: *psud, psud, psud*. Another group of seven (July 16, 1927) consisted of two adults and five young. The latter rested on the wires and were fed by the parents which skimmed the lake for food. A third family of five was on the wires at the Point on July 5, 1932, while the earliest appearance was on June 30, 1935, an adult and five young.

All through the summer young birds can readily be distinguished from adults by the rich rust-colored edgings to the wing feathers and the slight brownish suffusion on the breast.

We have spring records at Cape May Point as follows:

| | | | |
|---|---|---|---|
| 1924. May 10. | 1927. April 30. | 1933. May 6. |
| 1926. May 1. | 1928. May 5. | 1934. May 12. |
| | 1932. April 24. | |

Our latest occurrences have been:

| | | |
|---|---|---|
| 1924. August 16. | 1927. August 26. | 1929. August 17. |
| 1925. August 18. | | 1931. August 18. |

William Rusling has recorded one on September 6, 1935.

Nests of the Rough-wing with sets of five and six eggs have been found at Palmyra, near Camden, on May 23 and 27, and the bird has been reported nesting as far north as Plainfield, Morristown, Summit, Paterson and High Knob.

## BARN SWALLOW

Hirundo erythrogaster Boddaert

The Barn Swallow is a common summer bird in the Cape May region and a conspicuous and abundant migrant during August and September, especially close along the ocean front where a few are sometimes passing south as late as November. They nest about all the farms in the upland and locally along the coast where suitable situations are to be found. At Schellenger's Landing, where numerous boathouses are clustered, many pairs of Barn Swallows nest every year and during May they may be seen flying in and out through the doors which open on the water, carrying building materials. They are early risers and I recall one mid-May morning as Walker Hand and I were leaving the Landing for a trip up the sounds at about three o'clock when we could hear the swallows calling all about us although it was still too dark to distinguish them. Wherever there are houses close to the shore, with sheds or other outbuildings that furnish acceptable shelter, a pair or two of Barn Swallows are usually to be found, as well as about isolated Coast Guard Stations or deserted summer cottages. Some also nest under the platforms leading to the boathouses at Wildwood Crest and at Stone Harbor, while a pair apparently had a nest for several years under a low stone culvert arch where Cape Island Creek formerly entered the town at Grant Street.

While living in a gunners' cabin out on the meadows back of Two Mile Beach in May, 1922, a few Barn Swallows flew past every day but they did not seem to be nesting in any of the similar shacks which dot the meadows, and which were perhaps too much exposed for their liking; they were evidently wide ranging individuals from some mainland colony like many others that I have seen foraging far out on the meadows.

Turner McMullen gives me the following list of nests examined by him on Seven Mile Beach where the birds nest in boathouses and under elevated boardwalks:

May 30, 1911, four eggs.
May 30, 1912, nest just begun.
May 26, 1929, five eggs.
June 15, 1930, three eggs.
June 18, 1922, four eggs.
June 24, 1928, five fledglings.
July 4, 1929, four half-grown young.
July 4, 1931, five eggs.
July 4, 1932, six eggs.

On June 15, 1937, Julian Potter saw Barn Swallows entering the cabin of the wrecked concrete boat in the Bay opposite Cape May Point and doubtless they nested there.

I saw a pair preparing to nest in a boathouse at Sea Isle City as early as May 9 and Richard Miller has found full sets of eggs on May 30, June 17, and June 20, in different years. On July 2, 1921, I found a nest with young on top of a beam in a small shed north of Schellenger's Landing, a favorite position for coastwise Barn Swallows, possibly because of the danger of disintegration, due to the humid atmosphere, of nests built in the usual style against the side of a wall or rafter. The parents of this family were coming in constantly with food and at intervals could be seen removing the white excrement sacs which they dropped about a hundred feet away. Another pair at Frank Dickinson's barn at Erma fed several large young in the nest on June 21, 1931, and apparently the same pair had another brood in the same place on August 9. Other pairs still had young in the boathouses as late as July 22, 1921, and Barn Swallows are to be seen there all through August.

Fledglings, conspicuous for their swollen yellow gapes and shorter less forked tails, appear on telegraph wires during early July—July 3, 1920; July 1, 1921; July 5, 1922; July 5, 1923; July 4, 1927; July 29, 1932; June 20, 1933; June 30, 1935. One family of four, perched on a wire near an unoccupied cottage at South Cape May, was being fed at intervals by the parents which were gathering food along the ditches of the adjacent meadows As a parent approached with food all of the young fluttered their wings anxiously and one of them usually launched into the air but it seemed always to be one of the others that got the food. They all opened their mouths wide and uttered cries of a single syllable. When the excitement was at its height the other parent often flew up and sometimes two other adults which had been feeding in the vicinity. The commotion over for the time being, the young plumed themselves and stretched their wings to their fullest extent, first one and then the other, until they reached beyond the tip of the tail. Sometimes the young birds will perch on bayberry bushes and once I saw one fed while on the wing.

On July 2, 1923, a family of five young rested on a bare sandy spot on the Fill, one on a low weed, the others directly on the ground, where they were fed by the parents with much fluttering and elevation of wings. On

July 8, 1932, there were several young on the wing near the same spot and one adult repeatedly flew close to my head calling *sheep* as she fairly brushed my cheek with her wing. I could find no young on the ground or bushes and her concern seemed to be for the birds in the air. On June 24, 1924, the entire boathouse colony rallied to attack a Fish Crow which had unwittingly alighted on a nearby post and drove him from the neighborhood.

The flight of the Barn Swallow is marvellously accurate, swift and graceful, and apparently is effected with a minimum of effort. As a rule they fly lower than other swallows, frequently just skimming the ground or the top of the meadow grass, and with just enough wing action to keep them going and to steady them as they tilt now to the right, now to the left, on their drifting, gliding way, often reminding one of a lot of wind blown leaves rather than birds which are consciously directing their flight. Their favorite position is not over two to four feet from the ground but occasionally one will throw its body up into the wind and after a rise and momentary pause will shear off again on another tack and glide away as before. Often they will select some piece of roadway as their feeding ground, skimming back and forth only a few inches from the surface and their habit of flying immediately in front of an automobile proves fatal to many a Barn Swallow, in spite of the efforts of the driver to avoid them. I have sometimes seen single birds follow a path across a field for a hundred yards without deviating from the straight line.

Fields of cut hay furnish attractive feeding grounds for Barn Swallows and here, with Martins and Chimney Swifts for companions, they will gather in numbers, whirling in intricate evolutions. Sometimes where there are swarms of gnats in the air many Barn Swallows will gather in a surprisingly small area to feed upon them and I once saw fifty so engaged in a space not over fifteen feet square. The gauzy wings of the flies flashed in the sunlight and made them very conspicuous, so that it was possible to see the birds snap them up as they passed and repassed in a maze of flight.

On August 13, 1928, I came upon a mass of Barn Swallows concentrated over a patch of short grass on the meadows above the Point which varied their usual method of feeding by darting down continually to snap up some sort of insect, and on July 23, 1934, there were a great many scouring some fields near the Court House where swarms of voracious strawberry flies made progress by humans almost impossible. The swallows were snapping up the flies right and left. Again on August 2, 1934, an old wheat field near Cold Spring, the crop of which had proved a failure, was plowed up and a host of birds assembled to feed on the scattered grain and the insects turned up by the plow. Killdeers, Red-wings, Robins and even Kingbirds were present at the feast and a number of Barn Swallows found some small flying insects to their liking and flew around over the backs of the other birds or rested temporarily on the upturned clods of earth.

At rest on the wires Barn Swallows, like other swallows, have a habit of stretching the wing straight out from the shoulder and so short is the upper arm that it appears as if the long flight feathers arose from close to the shoulder of the bird. They also stretch the wing to full length out past the tip of the tail, spreading the tail feathers on that side simultaneously. They sometimes open the mouth in a wide gape or yawn and will scratch the head with the foot leaning the head back over the shoulder in the accomplishment.

I have seen Barn Swallows during May resting on the muddy shores of Cape Island Creek and in plowed fields gathering mud for their nests and have noticed them in early July, when still feeding young in the nest, alight on the ground to pick up food washed up on the edge of the meadows and even fly out on the sea beach and alight along the high water mark to catch the flies that gather about the ocean refuse left by the waves. They alight on the ground, too, at times of strong wind apparently exhausted by their efforts to keep on the wing under such conditions. I have seen spring migrants resting thus in plowed fields and waddling on their short legs to get to the shelter of clods of earth or tufts of grass, as the small sandpipers do on the meadows during a gale. On July 10, 1921, many Barn Swallows gathered on the side of a railroad embankment for protection from a strong wind, while on July 1, 1922, they settled on a gravel road on the edge of the town in the lee of a thick hedge. On August 9, 1920, during a heavy southwest wind numbers of Barn Swallows collected on a sand flat below South Cape May and skimming the surface of the ground came to rest continually, one at a time, until they covered a considerable area. They acted individually in taking wing and settling again and never all flushed at once. Again in April, 1919, they assembled in the same way in a field by the Cape May Point turnpike where once again they were protected from the wind by a hedge. They were so loath to leave or so exhausted that one could approach to within a few feet of them before they would take wing. On September 2, 1920, many migrant Barn Swallows settled on the sloping roof of a cottage below South Cape May and lay close to the shingles on the side away from the wind; later they flew down to the nearby sand flat and settled there, all heads to the wind, looking exactly like the scattered black and gray oyster shells that were strewn over the ground.

When most of the young are on the wing the Barn Swallows of the upland begin to collect in flocks, feeding together and resting on the roofs of the larger barns. On one barn at Fishing Creek, on July 24, 1923, I counted seventy-five birds, mostly young, and on a nearby house on August 19, about 150. Such assemblages prepare the way for the great southward movement along the coast, which is so characteristic of August. Indeed some of the later gatherings are doubtless migrating birds from farther north pausing to rest, such as a flock of fifty seen on a clump of poplar sprouts on the Fill on August 7, 1923, fluttering as they clustered there until they seemed to be only part of the quivering foliage; and the long lines, sometimes 150 together, which throng the wires at Cape May Point late in the summer.

Barn Swallows migrate by day and the flight at Cape May seems to be mainly confined to the immediate vicinity of the sea beach while most of the birds pass within a strip one hundred yards wide. I have recorded the movement in progress by:

| | | | | | |
|---|---|---|---|---|---|
| 1920. | August 5. | 1925. | August 9. | 1929. | August 17. |
| 1922. | August 3. | 1926. | July 23. | 1932. | July 28. |
| 1923. | August 4. | 1927. | August 3. | 1933. | July 26. |
| 1924. | July 18. | 1928. | August 13. | 1935. | August 8. |

The major part of the flight always occurs before noon. The birds often fly only a few inches above the strand and rarely over six feet. Their course is somewhat erratic, drifting right and left and sometimes tacking back again for a few yards but the general progress southward is steady and rapid. During one of the August flights I stationed myself back on the meadows below South Cape May, some fifty yards from the dunes, where I had a clear view all the way to the sea. Apparently all the Barn Swallows were passing in front of me and selecting a definite line of bushes as a base I counted the birds as they passed it and the average was seventy per minute. Again on August 27, 1926, I counted the swallows that passed along the dunes and beach and the average was forty-six per minute and, so far as I could see, the flight continued at this rate for the better part of the morning and part of the afternoon, although there may have been breaks or pauses in the stream.

On August 24, 1927, I followed the flight all the way to the Bay shore and in spite of a strong northwest wind the birds kept right on, dropping from the higher elevation that they had assumed in crossing the pine covered area of the Point and flying close to the waves, so close in fact that they seemed in imminent danger of being washed under. They seemed to head directly for Cape Henlopen, but on August 1, 1932, they left the coast nearly opposite the Lighthouse.

On several occasions the birds paused on arriving at the Point and lined the telegraph wires, but never in the numbers of the Tree Swallows. On August 26, 1921, I counted eighty-five near the Lighthouse; there were 160 on August 26, 1920, and 150 on August 31, 1925. In the first of these assemblages there were two Tree Swallows and frequently a few Barn Swallows are found in large gatherings of the latter species but for the most part the two remain separate. On August 17, 1920, for instance, an immense host of Tree Swallows had gathered at the Point but there were no Barn Swallows with them although out over the beach the latter were passing steadily southward.

I have referred in my notes to the southward flight as "streaming" or "pouring" down the beach and that is the impression one gets of it. On one day I estimated that one hundred birds were in sight at once and again that upon looking ahead at any minute twenty or more would be in the immediate range of vision. On one or two occasions there was a definite flight across the Fill following the line taken by certain shore birds which coincides with the edge of old Cape Island Sound, which was filled in thirty years ago, and this may be the regular flight line here although on Seven Mile Beach it is along the ocean strand as it is between Cape May and the Point.

On some evenings, during the southward migration, a certain number of Barn Swallows went into the Purple Martin roost which existed at the time on Washington Street, sometimes only two or three and at other times a considerable number. On August 8, 1924, at least 250 gathered and swirled about over the trees, just as the Martins do, and again on August 20 and 21, 1926, there were several hundred present which kept more or less to themselves both in their aërial evolutions and when roosting on the wires. They were later than the Martins in arriving and were the last birds to go into the roost. The northward flight in spring is by no means so conspicuous as the southward migration and it seems possible that the birds do not follow the coast at this season, with the exception of those that summer here. On May 10, 1924, however, there was an exceptional flight. It was a raw cloudy day and the Barn Swallows were as abundant over the beach as in August and curiously enough they were flying south with a strong northeast wind! They would gather on dead snags sticking up on the edge of the meadows while some took refuge on the ground. Others were attracted by a flock of Semipalmated Sandpipers which were endeavoring to walk on the soft mud of a shallow pond and flew close down over them.

The average date of arrival of the Barn Swallow in spring, according to the records kept by Walker Hand from 1901 to 1920, is April 20, while in the eight succeding years my average is April 23.

In the autumn individuals continue to drift down the beach long after they have disappeared from the upland and we have a number of records for November, usually of single birds—November 11, 1921; November 12, 1922; November 16, 1924; November 25, 1928; November 7, 1931; November 14 and 15, 1935. William Rusling recorded 1500 passing the Point on August 26, 1935; 2520 on August 30; 1500 on September 9; with smaller numbers for later and intermediate dates. My latest date is a single bird seen on December 1, 1923. They are widely distributed summer residents throughout New Jersey.

The color of the breast in the adult Barn Swallow varies greatly and I have noticed, in the lines of birds on the wires during the August flight, some in which the breast was almost white and others in which it was deep rusty. There is no molt so far as I have been able to detect before the southward migration and all adults retain the long outer tail feathers until they depart, although the tips are often broken off.

While the Barn Swallow does not exhibit the spectacular massing that we see in the Martin and the Tree Swallow, to one who appreciates what is going on, its steady streaming down the coast, without pause or evident destination, is no less impressive, while the home life of the swallows about our farmhouses is a delightful feature of the bird life of the Cape.

## CLIFF SWALLOW

Petrochelidon albifrons albifrons (Rafinesque)

A few Cliff Swallows apparently pass through Cape May every year on both the northern and southern migration, occurring in late April and May and again in August, the south-bound birds being usually young of the year. In August they are usually stray individuals in flights of Tree Swallows or Barn Swallows. I saw one on the western edge of the town on August 7 and another on September 3, 1920, the latter our only September record. An adult bird was seen on the telegraph wires at Cape May Point on August 15 and 16, 1921, in a flock of some three hundred Tree Swallows; while on August 26 one was found sailing back and forth over Lake Lily with other swallows. On August 24 and 25, 1927, I saw a young bird resting on a wire fence at the Point which allowed me to approach to within six feet of it. The top of its head was dull glossy green, back of head and neck dull gray in strong contrast, and there was a bluish black spot under the chin. The forehead and cheeks were chestnut and the rump reddish buff.

In spring the Cliff Swallows seem to occur in small groups by themselves and do not mix with the other species. Julian Potter saw six on April 23, 1922, and Richard Miller ten on May 13, 1923, while the Delaware Valley Club has recorded a pair near the Point on May 30, 1924. I saw two pairs at the Lighthouse Pond on May 13, 1928, and several pairs flying over the fields just back of the town on May 24 to 27, 1892. The lateness of these records might indicate nesting in the immediate vicinity, at least in the past, but we have no positive evidence.

The present day rarity of the bird at Cape May may be indicated by the fact that we have but eighteen records in the past eighteen years. In recent years the Cliff Swallow has very definitely lost ground in New Jersey, for some reason or other, and as demonstrated by B. S. Bowdish (Auk, 1930, pp. 189–193) its breeding range in the state is now restricted to a few barns in Passaic County, while it has become much scarcer as a migrant elsewhere. It would seem probable that the breeding birds pass south along the Delaware Valley rather than down the coast. It is today a rare bird anywhere in the East except in some of the mountainous districts.

The buff rump patch, paler in the adult, is the best identification mark but the bird has a peculiar habit of turning the head upward and mounting with vigorous beats of the wing for some feet and then shearing off on a long downward sail. They also skim the surface of Lake Lily and the Lighthouse Pond and on all of these performances the light rump is conspicuously displayed.

## PURPLE MARTIN

Progne subis subis (Linnaeus)

PLATE 105, p. 695

With the possible exception of the Laughing Gull, the Purple Martin is the most characteristic bird of Cape May. Though always local in its distribution it is much more abundant in the coastal plain region of New Jersey than in the upland country farther inland where Martin colonies are few and far between. To many visitors to the Cape, therefore, Martins are quite as much of a novelty as are the birds of the sea.

As usual the Cape May Martins occupy nesting boxes erected especially for their accommodation on poles in yards and gardens. Some of these are quite pretentious affairs with many compartments, low projecting roofs and broad porches; others are more modest structures housing only two or three pairs, while the house most popular with the birds, to judge by its many tenants, was an aggregation of old wooden boxes partitioned off into sections with suitable openings cut in them. Unfortunately this commodious residence was taken down by its owner some years ago and the nesting Martin population was thereby sadly decreased. From careful estimates in recent years there have not been more than fifty pairs of Martins breeding in Cape May while colonies farther up the peninsula are mainly at Dennisville, Court House and other towns and villages, doubtless because only in these places have nesting boxes been erected. The dates for first arrival of

Martins at Cape May, mainly from the records of Walker Hand, are as follows:

| | | | | | |
|---|---|---|---|---|---|
| 1902. | May 2. | 1912. | April 3. | 1923. | April 22. |
| 1903. | April 8. | 1913. | April 12. | 1924. | April 3. |
| 1904. | April 1. | 1914. | April 17. | 1925. | April 8. |
| 1905. | March 27. | 1915. | April 12. | 1926. | April 11. |
| 1906. | April 4. | 1916. | April 14. | 1927. | April 24. |
| 1907. | April 25. | 1918. | April 16. | 1928. | April 1. |
| 1908. | April 18. | 1919. | April 6. | 1931. | April 19. |
| 1909. | April 11. | 1920. | April 14. | 1932. | April 10. |
| 1910. | April 10. | 1921. | April 24. | 1933. | April 20. |
| 1911. | April 6. | 1922. | April 23. | 1934. | April 15. |

In 1924 I saw the first birds for that year, one perched on the railing of the deserted board walk and a pair on one of the nesting boxes on Lafayette Street. The early comers not infrequently make an inspection of the box and then disappear for a few days, or perhaps are replaced by others, and it may be well on in the month before they become permanently established. Even then they may be loath to begin nesting operations until assured that the weather is favorable and as late as April 30, in 1923, I have seen a number of the birds huddled together on the porch of a nesting box, trying to keep warm in the face of a strong, cold wind. May and June are occupied with the nesting and during the period of incubation the females stay pretty closely indoors while the males perch, during part of the day, on nearby wires or tree tops, or even on the porches of the boxes, though they are mainly occupied in sailing about overhead or skimming the marshes in search of food. They do not, however, seem to wander very far afield at this time. The females are also seen occasionally, especially toward evening, feeding over the meadows, leaving the nesting box precipitately and entering immediately upon their return. Males have been seen to enter the compartments at this time but whether to relieve the females I could not be sure. There may be a harsh note or two of greeting as the birds arrive or depart but the general quiet that prevails is in strong contrast to the bedlam of a few weeks later when the young begin to appear.

The Martin on the wing is deserving of careful study: a glorified swallow, he is a perfect master of the air and his flight is at all times a wonderfully graceful performance. I stood on the edge of the meadows, one day in June, while twelve males were skimming the tops of the salt grass, tilting now to this side now to that to maintain their balance in the air. Now one of them turns in his course and passes close to my head, swift as an arrow and uncanny in his blackness, which has no relieving spot of white, not even on the belly where most birds are lighter in color. His call uttered either in greeting or protest as he passes is a harsh *zhupe, zhupe*. Again he will mount upward with rapid strokes of his narrow pointed wings only to return again to the lower level on a long sloping sail. Sometimes at the very summit of the ascent he will come about into the wind and remain stationary, on rapidly beating wings, before sliding away on the long downward sail.  When flying high over the town, late in the summer, the Martins' mastery of the air is particularly noticeable.  They come in against the wind on set wings like small three-cornered kites, steadying themselves now and then with two or three short wingbeats, and then, apparently tiring of the sport, they will drop through considerable distances and, flapping rapidly, regain their former altitude.  While Martins flying low over the meadows are undoubtedly engaged in seeking food many of their aërial evolutions, like those of other expert flyers, seem to be for the shear joy of flight.  Certainly they can find no food far out over the sea where we not infrequently see them as we walk along the beach, and the wonderful mass flight at roosting time has nothing to do with food.  On July 29, 1916, too, I watched a single Martin associated with a band of Swifts maintaining a position directly over Congress Hall hotel, in the face of a strong south wind, for at least half an hour.  The birds would often remain absolutely stationary in the air for several minutes at a time, evidently supported by the upward currents of air deflected by the walls of the building.  Here was no search for food but some sort of enjoyment or play.

On June 29, 1920, and on several occasions before the young took wing, I noticed Martins, usually old males, coming down to the sea beach.  They came regularly to the high water mark at the edge of the wet sand and picked up food of some sort, probably insects washed up by the waves.  They waddled about in a clumsy fashion, as they often do on the porches of their houses, taking a few steps but remaining stationary most of the time, picking up whatever happened to be within reach.  They would fly down in the face of a strong wind off the water and sail on set wings until their feet would touch the sand, sometimes poising in the air a foot above the beach for a moment or two.  Again on July 6, 1921, I saw them sailing low down over the dunes just before sunset, catching insects of some sort but not alighting on the strand.  On August 10, 1922, a large number of Martins settled on the golf links and apparently fed on some sort of small insect but this was a very unusual occurrence.

When the young are hatched excitement in the Martin colony increases daily.  The parents are now continually scouring the meadows for food and are constantly arriving at the boxes or taking their departure, all of their movements accompanied by harsh challenges which are later mingled with the shriller calls of the young, as they become strong enough to stick their heads out of the entrances, or waddle boldly out onto the porches. Some young, at this time, are often crowded off onto the ground which adds to the excitement, as the parents swoop over them calling loudly. On July 17, 1922, the porches were full of young and I could see that both males and females fed them but only one young bird was fed on each trip. Young birds are seen poking their heads out of the entrance holes during the first week of July and by about the 20th of the month the first broods leave the boxes, the actual dates for the years 1920–1928 when I first saw the young away from the boxes being July 23, 21, 25, 12, 24, 20, 28, 27, and 25 respectively. By the end of the month all have departed and a strange stillness settles down over the once noisy nest boxes.

The families of young, accompanied by their parents, now take up positions on telegraph wires or on dead tree tops close to the feeding grounds on the meadows. The young seem to be able to fly fairly well as soon as they leave the boxes, as on July 26, 1920, I noticed a late brood being fed by their parents near the box, which upon my approach took wing and followed the old birds with only a suggestion of uncertainty in their flight.

On the wires the young birds sit very erect at first and are evidently not sure of their balance, their legs are spread wide apart and their tarsi are clearly seen from the ground below, as they hold their bodies clear from the perch. As the parents bring in food to the family on the wires there is much excitement, fluttering of wings and loud conversation. The young call *choop, choop*, and the females have a similar note which is sometimes doubled into *choop-choop*, while the old black males constantly cut in with their harsh rasping *zheee, zhudge, zhudge-zhudge-zhudge;* or again, *zhupe, zhupe, zhee-zhee-zhee*, a peculiar quality for a bird voice; almost guttural. When, as was usually the case, all called at once there was quite an uproar and when an intruder approached the whole family took wing in great and voluble excitement and passed on a little farther, alighting on the wires as before.

The increase of families of young on the wires and tree tops is noticeable during the last week of July, and the birds are more widely spread over the country than at any time earlier in the year. The young have a frosted appearance due to the grayish edgings to the feathers and to the presence of down, while their throats are paler, which serves to distinguish them from the old females.

I witnessed the feeding of the young in the air on several occasions and apparently they are induced to take wing in this way either intentionally or through the desire for food. As the young one would approach its parent in the air they would flutter up to one another, make the transfer of food, and then drift away again, the young one often returning to the wire. Several times I have seen an adult bring a large dragonfly in to its young as it perched expectantly on a wire and ram it down the wide open mouth. The insect with a body and wings three inches in length is forced head first down the throat while the young bird gulps spasmodically again and again, in an effort to swallow the meal, and often one will be found standing particularly erect with the tips of the dragonfly's harsh, rough wings protruding from either side of its broad mouth. The old Martins frequently follow closely after the flying dragonflies and once one of them in headlong pursuit of a flying cicada almost struck me in the face.

The dead tree tops are now the favorite resting places for the young and they return to them after their first foraging trips, and there the parents continute to feed them for some time longer. One young bird, roosting in such a situation, was seen to sidle along a branch toward a female that had just alighted, evidently in the hope of securing food. It moved its feet sideways, one at a time, and I have seen them do the same thing when shifting their position on a telegraph wire.

As soon as the young are able to secure their own food the Martins begin to disappear during the daytime and there will be many a day in August when not a single individual can be found between Cape May and the Point. Young and old sometimes return to the nesting boxes after they have left and roost there for a short time. On July 25, 1920, about 6:30 p. m., I noticed a number of Martins flying about one of the boxes and on August 6 following, early in the morning, some of the boxes were covered with roosting birds but this was probably due to heavy rains which had prevailed the night before and prevented the usual flight to distant feeding grounds.

I have seen Martins at sunset skimming back and forth over the sand dunes along the coast, apparently after insects while at Lake Lily on August 1, 1932, five hundred of them were assembled on the wires and every few minutes detachments sailed down over the water and dipped their bills to the surface apparently drinking.

The activities of nesting time and the care of the young, interesting as they are, fall far short of the spectacular performances incident to the roosting of the Martins in August and early September. Cape May has been fortunate in having in its immediate vicinity a roost of notable proportions and of long years standing. For many years it was located on the Physick property on the principal street of the town. Here there is a grove of silver maples about thirty feet in height and covering an area of some two acres, growing so close together that their tops join one another, making a dense canopy with constant shade. Extended grounds, screened from the public and supporting other trees and shrubbery, afford protection to the roosting birds. Between the grove and the sea beach, half a mile away, was formerly a stretch of salt meadow which has for thirty years past been converted into a slightly elevated tract of sandy brush-covered ground, known as the "Fill," and across its level surface the roost stands out conspicuously.

This roosting place was later abandoned in favor of other nearby locations as explained below and in 1936 the birds apparently deserted Cape May entirely as a roosting spot as no trace of a roost could be found anywhere in the county. The following account was prepared when the roost on the Physic property was at the height of its activity and it seems hardly worth while to alter it from the present to the past tense especially as the erratic birds may at any time return to their former haunts.

Here for some twenty years on every night during late July, August and early September, there gathered great flocks of Martins, Grackles, Robins, Cowbirds, English Sparrows and a few Red-wings, and in later seasons an increasing horde of Starlings. The Sparrows come in first, then the Grackles in compact flocks take up their position in the trees, next come the mixed flocks of Cowbirds and Red-wings, and close-packed bands of the Starlings glad of company and ever ready to mix into any assemblage of birds without inquiring into its character. The Robins come next in small detachments or singly, although many young Robins may be found feeding on the ground below the trees early in the evening. Finally come the Martins which outnumber all the rest together.

Were it not for this roost, the only one in South Jersey so far as I know, Martin history at Cape May would come to a close early in August when the last of the fledglings become self dependent and sail away with their parents. But as it is, though there may be many days in August when practically no Martins are to be found for miles around Cape May from sunrise to sunset, they will gather in ever increasing numbers to pass the night in this small grove which, so far as our eyes can detect, offers no advantages over hundreds of similar groves past which the birds must have flown. It would seem that most of these Martins must have come from areas far to the north of New Jersey, as the local breeding Martins could not have yielded such a crop of young. I estimate that there are not more than fifty pairs of the birds in Cape May and perhaps twice that number elsewhere in the peninsula and these hundred and fifty pairs could not produce more than six hundred offspring, making some nine hundred Martins in all, and yet at least 15,000 of the birds come to Cape May every night to roost. In the New York area, including northern New Jersey, Ludlow Griscom states that the Martin colonies are very locally distributed and that the birds are rare as transients, which further complicates the question of where our Martins come from! Another fact of interest is that on July 23, 1926, before any of the young had left the Cape May nesting boxes one thousand Martins had already assembled at the roost.

We have no means of ascertaining whether the same birds gather in the roost night after night, with constant additions to their ranks, and then pass southward when weather conditions seem favorable, or whether individuals are arriving and departing every day. Possibly the roost gathers all the Martins that pass south along the New Jersey coast and is maintained with the same personnel throughout the summer, until the entire assemblage leaves together early in September. There is undoubtedly some fluctuation in the number of birds present on different nights, and this might indicate that individual Martins remained in the roost only a few days, but on the other hand the evident familiarity with the roosting place would suggest that the same birds were present for the greater part of the summer. A curious feature is that, during the height of the roosting, Martins are exceedingly scarce about Cape May during the day and although I have traveled some miles to the north and west I have been unable to find any of the birds or locate any possible feeding grounds. Nevertheless at the approach of evening, at almost the same hour, night after night, they come to the roost by thousands from we know not where and almost always against the wind. It has been suggested that they fly very high, beyond the range of our vision, but it is hardly likely that any insect food could be found at such an altitude. In support of such a theory I must admit that on two occasions, August 28, 1928, and August 10, 1921, they did come to the roost at such an altitude that they looked like mere specks in the sky, while on August 14, 1932, a large number of Martins that had remained on the telegraph wires at Cape May Point until noon, took wing and at once ascended until nearly out of sight. These birds however may have been completing or beginning a long migratory movement.

As early as June 25 Martins have been observed going into the roost but these must have been either barren or non-breeding birds. They included both males and females and gathered on the wires opposite the roost and resorted to the upper branches of the maple trees at dusk. There were six on July 2, 1921; thirty on July 5, 1922; one hundred on July 9, 1922; a like number on July 4, 1923; twenty on July 10, 1924; fifty on July 5, 1925. The numbers present each night increased and fluctuated during the remainder of the month. Since the young Martins of the local colonies do not leave their boxes until about July 20 it is obvious that these roosting birds were not local breeders unless some of the males desert their families during the night. As the season advances the number of roosting birds increases steadily although it is usually August 10 before a really characteristic roosting occurs. The years 1925 and 1926 were exceptions, however, and we had an assemblage of at least 1000 birds on July 26 and July 23 respectively. Counts of the early gatherings indicate that there are about four females (or possibly un-molted young) to one black adult male.

On clear nights the birds come in a little before sunset heading straight for the roost, with their long powerful wing strokes carrying them directly into the wind, and so long as the twilight lasts they perform their remarkable evolutions over the tree tops or the streets of the town, preparatory to resting for the night.

My records show that the first arrivals may settle directly on the roosting trees, on isolated trees in the neighborhood, preferably those with dead tops, or on telegraph wires or the roofs of houses. Then, on some impulse or other, they all rise in the air and circle about overhead gradually dropping back again to their perches. As their numbers increase the repeated risings are like regular explosions of birds and as the whole mass goes circling—or "milling" as it is called, round and round high above the roost it resembles an immense swarm of bees. Finally the birds narrow their orbit with successive circles until they pour down into the tree tops in a great cyclonic cloud and as darkness creeps on they settle for the night. As one enters the grounds the chatter of the thousands of birds makes a great buzzing like the rush of water and if, on some impulse, they again arise in flight the rush of wings, to one standing immediately below, sounds like the crash of some great tree falling in the forest.

I have further details of the roosting during several seasons. On August 11, 1921, the Martins began to gather about 6:10 p. m. on the wires at various points near the roost, and by 7:00 the entire assemblage, numbering probably five hundred birds, had retired to the trees. A bunch of one hundred or more would circle about, drop in, and then take wing again, and spread out widely making a great circle 250 yards in diameter. Sometimes they would return to the wires for a few minutes and then swing around again to the roost. Part of the gathering would be milling regularly and the other detachments passing over the trees in a much larger circuit. On August 20, of the same year, there was an immense gathering, the largest of the summer. Up to 6:15 p. m. there were but a few individuals flying about overhead, but from sunset at 6:45 to dark at 7:15, the great flight arrived from the northeast. They came out of the gloom and haze, far away above Schellenger's Landing, and stretched out over both the meadows and the Fill. None came from the west or south, the wind being from the southwest. There was a continuous scattered flight augmented every now and then by a dense stream of birds, as if a great number had been suddenly liberated from some enclosure. Toward the end of the flight there would be a lull and then definite flocks would come in flying low. These late comers did not mill around like the early flight but plunged directly into the roost. At Schellenger's Landing the birds would pause and line the telegraph wires, doubtless tired by their long flight and in need of rest. Then they would rise all together and pass on to the roost. A few Barn Swallows were with them. On the 25th the wind was from the east and the birds all came in from the west. On the 26th there were absolutely no Martins in sight all day and I covered the country all the way to the Bay shore, yet at 6:00 p. m. they gathered by thousands at the Physick place, from where I could not determine, as I failed to see them arrive. The ground below the trees was by this time white with their droppings.

"August 30. Scattered birds present this morning but only a few. The wind was from the south and between 6:15 and 6:40 p. m. a great steady flight came in from the north. The birds alighted on the wires at the Landing for a few minutes and then passed on making a sudden congestion in the flight. Over the roost they appeared like a swarm of bees, or gnats, whirling round and round. Part of them had settled on the branches by 6:00 p. m. but the bulk did not go in until about 6:30. It became dark before 7 o'clock.

"August 29, 1922. There was a light southwest wind and the Martins began to gather very high over the roost by 5:30 p. m., descending to a lower level as their numbers increased. By 6:30 there were about six thousand over the Physick grove and probably two thousand farther out over the meadows to the west. They formed a huge maze like an immense flock of mosquitos and now and then about one third of the flock would veer off in a sudden surge to the right or left and back again, until finally the flying mass resolved itself into an irregular oval of moving birds. By 6:45 the flock had come down closer to the tree tops and great detachments began dropping into the roost like birds that had been shot and were falling to earth. By 7:00 p. m., the last individual had retired and there was a continuous hissing sound pervading the whole grove. In the morning there was scarcely a Martin to be seen.

"August 30. There was again a large gathering, but the birds came in suddenly and pitched down in large flocks, all within a few minutes, so that none was to be seen on the wing after 6:30.

"August 14, 1923. Great masses of Martins gathered on the wires on Madison Street below the roost and on Lafayette Street opposite. They seemed to occupy first the cross bars of the telegraph poles, and then to line the wires, all facing the wind and sitting as close together as possible. Some of them plumed themselves and stretched their wings one at a time down behind their bodies, while all of them raised and lowered their tails to balance themselves against the wind. By 6:00 p. m. they had all left the wires and the entire mass of birds was over the roost whirling about in a great irregular circle, large flocks pitch down into the trees and hundreds of birds on set wings sail slowly into the wind; suddenly something disturbs those already in the roost and the grove seems fairly to boil over with birds. Then they settle once more and all is quiet.

"August 15. Not a Martin was seen all day and by 5:45 p. m. none had arrived and I began to think that they had gone south when, far away over the golf links to the southwest, a few scattered birds came into view winging their way against the northeast wind, and immediately across the whole southwestern sky they appeared in a great scattered swarm, those in the rear mere specks on the horizon. They swerved about when over the roost and pitched straight down into the trees with no resting on the wires and no preliminary evolutions. The suddenness of their arrival and the short time required to settle in the trees were remarkable. Doubtless their progress had been delayed by the force of the wind." On August 26, occurred the largest roosting of the year 1923 and I estimated that there were at least 15,000 Martins present. On Madison Street they filled nine sections of telegraph wires, six strands wide, until the wires sagged perceptibly between the poles; the birds, with a very few exceptions, faced the wind which came from the northeast and they sat as closely as possible to one another. Suddenly, and with no apparent cause, the entire assemblage poured off of the wires close down over our heads with a great whir of wings, beating their way about fifty yards to windward and then drifting back again, they once more lined the wires. Some of them perched on the top of a nearby smokestack and its guy wires, as well as on the roofs of the houses. Once more they take wing and whirl close over our heads until we become dizzy as we gazed at the maze of moving wings, which like a black snow storm swept over the roost. When directly above us the impression was that the sky itself was in motion.

By counting the birds on one section of wires, and multiplying by the number of sections, one could form a pretty accurate estimate of the number present and tonight this showed four thousand on Madison Street, six thousand on Lafayette Street and at least five thousand in or over the roost. They seem to enjoy close quarters, like most birds of flocking tendencies, and would crowd onto a wire already apparently full in preference to making use of an adjoining wire which was still empty. Needless to say the sidewalks below the wires were all splashed with excrement and walking there was dangerous!

On September 4 it was cloudy and the Martins came to the roost early and by 4:30 they were all whirling high above the tree tops. Then they gathered in several tall silver poplars at the golf club, settling on the twigs and branches until the whole foliage appeared black, while their calls produced a constant twittering like escaping steam, now swelling loudly and then dying away again. When they crossed to the roost they went out in a great wave and the trees seemed to fairly belch forth Martins in a band forty feet wide, which continued long after one would have thought that all had flown. They swirled round and round on a great oval course mounting into the air until they seemed no larger than flies. None used the wires tonight.

In 1924, the flight of August 28 was notable. By 6:00 p. m., there were not over twenty Martins in sight. The Grackles, Red-wings, English Sparrows and Robins went into the roost and finally at 6:30 came the Martins all from the southwest like minute specks high up in the sky. The swarm of birds poured into the grove until 6:50 and by 7:00 all was quiet. The sun had set as a great red ball over the Bay at 6:30 and by the time the birds had retired darkness had settled down over the landscape. There was no preliminary gathering tonight and the birds milled around in a great surging swarm which constantly poured down into the trees like a huge funnel or the tail of a cyclone.

On September 1 the cyclone effect, as the birds entered the roost, was again marked. They seemed very nervous and again and again they rose from the trees to circle once more, so that it was quite dark before the last ones were settled for the night.

When thunder storms occurred at roosting time the birds acted differently and frequently came in earlier than usual, while on days of continuous rain they lined the wires early in the morning and remained there the greater part of the day. Whether they spent the night on the wires in preference to the tree tops I was not able to determine. On August 8, 1922, there was a heavy downpour of rain at roosting time and the birds gathered on the wires to the number of about seven hundred and later the whole assemblage coursed low over the golf links apparently feeding on some sort of insects. On August 12, during a northeaster there were 975 Martins lined up on the wires all day; and on August 27, under similar conditions there were 1900 on the wires at 6:00 a. m., but as the rain moderated they left and returned as usual at 5:00 p. m. to roost in the grove. On August

17, 1923, there was rain all afternoon and the birds began to come in to the wires by 2:00 p. m., until they numbered about five thousand.  They rested there until time to repair to the roost.  On September 2, 1924, just at the time that they usually assemble, a thunderstorm broke over the town and a south wind, which had prevailed all day, changed to a gale from the northeast, the direction of the storm center.  The birds were much bewildered and poised on set wings over the houses in broad columns, facing the wind. They did not seem able to circle in the usual fashion but gradually drifted into the roost.

When the time for their departure approaches there will be an evening when the Martins will appear in very much reduced numbers, many of them having apparently gone south after they left the roost in the morning.  After that each evening brought a smaller number of the birds until the last stragglers were recorded.  My dates for these are as follows; sometimes only a single bird:

| 1902. | September 6. | 1924. | September 15. | 1927. | September 11. |
| 1921. | September 8. | 1925. | September 3. | 1928. | September 8. |
| 1923. | September 15. | 1926. | September 11. | | |

In 1928, while some Martins made use of the roost, there were not more than two thousand present on any night during July or August and it was evident that there had been some change in their roosting habits.  Next year the conditions were similar but the birds coming into the Physick grove had still further decreased.  On August 22 I discovered large numbers of Martins circling over the bayberry thickets on the Fill, half a mile east of the roost, which had grown up in the past few years until they formed a dense "forest" eight to ten feet high.  In 1930 the birds were going through the same evolutions over the bayberry thicket.  Many of the Starlings and Grackles gathered first in the old roost on the Physick property and then crossed over to the bayberry roost all together.  It was discovered late in the summer that there was still another roosting place, a tract of woodland in West Cape May.  Thousands of Martins and Starlings and quite a number of Grackles repaired to this spot every night, and the bayberry roost on the Fill, as well as the original roost, were deserted.  The West Cape May woods being off the main road, with no convenient wires upon which to assemble, the birds came directly to the trees from gathering points at more remote spots but they went through the usual circular flights and other aërial activities, just as they had done over the Physick grove.  They used this roost during the summers of 1931, 1932 and 1933.

During the maintenance of the roost in the Physick grove the Martins used to assemble at Schellenger's Landing, at the old farm at the end of Mill Lane, and elsewhere, from which they would repair to the roost just before dark.  Similar gatherings now occurred nightly on the wires along the Bay Shore Road at its crossing with the Higbee's Beach Road, and at Cape May Point, and several thousand birds would assemble there nightly preparatory to the flight to West Cape May. As these detachments arrived at the roost the birds that had already settled for the night would take wing and join the milling throng, and great excitement would prevail until all had settled again.

During the severe winter of 1933–1934 the woods were cut down for firewood and when the Martins began to arrive in July, 1934, they returned to the bayberry thicket on the Fill, using the same places of assembly as in the previous year—at Cold Spring and Cape May Point. By locating on an open spot on the Fill one could obtain a wonderful close-up view of the roosting activities of the birds. The Grackles and Starlings came first, individually or in small bunches, followed by Red-wings and Robins and then the Martins, a few scattered bunches at first and finally the great flights from the gathering places already mentioned. They came in force at 7:00 p. m., and all were in by 7:15. There were the same restless flights as already described at the original roost. The birds swarmed high up in the air and circled over a course, one hundred yards of more in diameter, in several distinct flocks. These eventually united and the circuit contracted until it formed a great funnel-like mass of birds which poured steadily down into the thicket. Later the birds burst forth again and circled close over our heads in the increasing darkness, until a final settlement was effected and all was quiet. From previous experience we estimated that 10,000 Martins used the roost this year. In 1935 they again gathered in the Fill but in 1936 and 1937 no trace of a roost could be found. Curiously enough in these two summers no flocks of Grackels, Robins or Starlings have been observed anywhere in the southern part of the peninsula and it would seem that they have all followed the Martins to some new rendezvous wherever it may be!

The Martins left the roost quietly at a very early hour in the morning and I never saw them leave. On rainy mornings, however, a large number of them remained all day on the nearby wires.

The Purple Martins have been the most interesting land birds of the Cape and the study of their activities, especially during the great August assemblages, has been fascinating. In spite of years of close observation we are still in doubt about many of their movements. We should like to know whether the same individual birds return night after night to the roost or whether its personnel changes every day. We should like to know where the birds spend the day, if the same ones that leave the roost in the morning come back at night, and we should like to know just when they start on their southward flight.

## BLUE JAY

Cyanocitta cristata cristata (Linnaeus)

PLATE 106, p. 726

While the Jay is a resident of the woodland to the north of Cape May it is always most abundant in late summer and autumn and south of Cold Spring and Higbee's Beach it seems to be a transient only, occurring during September and October and occasionally, though rarely, at other times of year. Prior to 1927 I had never seen a Blue Jay at the Point but on September 25 of that year, to my great surprise, I found a flock of fifteen flying restlessly from one piece of woodland to another. They were repeatedly observed here during October and had increased to forty by the 23d while on October 10 two were seen about a deserted cottage at South Cape May close to the beach. This was our most notable Jay year and although they decreased in numbers as the autumn progressed a few established themselves in the Physick grounds in the heart of the town and remained throughout the winter until about May 1 when they disappeared. At the Point some of them lingered until May 10.

On October 5, 1929, there were at least one hundred Jays at the Point in a great drifting flock screaming as they flew about the pine woods. Smaller flocks of twenty-eight, twelve and eighteen were found on the 13th; nine on December 22 and seven on December 7. These winter birds were very quiet taking refuge in low thickets and feeding on the brown lawns of the summer cottages.

The record of the Delaware Valley Club's Christmas census is as follows:

December 27, 1931, thirteen.     December 23, 1934, four.
December 26, 1932, four.         December 22, 1935, fifty.
December 24, 1933, five.         December 27, 1936, four.

On May 2 and 7, 1932, I found two Jays apparently left over from a small number that had wintered at the Point and which seemed from their actions as if they might be nesting. They were very quiet sneaking through the woods and thickets until they encountered a red squirrel, a rare animal in these parts, which started them to screaming with a vengeance. They were not seen again.

Turner McMullen found a Blue Jay's nest at Rio Grande on May 29, 1926, which contained six young, and two nests near Camden on May 2, 1915, which held five and six eggs. These records will give some idea of their nesting time in this vicinity.

I was at first inclined to regard the scattered occurrences of Jays at the Point as the drifting down of resident birds from farther north in the peninsula but I later decided that they represented a regular southward migration and the observations of William Rusling, who was present during the autumn of 1935 and able to watch their fluctuations, abundantly confirm this view. He found Jays present every day in varying numbers from two to fifty and all apparently passed down the coast.

North of the Higbee's Beach Road Blue Jays are to be found in the deep woods every summer, especially in the coastwise patches of tall timber opposite Bennett, where one may walk through the shaded wood roads that lead from the inland fields to the salt marshes and hear the familiar cry of the unsuspecting Jay from close at hand. The cry is redoubled in its vehemence as the bird detects your presence. Blue Jays occur throughout the state in similar situations and it is probable that the migrants that appear at the Point may come from much farther north. Just where they come from and whither they are bound are problems for the bird banders.

## MAGPIE
### Pica pica hudsonia (Sabine)

A Magpie was shot on the meadows back of Atlantic City on November 16, 1933, by Mark Reed and reported to me by R. Dale Benson, Jr., and F. W. Laughlin. Unfortunately it was not definitely identified as the American race but it showed no evidence of captivity and in view of other occurrences in the East may well have been a wild bird, a straggler from the West. One had been seen on Edisto Island, S. C., early in May of 1934 (Sass, Auk, 1934, p. 524) and another was taken near Milwaukee, Wis., on November 5, 1934 (Mueller, Auk, 1935, p. 90), while one had been seen at Point Lookout, Md., on June 28, 1931 (Ball and Court, Auk, 1931, p. 604).

In September, 1935, Joseph J. Hickey tells me that two Magpies appeared in the Hudson Valley fifty miles north of New York City, one of which was eventually caught and identified as the American race, and in late November one was found in Vancortland Park, in the Bronx, and was observed by many persons daily until the time of the Christmas census after which it disappeared. On February 12, 1936, William A. Weber writes me that he and others saw doubtless the same bird on the Palisades below Alpine, N. J., directly across the Hudson, which constitutes a definite New Jersey record. There seems to have been a distinct movement of Magpies eastward during the above years as they were seen also in Ontario.

## RAVEN

Corvus corax principalis Ridgway

Walker Hand always spoke of Ravens coming out to the sounds above Cape May from somewhere in the interior of the peninsula and there is no possibility of his having been in error as he knew the birds well. This however, was about the time of my first visit to the Cape, in 1890. His latest observations of Ravens on the meadows were on November 8, 1908, and December 31, 1912, a single bird in each instance. On October 25, 1936, James Tanner, Roger Peterson and Robert Allen saw a single Raven at Cape May Point which soared overhead for some time and is the only recent Cape May record so far as I know.

Farther north in the state they probably still exist in very small numbers. One was seen as recently as October 30, 1932, by Fletcher Street, Arthur Emlen and myself, flying from the outer shore of Barnegat Bay to the mainland, about a mile south of Manahawkin. It kept low down over the water and interspersed its flapping with rather long sails in the characteristic Raven manner. Its large size was notable. Charles Urner has seen Ravens in this same general region on several occasions—a single bird on October 9, 1927; two on January 23, 1927; August 11 and November 10, 1928; three on September 7, 1929; while Ernest Choate saw one on February 12, 1935, and there are other records.

In December, 1892, and February, 1893, Samuel Rhoads and I visited May's Landing for the purpose of collecting small mammals and almost every day during our stay we saw a pair of Ravens winging their way from a dense cedar swamp, lying west of the Egg Harbor River, out to the river bank or to the coast, presumably to feed. Natives who were well acquainted with them told us that they had a nest in the swamp. We not only studied their flight and compared them with Crows but on several occasions heard their guttural croaks.

In May, 1889, George Benners secured two young Ravens from a nest in a gum tree, between West Creek and Tuckerton, which he reared in captivity and named them, appropriately, "Never" and "More," unfortunately they lost any love that they may have had for one another and, as they grew older, engaged in several conflicts and eventually "Never" killed "More" and partly devoured him. "Never" is now in the collection of the Academy of Natural Sciences of Philadelphia.

On a subsequent visit to Tuckerton, about 1905, we were informed by Jillson Bros., who procured Benners' birds, that the Ravens still occupied the old nest but we were unable to verify this statement although the later records of Ravens in the Barnegat Bay region tend to confirm it.

When visiting the meadows about Atlantic City with Norris DeHaven in 1892 and 1893, we several times saw a pair of Ravens come from the mainland and settle on the edge of the thoroughfares and had good views of them from our catboat which was anchored for the night nearby.

## EASTERN CROW

**Corvus brachyrhynchos brachyrhynchos** Brehm

PLATES 107–110, p. 727, 742

Crows are present about Cape May throughout the year but during the summer months they keep for the most part back in the woods and open farming country to the north, or out on the edges of the salt meadows, and shun the vicinity of the town and the beaches. They are at all times alert and wary birds and give man a wide berth, so that we see them mostly at a distance or crossing high overhead.

In May and early June they are scattered in pairs, nesting in the woodland and foraging about the farms for food, approaching quite close to the buildings where there is promise of scraps of garbage or, perhaps, a young chicken which they are not averse to carrying off. I have also seen a Crow making off with a young Robin which was struggling and squeaking while its parents and another Robin which had come to their help pursued the robber viciously.

By early July the Crows have already begun to flock and course over the country in ever increasing numbers, playing havoc with watermelon patches in remote spots where they are screened from view, though they seem to find most of their food at this season along the Bay shore or on the Pond Creek Meadows and other similar pieces of marshy land surrounded by woods. The summer flocks of Crows are almost always seen at evening flying south along the Bay shore and apparently have a temporary roost in some of the adjacent woodland. On July 26, 1920, a long line could be seen flying southward just after sunset when the western sky was still aglow.

They were out over the Bay shore and proceeded as far as Pond Creek Meadows where they suddenly wheeled and flew back north disappearing behind the intervening woods; a bunch of twelve came first, followed by the main flock of forty-two.   On August 18 a similar flock at sunset numbered four hundred and on July 9, 1922, and on the same day in 1924, a flock of seventy-five flew by in the same way.   Another flock of twenty-five came all the way to the Point flying high overhead but when they sighted the ocean they turned back in bewildered confusion.   The same thing occurred on November 16, 1929.   Early in August, 1930, if not earlier in the summer, the Crows of Cape May had established a summer roost in an extensive patch of woodland near Bennett where they assembled every evening about 6:00 p. m.   On August 19, I saw them coming in from a distance.   As they arose far off on the ocean side of the tall woods north of Bennett they looked like a swarm of swallows and I could not realize that they really were Crows until I had focused my glass upon them.   They came in two main detach-ments, great oval masses of birds which later spread out into long streams, about five hundred in each lot; other smaller detachments followed.   On October 28, 1928, I found a flock of one hundred in a nearby field of ne-glected corn which later repaired to the same woods so that the spot may have been a temporary roost for a number of years.   In 1930, however, it was abandoned by August 29, after a heavy gale and rain storm.   When the Egrets and white-plumaged Little Blue Herons roosted in the coastal wood-land opposite Bennett the Crows gathered with them and although in small numbers they made quite a contrast to the masses of snowy white birds that assembled there.

During the day these summer flocks seem to feed on the ocean side of the peninsula and on September 7, 1924, about eight hundred of them were gathered in an old field of stunted corn which the farmer had left to its fate. They were having quite a feast and finally betook themselves to a nearby woods where they settled and engaged in a curious low-voiced conference. Walker Hand and I, who had been watching them, managed to work our way through the underbrush until we were almost among them but they detected us and instantly became silent, retreating precipitately in great confusion.   On October 2, following, this same flock was seen from a dis-tance arising from the ground in a great square mass, the birds milling about like Martins at their roost.   At the same time a mass of Starlings arose and apparently flew back and forth right through the Crows, looking in the dis-tance like a swarm of gnats.   Then the whole assemblage settled down again. On September 4, the flock was divided in three, each in a square mass not drawn out in a long stream as usual, and in this formation numbering 512 individuals it drifted across to the Bay just at sunset.

On September 20, 1924, and on several days preceding, Walker Hand saw this flock resting on the rails of the branch railroad that carries the fisher-men's train to Schellenger's Landing, and on the adjacent marsh and fences. I later examined the spot and it seemed likely that the birds had spent one or more nights there. They had evidently been sitting very close together on the rails and all facing the wind, for on that side of the track was a long row of ejected pellets consisting mainly of poke berry seeds with some sumac seeds and fragments of corncob fibre. On the opposite side the ties and roadbed were splashed all over with white excrement evidently voided by the long line of Crows as they sat there.

As winter approaches the Crows seem to resort to the open marsh back of Hereford Inlet between Five Mile and Seven Mile Beaches where I have been informed that they have long roosted in winter. On January 2 and February 21, 1926, there were evening flights to the northeast from the vicinity of the Cape and on November 28, 1926, from the mainland opposite Stone Harbor I saw a long scattered line of Crows beating their way across from the northwest heading for the inlet and too far south to reach the wooded part of the island which one would think was more suitable for a roost.

On December 27, 1931, about one thousand Crows were counted by members of the Delaware Valley Club on their Christmas census, all of which were flying steadily south to the roost and on February 6, 1932, large numbers were gathered on the mainland edge of the meadows, as early as four o'clock, from which detachments left every few minutes flying southeast, and on December 26 of the same year Julian Potter found some five hundred on the meadows at Jenkins Sound which had evidently assembled *en route* to the same spot. This seems to be the only winter roost in the vicinity of Cape May although on November 8, 1930, I saw three Crows crossing over the Bay above the Point flying low over the water in the face of a light southwest wind, which may have been bound for one of the roosts in Delaware. Farther north, the vicinity of Salem, and, formerly, Pea Patch Island in the Delaware River, were notable Crow roosts.

Alexander Wilson, writing in 1810, says of the latter: "The most noted Crow roost with which I am acquainted is near Newcastle, on an island in the Delaware. It is there known as the Pea Patch, and it is a low flat aluvial spot, of a few acres, elevated but a little above high water mark, and covered with a thick growth of reeds. This appears to be the grand rendezvous, or headquarters, of the greater part of the Crows within forty or fifty miles of the spot. It is entirely destitute of trees, the Crows alighting and nestling among the reeds, which by these means are broken down and matted together. The noise created by those multitudes, both in their evening assembly and reascension in the morning is almost incredible." He also comments on the tenacity of the birds when, on the occasion of a severe storm and consequent rising of the water, the roost was entirely submerged and most of the Crows drowned. "Thousands of them were next day seen floating in the river; and the wind shifting to the northwest drove their dead bodies to the Jersey side, where for miles they blackened the whole shore. The disaster, however, seems long ago to have been repaired, for they now congregate on the Pea Patch in as immense multitudes as ever." (American Ornithology, Vol. IV, p. 82.)

In January, 1899, I attempted to locate a roost that was supposed to exist in the woods some five miles south of Salem, and which we thought might be the successor of the Pea Patch which had by this time been long abandoned. "By following the flight line taken by Crows passing Salem we finally located near a woods that we were assured was the one used by the birds, but although Crows were abundant flying about the adjacent fields there were none in the woods. We began to think that we had missed the roost after all when, upon emerging from the far side of the woods, we found an immense flight just beginning to pass overhead from the westward; evidently the river Crows had concluded that bedtime had come. They did not, however, alight on the trees, but passed over and dropped noiselessly into the low fields just before us, seeming to select a black burnt area on the far side. To our amazement this 'burnt' patch proved to be a solid mass of Crows sitting close together, and in the gathering gloom it was difficult to see how far it extended. Four immense flights of the birds were now pouring into the fields, in one of which we estimated that five hundred Crows passed overhead per minute, during the height of the flight, and the rate of the others seemed to be about the same.

"It was now quite dark, and we began to think that the birds had no intention of retiring to the woods, so we determined to vary the monotony of the scene and at the same time to warm our chilled bodies. We, therefore, ran rapidly toward the nearest birds and shouted together just as they first took wing. The effect was marvelous; with a roar of wings the whole surface of the ground seemed to rise. The birds hovered about a minute, and then entered the woods; we soon saw that but a small portion of the assemblage had taken wing. Those farther off had not seen us in the darkness and doubtless thought that the action of their companions was merely the beginning of the regular nightly retirement into the trees. The movement, once started, became contagious and the Crows arose steadily section by section. The bare branches of the trees, which stood out clearly against the western sky but a moment before, seemed to be clothed with thick foliage as the multitude of birds settled down. After all had apparently entered the roost we shouted again, and the roar of wings was simply deafening; another shout brought the same result in undiminished force and even then probably not half the birds took wing. They soon settled again and we were glad to leave them in peace." (Stone, Bird-Lore, 1899, p. 177.)

These winter Crow roosts and the long lines of Crows on their way to roost constitute one of the most impressive phenomena of our bird life. Unfortunately the popular prejudice against Crows, aided and fostered by manufacturers of fire arms and ammunition, has resulted in organized Crow shoots at many of the roosts which have brought about the slaughter of hundreds of the birds and the abandonment of several of the roosts. As long ago as 1810 Alexander Wilson describes the organization of farmers in Delaware to effect if possible the extermination of the birds and, while he claims that Crows are in many ways beneficial, he says "to say to the man who has lost his crop of corn by these birds, that Crows are exceedingly useful for destroying vermin, would be as consolatory as to tell him who had just lost his house by the flames, that fires are excellent for destroying bugs." While neither Crows nor corn fields are so abundant now as in his day the prejudice remains the same, even in spite of the careful analysis of the Crow's food by the U. S. Biological Survey which proves that the bird is just as beneficial to the farmer as it is injurious. We fear that it is the lust for killing, just as in the case of the hawks of Cape May Point, that is at the bottom of the Crow shoots, not the desire to protect crops on the one hand and song birds on the other! One Cape May farmer having provided himself with a stuffed owl as a decoy to bring Crows within shooting range found that the birds were diligently hunting and devouring cut worms on his fields and promptly abandoned all thought of killing them. Would that there were more like him! Protection against Crows and efforts to control their numbers are necessary in specific cases but may be accomplished by scarecrow methods and limited shooting, where the birds are actually committing depredations, but the wholesale slaughter at the roosts at a time of year when the birds are wholly beneficial is an outrage.

Julian Potter, in January 1924, described the historic roost at Merchantville farther north in the state: "Twenty years ago" he says, "it harbored from twenty to thirty thousand Crows. At that time one line of flight which passed over Collingswood was so long that it stretched in either direction as far as the eye could see. This roost was investigated on March 20, 1924. As near as could be determined only about three thousand Crows came in. Instead of the long flight lines of former years, the birds came in in flocks of two to three hundred. This roost does not contain one-tenth of the number of Crows that it did twenty years ago which means that the Crow population for a certain number of miles around has decreased that much." (Bird-Lore, 1924, p. 188.) And now, twelve years later, he tells me it has utterly disappeared.

One of the most curious things about roosting Crows is their habit of roosting in trees in one place and on grass-covered marshes or islands in others. Do the same birds resort to different styles of roosts or are the components of one roost always the same birds and their offspring? These are some of the many questions about roosting Crows that we should like to solve. Also why it is that in spite of rain, snow, sleet or gales the devoted birds will persist in seeking the regular roosting place and pass over many a spot apparently far better sheltered and far more suitable for their night's lodging. But no, they would even perish in the effort, as they often do, before they will abandon the ancestral roost. This trait makes the wanton assaults upon the roosts all the more despicable.

At all times of year, especially in winter, Crows about Cape May feed about the hogpens that flourish here and there along the edge of the salt meadows, where refuse from the hotels is carted in great quantity, while they join the Herring Gulls and Turkey Vultures to feed upon fish cast up on the shores of the Harbor or the sounds, and do not disdain to share in the Vultures' feast of carrion.

On the salt meadows their range meets that of the Fish Crow, easily distinguished when the two are side by side, by its smaller size and, when in voice, by its harsh choking call as if suffering from a severe cold, as compared to the clear cut *caw, caw, caw* of the larger bird. On April 29, 1923, I found both species feeding on the Fill, perched side by side on the top of a signboard. The difference in size was clearly recognized but there seemed to be no difference in actions. Investigation disclosed that the Fish Crow was feeding on a recently killed hop toad while the other had the carcass of a bird apparently killed sometime before by a hawk. Solitary silent Crows from an area inhabited by both species are not always easily identified and I fear that on some "daily lists," where both are recorded, the desire to add another species gets the better of strict accuracy.

The slaughter of hop toads on the concrete roads, that have come into being with the automobile, has been enormous and the toad once so numerous about the Cape is actually becoming rare. At the height of destruction, between Cape May and the Point, there was scarcely a square foot of roadway in over two miles that had not its flattened and disembowled toad and I then saw many Crows each day frequenting this turnpike to feed upon the luckless batrachians. Crows often pursue one another in their capture of choice bits of food and in January I saw two relentlessly following another which was possessed of a choice tidbit, wheeling and twisting with wonderful agility, and finally forcing the victim to drop his plunder, whereupon all three dived to the ground after it.

The deserted winter beaches are favorite resorts for roving bands of Crows and on March 20, 1924, I found a flock of some fifty of the birds accompanied by Herring Gulls, gathered on the beach at South Cape May, feeding upon the trash which the waves had washed up, while a similar gathering of forty was seen at the same place on March 17, 1927. As they fed they walked about in all directions each one for himself with no uniformity of action. When standing erect on the beach the Crow's body is roughly triangular in outline, the breast coming straight down to make an angle with the abdomen which is parallel to the ground. The wings are folded tight and their tips show above the base of the tail only when the bird is bent over forward in feeding. The upper line of the body is then a perfect curve from rump to bill. There are always some members of the flock which are temporarily alert with head erect so that at any given moment there is always at least one on the lookout for danger; he promptly gives the alarm and all respond instantly. In this feeding flock some individuals were always flying a few feet in advance and settling again but there was little or no quarreling, although occasionally one bird would rush at another which had gotten a choice morsel. Crows coming in from the marsh, where many more were scattered about, proceded with the usual slow flapping until near the beach when they set their wings and sailed gradually

PLATE 106

*J. K. Potter*

*Francis Harper*

1. YOUNG BLUE JAYS, CAMDEN CO., N. J.
2. BLUE JAY ON NEST; MILLER PLACE, LONG ISLAND, N. Y., MAY 29, 1910.

PLATE 107

*W. L. Baily*

*W. L. Baily*

GROUPS OF YOUNG COMMON CROWS.

PLATE 108

*Courtesy of "Bird Lore'*　　　　　　　　　　*C. D. Kellogg*

*Courtesy of "Bird Lore"*　　　　　　　　　　*A. C. Redfield*

1. CROW ROOST NEAR SALEM, N. J., PHOTOGRAPHED BY MOONLIGHT, PLATE EXPOSED FROM 4:00 TO 5:00 A. M., JANUARY, 1901.

2. NEST AND YOUNG OF THE COMMON CROW.

PLATE 109

*Courtesy of "Bird-Lore"*

*C. D. Kellogg*

CROW ROOST NEAR SALEM, N. J., PHOTOGRAPHED BY MOONLIGHT, PLATE EXPOSED FROM 10:00 TO 11:30 P. M., JANUARY, 1901.

down to earth. When about two feet from the ground they would give several rapid flaps and, with legs extended, alight on the strand. Several Crows gathered around a gull which was endeavoring to break open a mussel evidently hoping to share in its disposal.

It is difficult to approach Crows without being seen and my ability to study this group was due to the fact that I was partly concealed by a shed when they arrived and they did not see me. The moment I moved, however, they were off. I came upon two Crows on August 26, 1920, which were walking about in a pasture field looking for such food as might be there and, in the shelter of a hedge, I was able to approach within thirty feet of them undetected. They were excedingly wary holding their heads high and constantly on the lookout for danger. Presently they caught sight of me and, although I remained perfectly still, they immediately took wing. Their feet were at first dangling but after a few wingbeats were gathered up against the under side of the tail with the toes tightly clenched.

Single Crows passing the nesting places of Red-wings and Kingbirds are at once attacked and on one occasion fourteen of the former birds pursued a luckless Crow that had ventured to cross their marsh. On the other hand Crows will attack a roosting hawk or owl and pursue him relentlessly, gathering in a vociferous ring about his roosting place, and will apparently taunt him into flight and then follow to the next stand. Such attacks are usually in the autumn or winter and I can see no apparent reason for them. Wintering Red-tailed and Red-shouldered Hawks are frequent victims. On September 27, 1926, thirty Crows were busy mobbing a Barred Owl in some cedars on the Bay shore while on July 26, 1920, another band was harrassing a Great Horned Owl in the tall woods east of Bennett, flying at him with loud cries every time he took wing. Even the Bald Eagle does not escape their persecution; William Baily saw thirty Crows pursuing an Eagle on Seven Mile Beach in November and a large flock at Cold Spring followed another Eagle from perch to perch in early July.

There are few birds that present such opportunities for the study of behavior as does the Crow and it is unfortunate that his occasional lapses from grace have brought upon him so many enemies bent upon his extermination. As a matter of fact in the East all economic studies of the food of the Crow by qualified investigators show that he is as beneficial as he is injurious and he is economically, as we so often see him in actual life, on the fence!

Crows are resident birds throughout New Jersey and while most of their winter roosts have been located in the southern part of the state one was established as far north as Union County. Samuel N. Rhoads has published an excellent account of New Jersey Crow roosts in "The American Naturalist," 1886, pp. 691 and 777, while Herbert L. Coggins contributed a later account to "Cassinia," 1903, pp. 29–42.

## FISH CROW

### Corvus ossifragus Wilson

The difficulty in deciding whether a lone and silent crow is a Fish Crow or a Common Crow may as well be admitted for it is hard to judge of relative size unless two or more birds are present for comparison. If the bird is in voice the harsh, nasal, more or less subdued, *kouh, kouh*, of the Fish Crow is in strong contrast to the clear cut *caw, caw*, of the larger species and if in exceptionally good light and very close at hand the greenish instead of purplish reflections of the plumage may be distinguished.

The true resort of the Fish Crows is the vast expanse of salt meadows which stretches from the mainland to the coast islands and from the Harbor northward along the entire seaboard of the state, while they also follow what is left of the meadows south along Cape Island Creek to Cape May itself. At almost any time of year they may be seen flying low over the grass and, now and then, dropping to the ground in search of food which in spring and early summer consists to some extent of birds' eggs and young birds. Back of the golf links I have seen them on July 7, 1931, and June 27, 1932, evidently searching for nests of Red-winged Blackbirds and marsh sparrows with several pairs of the former in hot pursuit. In days gone by when the Clapper Rails were abundant Fish Crows were responsible for the destruction of large numbers of their eggs which they carried to a stake on the meadows and devoured, leaving the shells scattered all about. Fish Crows also associate with the Herring Gulls and Turkey Vultures to feed on refuse fish thrown out on the meadows by the fishing boats and here they sometimes meet the Common Crows which sally forth from their home on the mainland. While living in a little shack on the meadows in May, 1922, I had abundant opportunity to become acquainted with this small crow and not infrequently one would pause and alight on our roof, beating a hasty retreat when, to his astonishment, he found the building occupied.

Fish Crows resort to the woods of the mainland or the coast islands to breed. Many still make use of the scattered trees on Seven Mile and Two

Mile Beaches as well as a grove on a point projecting out into the meadows south of Mill Lane, known locally as Brier Island. The best known nesting place, however, is the pine woods at Cape May Point east of Lake Lily where for the past thirty years I have found from one to three pairs located. As soon as one approaches this woods the Fish Crows fly out to meet him and circle round and round overhead uttering their guttural cries as long as he remains.

On June 22, 1924, I found in the top of one of the trees a brood of four young about which the parents were greatly concerned. They were dull black, in strong contrast to the glossy plumage of the adults while the bills were short with swollen yellow bases. In other years the old birds have kept up their outcries as late as August 7, 1922; July 19, 1924; July 16, 1927; August 8, 1929; July 22, 1931. On two occasions a young bird was detected in one of the tree tops but on others no trace of young could be found although I am of the opinion that they were somewhere about. By the middle of August the wood is deserted. At the other breeding places the behavior is the same and on July 4, 1927, I saw two young at Brier Island which although just out of the nest managed to fluff up their plumage until they actually looked larger then their parents. Turkey Vultures or other birds which appear near the nesting trees are viciously pursued.

The following list of nests which they have examined on Seven Mile Beach has been submitted by Turner McMullen and Richard Miller:

May 13, 1927, seven nests with four to five eggs.
May 14, 1916, four eggs.
May 15, 1926, five and six eggs.
May 18, 1924, four, five and six eggs (seventeen nests).
May 21, 1922, three and five eggs.
May 31, 1920, two with five eggs each.
June 11, 1922, four eggs.
June 20, 1926, three, four, four, and five eggs; these were second layings from nests robbed on May 15.
June 21, 1925, young birds.
June 24, 1925, young birds, one third grown.

Most of these nests were built in red cedar trees, a few in hollies.

Miller tells me that Fish Crows never use earth in nest construction as does the Common Crow.

In winter the Fish Crows collect in small flocks on the meadows and on the island beaches and Julian Potter found no less than thirty roosting on the roof of a closed cottage on the edge of the Fill on November 14, 1920. The Delaware Valley Ornithological Club's count of Fish Crows on their Christmas census from 1928 to 1936 are as follows:

December 23, 1928, twenty-four.
December 22, 1929, four.
December 28, 1930, ten.
December 27, 1931, thirty.
December 26, 1932, ten.

December 24, 1933, sixty.
December 28, 1934, fifteen.
December 22, 1935, seven.
December 27, 1936, eleven.

While the Fish Crow is chiefly maritime and is resident all along the New Jersey coast it also occurs on the Delaware River and large numbers of the birds have been caught in winter for trapshooting, just north of Philadelphia. As to the extent of their nesting along the river I do not have satisfactory information.  (cf. Stone, Auk, 1903, pp. 267–271.)

Nests have been found as far north as Hudson and Union Counties (Eaton and Urner).

# * BLACK-CAPPED CHICKADEE

### Penthestes atricapillus atricapillus (Linnaeus)

The common Black-capped Chickadee of northern New Jersey occurs as a resident as far south as the Raritan River according to Waldron Miller, and reaches Haddonfield and Princeton during the periodic autumn migrations which bring it as a winter resident to the vicinity of Philadelphia and elsewhere in southeastern Pennsylvania.  Farther south in New Jersey I know of but one positive record, a specimen obtained at Vineland by Dr. Max Peet on February 1, 1914; the Carolina is the common Chickadee throughout southern New Jersey.

The Black-cap has been recorded once or twice in winter at Cape May Point by visitors to the Bird Sanctuary but the members of the Delaware Valley Club have been unable to detect it there or elsewhere in the vicinity and no Cape May specimen has ever been taken.  The two species can readily be distinguished when in song as the Black-cap has but two notes while the Carolina has four.  Relative length of tail, amount of white on the edges of the tertials and secondaries, and amount of frosting on the black throat patch—the most striking differences, are not very satisfactory field marks and I am inclined to think that in winter errors might easily be made, unless one had given a great deal of study to the birds.

## CAROLINA CHICKADEE

Penthestes carolinensis carolinensis (Audubon)

The Carolina Chickadee is a characteristic bird of the pine woods and swamps of the Cape May peninsula. It is a permanent resident and nests in old woodpecker holes or natural cavities in dead tree trunks, while in autumn and winter it ranges more widely, often in small parties, and may be found in orchards and gardens or wherever there is promise of hibernating insects. We have found Chickadees in every month of the year at Cape May Point and in late summer, after the nesting season is over or during autumn and winter, they will come into Cape May foraging in the shrubbery of the yards or in the shade trees along the streets. Philip Laurent found them throughout the year on Five Mile Beach before the woods were removed.

During a large part of the year we more frequently see Carolina Chickadees in pairs or as single individuals but in the colder months we may come across bands of six or eight, doubtless family groups, or they may associate with Myrtle Warblers, Tufted Tits, Red-bellied Nuthatches or Brown Creepers, all drifting through the woods in a concerted search for food, and now and then a Downy Woodpecker may join the group.

We may discover several such groups in the course of a winter's walk and on January 25, 1925, Henry Gaede counted no less than twenty-five Carolina Chickadees, while on December 27, 1927, Julian Potter saw twenty. On the Christmas census, when members of the Delaware Valley Ornithological Club cover all the country south of the Court House in a combined count, much larger totals are recorded:

December 23, 1928, sixty-eight.

December 22, 1929, one hundred and five.

December 28, 1930, fourteen.

December 27, 1931, forty-two.

December 26, 1932, eleven.

December 24, 1933, thirty-five.

December 23, 1934, fifty.

December 22, 1935, one hundred and forty-seven.

December 27, 1936, eighty-six.

While there is some fluctuation in numbers this is apparently due to local shifting of Chickadee population and to food or weather, and there is no evidence of regular southward migration which would cause a definite scarcity. The bird is here close to the northern limit of its distribution and there could be no influx from farther north to take the place of possible emigrants to the south. William Rusling, present daily at the Point from October 10 to November 14, 1935, saw the species on only nine days, from two to seven per day, which simply represents the normal population there at this season.

As we see the Carolina Chickadees at the Point they go drifting leisurely through the pine woods, stopping here and there to explore a branch from above or swinging upside down below an attractive bunch of pine needles, while they pick off minute insects that may be lurking there. Then we see one dangling from the end of a slender branch while he probes between the opening scales of a cone, and now he will drop into the undergrowth of bayberry bushes or even onto the ground where he hops about for a few minutes among the tussocks of grass ever on the alert for food. Their actions are sudden, almost instantaneous, and they will often turn completely around in a single jump with a rapid flirt of the tail. After swallowing an insect a Chickadee will wipe the bill on a convenient twig, first on one side then on the other, and is on his way again with the usual rapid low *ts'dee, dee, dee, dee*,—as it sounds to us close at hand. The song of nesting time is a double call "*tsee-dee, tsee-dee*" the second couplet being pitched a trifle lower than the first. I have heard it as late as August 7 but it is unusual after May or June.

Carolina Chickadees, like the Red-breasted Nuthatches, often feed on the seeds of the pine cones and carefully trim off the wings before swallowing the kernel so that when several are feeding at once there is more or less of a shower of discarded seed-wings floating down from the treetops. In the winter of 1905–1906 Walker Hand found a flock of fifteen Carolina Chickadees which took up their quarters in a privet hedge in the heart of the town and were seen daily for several weeks. Others have wintered in the shrubbery of the Physick place on Washington St. which offers adequate shelter and protection to many winter birds.

On February 7, 1932, I came upon two of these Chickadees in a swampy thicket at Cold Spring feeding on the berries of the poison sumac. They would seize a berry in the bill and, hopping out on a horizontal limb, would hold it against a twig with both feet while they picked at it and apparently ate it piece by piece as I saw no fragments drop. On March 5, following, I saw two feeding in the same way on berries of poison ivy which grew on the trunks of pine trees. They never carried berries away but clinging to the vines leisurely picked them to pieces and swallowed them bit by bit. The great abundance of poison sumac and poison ivy about Cape May should ensure these little birds a regular food supply when the store of hibernating insects grows less as the winter advances.

I have a record of a nest at Swain with five eggs on May 15, 1924; another at Rio Grande with six young on May 24, 1925; and one at Whitesboro, May 10, 1925, with six eggs (McMullen and Miller).

There is something very attractive about these little Carolina Chickadees in winter when we find them most abundant. They are very trim and sleek in their gray, black and white plumage which seems particularly fresh at this season. We note the duller gray instead of pure white edgings to the wing and tail feathers and the clear cut line of demarkation between the black throat and the white breast which distinguish this little southerner from his slightly larger cousin of the north—the Black-capped Chickadee. The two are, however, not so easily distinguished in life as might be supposed.

Waldron Miller, who was better acquainted than anyone else with the bird life of Plainfield, told me that the Raritan River apparently marked the division between the breeding ranges of these two Chickadees. The Carolina is resident at Princeton but apparently not abundant in the breeding season although Babson (Birds of Princeton) records a nest and six eggs found May 29, 1901.

## *ACADIAN CHICKADEE

### Penthestes hudsonicus littoralis (Bryant)

The unusual flights of this brown-headed Chickadee to New England and New York during the winters of 1913–1914 and 1916–1917, brought several to northern New Jersey. Waldron Miller recorded one shot November 1, 1913, at Ramsay (Auk, 1920, p. 593) and two were seen by him on December 17, 1916, in the vicinity of Plainfield and single birds on January 7 and 28, 1917, while another was seen by Charles Rogers on February 4. In the vicinity of Englewood one was found on December 23, 1916, by Lester Walsh and on January 1, 1917, by Charles Rogers (Auk, 1917, p. 218). At Princeton four were observed by Henry L. Eno from November 18, 1916, to March 31, 1917 (Auk, 1918, p. 231).

No others have been recorded, so far as I know, and it has, of course, not been seen at Cape May but, inasmuch as Evening Grosbeaks and Red Crossbills occurred with the Hudsonian Chickadees at Plainfield, both of which have been recorded from Cape May, its occurrence there, in some future wave of northern bird life, is not beyond the range of possibility.

## TUFTED TITMOUSE

Baeolophus bicolor (Linnaeus)

PLATE 110, p. 742

While the Tufted Tit occurs regularly throughout most of the peninsula of Cape May it is by no means universally abundant and becomes rather rare at the southern extremity, about Cape May City and the Point, and there may be some years when none at all are seen there. It seems more at home on the Delaware Valley side of South Jersey from Salem north but family parties drift down to the Point at intervals and some remain through the winter while a pair now and then nests there. There seems to be no true migratory movement and even at the northern limit of its range the Tit is resident. Its movements are apparently merely in search of food when parents and young unite in a foraging party.

On January 19, 1922, I came upon a flock of twelve, busily feeding in the pine woods beyond Lake Lily. They hopped from branch to branch with a rapid, nervous flip of the wings, carefully inspecting the trunks and limbs of the trees. Sometimes one of them would hold himself erect and peck at the bark like a woodpecker or hold a seed in his bill and hammer it against the branch. Now and then all would resort to the ground, hopping about with neck held high and crest erect, pecking right and left and rustling the dead leaves as they went. Their flight from tree to tree was somewhat undulating.

On April 3, 1924, there were two Tits associated with a Carolina Chickadee and some Myrtle Warblers. One of them worked for some time at a large scale of bark which he finally dislodged and then joined the warblers on the ground hopping about and feeding among the scattered pine needles which covered the woods floor.

The call of the "Tom Tit" is a loud clear whistle which sounds at a distance like the cry of a young Turkey—*weet, weet, weet, weet,* but which upon closer approach resolves itself into *peeto, peeto, peeto, peeto,* the "o" being unaccented which accounts for the difficulty in detecting it at a distance. In the midst of repeating this call over and over, the bird may suddenly alter its notes entirely substituting the more rapid, though less strongly accented, *toolée, toolée, toolée, toolée.* There is also a low *dee-dee* note like the latter part of the Chickadee's call.

In April I have records of single birds in six of the past seventeen years and sometimes a pair. In May, June and July all of my records are from the country north of Cold Spring and Higbee's Beach, where the Tits are always more plentiful. For August and September I have no records at all, doubtless due to the silence of the birds at this season, for we always hear more Tits than we see. In the late autumn more records have been obtained; two in October and two in November and the Christmas lists of the Delaware Valley Club give us December records as follows:

| | |
|---|---|
| December 26, 1927, two. | December 26, 1932, five. |
| December 23, 1928, two. | December 24, 1933, nineteen. |
| December 22, 1929, thirty-three. | December 23, 1934, five. |
| December 28, 1930, one. | December 22, 1935, forty-one. |
| December 27, 1931, thirty-four. | December 27, 1936, seventeen. |

The far carrying whistle of the Tit is its most striking characteristic and is a delight in cold winter days when so many birds are virtually silent. Like the Cardinal and the Carolina Wren, fellow Southerners, the Tit is here close to the northern limit of its range, being of only irregular occurrence in the northern counties, yet it shows no disposition to retreat southward in severe seasons, and doubtless some individuals pay the penalty and years of absence of any of these species may often be correlated with severe winters immediately preceding. It has bred as far north as Union and Essex Counties.

## WHITE-BREASTED NUTHATCH

### Sitta carolinensis carolinensis Latham

While one race or other of the White-breasted Nuthatch is resident from northern North America all the way south to Florida the species is absent, except as a rare transient, and still rarer winter resident, in southern New Jersey. In the Middle States the high hard wood forests seem to appeal more strongly to it than do the coastal pine lands. While a few probably pass through Cape May every autumn we have records for only seven of the twenty odd years that careful attention has been given to the birds of the Cape and only twice has an individual been seen in spring, one by William Yoder on April 11, 1926 and another on April 23, 1932. While this scarcity of records may be due in part to lack of continuous observation,

William Rusling's experience during the autumn of 1935 bears out our designation of the White-breasted Nuthatch as a rare species in this region. He saw it on but four days. Three on September 24 and two each on October 5, 17 and 19. Philip Laurent saw but two on Five Mile Beach before it was built over, both in autumn. It is a resident species in the northern counties.

Members of the Delaware Valley Club have seen White-breasted Nuthatches at Cape May as follows:

| 1923. | September 16, 30. | 1925. | October 18. | 1928. | October 7. |
| 1923. | October 1. | 1927. | October 23. | 1929. | November 16. |

All single birds evidently on migration.
Wintering birds as recorded on the Christmas census trips follow:

December 23, 1928, one.          December 26, 1932, one.
December 22, 1929, one.          December 22, 1935, three.
December 27, 1931, three.        December 27, 1936, two.


## *BROWN-HEADED NUTHATCH

### Sitta pusilla pusilla Latham

While this southern nuthatch occurs in Delaware across the Bay we have never been able to find it at Cape May. Beesley gives it in his list of Cape May County birds (1857) and Turnbull (1869) states that it is a rare visitant in the southern counties, but does not specify whether he refers to Pennsylvania or New Jersey. Neither writer is explicit as to the source or nature of his information.

The only definite record for the state is a single individual observed at Haddonfield by Samuel Rhoads in winter about 1876. The bird came to feed on suet fastened to a tree near the window and was carefully studied.

## RED-BREASTED NUTHATCH

### Sitta canadensis Linnaeus

The Red-breasted Nuthatch is an irregular or erratic autumnal transient about Cape May, abundant in some years and rare or absent in others; a varying number remain through the winter but there is no definite return flight in spring although occasionally an individual bird may be seen at this time. What becomes of the hordes of Red-breasted Nuthatches that move on to the south in some years and apparently never come back is one of the standing puzzles of bird migration. (cf. Nichols, Science, August 16, 1918.) The pine woods at the Point constitute one of the favorite resorts of these little birds but they are common elsewhere in the peninsula and at the height of their migration occur in numbers in the town, wherever trees are to be found. It was plentiful on Five Mile Beach in September and October when the island was wooded.

On September 9, 1921, a year when these birds were here in great abundance, a great many could be seen in the pine woods, where they crept about the branches exploring the clusters of pine needles and probing between the scales of the cones. Sometimes one would pause on the under side of a cone cluster and stretch his neck upward and backward, until he was looking out over his shoulders, while another would cling upright to a cone and probe into it after the manner of a woodpecker. A third bird followed out an old broken branch clear to the end, examining every inch of it with the greatest care, and then was off on his somewhat undulatory flight in which the shortness of his tail was conspicuous. Alighting on the trunk of the next tree he went round and round head down creeping like a mouse; now he pauses to pry off a loose scale of bark, seeking some lurking insect

( 737 )

hiding beneath, now he stops and daintily picks off a number of gray aphids from a bunch of pine needles and then is off to other feeding grounds. One of the few spring birds that I have noticed was hovering in the air as he pursued a small moth in the manner of a flycatcher.

On October 23, 1927, and on several previous occasions I have seen Red-breasted Nuthatches feeding on seeds from freshly opened pine cones. Picking the seed out with the bill the bird would carry it to a definitely selected spot on a nearby limb where he placed it in a notch or under the edge of a bark scale and proceeded to hammer it with the point of the bill, deftly cutting off the wing, and perhaps breaking the seed covering, before swallowing it. Each bird visited again and again the spot which he had selected to prepare his seed for eating, and when several were working in the same tree the loose seed-wings were constantly fluttering to the ground.

Several times I have seen a Red-breasted Nuthatch flying wildly round and round above the tops of the pines in an ellipse probably one hundred feet in length, covering exactly the same course several times before coming to rest. I could not guess at the meaning of this unless it is the recurrence of a flight song performance incidental to the mating time.

Our records for Red-breasted Nuthatches at Cape May are as follows:

| | |
|---|---|
| 1918. July 18. | 1927. August 26–October 23. |
| 1921. August 13–October 9. | 1928. September 30–October 21. |
| 1923. August 26–October 21. | 1929. September 20–October 25. |
| 1923. November 11. | 1930. August 11–October 5. |
| 1924. October 2 and 3. | 1931. August 27–October 18. |
| 1925. August 20–October 18. | 1931. November 28. |
| 1926. July 18 and August 8. | 1932. September 25–October 8. |
| 1926. November 13. | 1933. July 8–October 29. |
| | 1935. September 7–November 14. |

In some years it will be noticed that we had only one or two records during the entire season while in others there were days when the nuthatches fairly swarmed, such as September 16, 1923; September 22, 1925; etc.

While the usual time of arrival, on years when a pronounced migration occurs, is about the middle of August there were three years when a much earlier arrival was noted. On July 18, 1918, I found a single bird on a pine tree near the head of Lake Lily and on the same date in 1926, William Yoder saw one in the same vicinity, while on July 8, 1933, I found at least three in the pine woods at the Point.

Our winter records are as follows: On December 1, 1921, Fletcher Street saw a single bird while I saw perhaps the same individual on January 9 associated with a party of Tufted Tits. On January 25, 1925, Henry Gaede saw ten in the woods at the Point and I found one there on February 14. Records of the Christmas census are as follows:

| | |
|---|---|
| December 26, 1927, four | December 22, 1935, twenty |
| December 23, 1928, eight | December 27, 1936, one |
| December 27, 1931, two | |

In spring I found one in a spruce tree on the Physick grounds in Cape May on May 10, 1924, associated with a Tennessee and a Black-poll Warbler; and on May 2, 1932, there were three or more in the pine woods at Cape May Point and another in the Physick place, with several more there on May 5, 6 and 7 and several at the Point on the last date. On May 12, 1934, I found one at the latter spot and this record further illustrates the irregularity in the movements of the bird.

We naturally associate the Red-breasted Nuthatch with the crisp days of September and October when it appears in greatest abundance and with the pond pines of the Point which seem to be its favorite haunt.

As the Red-breasted Nuthatch does not breed anywhere in New Jersey the host of transients that arrive periodically in autumn must come from the north woods of Canada and the northernmost United States.

## BROWN CREEPER

**Certhia familiaris americana Bonaparte**

The Brown Creeper is a common and regular autumnal transient throughout the Cape May Peninsula, and formerly on Five Mile Beach, while occasional individuals remain as winter residents. There is no noticeable return flight in the spring and our five April records, all single birds, may just as well have been wintering individuals as migrants from farther south; I should certainly so regard the few March occurrences.

Our autumn records for the past fifteen years are as follows, the November dates being after the main flight may possibly indicate wintering birds:

| | | | |
|---|---|---|---|
| 1921. | September 14–October 16 November 11. | 1931. | October 18. November 7. |
| | | 1932. | September 25–October 14. November 13. |
| 1923. | September 30–October 21. November 4. | | |
| | | 1933. | September 30–October 29. |
| 1925. | September 22–October 18. | 1934. | September 19. November 3. |
| 1927. | October 30. November 21. | 1935. | September 29–October 29. |
| 1928. | September 27–October 27. | | November 3. |
| 1929. | October 25. | | |

The abundance of the Creeper varies considerably in different years. In 1935 William Rusling, with the exception of three days, when his count reached seven, saw only one to four per day, but Julian Potter saw at least one hundred on September 30, 1923. On the next day I found Brown Creepers all over the Point as well as in the shade trees of the town, sometimes three or four were to be seen hitching up the trunk of a single tree, while out on the Fill they were climbing up the stems of bayberry and marsh elder bushes. On October 18, 1925; October 23, 1927; October 25, 1928; they were also abundant.

On the Christmas census the Brown Creeper has been reported as follows:

December 26, 1927, one
December 24, 1933, three
December 23, 1934, one

December 22, 1935, eleven
December 27, 1936, twelve

Those that attempt to winter seem to meet with disaster as we have only a few records later than December—i. e. January 25, February 14, March 21–22, 1925, and March 19, 1932. Our April records are April 23, 1922; April 11, 1926; April 24, 1927; April 2, 1933.

While it breeds mainly north of New Jersey, P. B. Philipp has found nests in a tamarack swamp at Newton, Sussex County, in the summers of 1906, 1907 and 1908. Elsewhere it is a regular transient and less frequent in winter.

The Brown Creeper shows little variation in habit as we see him here on migration. He sticks to the tree trunks in a never ending search for hibernating insects or insect eggs concealed in the crevices of the bark, occasionally trying his luck on the stems of saplings or low bushes if he lands among them as he rests from his strenuous night flight. He not infrequently tries telegraph poles and once I saw one laboriously ascending an iron standpipe by the Lighthouse, following the perpendicular line of rivet heads that reaches from the ground to the top. But there was method in his madness as a search disclosed the fact that many spider eggs, with their thick white covering, and some insect pupae were to be found in the cracks between the rivets and the sheet iron.

Hitching ever upward like a diminutive woodpecker or a climbing mouse the Brown Creeper furnishes a wonderful example of protective coloration, disappearing from sight the moment he comes to rest and never conspicuous even when in motion. He is also the personification of patience and no sooner does he reach the limit of profitable foraging on one tree trunk than he drops to the base of the next one and begins all over again.

## HOUSE WREN

**Troglodytes aëdon aëdon Vieillot**

The House Wren is a common summer resident at Cape May Point and about farmhouses throughout the peninsula while there are usually one or two pairs in Cape May itself; Laurent found a pair on Five Mile Beach in 1891. In the northern parts of the state it is common and generally distributed.

It nests in bird boxes, when available, or in old woodpeckers' holes in trees and telegraph poles, as well as in holes in stumps or in old buildings. The most usual nesting materials are twigs with a lining of chicken feathers but a pair that occupied the box in Walker Hand's garden built a nest which was composed almost entirely of bits of wire from a discarded piece of chicken wire which had rusted to pieces on the ground nearby. A nest with six eggs was found by Richard Miller at Swain on June 6, 1920, and another with five eggs at Cape May Point on June 4, 1922, while nests with young were examined at Cold Spring on June 17, 1933; July 5, 1932; August 5, 1932; the last obviously a second brood. Young of the 1932 nest were on the wing by July 9 and another family on the 5th.

When the young are able to shift for themselves House Wren families accompanied by one or both parents often resort to the woods and thickets and we usually find one or two groups during the latter part of the summer at the Point, or along hedgerows back in the farmland. I have found young and old at the former locality on July 8, 1921, and July 24, 1920. The parents were much excited hopping nervously about in the thickets and

PLATE 110

A. C. Redfield

W. L. Baily

1. COMMON CROW ON NEST.
2. YOUNG TUFTED TITMICE, MEDFORD, N. J.

PLATE 111

J. K. Potter

W. L. Baily

1. YOUNG CAROLINA WRENS.

2. NEST OF THE LONG-BILLED MARSH WREN, DELAWARE MARSHES AT PENSAUKEN
   CREEK, N. J.

constantly uttering their alarm note, a complaining, rasping *chesh-esh-esh-esh-esh-esh* etc. or *shee-shee-shee-shee-shee-shee* etc. as I have written it on another occasion. They constantly bob or duck the body up and down as if their slender legs were wire springs and give an instantaneous flutter to the wings, so rapid that the eye catches it only as an indistinct blur. While these birds were tending full-fledged young another pair was caring for a nest, with the male in full song.

Birds have been heard in song as late as: July 24, 1920; July 27, 1922; July 22, 1923; July 16, 1927; July 19, 1931.

Our latest dates for the occurrence of House Wrens at Cape May are:

| | | | | | |
|---|---|---|---|---|---|
| 1913. | October 13. | 1927. | October 10. | 1932. | October 8. |
| 1920. | October 31. | 1928. | October 21. | 1935. | October 13. |
| 1925. | October 18. | 1929. | October 25. | | |

The majority have left by early October but we have had definite migratory flights on October 1, 1923; September 30, 1928; September 28, 1930. In other years there seemed to be no marked concentration.

Walker Hand has recorded the arrival of the House Wren at Cape May up to 1920 and I have recorded its appearance in several subsequent years. It is probable that his May records are late or that the birds arrive in the surrounding country a few days before they put in an appearance in the town itself. The list follows:

| | | | | | |
|---|---|---|---|---|---|
| 1902. | May 5. | 1914. | April 26. | 1922. | April 23. |
| 1904. | May 7. | 1915. | May 7. | 1923. | April 30. |
| 1906. | May 5. | 1916. | May 2. | 1926. | April 24. |
| 1907. | April 30. | 1917. | April 24. | 1927. | April 24. |
| 1908. | April 26. | 1918. | May 4. | 1928. | April 30. |
| 1910. | May 2. | 1919. | April 23. | 1933. | April 30. |
| 1912. | April 8. | 1920. | May 2. | 1934. | April 23. |
| 1913. | May 3. | 1921. | May 8. | | |

An exceptional date was one seen by Edward Weyl at Heislerville on November 29, 1931.

The House Wren is a common summer resident throughout New Jersey.

## WINTER WREN
### Nannus hiemalis hiemalis (Vieillot)

The Winter Wren is not a common bird at the Cape and our records are almost entirely of single individuals seen during the autumnal migration or during December.

Our autumn records are:

| | | | |
|---|---|---|---|
| 1923. | September 30, October 7, 21. | 1930. | October 5, November 8. |
| 1925. | November 14. | 1932. | November 24. |
| 1928. | October 12, 21, 27. | 1935. | October 5, 8, 10, 12, 19, 25. |
| 1929. | October 5, November 16. | | |

The 1935 observations are those of William Rusling who was present throughout the autumn. He saw quite a number of the birds on October 5, and there may have been similar concentrations in other years, had someone been constantly present at the Point to record them.

The observations on the Christmas census follow:

December 22, 1929, one.                December 23, 1934, five.
December 28, 1930, one.                December 22, 1935, two.
December 25–26, 1932, one.             December 27, 1936, four.
December 24, 1933, three.

In spring we have but few records: February 19, March 12, April 1, 1933. Winter Wrens are usually found in dense thickets especially along stream banks and I once found one in the very heart of the tall woodland at Cold Spring. Sometimes they frequent old buildings and one in search of spiders or insects was led to enter a shed through a crack in the wall and remained a prisoner there for some time, failing to find a way out. Another was found in a hedge in the Physick garden, in the town, where he went like a mouse in and out among the roots, so rapidly that it was difficult to decide whether he used his wings or legs in his progress.

The Winter Wren is a common transient and less common winter resident elsewhere in the state.

## *BEWICK'S WREN

### Thryomanes bewicki bewicki (Audubon)

The records of Bewick's Wren in New Jersey published by Dr. C. C. Abbott are so involved that I feel that an error in identification has been made (cf. Stone, Birds of New Jersey, 1909, p. 299). The only other record of the occurrence of the bird in the state is one seen by Samuel Rhoads at Haddonfield in 1890. William Baily secured a specimen at Wynnewood, Pa. not far from Philadelphia on April 12 of the same year. It is mainly a bird of the Middle West and southern Alleghanies and breeds regularly as far east as Fulton County, Pa., but seems to become scarce as the House Wren increases in abundance.

## CAROLINA WREN

**Thryothorus ludovicianus ludovicianus (Latham)**

PLATE III, p. 743

There are nearly always a pair or two of the big rusty Carolina Wrens about the old buildings of Cape May and especially in the negro quarters of West Cape May where they seem to find an environment more like that of the South. In the thickets of the Point, too, we come upon a pair or two and their clear whistle comes from the dense tangles of green brier and honeysuckle which flank the old farm buildings at Higbee's Beach. Everywhere in fact, throughout the peninsula, where old tumble-down sheds and dense thickets of vines or shrubbery are in proximity, we may look for the Carolina Wren. Philip Laurent found two on Five Mile Beach in autumn and I saw one on Seven Mile Beach in winter.

After very cold winters there may be a diminution in the number of Carolina Wrens and as they do not migrate I fear that most of them fall victims to the weather and it may be several years before they regain their normal numbers. They are here close to the northern limit of their range and with the Cardinal they hold to it regardless of all obstacles. Like the opossum, the persimmon tree and the country negro these birds are outposts of the South and have their boundary line beyond which they seldom pass—the northern limit of the Carolinian Faunal Zone. They are rare as far north as Princeton and Plainfield and absent in the more northern counties except in the lower Hudson Valley.

( 745 )

The Carolina Wren is a resident species and we have records of its presence in every month of the year while under normal conditions there is very little seasonal variation in its numbers except what may be due to the appearance of the young birds during the summer.   It is an active nervous bird delighting in brush piles and hedges and thick shelter of any sort, moving in and out like a mouse, or we may find it, when singing, perched on the top of some tree or bush in full view.   I have several times seen them fluff up the plumage and once in May this was apparently the action of a male before a female and was probably part of the sexual display.

Their feeding is usually done in the depths of the thickets, but one individual mounted the trunk of a pine tree and fed from the crevices of the bark like a creeper.

Holes in old buildings seem to be the favorite nesting places of this wren. One pair had built on the flat sill above the door of an old shack at the Point and the nest was found with a full set of eggs by Charles Page when he came to occupy the place for the summer.   The opening and shutting of the door was too much for the nerves of the birds and they deserted.   A roll of roofing paper was immediately put up on the trunk of a nearby pine with a tomato can at the end and within two hours the wrens had take possession and were soon at work on a new nest in which a brood was raised.   A nest seen by Turner McMullen at North Cape May on May 14, 1927, contained five eggs.

The song of the Carolina Wren, which is perhaps his outstanding character, is exceedingly variable but always reducible to a series of clear penetrating whistles, except for the long drawn rolling trill—*chirrrrrr, chirrrr* which he utters on occasion.

There is some resemblance to the song of the White-eyed Vireo, a frequent companion of the Carolina Wren in low damp woodland.   The resemblance lies in the clear quality of the notes and in the ability to make an instant change in the character of the utterance, but the make-up of the two is entirely different.   It is the call and song of the Cardinal, however, which the Carolina's music most closely resembles.   The most frequent song is the *twéedle, twéedle, twéedle, twéedle* with which all fellow residents of wren territory are familiar.   This I have written, on other occasions, *teedle,* and *cheedle,* as there is a good deal of variation in the syllables of different individuals.   The other familiar song of the bird, which seems to be fundamentally different since it is accented on the first of three syllables instead of the first of two, is—*túleeah, túleeah, túleeah, tóo.*   This has also been rendered effectively as *téa-kettle, téa-kettle, téa-kettle.*   One bird (August 16, 1921) was endlessly reiterating the *twéedle, twéedle* note when he suddenly stopped and sang *sweét-tel-ee, sweét-tel-ee, sweét-tel-ee* (a slight variant of the second song) and then as suddenly reverted to the first phrase to which he finally added two syllables: *twéedle-dee-dle, twéedle-dee-dle,* etc.   Other phrases that I have recorded are *whéet-a, whéet-a, whéet-a; séetilo, séetilo, séetilo; tsíleo, tsíleo, tsíleo;* and *pée-to, pée-to, pée-to.*

Several times I have heard these wrens shorten up the long trill into *chéer-up, chéer-up, chéer-up* and once (March 22, 1925) a bird executed a peculiar rolling song something like the gurgling of a Long-billed Marsh Wren or like the beginning of a House Wren's song: *tlit'l, tlit'l, lit, lit, lit, lit, lit.* I was quite at a loss to guess the author until I caught sight of him in the act.

A Carolina Wren at the Point (July 18, 1923) suddenly started a series of clear penetrating notes: *quip, quip, quip, quip,* etc. separated by several seconds. This was one of those bird calls, which, perhaps because of its peculiar character, attracts the attention of other birds whose curiosity is aroused. At any rate in the course of two or three minutes, while this performance was going on, there were gathered near the singer, four Towhees, four Thrashers, a Flicker, a House Wren, a Yellow Warbler and a White-eyed Vireo. Then as if satisfied the Carolina abandoned this call and launched into his familiar *túleeah, túleeah, túleeah,* and the other birds lost interest and immediately scattered. It would be interesting if we could interpret bird songs and calls or at least know just how the song of one species affects others.

While Carolina Wrens sing most frequently in the spring and summer it is not unusual to hear them burst into song at other seasons and even in midwinter we hear them on fine mornings, despite a snow covered landscape, vie with the wintering White-throated Sparrows in voicing their cheerful phrases. We have recorded their song in every month except January and February and doubtless constant observation would find them whistling then as well.

H. B.

# LONG-BILLED MARSH WREN

Telmatodytes palustris palustris (Wilson)

PLATE III, p. 743

None of our summer resident land birds has suffered such depletion in numbers within my recollection as has this little denizen of the marshes and cattail swamps. In 1890, when I first visited Cape May, Marsh Wrens were abundant all the way from Broadway to the Lighthouse nesting in the marsh elder bushes and in the taller sedges all along Cape Island Creek and in similar situations through the marshes behind the town nearly to Schellenger's Landing. On both sides of the turnpike as it traversed West Cape May their bubbling song could be heard continually while the great cattail swamps to the south of the road were alive with them.

By 1920 the draining of these marsh lands in the interests of mosquito extermination had sadly depleted the numbers of the Marsh Wrens and destroyed most of the fields of cattails so that the birds were found only in a limited area just east of South Cape May and around some of the ponds and sluices nearer to the town. Then came the unfortunate exploitation of this area of marsh which resulted in its being almost entirely filled in so that by 1926 Marsh Wrens were driven completely away from the Cape May district with the exception of a small colony immediately behind the golf links, in the marshes which border the railroad. So tenaceous of their nesting sites are these little birds, however, that there may be a few scattered pairs elsewhere which from their secretive habits and limited range have escaped notice.

( 748 )

On the upper part of the South Dennis marsh and doubtless at other spots on the peninsula, where "improvements" and ill-advised drainage operations have not ruined their native habitats, the Long-billed Marsh Wrens still abound and small colonies existed a few years ago on the upper part of the Pond Creek Meadows and along a creek that flows from the mainland opposite the middle of Seven Mile Beach and they probably still survive. Another colony formerly existed on this beach near Eighty-fourth St., not far from the ocean (McMullen).

While the songs of the Marsh Wrens are heard on every side as we approach one of their colonies it is not so easy to see the birds as they keep well down in the thick sedge but presently curiosity will bring one of them into view. He grasps an upright reed with both feet and leans out almost horizontally with tail cocked over his back until it nearly touches his head, the head is bent upward with the throat extended and the whole body sways slightly up and down. He has a short quick alarm note: *chip; chip; chip; chip;* which is uttered continually when the young are on the wing and is accompanied by an instantaneous flip of the wings with each note.

Every now and then one of the wrens will launch forth in flight, just skimming the top of the sedge like a great bumble bee, with wings beating so rapidly that they almost make a blur; the slender bill held out in front and the closely appressed tail behind make the bird appear distinctly pointed at each end. The flight is not long sustained and the bird drops back into the depths of the sedge. In the resting season a male will be seen to mount six or eight feet in the air, ascending in a curve over the marsh with head and tail held high and throat distended, pouring out the continued bubbling medley of the flight song and then sinking slowly down on fluttering wings into the grass.

The song has a peculiar spluttering, bubbling quality, like water gurgling out of a pipe or the rippling of a brook over a pebbly bottom. I have written it on several occasions: *possa-wat'l-wat'l-wat'l-wat'l-wéegal*. The first two short notes are unaccented and low, the four gurgle notes are higher, with the last couplet suddenly descending. Sometimes the preliminary notes sound more like *tick, tick*.

Again I have recorded the song: *witla-witla; watt'l—watt'l—watt'l—watt'l-was-it* and again: *possa-psilla—psilla—psilla—psilla—wisset*. It is difficult to detect how many low preliminary notes there are and the impression is that the bubbling might have been going on for some time in an undertone and has suddenly become audible. So, too, there is often a gurgle of incompleted song from the depth of the sedge. I have heard the song frequently to the middle of July and fragments of it as late as August 3, 1920; August 5, 1921; August 11, 1925.

I have seen young birds perched in the marsh elder bushes near their nest holding on to two twigs, one with each foot, with the result that their legs were spread far apart with the tail twitching nervously, and once a parent perched on a telegraph wire reiterating the alarm note as it turned to the right and left with a quick flip of the wings. The general appearance of the Long-bill in flight is dull brown but when perched head-on the silky whiteness of the throat and breast is very conspicuous and they fairly shine in the sunlight. The full-fledged young look very black with a rusty patch on the back and are much darker than the worn and faded adults of late summer.

I found many nests with fresh eggs in the cattail swamps on May 25, 1892, situated about three feet from the ground or water and Richard Miller has found them still with eggs on June 8, 1919. The regular nests are rather oblong with more or less cattail down for lining and this often protrudes from the entrance hole on the side. The sham nests are usually nearly spherical, unlined and often built in the low sedge. The usual number of eggs in a full set is six. One nest evidently deserted was found with two eggs on July 12, 1923, and another, possibly a sham nest, was started on July 22 and completed on July 31, but no eggs were deposited in it. I have also seen the Marsh Wrens carrying nesting material as late as August 7.

Young just able to fly were found on July 14 and in full juvenal plumage by August 28, 1917. From the last days of August through September there seems to be an increase in the number of Long-billed Marsh Wrens and they occur in the marshes nearer to the Lighthouse and even in the coarse grass and sedge immediately back of the sand dunes. These are obviously migrants from farther north and it is quite likely that the individuals that have been found here in winter are of this sort rather than birds that have nested at Cape May. On October 1, 1923, they were more abundant than I had ever seen them, taking wing constantly as I tramped through the short sedge, or broke my way through the marsh elder bushes. Sometimes from three to six flushed at once and in a short walk I counted more than one hundred yet they would not have been seen at all had I not happened to enter the area in which they had sought shelter after their night flight. They flew heavily and dropped back to the ground like miniature rails. Judging from their labored flight on such occasions one wonders how they can accomplish such long migrations. Similar flights occurred on September 21, 1929; September 28, 1930; September 19, 1934; while in several years a number of dead Marsh Wrens were picked up along the roads which had struck overhead wires or had been struck by automobiles in the night.

Our dates of arrival are not very satisfactory as few observers have been in the haunts of the birds in the early spring but they are obviously late migrants and our earliest dates are May 11, 1908; May 17, 1914; May 10, 1924. The breeding birds seem to leave by late September or early October but we have records for November 6, 1921; November 21, 1926; November 9, 1930; and on several Christmas censuses of the Delaware Valley Club there are December records of single birds—December 24, 1923; December 26, 1932; December 22, 1935; December 27, 1936.

The occurrence of the Long-bills at Cape May in winter has always interested me. They seem so out of place at this season. We look upon them as among the latest spring migrants, birds that seem to revel in the hottest and sunniest of open marshes and yet here they are thriving in the coldest days of the year. Samuel Rhoads and I first established them as winter residents in January, 1892, during a bitter gale from the northwest when the marshes were all encrusted with ice and one could scarcely stand against the wind. Making our first trip to Cape May at this season, we plowed through the acres of tall cattails back of South Cape May to see what might be lurking there. As we parted the close ranks of dry yellow blades we sent clouds of soft down from the ripened fruit drifting through the air and suddenly one of these little birds appeared before us and, pausing for a moment, plunged again into the thick vegetation. Then we found them every few steps swaying up and down on the dead stalks with tail cocked over back in the characteristic manner. Evidently there was insect food here sufficient for their support—hibernating flies, perhaps, on warmer days, and pupae of various sorts waiting to be sought out. We thought the occurrence of the Marsh Wrens at this time entirely unusual but subsequent experience has shown them to be regularly present in winter in small numbers. Thus was a summer resident species shown to be a resident but I still doubt that the birds that breed at the Cape are the same individuals as those that are to be found in the cold days of January.

The occurrence of Long-billed Marsh Wrens in winter is not peculiar to Cape May as Charles Urner found one at Manasquan on the northern coast on February 26, 1931, and John Gillespie saw another on the Tinicum marshes below Philadelphia on January 26, of the same year.

While they are summer residents in suitable localities throughout New Jersey their distribution is dependent upon the presence of cattail swamps. They are to be found in marshes all along the coast and up the Delaware as far at least as Trenton and along the larger rivers, sometimes above tidewater; above Mays Landing, near Princeton (Phillips), Plainfield (Miller), and even at Newton, Sussex County (Philipp). Their abundance in former times may be judged from the statement of B. B. Haines (O. and O., 1883, p. 204) that he knew a collector to obtain from 400 to 500 eggs in a day in the vicinity of Elizabeth!

## SHORT-BILLED MARSH WREN

### Cistothorus stellaris (Naumann)

This very different Marsh Wren is a local summer resident of open semi-brackish marshes about Cape May, inhabiting areas of fine low grass—*Distichlys spicata* and *Spartina juncea*—usually back toward the upland where stray bushes occur scattered about and never out on the main salt meadows; nor is it found in the cattail thickets where the Long-bill abounds. Like the latter it also occurs in winter usually in smaller numbers but frequenting the same haunts as in summer and never mixing with the other species.

Curiously enough it was in midwinter that I first discovered this little Marsh Wren at Cape May. Samuel Rhoads and I had been trapping shrews and mice on the marshes then lying between Cape May and the Lighthouse on January 28, 1892, when we flushed one of these diminutive birds from an open grassy spot back of South Cape May and, as we did not know it, it was promptly shot. The wind was blowing a gale from the northwest and it was bitter cold, hardly the weather to expect such a bird as this. But subsequent experience has shown that it is of regular occurrence here in small numbers every winter.

While Richard Harlow had found the Short-billed Marsh Wren nesting on the edge of the salt meadows in Burlington County in 1913 and Dallas Lore Sharpe saw two on the marshes of Salem County at the head of Delaware Bay, at a much earlier date, it was not until 1917 that we found them at the Cape in summer. On August 4, of that year Fletcher Street and I heard one singing near the site of my winter record. There was a large patch of fine grass flanked by an impassible muddy bog on one side and a cattail thicket on the other, where a few Long-bills were established. Search as we would we were unable to find a nest nor did we see more than a single bird and up to date no one has been able to locate a nest in this region. I visited this bird many times during the summer and studied it carefully, but failed to find a mate or young. Sometimes it would not be in evidence when I arrived, then suddenly I would hear the song and there was the bird on the top of a low bush or weed right in front of me, but when I looked again it was gone, dropped back into the dense mat of grass whence it had come, and where it remained silent, while no amount of tramping about would cause it to take wing. The habits of this and many other individuals observed on subsequent occasions was always the same, ever elusive and always singing from one or more definite perches, flying low over the grass when changing its position and eventually plunging into it to seek refuge and concealment.

A bird watched on August 28, 1929, gave a flip to the wings and tail that was so rapid that it seemed like a blur while the head was jerked to right and left so quickly that the action almost escaped the eye. Another individual was seen to climb up the stalk of a sedge by rapid jumps of an inch or two facing first to one side, then to the other, while the feet changed position with each jump and the head and body were "bobbed" up and down between them.

The notes of the rapid song are fine and insect-like but sharp and emphatic and give the impression of being chopped off short. The most frequent song as I have transcribed it is: *tchip; tchap; tchip, tchu-tchu-tchu* and at a distance when only a part of it is audible it recalls the *chís-eck* of the Henslow's Sparrow which inhabits the same region. On other occasions the song terminates with more of a trill: *tchip; tchap; tchip; churrrrrrrrr* or *chip; chap; chip; zizl-zizl-zizl*. One bird varied its song considerably, sometimes shortening it to *chap; chap; chappy-chappy*, or *chip; chap; zee-zee-zee-zee-zee*. Next day he sang *chap; chap; zeeda-zeeda-zee* and *chip; che-che-che-che*, the last notes of this song being much more deliberate than in any of the other renderings.

Another individual watched on August 15, 1921, began with *tchip; tcha; chu-chu-chu-chu-chu*, then changed to *tchip; tcha; tchip; churrrrrrrrr* and again to: *tchip; che-tzee-tzee-tzee-tzee*, with a noticeable pause after the first note. The alarm note *tchip* is often interpolated and repeated between the renderings of the songs. A short song was heard as late as September 5, 1926, by John Gillespie and a mid-winter bird was heard to render the alarm cry *chick, tick*.

A bird singing on August 13, 1921, had a mouth full of dry grass strands three or four inches in length and managed to utter his notes without dropping them; another carrying a longer strand was also singing. These birds may have been building sham nests although Richard Harlow's nests farther up the coast were found on August 4; one with four eggs, one with five and a third with five young.  He considered them as probably second breedings which may have been the case since a nest found in Salem County by H. M. Harrison contained eggs on June 4, 1922, and W. B. Crispin found another in the same vicinity on June 5, 1909.  Turner McMullen has examined nests near Cape May Court House on May 30, 1930 (seven eggs), June 7, 1931 (six eggs), and at Fortesque on Delaware Bay on May 28, 1932.

While Short-billed Marsh Wrens have been found in breeding colonies in Morris and Sussex Counties in the upper part of the state and scattered individuals have been recorded from various localities the bird seems to be rare and we have no definite migration records.  It may be that the summer birds at the Cape are the same individuals that winter here, certainly there is no such influx of transients as we see in autumn in the case of the Long-bill and birds summering to the north may pass to the southwest or down the Delaware Valley as seems to be the case with other species that are rare at the Cape.  (cf. L. K. Holmes, Cassinia, 1904, pp. 17–25.)

Our records follow, but absence of continual observations during the spring and autumn probably has much to do with the paucity of data at these seasons.

| | | | |
|---|---|---|---|
| 1917. | August 4–30. | 1928. | May 30–July 14.  September 1; October 7. |
| 1920. | August 15. | | |
| 1921. | July 30–August 19. | 1929. | July 27–August 28.  October 25. |
| 1922. | July 8. | 1930. | July 25–August 20, September 28. November 9. |
| 1923. | May 30–July 7. | | |
| 1924. | June 22–August 9. | | |
| 1925. | May 30–July 6. | 1931. | April 19, May 30, August 7. |
| 1926. | August 24–September 5. | 1932. | May 8, June 22. |
| 1927. | May 22–August 26. | 1933. | July 8. |
| | | 1934. | December 23. |

As a rule our records are of single birds but on May 30, 1925, a colony of six was found back of South Cape May as well as several individuals in other localities.

The counts on the annual census by members of the Delaware Valley Club are:

| | |
|---|---|
| December 23, 1923, one. | December 24, 1933, ten. |
| December 26, 1927, one. | December 28, 1934, twelve. |
| December 23, 1928, one. | December 22, 1935, four. |
| December 28, 1930, one. | December 27, 1936, ten. |
| December 27, 1931, one. | |

The Short-bill may be more abundant at all seasons than we suspect since its secretive habits, and ability to resort to shelter from which it is difficult to dislodge it, are characteristic.

# MOCKINGBIRD

### Mimus polyglottos polyglottos (Linnaeus)

We like to think of the Mockingbird as one of those austral birds, like the Gnatcatcher, Yellow-throated Warbler and the occasional Purple Gallinule, whose presence seems to make Cape May almost a bit of the South, but, as a matter of fact, it is hardly more plentiful or of more regular occurrence than it is at several points much farther north and it is only in unusual years that we can go looking for Mockingbirds at the Cape with any certainty of finding them.

With the exception of several nestings and the visits of family parties in late summer or early autumn our observations have been of single birds only, and so many of these have been in the colder months of the year, that we are forced to look upon the Mockingbird as a winter visitant quite as much as a breeding species. We have records at the Cape in all but two of the past twenty years—1919 and 1924, but the total number of our observations is not large. Arranged by months they are as follows: January, three; February, two; March, two; April, two; May, three; June, two; July, two; August, seven; September, four; October, two; November, one; December, five.

There are many tales of nesting Mockingbirds in the country about Cape May in the past and of men who, a generation or so ago, took the young from the nest and reared them for cage birds or for sale, but I find very few of the present day residents who know the bird at all and Otway Brown, who tells me of trapping Cardinals in the late eighties, says that no Mockingbirds

were obtained at that time.   Dr. Samuel W. Woodhouse some years before
his death, when asked about the abundance of Mockingbirds in past years,
told me that from about 1840–1850 when he was constantly in the field he
and his associates, John K. Townsend and George Leib, never found one
north of Maryland or Delaware.   In William Bartram's manuscript diary,
1802–1820, he mentions occurrences of single birds in his garden at Philadelphia but all in winter with the exception of one April and one October
record.   All of this testimony makes one wonder whether Mockingbirds
were ever really plentiful anywhere in Pennsylvania or New Jersey.   Peter
Kalm, it is true, mentions them as cage birds in this vicinity as early as
1748 and Alexander Wilson, writing in 1810, says: "the eagerness with
which the nest of the Mockingbird is sought after in the neighborhood of
Philadelphia has rendered the bird extremely scarce for an extent of several
miles around the city.   In the country around Wilmington and New Castle,
they are very numerous, from whence they are frequently brought here for
sale.   The usual price for a singing bird is from seven to fifteen and even
twenty dollars."   He also speaks of a man whom he had met on his rambles
"with twenty-nine of these birds old and young, which he had carried about
the fields with him, for several days, for the convenience of feeding them
while engaged in trapping others," but he does not state whether this was
in Pennsylvania, or in Maryland.

I have had several excellent opportunities for studying Mockingbirds at
the Cape.   One usually sees them perched on some telegraph wire or on the
top of a low pine or shrub or perhaps you may catch a glimpse of one on the
wing.   If it is your first view of the bird you think at first of a Robin—but
too light a gray, you say, and there is the longer tail, and as seen from the
back the conspicuous white on the wings, and finally the upward swoop as
the bird reaches his objective perch and comes to rest—all very unlike the
Robin.   You then think of the Thrasher—yes the pose and the proportions
are more like his but the color is of course very different and then there are
characters not shown by any other species which after all make the Mockingbird what he is.   The more you know him the better you realize his individuality and see that your first comparisons were merely the attempt to
describe the unknown in terms of the known.

Now he is up on the top of a pole standing high on his slender legs with
tail straight out behind, vibrating slightly as if moved by the breeze, a
veritable balancer; and now he is pouring out his song: *chuley, chuley-chuley-
chuley shee, shee, chu-aleé chu-a-leé chu-a-leé chee, chee, chee, tzit-tzit; tzit-
tzit* etc.   It is not the careful and consistent duplication of notes as given
by the Brown Thrasher but a repetition apparently dependent entirely
upon the pleasure of the performer.   Some notes he abandons at once,
the next perhaps will strike his fancy and he repeats it over and over, far
beyond the usual limit of repetitions, closing perhaps with some curious
attenuated *sotto voce* duplications of the note which he rolls out with great
apparent satisfaction.   Now he is hopping on tiptoe, as it were, along the

fence, singing all the while and then launches forth across the road, the notes still bubbling from his throat, and with wings flapping in an exaggerated effort as if it were all that he could do to transport such a load of song. With the usual upward swoop he comes to rest again on the telephone wire and begins all over again: *chuley, uley, uley, uley, cheer, cheer, cheer, whe-oo, whe-oo.*

The call of the Cardinal will be recognized in this effort but master mimics as are some Mockingbirds I have not detected the songs of many other birds on the few occasions on which I have heard Mockers sing at Cape May. The best singer that I have heard here was one of a pair that nested near the fire house at the Point in June, 1931, and was always in evidence singing at any hour of the day. I heard him on June 28, at 7 p. m. and on June 29 at 9 a. m. while William Shryock heard him at 9 p. m. on July 7, apparently the last day that he was in song. Sometimes he would leap into the air from his perch and turn an almost complete somersault making a great display of the white of both the wings and tail.

Single Mockingbirds that I have studied at other than nesting time usually perch on the top of some low bush or small pine tree or on telegraph wires or even on the ridge pole or chimney of a house, and from such a stand will drop suddenly to the ground, or to some fence post, and flap back again.

Sometimes I have been fortunate enough, in late August or early September, to have Migrant Shrikes and Mockingbirds under observation on the wires at Cape May Point at the same time. While the similarity in coloration causes those previously unfamiliar with these birds to mistake one for the other, their perching position and manner of flight are so strikingly different that they can easily be distinguished at long distances. To the alert, slender-legged Mockingbird, the perching Shrike, short-legged and heavy-headed, with tail drooping and head usually bowed over, is in striking contrast. The flight of the Mocker is steady and low, the beats reminding one of the leisurely strokes of the oars in an old row boat, and as the objective perch is reached the bird will set its wings and sail with a slightly undulatory motion terminating in the sharp upward rise that is so characteristic. The Shrike's flight, on the other hand, consists of a series of rapid wing beats and then a short pause in which the body falls slightly before the next series of pulsations. In both birds there is a conspicuous show of white in the wings but the slower flight of the Mocker produces a very different effect from the rapid flicker of the Shrike.

In one Mocker family that I studied an adult and young spent much of their time in the heart of a thicket, busy pluming themselves and the situation permitted close approach. Their quietness, and the length of time they remained under cover, demonstrated how easy it would be for them to escape the observation of one making but occasional visits to their haunts, and convinced me that they had thus escaped my attention on several previous visits to the spot.

Some dense thicket or cedar tree will furnish a wintering Mockingbird with satisfactory shelter and into these he will plunge when alarmed and refuse to emerge and, in spite of all our efforts to dislodge him, will remain safely out of sight in the depths of his retreat. I have observed this on not a few occasions.

Reviewing the several actual or probable nestings of Mockingbirds at Cape May; Reynold Spaeth, whose family lived at Cape May Point during his boyhood, told me that he found a Mockingbird's nest in the shrubbery of their garden in June, 1899, which contained four eggs. He took one of them and the birds promptly deserted. In other years about that time the birds were present and probably nested and that they did so in earlier years is suggested by the fact that I found a very worn bird there on August 27, 1891.

On August 25, 1917, Julian Potter found two old birds and a speckled-breasted young one at the Point. Two days later I found that there were five Mockers in this party, one a molting bird minus a tail, but with an exceptional amount of white on the wings; one in nearly full fresh plumage, possibly a bird of the year; two adults in worn plumage and the young one still being fed by the adults.

In May, 1918, a male was reported in full song near David Baird's residence on the western edge of Cape May not far from the beach, possibly the same bird that Walker Hand had reported as present during January and February. It disappeared, however, before summer set in.

On March 25, 1928, a Mockingbird was found in a thicket back of Second Avenue where it perched on the topmost spray of a bush and frequently indulged in those peculiar aërial somersaults for which these birds are famous. It was seen again on May 6 and by June 28 a pair had taken up residence amongst the shrubbery on the Mercur (Dougherty) place on Washington Street in the heart of Cape May and apparently nested, although I was unable to definitely locate a nest. Walker Hand told me that he had heard the male singing there since the end of April on nearly every time that he passed the premises and I heard it daily from June 28 to July 4 when both birds suddenly disappeared. Possibly their nest had been destroyed by one of the numerous marauding cats that are left every year by departing summer visitors to enrich the already too numerous cat population of the town. On June 26 I came upon this pair at 6 a. m. on Corgie Street immediately back of the yard in which the nest was supposed to be. They hopped about the low shade trees and down on the sandy ground where they progressed by a sort of running hop, with head and tail up, wings drooping slightly with the tips held just below the base of the tail. They exhibited the characteristic swooping, sailing flight of the species and the slow, measured beats of the wings. On the following day they were on the ground moving rapidly with heads stretched out in front seeking food of some sort.

On July 2, 1929, one was heard singing on Lafayette Street near Schellenger's Landing but was not seen later. On September 7, however, a family of four put in an appearance on the wires along Broadway near the beach, two adults one of which was molting, and two young with speckled breasts

PLATE 112

*W. L. Baily*

*W. L. Baily*

BROWN THRASHER; YOUNG AND NEST AND EGGS.

PLATE 113

*A. C. Redfield*

*Wharton Huber*

1. WHITE-EYED VIREO ON NEST.
2. RED-EYED VIREO FEEDING YOUNG AT THE NEST.

although in one the marks seemed more like streaks, perhaps due to the beginning of its molt. While perching they would now and then turn the head and point the bill diagonally upward. They also flirted the tail when excited and cocked it up over the back as if to aid in retaining their balance in the breeze. When one of them descended to the ground it literally dropped like a plummet with legs dangling. On October 3, there were five Mockingbirds in a yard on Lafayette Street, possibly the same family.

In June, 1930, William Schwebel told me that one had been singing at night at his cottage at the Point and kept his family awake and he thought that it must have had a nest nearby. Another sang from March 23 to April 25 in Walker Hand's yard in Cape May but was not seen later in the year.

In 1931 a pair nested at the Point near the fire house and the young were out of the nest by May 30 and were seen by William Shryock during June, the male being still in song and the young feeding in a garden close by. I noticed that they did not hop but ran rapidly over the ground pausing occasionally and spreading their wings, arching them slightly away from the body so that the white areas were displayed. On July 7 I saw six of this family at once. A single bird was there on July 17 and again on August 7 but none afterwards.

In 1932 we looked in vain for the pair of the previous year but no Mockingbirds were seen about the Point. On August 9, however, Charles Page found a pair with several full grown young among the dune thickets northwest of the Pond Creek Meadows and one or two were seen there later in the summer by James Bond and myself on several occasions.

On August 25, 1933, I found an adult bird with two spotted young, again in the same vicinity, and a single adult on August 20, 1934. My opportunities for following up the history of these birds were limited and they may have been present both earlier and later than the dates given.

June 1935, found a male Mockingbird in full song in a dense thicket in a yard on North Street which continued to sing until July 7 and was last seen on July 15 but no mate or young were detected. This may easily have been due, however, to lack of continued observation and the ability of the birds to conceal themselves. In the summer of 1936 the male was there again and was heard singing at various times, once as early as 1 a. m. by Ernest Choate.

During September and October one or two Mockingbirds have frequently visited the yard of David Baird on the western edge of Cape May where dense shrubbery close to the house furnished congenial shelter. One individual roosted there nightly from September 20 to October 2, 1925, and voiced his complaint when a light was turned on in the window near to his retreat. Two adults and several young appeared there on September 17, 1927.

In winter the Mockingbirds seen at the Cape are solitary individuals which select a suitable spot and are resident until spring time when they

apparently depart to seek mates.    One remained in the vicinity of Walker
Hand's home all through the winter of 1929–1930, coming regularly to a
table on the back porch, where a bunch of Christmas holly had been placed,
to feed on the berries.    Another individual located in a yard on Lafayette
Street in January 1922, and came regularly to fight his image in a window
of the house next door.

As many of these wintering Mockingbirds and the others that are seen
singly or in family parties, in late summer, are not observed earlier in the
year, when many persons are making daily studies of the bird life of the
region, it would seem that they must have drifted in from more remote
localities back in the country.    This could hardly be termed migration,
especially as the young birds in the late summer groups are still in the
juvenal plumage and are being fed by their parents.    Furthermore they could
not have come from greater distances to the north because there are no
breeding Mockingbirds there, while a northward movement, say from Delaware or Maryland, such as we see in the case of various herons after the
breeding season is over, is hardly likely.

On the other hand they may have come from quite near at hand since
Mockingbirds are so local, when nesting, that they might easily escape
notice except from those immediately on the spot, who as a rule would pay
no attention to them.    The pair found on the Dougherty property, for instance, scarcely wandered away from the yard in which they had established
themselves during the whole time that they were under observation, and
not more than half a dozen persons in the town recognized them.    Again, a
single bird seen by Alexander Wetmore, at Pierce's Point on the Bay shore
on August 11, 1926, might easily have reared a brood there without anyone
being the wiser.

While departure from the Cape, after the summer is over, has prevented
my continous observation of the activities of the late summer family groups,
week end trips by myself and various members of the Delaware Valley Club
during the autumn and winter have furnished fairly accurate records of the
occurrences of Mockingbirds throughout the year.    It would seem from these
that the bird is in no way gregarious and after the young have been reared to
the point that they are self reliant, they scatter and become solitary hermits
during the winter months.

That Mockingbirds have some preference for the immediate vicinity of
the sea is suggested by the records of a pair on Long Beach in the summer
of 1906, seen by Norris DeHaven; and on Sandy Hook at least until 1892,
according to Rev. Samuel Lockwood; at Point Pleasant, through the winter
of 1902–1903, reported by Miss Caroline Murphy; at Barnegat through the
summer of 1900 according to John Lewis Childs; at Stone Harbor, September 4, 1903 seen by David McCadden and on Five Mile Beach on December
27, 1903, seen by William Baily.    The latter also found a young spotted-
breasted bird just able to fly on Five Mile Beach on September 14, 1895, and
I saw one in full juvenal plumage with wings and tail fully developed on

Seven Mile Beach on September 10, 1927. These last records would seem to indicate nesting on the two islands.

There are scattered records of Mockingbirds in winter and more rarely in the breeding season in northern New Jersey as well as north to New England, but as the bird is a resident wherever found, there is no definite migratory movement.

In spite of the rather numerous records of the Mockingbird at the Cape it is still a red letter day when the bird watcher is lucky enough to find one, whether a solitary winter sojourner or a family in the warm days of late summer and early fall, and the puzzling irregularity of the occurrence of the species always arouses our curiosity and interest.

## CATBIRD

### Dumetella carolinensis (Linnaeus)

Catbirds are as universally distributed throughout the Cape May Peninsula as are the Thrashers but are more plentiful. In the town they nest in most of the gardens where there is thick shrubbery, while at the Point and back in the country nearly every thicket has its pair of Catbirds. The Catbird is more sociable than the Thrasher and delights in the immediate vicinity of old houses if suitable cover is left for its shelter.

It does not seem to occur close to the beaches except in migration, as bayberry bushes are not adapted to its needs, and Laurent saw only a few on Five Mile Beach in the old days when the island was wooded.

While mainly a summer resident and abundant transient, a few Catbirds usually remain through the winter in the dense tangles of greenbrier and holly about Cape May Point and along the Bay shore, and to a lesser extent in similar situations elsewhere. The familiar song of the Catbird is in evidence from late April to mid-July—July 16, 1927; July 14, 1923; July 19, 1924; July 23, 1926; July 16, 1927; etc, while fragments of song have been heard as late as August 9. The long drawn mewing alarm call—*tweeee* or *shreeee* is heard at all times through the summer when the bird is disturbed by an intruder. Catbirds sing frequently from the interior of a thicket but also from the top of a bush, with head up, wings slightly drooping and held a little away from the body. Perhaps no bird is more ready to respond to a cry of distress and a call of this sort from any bird will bring all the Catbirds in the vicinity "mewing" in sympathy, or more likely in curiosity.

The abundance of Catbirds at the Cape varies greatly in late August and during the autumn. Definite increases have been noted on August 20,

1927; August 21, 1922; etc., and then with the apparent departure of the summer population they may be almost absent until a great migratory wave brings others from the north and we marvel at the number of Catbirds that must summer in eastern North America! Such a flight occurred on October 5, 1927, when Walker Hand reported the town full of them and counted eleven in one small yard. Again on October 8, 1932, when I found them swarming in the thickets of Cape May Point, the wood edges were fairly vibrant with them as they continually darted up into the sour gum trees and dropped back again into the bushes. I estimated that there were at least one hundred in two gum trees which bore a generous crop of berries. There were many also at Cold Spring and a large number in the Physick yard while I picked up three on the road, victims of the wires. William Rusling observed a similar flight on October 5, 1935, and I saw a congested migration on September 28, 1930, and September 27, 1926.

I have seen fully fledged young being fed by the parents as late as July 17, 1920, and have seen an adult feeding with a Water-Thrush on the dry bottom of a woodland pool near Bennett, tossing the leaves aside vigorously. Another alighted on our porch roof in search of caterpillars which dropped there from an adjoining tree and he also tossed away the leaves that often covered his prey.

Five nests with fresh eggs, three or four in number, were found by Richard Miller at Rio Grande on May 27, 1923, and others on June 3 with eggs partly incubated. At the same locality Turner McMullen has found four nests with eggs as late as June 10 and one on May 23; two on June 8 contained young.

Walker Hand's arrival dates for the Catbird are as follows, with several additional records for recent years:

| | | | | | |
|---|---|---|---|---|---|
| 1902. | April 24. | 1908. | April 26. | 1914. | April 23. |
| 1903. | April 20. | 1909. | April 6. | 1917. | April 23. |
| 1904. | April 27. | 1910. | April 28. | 1920. | May 1. |
| 1905. | April 23. | 1911. | April 24. | 1923. | April 30. |
| 1906. | April 21. | 1912. | April 30. | 1926. | April 24. |
| 1907. | April 25. | 1913. | April 30. | 1932. | April 30. |

Concentrated spring migrations of Catbirds have been noted on May 1, 1914; May 8, 1915; May 6, 1930; May 7, 1932; but these did not compare with the autumnal flights. From their abundance as transients I assume that the coast line is one of their chief avenues of migration.

The usual date of departure is about the middle of October:

| | | | | | |
|---|---|---|---|---|---|
| 1920. | October 31. | 1925. | October 18. | 1931. | October 19. |
| 1921. | October 16. | 1927. | October 23. | 1932. | October 14. |
| 1922. | October 1. | 1928. | October 28. | 1933. | October 29. |
| 1923. | October 21. | 1929. | October 25. | 1935. | October 29. |
| | | 1930. | October 11. | | |

We have later records which may probably all be regarded as wintering birds:

| | | | |
|---|---|---|---|
| 1903. | March 9. | 1926. | December 26, two. |
| 1914. | December 9. | 1927. | January 23. |
| 1922. | December 9, 30. | 1927. | February 3. |
| 1923. | December 2. | 1927. | December 26, three. |
| 1925. | February 14. | 1928. | December 6, 9. |
| 1926. | November 14, 21. | 1928. | December 23. |
| | | 1929. | November 7. |

| | |
|---|---|
| 1930. | December 28. |
| 1932. | March 5. |
| 1932. | December 26. |
| 1934. | January 24. |
| 1934. | December 23. |
| 1935. | November 4. |

The February 1925 bird was in company with a small flock of Cedar Waxwings and some Robins. Winter records elsewhere are: Atlantic City, December 26, 1892 (Rhoads); Seven Mile Beach, February 11, 1894 (McCadden) and December 31, 1905 (Hughes); Five Mile Beach, several in the winter of 1897–8 (Baily). Also Plainfield, December 30, 1897 (Miller), and Moorestown, December 25, 1903 (Evans).

The Catbird is a common summer resident throughout New Jersey, including the coastal islands.

# BROWN THRASHER

*Toxostoma rufum* (Linnaeus)

PLATE 112, p. 758

Thrashers are common summer residents throughout the Cape May Peninsula all the way down to the pine woods and thickets of the Point. They also occur here and there in the gardens of the town and in clumps of bayberry and brambles just back of the sand dunes, from which they occasionally repair to the sea beach itself in their search for food. I have found them breeding on Two Mile Beach and on the other island beaches to the north where they find satisfactory shelter. Occasional Thrashers also remain throughout the winter in dense thickets at the Point and along the Bay shore.

They are in full song from their arrival in April until the middle of June. It is their habit here, as elsewhere, to mount through a tree from limb to limb until they attain the topmost twig and there, with head up and tail straight down, they pour out the familiar medley of couplets that constitutes their song. They stop singing, I think, sooner than any of our other breeding birds and my latest dates are June 22, 1924; June 30, 1920; July 2, 1921; July 4, 1928.

As there is usually more or less of a breeze near the shore it is sometimes amusing to see the efforts of the Thrasher to maintain his exposed singing perch. One observed on May 9, 1925, swung his long tail up and down like a veritable balancer, now almost vertical above his back and then straight down beneath his body. Another on May 24, 1918, was pouring out his song in the face of half a gale and had great difficulty in keeping his balance. At one moment his tail would be blown forward over his back until it nearly touched his head and then he would bring it around below his belly while he fairly leaned back against the wind.

The gait of the Thrasher on the ground varies. I have seen them, when feeding deliberately on the lawns on Washington Street, walk slowly and occasionally take a half-running step, while others on the sandy roads of Cape May Point progressed by a series of vigorous hops for a few yards and then seemed to combine a hop and running step until it was difficult to define their progress as either. Thrashers delight in sandy and dusty roads and before these were so generally replaced by hard concrete they were much more in evidence than they are today. They come to such places to dust themselves and rid their bodies of the lice that infest the nest. A full plum-aged young bird of the year was found on July 29, 1920, squatting full on his belly in a hollow in the sandy road east of Lake Lily. He fluffed out his feathers in the dust and every now and then would preen his plumage, prob-ing the bill well under the wings, after which he would poke it down into the sand as if to cleanse it. Then he arose and hopped vigorously for a few yards returning to the same spot where he rolled partly over on one side and remained so for several minutes holding his bill open the while. I saw an adult bird going through the same performance in a sandy wood road on July 7, 1928, and was in some doubt whether he was cleansing his bill or swallowing some of the sand. I have several times seen Thrashers bathing in rain water pools by the roadside.

Nests with four fresh eggs were found by Richard Miller at Rio Grande on June 6, 1920, and June 3, 1923, while in another nest found on May 27, 1923, the eggs were just hatching. Two nests found there by Turner McMullen on May 24, 1925, contained eggs and two on May 29, 1932, held young. I have seen full-fledged young birds in gardens on Washington Street on July 11, 1922, and July 5, 1925; in the former case they were feeding themselves. The duller coloration of the young Thrashers and the looser structure of their feathers are quite noticeable but not so striking as the different color of the iris which is gray in the young and bright yellow in the adult.

On July 3, 1920, I came upon two Thrashers in a thicket which were very much concerned at my presence and constantly uttered their alarm note—*chut, chut*, a sound almost exactly like that produced by sucking the tongue against the roof of the mouth and suddenly removing it. Doubtless they had young in the vicinity as on July 15, I found them there again, both carrying food in their bills although one of them soon swallowed his mouth-ful and wiped his bill on a twig. They again uttered the monotonous *chut, chut*, but this time there was also a peculiar mellow note *chuuurl* which had a curious ventriloquial character. I heard precisely the same note on July 8, 1916, and July 21, 1917, and on each occasion the birds were feeding young. Again I detected it on July 18, 1923, and recorded it as *churrly*, interposed among the numerous sucking alarm notes.

One individual came to our bird bath in mid-July 1937, and fed on scraps of bread thrown out to Grackles, Red-wings, etc. The former of these were cock of the walk so far as Red-wings, Starlings and Sparrows were concerned but they always deferred to the Thrasher when he appeared on the scene.

A family of three young Thrashers visited our garden on July 5, 1925, showing that they soon begin to wander from the nest site as we had had none present earlier in the summer. Another family was full-grown, but still in the juvenal plumage, on September 1, 1928. Thrashers are most abundant after the middle of July when the broods of young are on the wing. Later, in August, they become quite scarce, perhaps due to the retiring habits of the adults while molting, but it is my opinion that Thrashers like a number of the breeding birds begin to move south before the migrants from farther north arrive along the coast; with the great flights of late September and October they again become plentiful.

Walker Hand's records of first arrivals at Cape May up to 1920 with a few other records for more recent years are:

| | | |
|---|---|---|
| 1902. April 24. | 1911. April 27. | 1920. April 25. |
| 1903. April 20. | 1912. April 5. | 1921. April 24. |
| 1904. April 24. | 1913. April 18. | 1922. April 23. |
| 1906. April 21. | 1914. April 13. | 1923. April 22. |
| 1907. April 25. | 1916. April 23. | 1926. April 24. |
| 1909. April 23. | 1917. April 19. | 1932. April 30. |
| 1910. April 28. | 1918. April 16. | 1934. April 23. |
| | 1919. April 23. | |

Our latest dates are:

| | | |
|---|---|---|
| 1913. October 13. | 1925. October 18. | 1930. November 9. |
| 1920. October 17. | 1927. October 30. | 1931. October 19. |
| 1921. October 16. | 1928. October 13. | 1932. October 12. |
| 1923. October 21. | 1929. October 25. | |

We have several November and December records and a few for January and February, all apparently of wintering birds; and usually single individuals; Christmas census data are included.

| | | |
|---|---|---|
| 1915. February 3. | 1926. November 21. | 1932. March 5. |
| 1919. January 19. | 1926. December 26. | 1932. December 26. |
| 1923. February 22. | 1927. December 26. | 1933. December 24. |
| 1923. November 4. | 1928. December 23. | 1934. December 23. |
| 1924. December 28. | 1929. December 22. | 1935. December 22. |
| 1925. January 25. | 1931. December 27 | 1936. December 27. |
| 1925. December 27. | (eight). | |

On Five Mile Beach William Baily saw several during the winter of 1897–98, one on February 22, 1894, and two on December 27, 1903.

The abundance of Thrashers at the Point during the autumn migration is evidence of the great numbers of these birds that must nest in northern New Jersey and the states to the north, while it also indicates that the shore line is a regular migration route for south-bound Thrashers.

# ROBIN

Turdus migratorius migratorius Linnaeus

While varying in numbers from year to year, the Robin seems to have increased very noticeably in Cape May within my recollection, and is now the most plentiful and generally distributed breeding bird within the town limits. Originally there were probably few if any summer Robins on "Cape Island," judging by their status on those parts of the other coast islands where original conditions still prevail, but the wonderful development of shade trees in Cape May and the steady increase in dwellings with gardens and shrubbery and well-kept lawns have caused a corresponding increase in Robins. We find them feeding on the lawns and building their nests in the trees along the streets; we hear their cries of alarm when the young are starting to shift for themselves; their evening song in the days of early spring and, during May and June, their early morning chorus from 4:00 to 4:30 a. m., notable for its volume and drowning out all competition. In fact an occasional Red-wing, Catbird or House Wren voice is about all that can be detected in the prevailing wealth of Robin song. Laurent found them only in spring and autumn on Five Mile Beach in the eighties.

Robins in the East have become so closely identified with man's habitations that it is in close proximity to dwellings that we usually look for them, and so we find them about the houses at Cape May or at the Point, or in the orchards and gardens about the farms of the upland, nor do they stray far except for food until the flocking begins and the drifting bands of autumn and winter are forming.

Robins are incubating eggs by the last week in April at Cape May and young are hatched by May 8. They, however, have two and often three broods in a season and freshly hatched young have been found as late as July 10, while young were still being fed in the nest on August 13 and August 23, in different years, and parent birds have been seen on the lawns caring for full-fledged, active young as late as September 1, 1925. The young in a nest in a sycamore tree in front of our cottage took their first flight early in July, 1932, and the old birds were soon busy building another nest in the next tree pulling material from the first one to aid in its construction. The second brood had hatched by July 28 and were still being fed by August 1. A nest in the same tree held nearly fledged young on July 29, 1934, as did another on July 10, 1935.

Robins have been heard in full song as early as March 13, 1921; March 19, 1924; March 21, 1925; March 11, 1929; March 23, 1935; while our latest dates for singing are July 26, 1922; July 26, 1925; August 7, 1926. While there is more variation in bird song than we realize there are usually certain dominant phrases that are always the same and this gives us the impression that all songs of a species are identical. Occasionally, however, one individual will utter a song so peculiar that we at once recognize it as different. So it was with a Robin at the Point on July 14, 1923, and on several days following which sang *chíl-o-wit, chíl-o-wit, chíl-o-wit*, each triplet exactly like the others, with none of the customary change of pitch. In autumn, winter and early spring, while not singing, the Robins have a series of subdued calls, *twit, twit, twit*, three or more together and accompanied by a flip of the wings as they sit on a perch or as they take flight. The loud screaming alarm cry seems to be limited to the breeding season and uttered mainly when nest or young are threatened.

The first full-fledged young have been seen on the lawns as early as May 23, 1921, and May 28, 1923, while others evidently but recently out of the nest, seen on June 21, 1932, and June 23, 1929, were probably second broods. By early July—July 8, 1921; July 11, 1922; July 11, 1924; July 18, 1925; they assemble in considerable numbers. On the shaded grounds of the Physick place I have frequently counted upwards of fifty or sixty on a single evening with very few adults, the latter doubtless still engaged with later broods. Some of the full-fledged young are in beautiful plumage, the dark spots below and the white ones on the back arranged in perfect rows. I have seen one of these speckled-breasted young bathing with an adult in Lake Lily on July 8, 1921. He stood in shallow water facing the shore, ducked his head completely under and fluttered his wings, fluffing up his plumage meanwhile. Another young Robin sat on a lawn with wings partly spread in bright sunshine while still another rested flat on his belly while he preened his plumage, both probably trying to rid themselves of lice.

In June Robins make free with the garden cherries, carrying them away one at a time in their bills and they also feed on the black mulberries which are frequently found along the wood edges, especially those that face the salt meadows. Later on wild cherries form an important part of their diet while in autumn poke berries are a favorite food and in winter the berries of the holly. They are to be seen too in July feeding on fields of new mown hay where insects are evidently the attraction. Their main staple of food however, throughout the spring and summer, is the earthworm and Robins may be seen constantly in search of them on the lawns and on the greens of the golf links. They gather in numbers on the close-cropped sod, running here and there, especially where a water sprinkler has brought the worms to the surface. They stop suddenly with head on one side as they detect their prey; and soon they are busy dragging the luckless worms from their burrows. With the advent of the Japanese beetle the Robins vie with the Starlings and Grackles in digging out the larvae from the ground. Unlike these birds, however, the Robin is not interested in scraps of bread thrown out on the lawn and while they are enjoying a feast of this sort nearby Robins persist in their search for worms or beetle larvae.

The usual gait of the Robin is a run, the feet moving with great rapidity, but they also hop, and a bird about to take wing from the ground usually changes from the run to the hop seeming to get a better start from both feet at once.

The roosting habit of Robins in late summer is well known and at Cape May, at this time, they associate with the Martins, Grackles and Starlings. At the time my observations began, they made use of the grove on the Physick property on Washington Street. Later they followed the other birds to a patch of woodland in West Cape May and finally back to the tall bayberry thickets on the Fill just east of the original roost. The young birds that assembled in July on the lawns of the Physick property increased in numbers as summer advanced and each evening flew up into the trees which shaded their feeding grounds. Hosts of other Robins both old and young came to the roost from farther off, some of them resting for a short time on the golf links where they stood listlessly and fed but little. I have counted thirty on a single green on July 29, 1921, eighty-six on August 21 and sixty on August 29—approximately one for every two foot square. Another gathering place was a lawn immediately opposite the roost where I have often seen as many as 250 crowded into a comparatively small area. All of these birds eventually repaired to the roosting trees while the latest comers went directly into them pitching down precipitately onto the branches. They seem to be the last birds to go to roost, with the possible exception of the Martins, and often I have seen flocks of Robins come in after the last Martin had settled for the night, while in the roost on the Fill I have seen Robins flying about from bush to bush in the gathering gloom when it was almost impossible to distinguish them ten feet away. They leave the roost with the other birds shortly before sunrise and scatter over the country, sometimes perching for a short time on chimneys, house tops and isolated trees or out once more on the golf links.

Young Robins have been found molting by August 12 and 17 in some years and adults were in full molt during the first two weeks of September, 1927. Old birds have been seen entering the roost on August 21, 1926, and

August 27, 1924, which exhibited forked and wedge-shaped tails indicating successive stages in the progress of the annual molt. As the young birds do not molt the flight feathers in their first year they showed no such peculiarity.

In late August there seems to be a diminution in the number of Robins about Cape May as the breeding birds begin to flock and scatter farther afield for the day's feeding. We then find them more common on the edges of the woodlands, in the pine groves of the Point, and even out on the mud flats of Pond Creek Meadows with the Killdeers. Later the breeding Robins of Cape May probably leave the neighborhood entirely and their places are taken by migrants from farther north.

These great flights of northern Robins begin to arrive in late October and continue to pass throughout the first two weeks of November. We have records of great flights on October 31–November 7, 1917; November 7, 1922; November 11, 1923; November 6, 1927; October 25, 1929; November 8, 1930; November 7, 1931; October 24–25; November 3 and 14, 1935. They are often accompanied by Bluebirds and, both being day migrants, their time of occurrence does not coincide very accurately with the flights of the smaller night migrants. On October 2, 1924, for instance, when the woods of the Point were thronged with small birds that had arrived during the night, there were only a couple of Robins to be seen anywhere in the vicinity, and on October 8, 1932, I could find only one. Indeed October, with the exception of the last few days, seems to mark the lowest point in Robin population at the Cape; and the contrast of great flights of November is striking.

William Rusling who was present at the Point continually during the autumn of 1935, watching the hawk shooting as the representative of the Audubon Association, has given me an excellent account of the Robin flight of that year, he states that "on October 24 there was a drop of twelve degrees in the temperature accompanied by a fairly strong north-north-west wind. A great flight of Robins came in flying north across the turnpike and into the wind, the birds were everywhere in the air from the ground up as far as the naked eye could see, while the glass showed more Robins at still greater altitudes. The flight lasted until about 10 o'clock in the morning." He estimated that, between 6 and 10 o'clock, fifteen thousand Robins passed; his actual count being 9815 with three thousand more between 5 and 5:30 p. m. The next day there was a similar flight between 6 and 6:30 a. m. and he counted 9150 all flying northwest, his total count of south-bound Robins for the autumn was 30,334; some were still passing November 14–16 but the bulk had gone before that. His daily counts from the first big flight until the end of his stay are as follows:

| | | |
|---|---|---|
| October 24, 9815. | November 2, 480. | November 6, 1100. |
| October 25, 9150. | November 3, 2385. | November 14, 2150. |
| October 30, 650. | November 4, 800. | November 15, 2000. |
| November 1, 665. | November 5, 75. | November 16, 100. |

On the other days the number present was negligible.

The Robin flights are exactly comparable to the flights of Flickers, Kingbirds, Woodcock etc., and their direction is always northward along the Bay shore. The theories advanced to explain this apparent reverse migration are discussed elsewhere (cf. pp. 38–46). Otway Brown records a similar concentrated flight which took place on November 7, 1931, when very large flocks passed the Point all morning flying, as usual, into a northwest wind. The birds were also plentiful at Cold Spring, and many rested there on the ground fighting and feeding on fallen apples. At the time of the visit of the American Ornithologists' Union to Cape May Point on October 25, 1929, a similar flight, but of lesser proportions, was in progress with many flocks of Bluebirds mixed with the Robins. Sometimes these flights, just as in the case of the night flying warblers, get blown out to sea by the northwest winds and struggle valiantly to beat their way back to shore. I was fortunate enough to witness one of these occurrences on November 6, 1927, when from 10 a. m., and probably earlier, until 2 p. m. Robins came in great flocks across the boardwalk from far out at sea heading directly into the gale. They appeared at first as mere specks high up in the air, fifty, one hundred, and two hundred, in scattered flocks with gaps and pauses between them. As they came nearer one could see that they were birds and buffeted this way and that, rising and falling, they struggled on, coming nearer and nearer and finally when approaching the shore they dropped low over the beach, probably to get in the lee of the buildings and hedges. Then they coursed over the marshes and sand flats in a generally northwest direction crossing Lake Lily and the pine woods at the Point and on northward along the Bay shore. Apparently they all came in where the beach faces south, between the pier and South Cape May. Now and then some of them were turned about or blown back by the wind when they had all but reached their goal and, drifting along with the wind, losing ground every moment, they would once more face about and make another supreme effort.

In spring Walker Hand's records show a distinct northward movement of Robins on March 9, 1904; March 10, 1905; February 25, 1906; March 14, 1907; March 9, 1908; March 3, 1909; March 16, 1916; and the migration continues after the earlier arrivals are established in the town for the summer and are in full song. On April 2, 1922, for instance, a flock of these silent transients passed north over the Fill and on April 2, 1924, I came upon a similar flock resting in the pine groves of the Point near Lake Lily. With some Robins present all winter, however, it is difficult to give actual dates of first arrival or of latest departure. In some years, when very severe weather has prevailed during January and February, the usual appearance of migrating Robins, which we recognize about the middle of the latter month, is delayed until March, as was the case in 1936. There are also curious influxes of Robins in the late winter months, at times of severe cold, which are certainly not composed of birds from farther south, and which appear to be birds that had wintered to the northward and had been forced back by severe weather, snow and lack of food.

Wintering Robins are usually to be found about Cape May in small flocks in the dense thickets and wooded dune hollows between Higbee's Beach and Cape May Point on the Bay shore, where red cedars, hollies and greenbrier make an impenetrable shelter with food in abundance. On calm, sunny winter days, too, they may be seen in the same general neighborhood, flying overhead, pausing in the tree tops as they pass from one piece of woodland to another, or chasing one another over the bare fields, and stopping to feed on the low berry bearing bushes. Then in exceptional years we may have the winter influxes referred to above as in mid-January, 1922; January 14, 1923; January 25, 1925; January 3, 1926; when flocks of one to three hundred coursed over the open country sometimes to remain for weeks in the same neighborhood, sometimes to disappear as mysteriously as they came.

The numbers of Robins counted in the Cape May region on the Christmas census of the Delaware Valley Ornithological Club are as follows although with such active birds there is probably some duplication:

December 22, 1929, 130.
December 28, 1930, sixty.
December 26, 1927, thirty-four.
December 23, 1928, 279.
December 27, 1931, twenty-four.
December 26, 1932, 450.
December 24, 1933, eighteen.
December 23, 1934, 154.
December 22, 1935, 597.

It is always one of the pleasures of winter bird study at the Cape to come upon these bunches of the familiar Robins in their winter quarters, familiar and yet somehow different from the sociable Robins of summertime; no longer dependent upon human environment but shifting for themselves in the wild Bay side dunes and marsh-lands; their breasts dulled by the brown suffusion of the winter plumage; their voices stilled but for the occasional flight call.

## *VARIED THRUSH

### Ixoreus naevius meruloides (Swainson)

It is a remarkable thing, one of the mysteries of bird migration, that three individuals of this bird of the far Northwest should have found their way to New Jersey. As early as March, 1848, Dr. Samuel Cabot procured a specimen in Boston, Mass., which had been shot in New Jersey (Proc. Boston Soc. Nat. Hist., 1848, p. 17) and in December 1851, another was taken at Hoboken, and recorded by George N. Lawrence (Ann, Lyc. Nat. Hist., N. Y., 1851, p. 221).

While three specimens were recorded from Long Island no others were seen in New Jersey until November 26, 1936, when one appeared at Mr. M. L. Parrish's cottage at Pine Valley, near Clementon. It was identified from plates in standard bird books and from an examination of specimens at the Academy of Natural Sciences and was later seen by Mr. and Mrs. E. S. Griscom.  It remained until March 20, 1937 (Auk, 1937, p. 395).  Curiously enough on November 24, 1936, another Varied Thrush appeared in the garden of Mrs. John H. Boesch in Richmond, Staten Island, N. Y., where it remained until December 6, and was observed by many persons.  (Bull. Staten Isl. Inst. Arts and Sci., January, 1937.)  While none of these individuals was identified subspecifically it seems probable that they all belonged to the more eastern race which ranges to northwestern Montana.

## WOOD THRUSH

### Hylocichla mustelina (Gmelin)

The Wood Thrush occurs as a summer resident in moist woodlands from Higbee's Beach, Cold Spring and Bennett, northward through the peninsula, but never about Cape May or the Point except as a very rare transient in autumn.  It is not adapted to the dry pinelands of south Jersey and does not find congenial surroundings close to the farmhouses, while in the Pine Barrens to the north it occurs only occasionally in deep cedar swamps. It is a bird of West and North Jersey and occasional in the narrow coastal strip where deep deciduous woods are to be found, as opposite to Rio Grande, and Bennett and in the Manahawkin Swamp in Ocean County, farther north.  We have heard the song of the Wood Thrush as late as July 12, 1925, at Goshen; July 14, 1927 at Bennett; July 28, 1922 at Erma; and as early as May 2, 1926, at Cold Spring.

In the autumn, at Cape May Point, William Yoder saw a Wood Thrush on October 25, 1929, and David Baird one on October 8, 1932, while one was picked up at the Lighthouse on September 18, 1932.  William Rusling through the autumn of 1925 saw it but four times—September 8, one; September 10, three; September 17, one; October 23, one.  Our only spring record for the town is a single bird that I saw in the Physick garden on May 10, 1929.

We have records for three nests all at Rio Grande and all containing four eggs, one on May 27, 1923, seen by Richard Miller, and two on May 30, 1925, and May 29, 1926, by Turner McMullen.

When we realize the numbers of Wood Thrushes that breed in the northern counties and in the states to the north of New Jersey we are at a loss to explain the scarcity of the bird in migrations at Cape May and are inclined to think that it must pass in a southwesterly direction north of the Pine Barrens and down the Delaware Valley or along Chesapeake Bay, and back in spring by the same route.

## HERMIT THRUSH

*Hylocichla guttata faxoni* Bangs and Penard

The Hermit Thrush is a common transient and a less abundant winter resident. It occurs in suitable localities all through the peninsula and even in the gardens of Cape May, but is most plentiful in the dense thickets of the Point and it is there that wintering individuals are most likely to be found. It was also found in migration on Five Mile Beach (Laurent). We may see many Hermits during the autumn migration but as we traverse the wood road through the sanctuary at the Point there are so many other birds present at this time that the silent south-bound Hermits do not impress us as do those that we come upon in midwinter. Then each individual seems to have selected a territory of his own where others shall not intrude, and where he may live up to the name that Alexander Wilson bestowed upon him. The presence of such an apparently delicate bird at such a season also impresses us and makes us associate the Hermit more with the stillness of his winter retreat than with the bustle of the autumn migration.

On one of those rare days of December or January when no wind blows and the sun warms up the pine woods and holly thickets until we think that spring has come, we may be fortunate enough to startle a Hermit Thrush from one of the dark tangles of vines and briers which are to be found along the Bay shore and we stop instantly to watch. With a few strokes of his wings he has alighted again upon some low limb or fallen tree trunk and so suddenly does he come to rest that the effect is almost startling. There seems to be no movement after his feet first touch the perch and with wings slightly drooping he remains motionless in his statue-like pose, the brown russet of his back blending with the dead leaves of the woods floor until we all but lose sight of him.    Presently there is a slow lifting of the tail, an interrogatory *put* and reassured he slips lightly to the ground. Now he pecks rapidly at some choice morsel among the leaves and is suddenly still again as if carved out of stone, or occasionally he will raise his head high up and stand as if on tiptoe to gain a better view when some sudden noise startles him.    At this season the term Hermit is peculiarly appropriate.    Even during the migrations he does not mingle intimately with his kind.    There may be several Hermits in the woods but each one seems engrossed with his own affairs and there is no flocking in the true sense of the word.    The Hermit, moreover, does not seek the vicinity of man's abode and when, through some accident of migration, he finds himself in the garden he shows none of the confidence of the familiar home birds but holds himself aloof full of an air of mystery, as if aware that the spell of the "wanderlust" is upon him and that his place is not with us.

Silence is one of his characteristics, when with us in the autumn and winter, but on a bright spring morning when a warmth as of midsummer makes all nature leap forth into early leaf and flower, there has come to me a vision of hemlock woods, of dark forest floors with sunlight filtering through the canopy of boughs high over head, and the tinkling of a mountain brook—and as I try to account for the mental picture I realize that a Hermit Thrush is singing—not the ethereal melody that will mark his homecoming in the north woods but a delicate imitation of it—his whisper song. There he stands on a bough not ten feet away, his bill closed but his throat swelling out with his song half-formed and ventriloquial but with sufficient of the true quality to bring back at once the vision of his mountain home. Just as the breath of summer has drawn forth the buds and blossoms a bit before their time so it seems to have forced our silent transient to try his voice before he reaches those surroundings amidst which he is accustomed to pour forth his music.    In autumn Hermits, like many other transients, linger longer than in spring.    They mingle more with other birds, exhibit more activity and are less secretive than on their northward flight.    We find them pulling at the pokeberries and belated sassafras fruits or flitting about the dogwood trees looking for the red berries, but there is always the same grace, the same dignity, and the same statue-like pose in moments of inactivity that are characteristic of this and the other small thrushes that grace our woods in the flights of spring and autumn.

The December Hermit Thrush records as reported on the Christmas census of the Delaware Valley Club are as follows:

| | |
|---|---|
| December 24, 1922, one. | December 27, 1931, thirteen. |
| December 26, 1926, two. | December 26, 1932, three. |
| December 26, 1927, one. | December 24, 1933, six. |
| December 25, 1928, one. | December 23, 1934, two. |
| December 22, 1929, three. | December 22, 1935, thirty. |
| December 28, 1930, four. | December 27, 1936, seven. |

We have scattered records of Hermit Thrushes for January, February and early March and on January 25, 1925, Henry Gaede saw as many as twelve in the course of a morning's walk at the Point. As in the case of several other wintering species there is little doubt but that they would be found to be quite as common in January and February as in December, had we been present continuously or had made more visits to the Cape at this time. It is not very likely that there is a southward migration of birds of this sort after December but some may fall victims to predatory enemies or perish from unusual weather conditions as winter progresses.

William Rusling's observations throughout the autumn of 1935 show the height of the autumn flight to be in late October. His daily counts are:

| | | |
|---|---|---|
| October 12, three | October 24, three | October 29, four. |
| October 14, fourteen. | October 25, thirty-two. | November 3, three |
| October 19, seven. | October 26, fifteen. | November 9, two. |
| October 21, three. | October 28, eight. | |

The spring migration seems to take place in late March and April and Hermits were reported as very numerous on April 24, 1926; April 1, 1928; March 19, 1932. On March 3, 1935, twenty-five were seen in the Physick garden by Otway Brown which may have been a migrating group but more likely wintering birds driven in for shelter or food by the excessive cold and snows of the preceding February.

While the Hermit Thrush is a summer resident in the mountains at New-foundland, Passaic County, near the northern boundary of New Jersey (Miller, Auk, 1922, p. 116), and perhaps elsewhere in the same vicinity, it is only a transient or casual winter resident in other parts of the state, and the host of Hermits that spread over the state during migrations must come from much farther north.

## OLIVE-BACKED THRUSH

### Hylocichla ustulata swainsoni (Tschudi)

A regular transient especially in the autumn at times of strong north-west winds and less abundant on the return flight in May. They come with the Veeries in late August and early September although the peak of their migration seems to be a little later, and like them they frequent the gardens of Cape May, although most common at the Point. They nest entirely north of New Jersey and migrate both down the coast and through the interior.

Our autumn dates are as follows:

| | |
|---|---|
| 1913. October 13. | 1928. September 5–October 21. |
| 1920. September 2. | 1932. September 7–October 14. |
| 1921. August 31–September 14. | 1934. August 26. |
| 1924. September 4–October 2. | 1929. September 6–October 5. |
| 1925. September 20–October 18. | 1930. September 28. |
| 1926. September 11–27. | 1931. September 7–October 19. |
| 1927. August 26–October 16. | 1935. September 7–October 5. |

Spring records are:

| | | |
|---|---|---|
| 1915. May 15. | 1916. May 16. | 1930. May 15. |
| | 1927. May 20. | |

Philip Laurent found them on Five Mile Beach in spring and autumn in the eighties.

## GRAY-CHEEKED THRUSH
### Hylocichla minima aliciae (Baird)

Occurs with the Olive-back but apparently not so abundant. I have seen them at Cape May Point on September 25, 1927; September 27, 1928; September 19 and 21, 1934; while William Rusling as a result of his continued observations during the autumn of 1935 reports them on September 7, 29 (seven), 30, October 4 (nine) and 5 (six) with one on the unusual date of November 2. These were all single birds except as indicated. I also saw several on May 20, 1927. The Gray-cheek breeds far to the north and northwest and probably only a small proportion of them traverse our coast line in migration.

## BICKNELL'S THRUSH
### Hylocichla minima minima (Lafresnaye)

William Rusling found five thrushes that had been killed by flying against wires or the Lighthouse, and that agreed in measurements with this small edition of the Gray-cheeked Thrush which breeds in the mountains of New England and New York. It would be impossible to satisfactorily identify them in life unless one had the two forms close together for comparison. His birds were found on September 23 (two), 24, 30 (two), 1935. At Barnegat light Charles Urner found a single Bicknell's Thrush among some five hundred birds killed there during a storm on October 28, 1925. Babson has recorded it at Princeton on September 10 and October 5 (Birds of Princeton).

## VEERY
### Hylocichla fuscescens fuscescens (Stephens)

An autumnal transient occurring in numbers at times of northwest winds in late August and September especially at Cape May Point but also in the gardens of the town and on the Bay shore north to Higbee's Beach. Walker

Hand and William Rusling have both commented upon the frequency of the call of the Veery on still nights when the fall migration is in progress and it would seem that far more of these birds pass overhead than are brought down by adverse winds. Veeries exhibit an unexpected spirit of hostility on occasion, and I have seen two of them, that settled on a sassafras tree to feed on the berries in late August, drive off Kingbirds that came to the tree for a similar purpose. Both species feed largely upon these berries during the autumn flight.

Our inclusive autumn dates for Veeries are as follows:

| | | | |
|---|---|---|---|
| 1891. | August 26. | 1927. | September 12. |
| 1920. | September 1–2. | 1928. | September 5–8. |
| 1921. | August 19–September 4. | 1929. | September 2. |
| 1922. | August 29–September 17. | 1930. | August 11–September 28. |
| 1923. | August 27. | 1931. | September 1–7. |
| 1924. | September 4–7. | 1932. | August 29–September 17. |
| 1925. | August 29–September 7. | 1934. | September 6–13. |
| 1926. | September 1–27. | 1935. | August 30–October 4. |

The earliest date, August 11, was of three in the Physick garden and my only spring record was of two that I saw in the same place on May 11, 1929. William Rusling's continued observations during the autumn of 1935 showed a single Veery on August 30, thirty-five on September 2, ninety-two on September 7 and from two to eight on five dates up to October 4.

While the Veery nests in the mountainous parts of northern New Jersey and as far south as Plainfield, Paterson, and possibly Princeton, the number of the transients that pass the Cape indicates that many of them come from still farther north. The Atlantic coast seems to be a regular highway of migration.

## *WILLOW THRUSH

### Hylocichla fuscescens salicicola Ridgway

While all of the specimens of Veeries that I have seen from Cape May County are the familiar eastern race one found on the campus at Princeton by Charles Rogers, on September 10, 1934, proved to be the darker western form known as the Willow Thrush (Auk, 1935, p. 191).

So far as I know this is the only record for the state.

## BLUEBIRD

### Sialia sialis sialis (Linnaeus)

Bluebirds are quite local about Cape May in summer. There are usually a pair or two nesting along the railroad between the town and Cold Spring and sometimes one or two at the Point and during July and August family parties may be seen on the telegraph wires but of late years none has been seen there.   Their favorite nesting places seem to be old woodpecker holes in telegraph poles or cavities in apple trees in the orchards.   Philip Laurent found them in spring and autumn on Five Mile Beach in the eighties but none bred there.

At the time of their arrival in March they sometimes occur in flocks of a dozen or more, most of which pass on farther north, and in autumn when the late October and November flocks of Robins are flying south we always find flocks of Bluebirds mingling with them.   It is at this season that they reach their maximum abundance at the Cape although they are then only passing transients and escape general notice.   A few remain through the winter along the hedges and fence rows of the uplands usually associating with winter sparrows, Juncos, Goldfinches, and other hardy species.   As the winter wanes these birds break into fragments of song but the "melting music of the Bluebird" is never at Cape May the herald of springtime as it is, or used to be, farther north.   Indeed our harbinger of spring would seem to be the male Red-winged Blackbird returning to his nesting ground close to the town and announcing the fact to the world.

It is difficult to distinguish spring arrivals from winter resident Bluebirds but I have listed all of our February and March dates below:

| | |
|---|---|
| 1921.  March 31. | 1930.  March 22. |
| 1923.  February 22. | 1931.  February 1, twenty. |
| 1924.  March 20. | 1932.  March 5. |
| 1925.  February 8. | 1933.  February 19 (with a flock March |
| 1927.  March 18. | 12). |
| 1929.  March 11. | 1934.  March 8, flock. |
| | 1935.  March 23. |

The state of the weather affects the time or arrival of the Bluebird and in some years continued snow and ice throughout February undoubtedly set them back, while in other years, when upwards of twenty species of wild flowers bloomed in this month, the Bluebirds pushed northward early.

Our winter Bluebird records are as follows:

| | |
|---|---|
| 1921.  January 9, three; January 10, four. | 1929.  December 22, six; December 26, four. |
| 1922.  December 24. | 1930.  December 28, twenty-one. |
| 1923.  December 2, three; December 23, two. | 1931.  December 27, thirty-one. |
| | 1932.  December 26, twenty-nine. |
| 1924.  January 19, three. | 1933.  December 24, forty-two. |
| 1926.  December 26, four. | 1934.  December 23, sixty-six. |
| 1927.  January 23, two. | 1935.  December 22, eighty-four. |
| 1928.  December 23, sixteen. | 1936.  December 27, 165. |

The late December counts were made on the Christmas census of the Delaware Valley Club and represent the combined observations of an increasing number of individuals.   Most of the individual returns were of a few birds only but flocks of as many as twenty were seen in several instances.   The possibility of duplications by several observers must also be considered in comparing the totals.

Winter Bluebirds either associate with other species or are sought out by them, and on January 19, 1924, three Bluebirds seen along a fence row, back of the town, were associated with two Myrtle Warblers and a Palm Warbler. While steadily decreasing as a breeding bird about Cape May the heavy autumn flights and the number of winter residents indicate that they must still breed in abundance in the country lying to the north of us, more especially north of New Jersey, and that the Atlantic coast is one of their regular migration routes.

I have seen Bluebirds with nests in telegraph poles on May 10, 1931, and May 25, 1922, while Turner McMullen has seen a nest with a full set of five eggs at Wildwood Junction on May 9, 1926, and one in the same place on May 8, 1927, containing five young. In Salem County and farther north, in West Jersey, Bluebirds have eggs as early as April 22 but those nesting near to the ocean seem to be a little later. I have seen the speckled-breasted young on the wires being fed by the parents from June 30 to July 27 and once on September 2, 1920, although they are most frequently observed during the first week of July.

The south-bound flocks have been recorded, usually with Robins, on:

| | |
|---|---|
| 1923. October 21 and 26. | 1931. October 31. |
| 1927. October 22. | 1932. November 12. |
| 1928. October 27 and November | 1933. October 28. |
| 1 and 10. | 1934. November 25. |
| 1929. October 25. | 1935. October 24–25, November 1, 2, |
| 1930. October 26. | 6, and 14–15. |

The 1935 record is that of William Rusling who was present at the Point throughout the autumn. His counts were as follows September 19 (seventy-five); October 24 (352); 25 (440); November 1 (710), 2 (220), 3 (forty-five), 6 (245), 14 (125), 15 (135), with scattering individuals on other days. The big flights occurred with Robins on days of north winds.

## BLUE-GRAY GNATCATCHER

Polioptila caerulea caerulea (Linnaeus)

The Gnatcatcher is one of those southern species whose presence at Cape May adds to the interest of its bird life and gives to the southern counties of New Jersey a character all their own. It is most frequently and regularly seen in the pine woods of Cape May Point surrounding Lake Lily though it occasionally visits the gardens of the town and may be seen as a rare transient farther north in the peninsula. On the Bay shore it ranges north at least to Bridgton where it has nested for several years and doubtless has always been a summer resident. Bennett Matlack has found four nests in this vicinity; one in Bridgeton Park on May 6, 1910, on the horizontal limb of an oak, twelve feet up and another back of Fortesque on a similar limb fifteen feet from the ground. In the latter instance "both birds carried nesting material and through the glass the shiny cobwebs and other material could be plainly seen." On May 27, 1933, a third nest was found in the park on an oak limb eighteen feet up and still another May 30, 1933, on a small limb of a tree which held four eggs. We have another Bridgeton record, May 12, 1935. The first nest found in the state was discovered by William Baily in the same neighborhood on May 19, 1885. For the vicinity of Cape May we have but two breeding records, a nest with four eggs found at the Point by Samuel Rhoads on May 17, 1903, and a brood of young just out of the nest June 13, 1937, seen by Frederick Schmidt and others. Julian Potter and Fletcher Street saw a family being fed near Court House on June 16 of the same year. It probably nests also at Dias Creek and elsewhere in the intervening country as Walker Hand and Henry Fowler found six birds there on May 28, 1911. Julian Potter found a Gnatcatcher singing at the Point on June 9, 1929, and another at Medford Lakes on June 16, 1935, while Fletcher Street showed me a nest at Beverly on May 2, 1936, which contained eggs. On the Atlantic side of the state it has been recorded on Five Mile Beach on April 12, 14 and 15, 1879 (W. L. Abbott), and April 7, 1901, while Norris DeHaven and I found a number in the strip of woodland that formerly stood back of Chelsea, just below Atlantic City, on April 8 and 16, 1893. While these birds may have been migrants the fact that the Gnatcatcher does not breed north of New Jersey, in the east, makes it likely that they spent the summer where they were found. Straggling migrants have been seen farther north, as one at Manasquan on September 5, 1927 (Urner); Princeton, April 28, 1875 (Scott); Woodbury, May 1, 1880 (Abbott); Haddonfield, April 10, 1882) Rhoads); and Mt. Holly, April 25, 1920 (Pumyea); also four records for Essex Co. (Eaton) and two for Union (Urner).

The Gnatcatcher is an exceedingly active little bird, hopping from twig to twig as it moves through the woods, peering from right to left with its prominent black eyes and swinging its long tail forcibly from one side to the other, usually keeping the feathers tightly closed although they are sometimes slightly spread. The tail seems entirely out of proportion to the body and its constant action is most characteristic; sometimes the bird is swung completely around by the force of the effort. The head is usually bent over with the bill pointed downward, and the tail, between flirts, is cocked up at an angle while the wings droop slightly.

Once I saw two Gnatcatchers fly up fighting in the air with a great show of white tail feathers (September 1, 1926). And again one was seen hovering over a stalk of golden-rod catching some small insects in the air. Seen from below the Gnatcatcher displays only the silky whiteness of its breast and belly but from the side, especially in spring, the blue of the upper parts is quite intense. Young of the year are grayish blue not nearly so brilliant as old birds in spring. A young bird in full juvenal plumage was seen on August 7, 1931, and adults in molt, with new tail feathers not fully grown, on August 7 and August 4, in different years.

The wheezy squeek which constitutes the Gnatcatcher's song has been heard in the spring and early summer but in August and September when the little bird is most frequently seen at the Cape it is silent.

One that I studied intimately on May 2, 1932, remained for some time in a small bush, and on the lower limb of an adjoining pine tree, feeding diligently. It peered intently with its beady black eyes at every twig and as it hopped about, the tail was flipped slightly up and down, and every now and then there was a much more violent rotary swing to one side or the other. The bird then came to rest and plumed the feathers of the breast and back, down to the base of the tail; it also scratched the head with its left foot. After this it became more active than before with much more flirting of the tail. The colors were very bright and contrasting, the blue of the back, white breast and black tail. The white feathers of the latter were seen only when the bird flew from one twig to another.

With the exception of the records already referred to our earliest dates for summer Gnatcatchers at the Point have been:

| | | | | | |
|---|---|---|---|---|---|
| 1922. | July 15. | 1927. | July 29. | 1934. | July 29. |
| 1923. | July 18. | 1928. | July 18. | 1935. | August 4. |
| | | 1932. | July 17. | | |

They become more plentiful in August, though never abundant, and our latest dates are:

| | | | | | |
|---|---|---|---|---|---|
| 1922. | September 17. | 1928. | September 1. | 1934. | September 20. |
| 1924. | September 1. | 1929. | September 29. | 1935. | September 6. |

While most of our observations of Gnatcatchers have been of single birds or parties of two or three, John Gillespie saw five on September 5, 1926, Julian Potter eight on April 23, 1922, and Ernest Choate five on August 3, 1935.

Our earliest spring arrival dates for Gnatcatchers at the Point are:

| | | | | | |
|---|---|---|---|---|---|
| 1903. | April 11. | 1926. | May 1. | 1932. | May 2. |
| 1921. | April 24. | 1927. | April 24. | 1934. | April 14. |
| 1922. | April 23. | 1928. | April 6. | 1935. | April 15. |
| 1923. | April 22. | 1929. | April 14. | | |

With no competent observer in the field continuously through the spring some of these dates are undoubtedly late.


## GOLDEN-CROWNED KINGLET

### Regulus satrapa satrapa Lichtenstein

The Golden-crowned Kinglet is a regular autumn transient, especially about Cape May Point, but occurs also in Cape May and in the wooded country to the north as well as, formerly, on Five Mile Beach. A small number remain through the winter in cedar groves and orchards but it is much less abundant then, as well as on the northward migration in spring.

Our earliest arrival dates are:

| | | | | | |
|---|---|---|---|---|---|
| 1921. | October 9. | 1925. | October 1. | 1930. | October 5. |
| 1923. | September 30. | 1927. | October 10. | 1932. | September 24. |
| 1924. | October 2. | 1928. | September 30. | 1935. | October 5. |
| | | 1929. | October 5. | | |

We have many records for November and December but our Christmas census lists usuually show only a small number present:

| | |
|---|---|
| December 23, 1928, five. | December 24, 1933, one. |
| December 22, 1929, two. | December 23, 1934, eight. |
| December 27, 1931, one. | December 22, 1935, eighty. |
| December 26, 1932, five. | December 27, 1936, eleven. |

I seldom see over six on a day's walk in autumn and on only three days did the number ever exceed ten.

In spring we have only two records—April 1, 1928, one seen by David Baird, and March 18, 1933, when I saw several. This is in part due to lack of field work in early spring and partly, no doubt, to the fact that the bird passes through rapidly at this time or travels farther inland, but it is unquestionably scarce.

The Golden-crown is at home in the north woods and the higher mountain forests of the eastern United States but does not nest in New Jersey. For some reason or other it does not seem to be as abundant in either migration as it is farther inland.

## RUBY-CROWNED KINGLET

### Corthylio calendula calendula (Linnaeus)

The Ruby-crowned Kinglet is a regular transient, more abundant in autumn; occasionally an individual remains through the winter, or at least through December, but this is very unusual. While here its habits and haunts are like those of the Golden-crown and they often associate.

Arrival dates:

| | |
|---|---|
| 1923. September 30. | 1928. September 27. |
| 1924. October 2—numerous with Chickadees. | 1929. October 5. |
| | 1930. October 5. |
| 1925. September 22. | 1934. September 28. |
| 1926. September 27—abundant. | 1935. September 27. |

Our latest dates for migrants are:

| | |
|---|---|
| 1923. November 11. | 1934. November 7. |
| 1931. November 7. | 1935. November 3. |
| 1932. November 13. | |

Single individuals were seen December 26, 1927 by Julian Potter and December 23, 1934, on the Christmas census.

In spring we have the following records:

| | |
|---|---|
| 1922. April 23. | 1932. May 8—three. |
| 1927. April 30. | 1933. May 7—several. |

The Ruby-crown breeds still farther north than the Golden-crown while its route of migration appears to be the same.

## PIPIT

Anthus spinoletta rubescens (Tunstall)

Flocks of Pipits are of regular occurrence about Cape May from October to January but curiously enough none have been recorded during the northward flight of spring. Most of our records are of two or three birds flying overhead, or flocks of a dozen, thirty, or forty, but in December and January there may be great flocks of several hundred apparently spending the winter in the Cape region. Whether we have simply failed to come upon them in February and March, or whether the flocks have moved off to the south and then gone north rapidly or by a more inland route, I cannot say.

To me the Pipit seems to be the embodiment of three impulses of bird life: gregariousness, the restless spirit of migration, and protective coloration. On some day of midwinter when there has been no blanket of snow such as sometimes covers the landscape, even at such a supposed "semi-tropic" region as Cape May, we gaze over the broad monotonous expanses of plowed fields and conclude that here at least bird life is absent. We contrast these silent brown stretches with the swamp edges and their bursts of sparrow conversation or with old pasture fields where Meadowlarks are sputtering. But let us start to cross these apparently deserted fields and immediately with a weak *dee-dee, dee-dee*, a small brown bird flushes from almost beneath our feet, then another and another, displaying a flash of white feathers in the tail as they rise. In a moment they have settled again farther on and are lost to sight against the brown background as suddenly as they appeared. We advance again and now the ground before us seems fairly to belch forth birds, as with one accord, the whole flock takes wing, and with light, airy, undulating and irregular flight, courses away over the fields, now clearly defined against the sky, now swallowed up in the all pervading brown of the landscape.

On January 3, 1893, I came upon an enormous flock of Pipits back of South Cape May feeding on black grass stubble. After following them about for a few minutes they all took wing and mounting high in air, until they looked no larger than flies, they disappeared to the southward. On January 7, 1922, I encountered a similar flock on the Fill feeding in a burnt over area several acres in extent. In places the grass had been burned down to the ground, which was black with the ashes and traversed everywhere by the winding runways of meadow mice, now mere channels in the earth. There were scattered bayberry bushes, clumps of low willows and occasional tufts of ruddy buff Indian grass which had escaped the fire. I had deliberately approached the spot with the expectation of finding Pipits but they had all taken flight before I was able to distinguish a single bird on the ground. A large part of the flock arose first and the others joined them in succession, rank after rank. They formed a long rather dense flock and did not fly high above the ground, as they often do, the individual birds rising and falling slightly which produced a somewhat undulating effect, while all were chirping in their thin wheezy manner.

After circling in a large arc they came drifting back and settled down near where they were before. Several times later they flushed but always returned to the burnt area. By watching exactly where they alighted I was able to detect them scattered all over the ground, about one bird to each square foot, where thickest. Their backs had a distinct olive cast in the strong light but the streaks on the under parts were only seen clearly when the birds were breast on. They all walked deliberately or sometimes took half a dozen steps in rapid succession, almost a run, though less regular. They all moved in the same general direction and as I moved parallel with them I could see them pressing straight ahead through the grassy spots and between the grass tufts and the stems of the bushes that had escaped the fire. They kept their heads pretty well down on the shoulders and leaned forward, dabbing at the ground with the bill, to one side or the other, apparently picking up scattered seeds of grasses and sedges. The tail was carried parallel with the ground or tilted up a trifle while the tips of the wings hung just below its base. The tail moved a little as the bird advanced but there was no distinct tilting as in the Palm Warbler or the Water-Thrush. Only just as the bird took wing was it possible to see the white on the outer tail feathers. Sometimes the neck was outstretched and the head held erect while the bird made a hasty survey all around. Just how the Pipits took wing I could not ascertain as the individuals that broke into flight were never the ones upon which I had my glass focussed, and once the start was made it became contagious and all were on the wing in a moment.

Once or twice a few Pipits took after a nearby Meadowlark that had flushed at the same time but usually they made no mistake and hung closely together. Eventually, three days later, the flock disappeared, rising high in air as did the other flock and made off for the shores of Delaware. They have a certain sparrow-like appearance on the ground but their walking and their systematic and concerted activities are characteristic.

The Pipit is a typically gregarious species and exhibits that peculiar simultaneous response to some signal that we cannot detect but which causes the entire flock to act as a unit with such beautiful precision. The action, however, is not developed to quite the perfection that we see in some of the smaller sandpipers.

The Horned Lark is the bird with which the Pipit would naturally be confused as they have much the same habits. Julian Potter writes me that in his opinion the flight of the Pipit is more uncertain and erratic than that of the Lark while the call note of the latter is higher pitched and clearer, the Pipit's call being thinner and slightly harsh.

It seems to me that the Pipits look much darker, almost black in certain lights, when on the ground, while they stand higher and do not appear to "creep" as the Larks seem to do.

Our arrival records are as follows:

| | | |
|---|---|---|
| 1921. November 11. | 1926. November 21. | 1933. October 29. |
| 1922. November 7. | 1927. October 23. | 1934. November 25. |
| 1923. October 21. | 1928. September 30. | 1935. October 8. |
| 1924. September 22. | 1929. October 25. | |

They have remained every year until the last of December and our Christmas census returns are:

December 26, 1926, forty-four.  
December 26, 1927, one hundred.  
December 23, 1928, fifty.  
December 22, 1929, one.  
December 28, 1930, nineteen.  
December 26, 1932, one hundred and ten.  
December 23, 1934, flock.  
December 22, 1935, four.

While I have no spring records for Cape May and only two for January, Julian Potter saw a flock of thirty near Salem, on April 28, 1918, which indicates the time of their northward flight.

Our Pipits come to us from breeding grounds north of the United States and while they occur inland, as well as on the coast, in migration, the latter is evidently one of their principal highways.


## *BOHEMIAN WAXWING

### Bombycilla garrula pallidiceps Reichenow

There have been several records of the Bohemian Waxwing in New Jersey but none of them is satisfactory. Dr. C. C. Abbott records one obtained in Cape May County and another in Morris County (Birds of New Jersey, 1868) and adds two more from Mercer County in his list of 1884, but there are no details regarding any of them. T. M. Trippe states that a pair was "observed in the vicinity of Orange, April 28, 1867" (Amer. Nat., II, p. 380), whether by himself or someone else is not stated.

These Waxwings often accompany the Evening Grosbeaks in their southward winter flights from their home in the far northwest but we have no record of them among the recent flights of the Grosbeaks.

## CEDAR WAXWING

**Bombycilla cedrorum** Vieillot

Cedarbirds about Cape May are found mainly in the pine woods of the Point although they occur irregularly and sporadically northward along the Bay shore and in the farming district farther inland. In Cape May itself I have seen them but once or twice; a flock came to rest in a wild cherry tree in the Physick garden on August 30, 1932; and Walker Hand told me that a flock of seven spent the winter of 1904–1905 there; while during March 19–24, 1906, they were common all over the town feeding on the berries of the Japanese honeysuckle and he counted fifty-two in one flock. They were also common during the winter of 1921–1922.

At the Point I have records of Cedarbirds for every month of the year but they are irregular there, as elsewhere, and vary greatly in numbers. They seem to be most abundant from May 20 to June 1 and from late July or early August to October. During some years there may be periods of several months when no Cedarbirds are seen and in some summers they have been recorded but once or twice. Usually, in summer, they occur in flocks of six or eight or as many as twelve or fifteen may be seen together; our largest flocks, however, have been in spring or fall: seventy on May 22, 1927; sixty on March 20, 1924; forty-five on May 10, 1924; thirty on September 11, 1924; while the largest winter flock was on December 26, 1926, when twenty-seven were counted. The largest flocks are obviously on migration and William Rusling who watched the Cedarbirds continuously during the autumn of 1935, found that during that year, at least, the height of the flight was in September.

His counts per day were as follows:

| | | |
|---|---|---|
| September  6, 125. | September 16, 160. | September 29, 120. |
| September  7, 830. | September 17, 225. | September 30, 180. |
| September 10, 531. | September 23, 191. | |

and in smaller numbers to November 15.

While the spring Cedarbirds are in beautifully fresh plumage, many of them with conspicuous red "wax" tips to the secondaries, the flocks that arrive in August are composed of both old and young.

On only one occasion have I any record of the Cedarbird's nesting in the Cape May district. On August 19, 1921, I found a nest on the horizontal branch of a pine tree about ten feet from the ground upon which the female was sitting. It contained no eggs and by the 25th had been deserted. There were migrant flocks of the birds in the woods at the time.

Cedarbirds are usually seen flying rapidly overhead in compact flocks, passing from place to place, and uttering their faint wheezy notes. With the glass it is usually possible to distinguish the yellow tips to the tail feathers of the flying birds, especially in strong sunlight. When at rest the birds occupy some dead pine top or in winter any leafless tree, where they perch upright, usually with crest erect and slightly recurved forward. When preening the wings and body plumage hang loosely, at other times they are closely appressed and the neck is drawn out so that with the erect crest the bird looks somewhat top heavy. A single Cedarbird when it reaches a perch will often remain rigid for long periods. On September 7, 1931, one was detected on the very top of a dead pine at 10:30 in the morning which failed to move for over ten minutes. It was observed at intervals until 12:40 and although it turned once, so as to face the other way, it apparently never left its perch.

When feeding on flying insects, as Cedarbirds often do, especially over ponds, they will fly in circles like swallows remaining on the wing for some time but returning at short intervals to their perches. In flight the Cedarbird rises and falls, there is a rapid flicker of wings and then they are closed against the body for an instant, but there is not the marked undulation of the Goldfinch. They will also set the wings and sail as they whirl into a tree to rest, much in the manner of a flock of Starlings, and present somewhat the same triangular wing outline.

I have seen Cedarbirds in early August feeding on wild cherries and on August 27, 1934, they were associated with migrating Kingbirds devouring the berries of the sassafras which are abundant at the Point. On March 20, 1924, there was a large flock busy picking off the holly berries that still persisted on the bushes. They held the berries between the mandibles for some little time, whether to break them or simply preparatory to swallowing I could not determine. On May 10, 1924, a flock of forty-five was feeding in a patch of shrubbery eating the soft leaf buds; one bird was noticed moving sideways along a limb to another which he proceeded to feed apparently ejecting a partly masticated bud from the throat into the bill. Other birds in a wild cherry tree in early August craned their necks high up and twisted the head half way round as they did so. Several times they were noticed to break off little pieces of twig or pull off fine shreds of bark with their bills for what object I was unable to determine. I have seen them in November persistently devouring chicken grapes at spots where the vines were growing abundantly and also feeding on the berries of Ampelopsis on the walls of a house, remaining until the crop had been entirely consumed.

Here as elsewhere Cedarbirds seem to be erratic both in habits and occurrence and might well be rated as vagrants rather than as migrants.

The first dates for south-bound migrants for a number of years are:

| | | | | | |
|---|---|---|---|---|---|
| 1921. | August 5. | 1925. | July 18. | 1930. | July 24. |
| 1922. | July 27. | 1926. | August 9. | 1931. | July 22. |
| 1923. | August 4. | 1927. | July 19. | 1932. | August 9. |
| 1924. | August 9. | 1929. | July 20. | 1935. | August 12. |

The results of the Christmas census of the Delaware Valley Club follow:

| | |
|---|---|
| December 27, 1931, one. | December 23, 1934, nine. |
| December 26, 1932, two. | December 27, 1936, twenty-six. |
| December 24, 1933, twelve. | |

## NORTHERN SHRIKE

Lanius borealis borealis Vieillot

An occasional winter visitant on the Fill and about Cape May Point, perching on low bushes or telegraph wires.

All that I have seen in southern New Jersey are birds in the plumage of the first year with dusky vermiculations on breast and belly.

Walker Hand reported single individuals on November 6, 1917; December 27, 1919; December 13, 1928; while I saw one daily on the Fill January 8–10, 1922, which was eventually collected and another December 24 to 27, 1929. Julian Potter saw one on December 26, 1926, and David Baird another on January 22, 1921.

At Beach Haven, farther north along the coast, where Charles Urner had counted sixteen on January 22, Richard Erskine and I saw five perched at intervals on the telephone wires on March 13, 1927. These were probably north-bound migrants as were single birds seen at Cape May on March 18, 1927, and March 23, 1930.

Northern Shrikes breed far to the north and while they occur more frequently in the northern part of the state New Jersey is near the southern limit of their winter wanderings.

## MIGRANT SHRIKE

### Lanius ludovicianus migrans Palmer

This representative of the Loggerhead Shrike of the South is a regular transient at Cape May from mid-August to late September. We have five records for October and I saw one in an orchard at Cold Spring on November 13 and 14, 1932, which may have been established there for the winter, as probably the same individual was seen in the same place on February 5, 19 and March 12, following. Julian Potter found two at Pennsville on December 7, 1930, and we have a few midwinter records of shrikes which were not positively identified as to species but were probably referable to the Northern Shrike which seems to be the more likely bird at this season. In spring I identified a Migrant Shrike on March 25, 1923, and another on April 2, 1933, and William Baily saw one at Ocean View on April 30, 1901. Farther north in the state Charles Urner has recorded one as late as May 11, 1929. They are, however, much rarer at this season than in late summer and early autumn.

Elsewhere in the state they are transients, just as they are at Cape May.

Migrant Shrikes are solitary birds and we usually see but one at a time but in the course of a day's walk we may come upon two, three or five while Conrad Roland saw six in the Cape May Point region on September 16, 1934. Their favorite perch is a telegraph wire or the top of a bush or small tree, always in a location commanding a clear view of the surrounding country. The bird's position is erect usually with the head bent over forward in the posture of a Bluebird, as if in deep meditation, while the tail hangs straight down with feathers tightly closed so that it appears very slender.

When the Shrike first alights it seems to stand higher while the tail is held horizontally and flirted sharply once or twice before the usual attitude of rest is assumed. Occasionally the bird will turn its head when danger threatens and may also drop diagonally to the ground, apparently after a grasshopper or other prey, but returns at once to its perch.

I have not often observed Migrant Shrikes caching their prey on thorns nor can I testify as to their returning to feed upon it later. One bird watched for some time on August 13, 1921, had a large grasshopper in its beak which it was trying to impale upon some of the twigs of a bush. Failing in this it wedged the insect into a fork of a branch and left it there. It held its prey in its beak during the attempts to impale it but between these efforts it grasped it with its feet holding it against the side of the branch. Another bird dropped onto a haycock in pursuit of a grasshopper and remained there for several minutes apparently searching for it. Another Migrant Shrike, that was in the usual attitude of repose on a wire just west of the town, was struck at by a passing Sparrow Hawk and it was amusing to see how quickly he dodged and how amazed he seemed to be as he again took up his position on the wire. The hawk did not renew the attack.

The flight of the Migrant Shrike is low and distinctly undulating with several rapid wing beats between the dips, producing a conspicuous flicker of white and recalling that produced by the Mockingbird although the flight of the latter is not undulatory, the wing action more deliberate, and the flashes of white continuous.

Adult Migrant Shrikes have very white breasts while immature birds are much darker due to the narrow gray vermiculations on the lower parts. The black eye stripe in this species runs clear to the nostril a character which distinguishes it from the larger Northern Shrike in which the lores are pale. This difference in the adults, at least, can usually be detected with the glass.

Our dates of arrival at Cape May for a number of years run as follows:

| | | |
|---|---|---|
| 1917. August 25. | 1922. August 21. | 1930. August 22. |
| 1918. August 23. | 1923. August 23. | 1932. August 20. |
| 1920. August 15. | 1926. August 27. | 1934. August 27. |
| 1921. August 13. | 1927. August 19. | 1935. August 29. |
| | 1929. August 20. | |

Our latest records for migrants are:

| | | |
|---|---|---|
| 1917. September 29. | 1925. October 2. | 1932. September 25. |
| 1920. October 3. | 1928. October 21. | 1935. October 14. |
| | 1929. October 5. | |

## STARLING

Sturnus vulgaris vulgaris Linnaeus

The Starling, which man so unwisely introduced from the Old World in 1890, is now one of the most abundant birds of South Jersey and bids fair to be the most destructive. Our other introduced species, the English Sparrow, seems to be distinctly on the wane, particularly in the towns and cities. The Starling, however, has been increasing ever since its first appearance and with its gluttonous appetite and generally hardy nature is in danger of crowding out many of our native species by sheer force of numbers, while by consuming the winter food supply it makes it difficult for many of our former winter residents to survive the cold months.

Introduced in Central Park, New York City, on March 6, 1890, they had reached Red Bank and Princeton by 1894, and Tuckerton and Vineland by 1907, if not before.

Walker Hand recorded the first Starlings at the Cape on April 4, 1909, when a pair nested in the woodwork of the old Stockton Hotel. By 1911 they had increased rapidly and in the summer of that year flocks of at least one hundred were to be seen. Since then they have been familiar birds at all times of year and are as regular in occurrence as the English Sparrows about every farm in the country. Single birds or pairs may be seen flying continually back and forth over the town from early spring to the end of July. They nest about buildings, in all sorts of holes and cavities, and take advantage of broken weather boarding which opens a way to inner spaces in walls. Flicker holes in telegraph poles along the railroads, or in old trees, are also acceptable nesting places, and Richard Miller tells me that they occupied one telegraph pole nest for six consecutive years and had young there on May 18, 1924. Old birds are busy all through the spring feeding on the lawns and in the gardens, and I have seen them carrying food as early as May 9, while others were feeding well-fledged young in the nest as late as June 20.

When the young first leave the nest they follow a parent, presumably the female, on the lawns of the town, running rapidly after her and jostling one another in their greed to get the food that she is finding for them. This often continues until the birds are full-grown and seem perfectly able to shift for themselves. By July 1 we may see flocks of young numbering one hundred or more, all in their plain gray dress, arising from the fields of cut hay where they find an abundance of insect food; other flocks all composed of young were seen on July 2 and 7 in different years about the hogpens which are to be found on the edges of marsh and woodland, where the garbage from the town is hauled. Similar flocks have been recorded as late as July 27 which had not yet begun to molt and young about half molted have been seen by August 5, while others on August 16, 1925, had conspicuous patches of glossy black feathers appearing in the gray plumage.

Adults and young seem to flock separately from the time the latter are on the wing, at least, until the late summer molt when they assume the black plumage. Flocks of both young and old birds are increasingly common throughout the summer and autumn and on the Fill, before the bushes attained such a growth, Starlings occurred in immense flocks during the autumn, many of them doubtless moving south as winter approached. On September 1, 1920, I saw at least a thousand rolling along over the ground, the rear ranks constantly rising and settling down in front, and curiously enough two Meadowlarks kept always in the van separated from the black horde by a small interval as if acting as leaders. Starlings also gather in flocks on the golf links, and about the aviation station, where they swarm over the roofs of the buildings and perch in rows on the fences, doubtless attracted by some refuse food.

As soon as the Grackles and Martins began to gather at their summer roost, formerly on the Physick place and later in the bushes on the Fill, the Starlings joined them every evening and spent the night with them. I have seen them coming in as early as July 7, 1923, and by August there were good sized flocks. On August 19, 1921, from 7 to 7:20 p. m., I counted 382 in detachments of from ten to one hundred and by September upwards of 1500 came in every night. Probably double that number came to the roost later. They usually come in before the Martins and did not rise and settle again as the latter do for some time before they rest for the night. When the Starlings did arise they took wing in a solid mass. When the Martins, after many years occupancy of the Physick grove, left for a piece of woods in West Cape May and later adopted the bushes of the Fill for a roosting place, the Starlings always went with them. It would seem possible, in the absence of any other explanation for this shifting of roostings, that the Martins may have resented the intrusion of the Starlings since their constantly increasing numbers must have crowded the Martins severely. They may also have forced the Martins to finally abandon their local roost. When occupying the Physick property the Starlings were seen to gather in considerable numbers on the roof of the greenhouse and if left to themselves they may prefer buildings to trees as night quarters, as they evidently do when they fly from the open country for miles around to roost on tall store and office buildings in the heart of Philadelphia.

A Starling flock is a unique sight. The birds seem to be the only land birds that can equal the lesser shore birds in unity of action and the sight of a flock of Starlings rising and falling, turning and pitching in perfect harmony cannot fail to arouse enthusiasm. Every bird moves instantaneously in exactly the same evolution that all the others are performing, yet we detect no possible guiding signal. There are no stragglers, no ragged edges to the flock, and at a distance it maintains its square, round or oblong shape, as the case may be, and drifts about like a swarm of bees. A great flock arose over the mainland, back of the Lighthouse on August 31, 1925, which looked from a distance exactly like a cloud of smoke. It came across the meadows and settled near the pond and later arose and covered the branches of some low dead trees, nearby, until they seemed to be clothed with foliage.

On July 27, 1920, a flock of some two hundred Starlings mingled with a large number of Red-wings on a field of freshly cut hay. When the whole mass of birds arose together they seemed inextricably mixed but in a moment the Starlings were in their own compact flock, still associated with the Red-wings but in a unit of their own. And so it is when they came into the roost with the Grackles, the bunches of Starlings formed compact units which cut through and around the slower moving Grackles in an astonishing manner, traveling, apparently, at least twice as fast.

The great flocks of Starlings drift about the country until the approach of winter when they apparently move off as they are much less frequently seen in cold weather although small flocks are to be found about villages and farm houses all winter.

As soon as the nesting period is over the Starlings become social birds willing and anxious to associate with any flocking species that will tolerate them and apparently forcing themselves upon some. There is rarely a flock of Red-wings, Grackles or Meadowlarks that does not contain Starlings and sometimes I have seen a stray Starling take up with a flock of English Sparrows. Starlings, too, have, to some extent, replaced the Cowbirds in the cattle yards and fields where cows are grazing, and during June and July most of the birds attendant upon the cattle will be found to be Starlings. On July 3, 1935; July 6, 1928; and July 5, 1931; such was the case and on the last occasion, only, were there any Cowbirds present. The Starlings, moreover, were all adults.

Starlings are omnivorous and seem to be adapted for feeding in a variety of ways; insects of various sorts and garbage they pick up from the ground; where Japanese beetle larvae are plentiful they will dig them out of the soil; while when other fare is scarce they will strip berry-bearing bushes of their fruit. So, too, when the flying ants take to the air on their nuptial flight the Starlings rise to the occasion and catch them on the wing with the agility of a flycatcher. On August 12, 1929, there were at least one hundred of the birds out over the Fill, circling continually as they snapped up the insects which were swarming everywhere. Many of the old birds were molting and their tails presented a peculiar wedge-shaped outline while the wings of both old and young, especially the latter, appeared curiously semi-translucent with the strong sunlight behind them. One young Laughing Gull joined them in their evolutions as these birds, too, seem to be not averse to catching insects in the air or to engaging in aërial evolutions.

Starlings are easily recognized in flight. Their wing action is more rapid and more sustained than that of the other "blackbirds" and there is no dropping of a beat as in the Grackle, no undulatory motion as in the Red-wing, while the long tail of the Grackle is missing; indeed the Starling's tail is so short that the body appears to be shaped the same at each end and to taper symmetrically to bill and tail with the rather narrow wings in the middle.  The wings are pointed and when the bird is at rest they seem to be joined closely at the shoulder, with a short upper arm, like that of a swallow; when spread they are strikingly triangular.

While the Starling has gained appreciation on account of its sociable nature and its fondness for Japanese beetle larvae, those who can see further into its life history realize that it is a serious menace to our native birds by devouring the food that formerly served as their winter support, while Robins and Grackles, relieved from the pressure of Starlings, would, I believe, be just as efficient in destroying the beetles.  In addition there is the danger that the Starling will become a destroyer of garden products, as it has in its native country.  All in all the addition of the Starling to our avifauna seems to me an excellent example of the folly of introducing the birds of one country into another and thereby upsetting the balance of life that nature has so carefully developed.

## WHITE-EYED VIREO

### Vireo griseus griseus (Boddaert)

PLATE 113, p. 759

The White-eye is the characteristic vireo of the Cape district and every piece of low swampy woodland has a pair or more. It is common at Cape May Point and northward along the Bay as well as in the woodland strip that borders the meadows above Cape May on the ocean side, and in moist spots inland—a summer resident from mid-April to late September and occasionally until early October.

Julian Potter counted thirty White-eyes in thickets bordering the Pond Creek Meadows on June 21, 1923, and nests, each with four eggs, have been examined by Turner McMullen and Richard Miller on May 20, 1916; May 21, 1926; and one with three eggs and one of the Cowbird on May 29, 1932. They were swung from forks of low bushes, rarely more than three feet from the ground. I have seen old birds feeding young on July 15, 1922, and a female carrying food on July 18, 1923, while young were shifting for themselves on the same date in 1935.

The White-eye is a favorite fosterer of the Cowbird and I found one feeding a well-fledged young parasite on August 3, 1927, while another on August 5, 1929, was being closely followed by a husky young Cowbird begging for food. On August 5, 1933, F. C. Lincoln and I found a pair feeding two Cowbirds! The actions of the White-eye are slow and deliberate. He hops leisurely from twig to twig of the low bushes with an occasional flirt of the tail, always peering this way and that, turning his head to one side or the other. A pair studied on July 13, 1920, apparently had young nearby as they were very nervous and excited. Their plumage was constantly ruffled so that their bodies seemed larger than normal; the tail was carried partly erect. Another individual, with plumage smooth and sleek, gave a nervous flip of both wings and tail as it hopped heavily from one branch to another.

The white iris, the blue gray feet, and the light wing bars are satisfactory identification marks but the vocal accomplishments of the bird are still more characteristic and one is at once attracted by the peculiar, emphatic, penetrating song—if song it may be called; it is surely not soft enough to be termed a warble.

After repeating one phrase a dozen times or more the bird will suddenly stop short or, after a pause, may change to an entirely different phrase so that one would feel sure that he had been listening to another individual had he not had the performer constantly in view.

The peculiar character of the songs renders them easy for syllabic representation and I have recorded quite a number. All have the same loud penetrating quality which makes the White-eye, as it were, the voice of the swamp. The simplest songs run: *tick, che-weéo, sick; chuck, che-weé-ju; ill, chee-whéo, chip; seé it, see, weé-ah;* and a shorter: *chick, wissa.* Other more complicated phrases are: *chick, che-weary-o-wisset; chuck, see, chur-a-lury, stick; che-wírra, chu, weé; che switz, ah, weé; pechítcha wirra, wée; sweé-a, sípititulia, síp.* The last was shortened in various ways sometimes the first note only was uttered, *sweé-a* or *sweé,* while the middle phrase was often cut in a variety of ways.

As an illustration of the changing of phrases, a bird heard singing on May 8, 1925, began with: *chéri-lo-wísset* and then added a couple of preliminary notes: *chip, sweé, chéri-lo-wísset* and then after several repetitions changed entirely to *weét, se-cheéa, sík.* In all of the "songs" the sharp preliminary note *tick, chick,* etc., is always followed by a pause while the similar final note when present is preceded by a pause.

Other notes are an interrogatory *cheee* which is often uttered as the bird catches sight of an intruder on his domain, and a curious guttural *zchurrrrrr,* to which is sometimes added one of the common final phrases, *wée-ah.* A bird with young kept up a constant chatter *shi-shi-shi-shi-shi* resembling one of the notes of the Chat when heard far off, while a young bird had a somewhat different chatter note: *chip-chip-chip-chip.*

Conrad Roland heard one still in song on September 6, 1934, which is unusually late.

Young birds were seen on the wing on July 18, 1935, and in the molt by August 13. An adult in the molt on August 14, 1932, had faded to a very pale gray and the new yellow feathers on the sides shown out in very brilliant patches. Another adult with a bob tail was seen on August 27 and a fully molted individual on August 30.

We have spring arrival records for the White-eye as follows:

| | | |
|---|---|---|
| 1908. April 26. | 1921. April 24. | 1923. April 30. |
| 1919. April 23. | 1922. April 22. | 1927. April 30. |

Late autumn records are:

| | | |
|---|---|---|
| 1928. September 27. | 1930. September 28. | 1932. October 12. |

The height of the migration seems to be during the first week of September.

While the White-eye breeds as far north as southern New England, it is more plentiful in southern New Jersey than in the northern counties.

## YELLOW-THROATED VIREO

### Vireo flavifrons Vieillot

I saw one Yellow-throated Vireo on October 5, 1929, at Cold Spring during a remarkable flight of migrants, while Fletcher Street found one singing in the woodland west of Cape May Court House on June 7, 1936, which would indicate that it was nesting there. It is apparently much rarer in the Cape district than the preceding.

It would seem that this species and the Warbling Vireo, of which we have no records for Cape May County, must migrate along the Delaware Valley rather than along the coast, although they probably cross the state north of the Pine Barrens. While it is a summer resident in most parts of the state, it seems to be rather local in its distribution.

## BLUE-HEADED VIREO

### Vireo solitarius solitarius (Wilson)

The Blue-headed or Solitary Vireo is an uncommon transient at Cape May and is more frequently seen in autumn. It is a bird of the north woods and does not breed in New Jersey, being everywhere a transient, although Dr. F. M. Chapman did find it at High Knob, Sussex Co., in June, 1890 (Abst. Proc. Linn. Soc., 1890–91, p. 4). From its abundance in the north and its scarcity along the New Jersey coast I infer that its migrations follow the Delaware Valley or regions farther west and that it pushes north in spring up the Susquehanna and Delaware Rivers to reach its summer home.

Our Cape May records, all single birds, are as follows:

| | |
|---|---|
| 1920. October 31 (Stone). | 1934. May 5 (Stone). |
| 1930. October 5 (Potter). | 1935. October 10 and 27 |
| 1932. September 25 (Roland). |    (Rusling). |

## RED-EYED VIREO

### Vireo olivaceus (Linnaeus)

#### PLATE 113, p. 759

While not an abundant summer bird about Cape May there are usually one or two pairs of Red-eyed Vireos breeding in the shade trees of the town and a like number at the Point. In the woodlands farther north in the peninsula they are more frequent.

Nests with incomplete sets of eggs have been found on June 3, 1923, and June 8, 1924, while parents were seen feeding young in the heart of the town on August 11, 1924, and again August 7, 1934. On the latter occasion they made a vicious attack on an English Sparrow which had alighted on a wire close to where the young Vireo was perched and drove it away. Later one of them caught a white moth and after clipping off the wings fed it to the young bird. Red-eyed Vireos have been heard singing in the shade trees along Washington Street as late as August 21, 1924, and August 10, 1926, and another at the Point on August 7, 1922, but they are usually through singing by the middle of July.

The northwest winds of late August and September bring many Red-eyes along with the host of migrant warblers, flycatchers etc., and it is then that the bird is most conspicuous in the avifauna of the Cape. This influx was especially noticeable on September 1–2, 1920; September 4, 1921; August 29, 1922; August 31, 1923; August 27, 1924; September 1, 1925; September 27, 1926; September 27, 1928, September 28, 1930; September 17, 1932; on all of these dates the birds were abundant in the woods at the Point and in some seasons there are several "waves" in which Red-eyes are conspicuous. Their deliberate movements and slow progress through the foliage, with no nervous action of wings and tail, is in sharp contrast to the warblers which are migrating with them. During these congested flights they crowd together in remarkable numbers, where food is obtainable, and are not particular as to its character. On one occasion as many as twenty-five were found in one small Sassafras tree, some of them hanging upside down while they pecked at the fruit, and I have seen them fluttering in the air close to berry bearing branches in a manner very unlike the usual habit of a vireo.

We have records of their arrival in spring on:

| | | | |
|---|---|---|---|
| 1924. | May 10. | 1932. | May 7. |
| 1928. | May 5. | 1934. | May 5. |

The latest records for autumn are:

| | | | |
|---|---|---|---|
| 1924. | October 2. | 1929. | October 5. |
| 1927. | October 10. | 1935. | October 13. |

The Red-eyed Vireo is nowhere in Cape May County the characteristic woodland bird that it is in the northern counties or in Pennsylvania and the states to the north. It is from the latter region that come the great waves of Red-eyes that throng the Point and the Bay side woods in autumn—silent berry eating birds, very different from the vociferous "preacher" of the more northern forests who keeps up his vocal efforts long after other singers have subsided in the heat of midday.

## *WARBLING VIREO

Vireo gilvus gilvus Vieillot

While the Warbling Vireo is a common summer resident of Warren and Sussex Counties according to Griscom and doubtless nests in other sections of northern New Jersey, the village shade trees which constitute its favorite habitat in most sections where it breeds, do not seem to attract it in South Jersey, and I have been unable to obtain a single nesting record. Julian Potter has recorded transient individuals at Camden on May 10, 1909; May 25, 1913; May 15, 1914; and Fletcher Street has observed it in spring at Beverly but none has been yet recorded from Cape May County although autumn stragglers should certainly occur here.

## PHILADELPHIA VIREO

Vireo philadelphicus (Cassin)

The Philadelphia Vireo does not breed in New Jersey but occurs as a rare transient throughout the state. We have but two records for Cape May County, a specimen shot on Five Mile Beach by H. W. Wenzel on September 21, 1889, and contained in the Laurent collection in the Reading (Pa.) Museum; and one shot on Seven Mile Beach by Dr. William E. Hughes, on September 11, 1898, now in the collection of the Academy of Natural Sciences of Philadelphia.

Specimens were taken at Princeton by W. E. D. Scott on September 21 and 28, 1876 (Babson, Birds of Princeton, 1901) and others, I believe, have been seen and collected in the northern counties.

## WARBLERS OF CAPE MAY

All of the warblers recorded for the state of New Jersey have occurred at Cape May with the exception of the Mourning and the Cerulean. There is every probability that a few of the former occur occasionally in the migrations but the latter, which is an accidental straggler from the south and west, is of unlikely occurrence.

Six warblers occur as summer residents and nest at the Cape while several others nest in small numbers a little farther north in the peninsula. These in the order of their abundance as breeders are:

Maryland Yellow-throat.
Yellow Warbler.
Prairie Warbler.
Pine Warbler.
Hooded Warbler.
Ovenbird.

Yellow-breasted Chat.
Black and White Warbler.
Parula Warbler.
Blue-winged Warbler.
Louisiana Water-Thrush.

Others which may nest in the Cape May region are:

Yellow-throated Warbler.
Prothonotary Warbler.

Redstart.

The most abundant transients are:

Black-and-White Warbler.
Redstart.
Myrtle Warbler.
Black-throated Blue Warbler.
Maryland Yellow-throat.

Northern Water-Thrush.
Palm Warbler.
Yellow Palm Warbler.
Ovenbird.

We do not have at Cape May, in either spring or autumn, the great warbler waves that are so characteristic of the migrations in the vicinity of Philadelphia and elsewhere, except so far as the above species are concerned, and the many other species are usually represented by but a few individuals. It must be admitted that we have not had competent observers constantly on the ground during the periods of migration but we have gathered enough data, I am confident, to justify the above conclusions.

As stated elsewhere, I am of the opinion that in the spring flight the great majority of the northern-breeding warblers turn north through the Susquehanna Valley or along the western border of the Delaware Valley, leaving only a few to reach the coast, while in the autumn the presence of these species on the coast of Cape May is largely due to strong northwest winds during the progress of their flight which either blow them from a more westerly course or force them to concentrate at the Point.

As W. W. Cooke has shown (Distribution and Migration of N. A. Warblers, Bull. 18, Biol. Survey, 1904), there are two main highways of warbler migration in the East; one up the coast and the other crossing the Gulf of Mexico and extending northward along the Alleghanies to cross somewhere in Virginia or West Virginia and thence, by the great river valleys mentioned, and across central New Jersey, to the Hudson and Connecticut Valleys.

The warblers that are supposed to follow the coast line and winter mainly in the West Indies (although some individuals take the other route and winter in Central America) are:

Black-and-White Warbler.            Palm Warbler.
Redstart.                           Northern Water-Thrush.
Parula Warbler.                     Maryland Yellow-Throat.
Myrtle Warbler.                     Ovenbird.
Black-throated Blue Warbler.

This group it will be noticed contains all of the species most common during the migrations at Cape May and all of them occur on the coast of South Carolina (*cf.* Wayne, Birds of South Carolina) both of which facts confirm the theory of their coastal migration route.

The species that are supposed to cross the Gulf and proceed north along the mountains are:

Golden-winged Warbler.              Bay-breasted Warbler.
Blue-winged Warbler.                Blackburnian Warbler.
Magnolia Warbler.                   Black-throated Green Warbler.
Chestnut-sided Warbler.             Canada Warbler.

None of these is a common transient at the Cape and none I believe has yet been recorded from the South Carolina coast.   The former fact would seem to show that in coming from their summer home in Canada and the mountainous portions of our northern states, where all but the first two breed, they must cross central New Jersey in a southwesterly direction and proceed down the western edge of the Delaware Valley, or even farther west, and then down the Alleghanies, thus for the most part keeping clear of Cape May, while their absence from the South Carolina coast shows that such individuals as do reach the Cape must, like the rest of their kind, cross the mountains in Virginia on their way to the Gulf of Mexico.

In the southward flight, as already suggested, the greater abundance of warblers at the Cape and along the coast to the north is probably due to the action of northwest winds in diverting them from their normal course.

# BLACK AND WHITE WARBLER

**Mniotilta varia** (Linnaeus)

The Black and White Warbler and the Redstart are the most regular and abundant transient warblers at Cape May on the southward flight and from the first week of August until the end of September they may be found in the pine woods at Cape May Point almost continuously, although they vary in numbers from day to day, in accordance with changes in the weather and direction of the wind. During the latter part of this period they may be found also in the shade trees and gardens of the town as well as throughout the wooded parts of the peninsula to the northward, though their center of abundance is always at the Point.

Upon the first northwest wind of August we shall find the Black and Whites circling the trunks of the pine trees and exploring the limbs and cone clusters, sometimes hanging over them like Chickadees. Their strongly contrasted black and white striping makes them very conspicuous against the dark trunks and branches of the pines. Their progress through the woods is more deliberate than that of the Redstarts with which they are so often associated and they spend much time climbing out and exploring the limbs of one tree and then moving to another in a long undulating flight, showing much white when on the wing. They are abundant on one day and rare or absent on the next as successive waves of migrants pass through. The dates of first arrival of south-bound birds at the Point for sixteen years are as follows:

| 1920. | August 1. | 1925. | July 30. | 1931. | August 8. |
|-------|-----------|-------|----------|-------|-----------|
| 1921. | August 4. | 1926. | August 14. | 1932. | August 9. |
| 1922. | August 9. | 1927. | July 30. | 1933. | July 26. |
| 1923. | August 4. | 1928. | August 13. | 1934. | July 28. |
| 1924. | July 28. | 1929. | July 27. | 1935. | August 5. |
|       |           | 1930. | July 24. |       |           |

Our latest autumn records are:

| 1917. | September 29. | 1924. | October 2. | 1929. | September 20. |
|-------|---------------|-------|------------|-------|---------------|
| 1921. | September 14. | 1925. | September 29. | 1932. | September 25. |
| 1922. | September 17. | 1926. | September 27. | 1934. | September 19. |
| 1923. | October 1. | 1928. | September 30. |       |               |

In spring Walker Hand and I have recorded the Black and White Warbler on:

| 1911. | April 26. | 1916. | April 30. | 1926. | April 24. |
|-------|-----------|-------|-----------|-------|-----------|
| 1912. | April 28. | 1917. | April 29. | 1927. | April 24. |
| 1914. | April 24. | 1923. | April 30. |       |           |

The Black and White Warbler breeds occasionally just north of Cape May but cannot be regarded as a common summer resident anywhere in the peninsula. Richard Miller found a nest with four fledglings at Rio Grande on June 3, 1923, which was tucked away among dead leaves at the base of a huckleberry bush in thick dry woods, and also saw a young bird fed by a parent at the same place on June 10. Turner McMullen found two nests with three eggs each in the same locality on June 8, 1924, and May 27, 1928, and one with four young on May 30, 1925.

Mark Wilde saw a number of the birds at South Dennis on May 18, 1894, and found one nest. I saw an adult and young at Erma on July 7, 1929, and other individuals at Goshen and South Dennis as early as July 12, 1925, while Fletcher Street and others, on an all day survey of the central part of the peninsula on June 7, 1936, saw no less than five of these warblers in the woodland from one to two miles west of Court House, one near Bidwell's Ditch and another near Seaville. Julian Potter informs me that he found a single bird in the woods on the eastern side of Pond Creek Meadows on June 11, 1923, and another at Ocean View on June 10, 1928. It is probable that all of these birds were nesting.

In northern New Jersey the Black and White Warblers are common summer residents in most tracts of woodland but judging by the numbers that pass through Cape May in the autumn the migrant flocks must include birds from wide areas to the north of the state as well.

## PROTHONOTARY WARBLER

**Protonotaria citrea (Boddaert)**

The Prothonotary Warbler is well known to nest along the Choptank River near the Delaware-Maryland line, at Marydel, where it was first detected by Gordon Smith on July 18, 1898, and at Seaford, Delaware, where Samuel Rhoads found it on June 18, 1903, but that would seem to be the northern limit of its normal breeding range in the East. The bird however has the habit of occurring, and even breeding, sporadically farther north, as witness the nest recorded by Howland and Carter (Auk, 1925, p. 138) in Morris County, in the northern portion of New Jersey, on June 30, 1924, and records of single birds by Samuel Rhoads at Haddonfield in the eighties; by A. H. Phillips, at Princeton, on May 8, 1894; by H. C. Oberholser (Auk, 1918, p. 227) at Morristown, June 14, 1888; at Mt. Holly, by Nelson Pumyea, April 25, 1920; by Reimann, at Marshalltown, April 29, 1934; by R. K. Haines, at Pemberton, May 11, 1930; and by Roger Peterson, at Pennsville, on June 9, 1935.

Arthur Emlen and I also saw a brilliant male on the Egg Harbor River near the Fourway Lodge above Mays Landing, on May 16, 1931, which dodged in and out of the shrubbery that overhung the banks of the river, keeping just abreast of our canoe as we paddled slowly up the stream. We have two instances of the possible breeding of this southern warbler in the lower counties of New Jersey although no nest has ever been found. On June 19, 1914, while Julian Potter was exploring a wooded swamp close to the Maurice River, two miles west of Vineland, a Prothonotary Warbler appeared, attracted by the chirping of a pair of Redstarts with young (a noteworthy record in itself!). The bird not only gave every opportunity for careful observation, but uttered its characteristic alarm note which Potter likened to that of a Water-Thrush. The swamp was overflowed by a few inches of water, a most likely place for a Prothonotary to breed.

On June 15, 1924, Richard Miller, in the heart of the Timber and Beaver Swamp at South Dennis, Cape May County, came upon a pair of Prothonotaries the female carrying a bill full of insects. They approached to within a few feet of him and gave every indication of having young in the immediate neighborhood. This swamp, with which I am well acquainted, is an ideal habitat for these warblers, with deep sluggish streams and many overflowed areas.

The Prothonotary is not a bird of the pinelands and judging by the character of the country I should think that the southwestern section of the state in Salem and Cumberland counties, or northwestern Cape May County, would be the most likely area in which to expect its nesting.

## WORM-EATING WARBLER

### Helmitheros vermivorus (Gmelin)

I have only twice detected this bird in Cape May County, both times during the early autumn migration. One was seen in a moist thicket at the Point on August 27, 1926, and the other in a tangle of greenbrier in the tall moist woodland east of Bennett, on September 2, 1930. It is a regular summer resident in parts of southern Pennsylvania and in some of the northern New Jersey counties but is not a bird of the pineland and is very rare even in West Jersey, across the river from Philadelphia. I am inclined to think that its normal route of migration is down the Delaware and that my Cape May birds had been diverted to the coast by northwest winds. As but few birds breed north of New Jersey, however, there must be very few migrants passing through the state.

## GOLDEN-WINGED WARBLER

### Vermivora chrysoptera (Linnaeus)

A rare but probably regular transient at Cape May Point in autumn and twice observed in spring. Our records are as follows:

| | | | |
|---|---|---|---|
| 1921. | August 15–16, two. | 1929. | August 17, one. |
| 1922. | August 21, one. | 1934. | August 27, one. |
| 1927. | May (early), one. | 1935. | August 23, three (W. Rusling). |
| 1927. | May 20, one. | 1935. | September 7, one (W. Rusling). |

It nests in Essex, Passaic and Sussex Counties in northern New Jersey.

## BLUE-WINGED WARBLER

### Vermivora pinus (Linnaeus)

It is probable that a few Blue-wings occur at Cape May Point every autumn and a lesser number in spring, although we have observed none at that season. Our records are as follows:

| | | | |
|---|---|---|---|
| 1920. | September 1, two. | 1927. | August 3, 6 and 17, one each. |
| 1921. | August 15–16, several. | 1929. | August 17, six. |
| 1922. | August 9 and 28, one each. | 1931. | August 7, one. |
| 1923. | August 31, one. | 1932. | August 29, one. |
| 1925. | August 18, one. | 1934. | August 7, one. |
| 1926. | August 27, one. | 1935. | August 30, two (W. Rusling). |

A few may nest in moist thickets farther north in the peninsula as I found several singing at Goshen on July 12, 1925, and Fletcher Street found one in the same vicinity and three in swamps west of Court House on June 7, 1936. While a common breeder in southeastern Pennsylvania and in the central and northern counties of New Jersey the Blue-wing does not range north of the Carolinian Fauna and would naturally not be a common transient at Cape May.

## *LAWRENCE'S WARBLER
### Vermivora lawrencei (Herrick)

## *BREWSTER'S WARBLER
### Vermivora leucobronchialis (Brewster)

While no individuals of Brewster's or Lawrence's Warblers, hybrids between the Blue-wing and Golden-wing, have been recorded in Cape May County, or elsewhere in southern New Jersey a number have occurred in the northern part of the state where both of the parent species nest. The type specimen of *Vermivora lawrencei* (Herrick), essentially a yellow-breasted Golden-wing, was taken by Aug. Blanchet at Chatham, May 1874 (Proc. Phila. Academy, 1874, p. 320), another by D. B. Dickinson, at Hoboken, September, 1876 (Bull. N. O. C. 1877, p. 19) and a supposed cross between *lawrencei* and *pinus* by Frank Blanchet, at Morristown, May 15, 1884 (Auk, 1886, p. 411).

Specimens of *V. leucobronchialis* Brewster, a white-breasted Blue-wing with yellow wing bars, have been taken or seen at Morristown, May 1859, (A. Blanchet) and May 15, 1887 (E. C. Thurber) and at Englewood, May 15, 1886, June 26, and July 31, 1887, May 11, 1890 (F. M. Chapman) and May 13, 1905 (G. E. Hix) (cf. Auk, 1886, p. 411; 1887, p 348 and 349; 1890, p. 291 and 1905, p. 417). C. B. Riker has recorded a cross between *leucobronchialis* and *pinus* at Maplewood, May 11, 1883 (Auk, 1885, p. 378) and Dr. Chapman a pair representing these two forms breeding at Englewood in 1892 (Auk, 1892, p. 302). There have, I believe, been other later records.

## TENNESSEE WARBLER
### Vermivora peregrina (Wilson)

A rare transient during late August and September with a single record in spring. Observed mainly at the Point but found also in trees in the town.

| | | | |
|---|---|---|---|
| 1920. | September 1–2, one each. | 1931. | September 1, one. |
| 1922. | August 21, two. | 1932. | August 29, one. |
| 1922. | August 29, six. | 1932. | September 17–18, an unusual |
| 1923. | September 16 and 30, one each. | | number. |
| | | 1932. | October 8, three. |
| 1924. | September 7, one. | 1924. | May 9–10, one. |

The spring individual was feeding continually with some Black-polls in an ornamental spruce tree in the Physick garden.

It occurs only as a transient in New Jersey.

## ORANGE-CROWNED WARBLER

Vermivora celata celata (Say)

I have always expected to come upon this warbler in the flocks of Myrtles feeding in the bayberry bushes in midwinter but have been unsuccessful. Philip Laurent however collected a specimen on Five Mile Beach (now in the Reading, Pa., Museum) on October 6, 1889, while it has been seen in winter at other points along the sea coast both to the north and south of New Jersey and Frank E. Watson has recorded one at Point Pleasant on the northern part of the coast on December 5, 1926. There is also a specimen in the American Museum of Natural History secured at Hoboken, May 1865, by C. S. Galbraith (Howell, Auk, 1893, p. 90); two May records for Union Co. (Urner) and three records for Essex Co. (Eaton). It is a very rare transient in the Delaware Valley—at Philadelphia about March, 1876 (McIlvaine, cf. Bull. Nutt. Orn. Club, 1879); at Haddonfield, New Jersey, March 22, 1883 (Samuel Rhoads, Bull. Nutt. Orn. Club, 1883) and February 25, 1909 (R. T. Moore, Cassinia, 1909, p. 53); at Rancocas Creek, New Jersey, February, 1860 (Turnbull).

## NASHVILLE WARBLER

Vermivora ruficapilla ruficapilla (Wilson)

One seen at Cape May Point by Julian Potter on September 30, 1928. It is a regular transient north of the Pine Barrens and in the Delaware Valley while Dr. F. M. Chapman took a breeding female at Englewood, on June 16, 1887, the only summer record for the state (cf. Auk, 1889, p. 304).

## PARULA WARBLER

Compsothlypis americana pusilla (Wilson)

The Parula is a spring and autumn transient at Cape May Point and in the trees of the town, occurring usually from September 8 to 18, with scattering individuals as late as October 14; and in spring from May 1 to 20, with a few throughout the month.

They vary in abundance and while our records are for the most part of a few individuals they have occurred in abundance on October 2, 1924; September 20 to October 2, 1925; September 27, 1926; September 17 to 18, 1932; and in spring on May 20, 1927, and May 5, 1934. We have but one August record—August 23, 1924.

Immediately about Cape May I know of only one nest which I found on May 26, 1892, at the Point. It was about ten feet up in a tree and contained three eggs and, curiously enough, one of the Cowbird, although how the latter bird managed to deposit its egg in such a frail structure without damaging it I am at a loss to explain.

Parulas have been seen at the Point on May 29, 1921, and at Higbee's Beach on May 30, in 1923, 1924, and 1925, while Julian Potter heard one in full song at the latter place on June 21, 1923, and I heard several at Goshen on July 12, 1925, all of which indicate probable nesting.

The swampy woods of the Great Cedar Swamp, a little farther north, and the borders of the extensive lake at South Dennis were favorite nesting places of the bird in years past but lately they do not seem to be so plentiful there, while similar localities at Mays Landing, Browns Mills and elsewhere in the Pine Barrens were, and doubtless still are, breeding grounds of the bird. Many also nested in the wooded swamps that existed on Five Mile Beach in the eighties, according to Philip Laurent.

The Parula's nesting seems to be governed by the presence of the pendant lichen or "beard moss" (*Usnea*) which formerly festooned all of the bushes that grew along the edge of the lake, and in the water, at South Dennis. In May, 1892, I spent some days exploring this attractive spot in company with Charles Voelker and Harris Reed and I never saw the Parula so abundant as it was at that time.  We pushed our flat-bottomed boat in among the maze of moss-draped bushes, shoving it through billowy, water-soaked beds of sphagnum, with cranberry vines and clumps of pitcher plants all about, and through great patches or wiry Cassandra tangles until we seemed to have penetrated to the innermost recesses of the Parulas' retreat and to be able to share the secrets of their home life.  They flit about on every side; here we see one entering its dainty moss basket nest while in another the female is sitting deep down in the delicate pocket engaged in incubation, her bill just protruding from the narrow opening.  Besides the constant *buz-z-z-z-z-z----zic* of the little warblers there comes to our ears the harsh cry of a Kingbird balancing himself on the topmost twig of a partly submerged gum tree; the emphatic song of the White-eyed Vireo, rises with startling intensity from the bushes only a few feet from us and from farther away, close to the black shade of the cedar swamp, come the clear phrases of the Hooded Warbler.  Hummingbirds dart back and forth and Martins, black against the sky, pass on rapid wings, while far overhead an Osprey with labored flight carries a fish from the coast to his nest farther inland.

Mark Wilde who made a thorough study of the bird at this spot has written as follows of the nesting of the Parula: "The nest is invariably placed in a hanging position usually in a bush on which the beard moss grows quite thickly, and here, within a dense tuft, the birds loop and weave the strands to form the nest.  They are careful to leave the moss on the bush hanging about the nest so that it may be well concealed and it can only be found by diligent search.  Building material is carried from other bushes and not taken from the one in which the nest is located, and while many nests are lined exclusively with strands of the moss others contain horsehair and yellow down from the stems of swamp ferns.  The entrance, always level with the top of the bowl, is through the moss on the side, very often directly under the limb from which the tuft is hung.  Very rarely the entrance is from the top and occasionally a nest is hung from a limb with very little moss, all of the material being carried from elsewhere; such a nest is much more conspicuous" (Auk, 1897, pp. 289–294).  Of the thirty-three nests that Wilde examined sixteen were from one to four and a half feet from the ground or water; eleven from six to fifteen feet up and one twenty feet high.  The eggs are usually four in number sometimes three and the average date for full sets was found to be May 20 while young were hatched in one nest by June 4.

The vegetation on the South Dennis lake has grown much taller in the past few years and the moss has to a great extent disappeared which doubtless accounts for the scarcity of the birds here, and as migrants at Cape May Point.  They still nest, however, where suitable environment can be found and Turner McMullen has found nests with full sets of eggs at Swain on June 6, 1920, and June 15, 1924, and Richard Miller at South Dennis on June 13, 1926.

The Parula is a common transient throughout the state and nests locally in the northern counties, at Newton, Highknob, etc.

## YELLOW WARBLER

**Dendroica aestiva aestiva (Gmelin)**

PLATE 114, p. 838

The Yellow Warbler is the most generally distributed summer warbler about Cape May unless it be the Maryland Yellow-throat. Ever a lover of the vicinity of water, it is found in the thickets of marsh elder and bayberry which border Cape Island Creek, as well as in the shrubbery surrounding the ponds at the Lighthouse and along the banks of Lake Lily at the Point. In the gardens of Cape May, especially those which back on the meadows or on the Fill, it is a familiar bird and its cheerful *sweet, sweet, sweeter, sweeter,* is constantly to be heard in the spring and early summer. It has always been common on Two Mile Beach and the other island beaches to the north, and in a small area at the southern extremity of the former island I counted ten pairs on May 22, 1922. In the orchards and gardens of the farmhouses of the upland a pair or two are almost always to be found. To those who know the bird only in such surroundings, among a wealth of green foliage or by clear ponds and little brooks, it seems strange to find it equally at home in marsh elder thickets overhanging the black mud of the tidewater creeks.

While usually a bird of low bushes the Yellow Warbler is often seen exploring the branches of the pine trees of the Point, after the nesting season is over, and I have also seen it feeding on the ground in the plum thickets of the Bay shore dunes.

In early May when the bushes of the coastal region, always backward as compared with more inland localities, are largely bare of foliage, the golden yellow of the bird's plumage stands out most conspicuously but later in the season it is not so noticeable. It is in full song during May and June and was once heard as late as July 24, doubtless a belated breeder.

( 813 )

Turner McMullen found a nest with four eggs at Cape May on June 4, 1922, another with a like number of young on June 8, 1919, and two with eggs, at Rio Grande, on May 20, 1923, and June 8, 1924.

I have seen full-plumaged young as early as July 6, 1925, and July 26, 1923, and an adult in freshly molted winter plumage on August 7, 1920. I have come upon very few birds in this plumage, however, and am inclined to think that the old birds move southward as soon as their annual molt is completed, or perhaps before, as almost all Yellow Warblers seen in late summer and autumn are birds of the year. Perhaps the breeding birds from farther north travel down the Delaware or Susquehanna Valleys.

Walker Hand's dates of spring arrival with supplementary dates by others are as follows:

| | | |
|---|---|---|
| 1905. May 8. | 1917. April 24. | 1926. April 24. |
| 1908. April 26. | 1918. April 30. | 1927. April 24. |
| 1909. April 29. | 1919. April 23. | 1932. April 30. |
| 1910. May 4. | 1920. May 1. | 1933. April 30. |
| 1911. April 30. | 1922. April 23. | 1934. May 1. |
| 1914. April 27. | 1923. April 29. | |

Our latest autumn records are:

| | | |
|---|---|---|
| 1922. September 17. | 1925. September 30. | 1930. September 28. |
| 1926. September 25. | 1927. October 10. | |

The birds are, however, scarce after September 5.

## MAGNOLIA WARBLER

### Dendroica magnolia (Wilson)

Apparently a regular transient passing through on the southward flight, mainly in September, at times of concentrated waves of small passerine birds, and seen on the return migration in May.

Our records are as follows, single birds unless otherwise stated:

| | |
|---|---|
| 1921. September 1, 9, 14. | 1930. September 27. |
| 1922. September 17. | 1931. September 7. |
| 1923. August 26. | 1932. August 29, several. |
| 1924. September 6. | September 17, 18, many. |
| 1925. October 1. | October 12. |
| 1927. September 1, 5, 8. | 1934. August 27, several. |
| October 7, several. | September 6, 19, several. |
| 1929. October 5, four. | |

In spring they seem to be much rarer and we have but four records:

1927. May 20 and 22.    1932. May 8.    1934. May 15.

The Magnolia Warbler is a common transient throughout northern and western Jersey and nests sparingly in the mountains of Sussex and Passaic counties.

## CAPE MAY WARBLER

### Dendroica tigrina (Gmelin)

A specimen of this little bird was shot in a maple swamp in Cape May county by George Ord, later president of the Academy of Natural Sciences of Philadelphia, in May 1809, and presented to his friend Alexander Wilson, who was at the time engaged in publishing his classic "American Ornithology." The bird was quite unknown to him and he prepared a painting and description of it which appeared in his great work. He named it in honor of the place at which it had been found, and the specimen was preserved in the famous Peale's Museum in Philadelphia. The bird thus became known to scientific men throughout the world and served to advertise the name of Cape May probably more widely than has been done in any other way.

It later developed that a specimen of this same bird had flown onto a vessel sailing off the coast of Jamaica and had been painted and described by an English naturalist George Edwards some years before Ord secured his specimen. This resulted in the publication of an earlier technical name but Wilson's English name, Cape May Warbler, has been retained for it ever since. We now know that the Cape May Warbler is a native of New Brunswick and other parts of Canada and that it occurs in New Jersey and other Eastern States only on its migrations to and from its winter home in the West Indies.

Curiously enough it seems never to have been recorded again at Cape May until September 4, 1920, when I recognized one in a shade tree on Perry Street in company with some Chestnut-sided Warblers. Since then we have seen a few nearly every year in spring and fall both at Cape May and at the Point. The birds had doubtless always been passing the Cape and the lack of any records has been due to the lack of ornithologists.

Our autumn records follow:

| | |
|---|---|
| 1920. September 4, one. | 1926. November 21, one. |
| 1921. September 16, one. | 1927. September 25, one. |
| 1922. August 28, one. | 1929. October 25, one. |
| 1924. October 1 and 2, one each. | 1930. October 5, one. |
| 1925. September 30, two. | 1932. September 17–19, six. |
| 1925. October 1, six. | 1934. September 28, one. |

The November record was a bird found by John Gillespie which was studied at leisure for some time as it searched for insects in a sycamore tree near the depot. It had a rather loud squeaking note which attracted attention to it.

From September 17 to 19, and probably later, in 1932, there were several young birds of the year feeding in the flower beds of the Physick garden on Washington Street, plain gray birds with very faint dusky streaks below and the telltale lighter crescent-shaped mark on the ear-coverts. They had a constant slight tilting motion of the tail which was also noted by Julian Potter in birds that he observed.

In spring I saw an exceptionally brilliant male in the pines at Cape May Point on May 1, 1926, in company with Myrtle Warblers, and on May 15, 1928, two beautiful males in an old deserted nursery near Schellenger's Landing. In these birds the tail tilting was very pronounced. They were so tame that they approached within arm's length of me as they fed in the privet bushes.

## BLACK-THROATED BLUE WARBLER

### Dendroica caerulescens caerulescens (Gmelin)

The Black-throated Blue Warbler is a regular transient through the wooded parts of the Cape May peninsula and is seen most frequently at the Point and along the Bay shore. Its line of migration follows the coast to its winter quarters in the West Indies.

Our autumn records are as follows:

| | | | |
|---|---|---|---|
| 1921. | August 27. | 1925. | October 1. |
| | September 4. | 1926. | September 11, 27, two. |
| 1922. | September 17. | 1928. | September 30. |
| 1923. | September 30. | 1929. | October 4, 5. |
| | October 1. | 1931. | September 1, 2. |
| 1924. | August 30. | 1932. | August 29, nine. |
| | October 2. | | September 17, 18, 25, 30. |

Spring occurrences:

| | | | |
|---|---|---|---|
| 1925. | May 8. | 1929. | May 10. |
| 1927. | May 8, 20, 22. | 1932. | May 7. |
| 1928. | May 6, 20. | 1934. | May 5. |

It is a common transient throughout the state and breeds in the mountains of Sussex and Passaic Counties.

## MYRTLE WARBLER

### Dendroica coronata (Linnaeus)

The Myrtle Warbler is an abundant winter resident and autumn transient throughout the Cape May area and may justly be termed the most conspicuous small land bird of the coastal district in late fall and winter. As one follows the shore line from Cape May to the Point they arise from the low bushes back of the sand hills at every step, while the dense growth of bayberry near the Lighthouse simply swarms with them. Out on the fields, east of the pine woods at the Point, they collect in large numbers in the shelter that is there offered against the wind, and as we advance they get up in a continuous succession and drift onward through the woods and into the bushes bordering Lake Lily.

Following the old sand road leading north from the Lighthouse Pond it seems at first as if birds of various kinds were taking wing ahead. Some of them dart out of the thickets like scattered flocks of sparrows; others cling to the pine cones like Chickadees; some cross the sky line like drifting swallows; and still others pause to flutter in the air in the manner of flycatchers; but we realize ere long that they are all Myrtlebirds and we marvel at their abundance and at their varied activities. In color, too, they vary not a little; the birds of the year in dull brown dress; old males showing slate-blue below the brown fringes of the winter plumage; females in a plumage between the two; while there is not a little individual variation in the intensity of shades. In some the black blotches and yellow breast spots of the spring livery show up strongly while in others they are scarcely evident, but when flying directly away from us, so that a good view of the back is afforded, the yellow rump always catches the eye and it, with the white spots at the extremity of the outer tail feathers, make a triangle of identification marks that stamp them all as Myrtle Warblers.

We soon learn to identify their rather jerky flight as they rise from the bushes, and with a series of short wing flips turn now to the right now to the left, in their zigzag progress, rising somewhat with the beats, and falling in the intervals. Sometimes a bird will go but a short distance, flitting from bush to bush, while others will climb higher and higher in the air, drifting on their jerky way cross the sky like wind-blown leaves.

I have seen the Myrtle Warblers down among the bases of the bayberry bushes gleaning from the ground, as well as up among the clusters of berries which are supposed to form the greater part of their winter food, and I have also seen them dropping down onto the muddy flats along the banks of Lake Lily where some sort of choice food was evidently available. As soon as a Myrtlebird alights on a bush there is a short, sharp flip of the tail, not a seesaw action, but one involving the body as well, and as it comes to rest the head is drawn in and the plumage ruffled up making the outline more nearly globular, while the wings are dropped slightly so that their tips are a little below the base of the tail.

October 31, 1920, was a characteristic Myrtle Warbler day. All day long they were present in abundance. The air seemed full of them wherever one went. Thousands were flitting here and there in the dense growth of rusty Indian grass (*Andropogon*), in the bayberry thickets, in pine woods and in dune thickets. As the dusk of evening began to settle down I found them flitting on their zigzag way to the bushes about the Race Track Pond where they were apparently settling for the night.

On October 13, 1913, Julian Potter encountered a great flight of Myrtle Warblers which he estimated at 3000. Upon reaching the coast he found numbers of them right in town, and, walking up the boardwalk, he encountered an almost continuous flight going down the coast in loose flocks. Some appeared to be coming in from the ocean as if they had been blown out to sea by the strong northwest wind of the night before. Many of them were very much exhausted and alighted on the beach, on the boardwalk, and on any conceivable perch, permitting one to approach them very closely. The flight continued until 11 a. m. when it had practically ceased, although there were straggling flocks to be seen all day. Some Juncos and White-throated Sparrows were pursuing the same course and along the boardwalk he found a number of dead birds evidently killed by striking the telephone wires. They consisted of three White-throats, three Juncos, four Savannah Sparrows, two Myrtle Warblers, one each of the Golden-crowned and Ruby-crowned Kinglets, and a Field Sparrow. At Cape May Point the Myrtle Warblers fairly swarmed.

On October 23, 1927, they were again in full flight, a steady scattered stream crossing the town and continually alighting on houses, hedges, fences etc., and winging their way on down the coast. Passing through the woods and thickets they made a rustling like falling leaves. Many were on the ground and clustered about rain water pools on the roads.

While the Myrtlebirds are most abundant on the southward migration an immense number remain all winter and shift here and there so that one may not realize how numerous they are until he comes upon one of the main flocks. On January 9, 1922, the majority of the Myrtlebirds of the Point were feeding on the ground along the road above the Lighthouse hopping rapidly about and picking up food like sparrows. Then all flew up on the wires and perched for a moment, and then off again over the meadows, and later they were seen crossing the turnpike into thickets east of the pine woods. While we speak of flocks of Myrtle Warblers they do not move in the simultaneous manner of true flocks but rather each bird for himself so that the movement of a flock is a continuous straggling performance, some birds alighting and others taking wing at every moment.

At times, often in midwinter, they swarm on the Fill east of the town where bayberry bushes have formed many dense thickets and from here they may flood the town in stormy or windy weather, flocking into gardens and shade trees and close about the houses, even thronging the porches of unoccupied buildings. They also, at times, cover the old weedy fields back of the meadows flying up onto fences and hedgerows when disturbed. These wild winter flights often seem to be without rhyme or reason but they are so extensive and so spectacular that they challenge our ability to explain them.

Entirely aside from the usual feeding habits of the Myrtlebirds was the case of an individual observed on April 2, 1924, which was systematically visiting the holes just drilled in some hickory trees by a Yellow-bellied Sapsucker, feeding either upon the sap that exuded from them, or possibly upon small insects that might have been attracted by it. The bird made regular rounds and could be seen repeatedly poking his bill into the holes, but he retreated whenever the Sapsucker returned to make his own rounds.

The Myrtles arrive from the north in late September or early October and our records of first arrival run as follows:

| 1920. | October 3.     | 1925. | September 22. | 1930. | September 28. |
|-------|----------------|-------|---------------|-------|---------------|
| 1921. | October 9.     | 1927. | October 10.   | 1932. | September 17. |
| 1923. | September 30.  | 1928. | October 7.    | 1934. | September 28. |
| 1924. | October 2.     | 1929. | October 5.    | 1935. | September 29. |

The great flights, however, take place toward the end of the latter month. In the spring we do not notice any marked increase in the winter population and they begin to thin out and then pass on to the north almost before we realize that they are going. In late April and May, however, there is evidence of a flight from farther south, birds that are associated with migrant warblers of various other species and obviously not left-overs from the local winter population. Our latest records for the spring are:

| 1921. April 24. | 1926. May 1. | 1931. May 9. |
| 1922. April 23. | 1927. May 20. | 1932. May 7. |
| 1923. April 30. | 1928. May 14. | 1933. May 7. |
| 1924. April 20. | 1929. May 11. | 1934. May 5. |
| 1925. May 10. | 1930. May 6. | |

In the summer of 1921, Earl Poole discovered some Myrtle Warblers in the pines at the Point, associated with Red-breasted Nuthatches, on the extraordinarily early dates of August 10 and 11, and they were seen there frequently until the time of my departure on September 5, but with no increase in numbers, never more than six present at a time. They had evidently come with the Red-breasted Nuthatches and these birds, notoriously irregular in the time of their migration, may in some way have influenced the warblers to come south far in advance of their usual time of flight. They had evidently left their breeding grounds before the beginning of the annual molt as they were all changing plumage and completed the molt while here. In 1924, three were found in the same wood on August 29, busily exploring the pine cones and bunches of needles and on August 20, 1925, two were present associated again with the Nuthatches; a few were present on August 26, 1927, and August 30, 1932, so that this early movement may be more frequent than was at first supposed.

In the spring the birds of the year shed their dull brown plumage and assume the more brilliant dress of the adults. I have collected specimens in all stages of this molt in the woods that formerly stood on the edge of the meadows between Atlantic City and Longport on April 9, 1892, and April 8, 1893, and birds at Cape May at this season were evidently in the same condition although the late migrants of early May are all in full nuptial dress.

While the Myrtlebirds are always found in abundance on the Christmas census of the Delaware Valley Ornithological Club it is interesting to note the estimates of numbers seen on these occasions although the relative number of observers and the thoroughness of the search accounts for much of the variation, the census of 1935 being by far the most thorough. In the case of such free moving birds, however, there is bound to be duplication.

| 1931. December 27, 7,500. | 1934. December 23, 820. |
| 1932. December 26, 6,000. | 1935. December 22, 7,257. |
| 1933. December 24, 996. | 1936. December 27, 1,556. |

The Myrtle Warbler does not breed in the state but is everywhere an abundant transient and winters all along the coast and less commonly inland.

## BLACK-THROATED GREEN WARBLER

### Dendroica virens virens (Gmelin)

The Black-throated Green Warbler is a rather rare transient. Spring records: May 20, 1927; May 14, 1928; May 8, 1932; May 5, 1934 (three).

Autumn records: September 8 and 25, October 8 and 9, 1932; September 19, 1934.

While outside the limits of Cape May County, the record of a Black-throated Green Warbler in the Pine Barrens of Ocean County on July 4, 1935, by Julian Potter, and another in the same region on June 6 of the same year by Charles Urner, are of particular interest since the former, especially, is too late to be regarded as a belated transient. If the bird was located there for the summer it may possibly have been nesting and that raises the question of its relation to Wayne's Warbler (*Dendroica waynei* Bangs) of the South Carolina lowlands and the Dismal Swamp of Virginia, which is at best scarcely more than a Black-throated Green summering far south of its normal breeding area.

Another was seen near Camden, N. J., however, as late as June 2, 1929 (Potter).

The Black-throated Green Warbler is a common transient through most of the state and breeds in the mountains of Sussex and Passaic Counties.

## BLACKBURNIAN WARBLER

### Dendroica fusca (Müller)

This beautiful warbler is a rare transient in the Cape May region. Autumn records: September 30, 1928; October 6, 1929; September 4, 1930; August 25, 1931; August 29, September 17, and October 8, 1932.

Our only spring record is a bird found in song in the pine woods at the Point by Julian Potter on the unusually late date of June 9, 1929.

In most parts of the state the Blackburnian Warbler is a common transient and it breeds locally in the mountains of the northern counties.

## *CERULEAN WARBLER

### Dendroica cerulea (Wilson)

The Cerulean Warbler is an exceedingly rare bird in New Jersey. The only published records of specimens taken in the state are one at Trenton, C. C. Abbott (Birds of New Jersey, 1868) and one taken by S. D. Judd, at Boonton, Morris County on September 1, 1887 (Auk, 1897, p. 326). The record of five seen at Cape May Point on May 23, 1936, which is our only Cape May record, need hardly be taken seriously (Bird-Lore, 1926, p. 299).

The Cerulean Warbler has been found nesting on the Hudson River in Dutchess County, N. Y. by M. S. Crosby (Auk, 1923, p. 104) and G. W. Gray (Auk, 1924, p. 161) and the birds of this, the most northern breeding place, may travel through New Jersey, but most likely down the Delaware or Susquehanna Rivers. The bird also nests on the Choptank River near the Delaware-Maryland line and at Seaford, Delaware (Rhoads, Auk, 1905, p. 203), also on the lower Susquehanna River near the Maryland-Pennsylvania line. Stragglers might be expected to reach Cape May from Delaware but we have as yet no satisfactory evidence.

## YELLOW-THROATED WARBLER

Dendroica dominica dominica (Linnaeus)

This southern warbler is a rare summer resident at Cape May Point, where it apparently reaches its most northern limit.   While no nest has yet been found, nor young seen, it seems hardly possible that the numerous individuals that have been observed can all be solitary birds that have overshot their normal limit in the northern migration, like the one found by Col. Theodore Roosevelt on Long Island, on May 8, 1907 (Scribner's Magazine, 1907, p. 387).   There are several records for North Jersey.

Our first record for the Cape May district was made on July 13, 1920, while I was making a census of the birds at the Point.   I had been studying some Pine Warblers in the tops of the trees when I noticed a bird agitating a bunch of pine needles at the extremity of one of the limbs and focussing the glass on it I was amazed to have a Yellow-throated Warbler emerge into the field.   The exceptionally long bill, blue gray back, yellow throat and black stripes on the sides of the breast, were all clearly observed.   Just previous to seeing it I heard a fragment of song coming from the same tree and resembling that of the Indigo Bunting but I did not hear the bird sing again.   I watched it for nearly ten minutes and during this time it moved deliberately about the branches, especially among the cone clusters, now and then fluttering in the air for a moment or two opposite the bunch which it was examining.   Finally it caught a green caterpillar about an inch in length and hopped with it back of the main trunk of the pine amongst some ampelopsis vines.   From there it apparently flew away in the opposite direction as I lost it completely.

While I watched it it came down to the lowest branches of the tree and followed them out to their tips until it was within ten feet of my face and showed no trace of fear.   On July 15 I returned to the spot and searched for about half an hour when I again found my bird.   It was moving deliberately as before and seemed to prefer the larger limbs and the clusters of needles and cones which grew close to them, in its search for food.   Regarding this bird as a purely accidental straggler I collected it and found that it was a male in worn plumage but with no signs of molting.   I saw no other individual during the summer although the region was pretty thoroughly studied.   Since then we have had twelve observations of the bird, all at Cape May Point.

On May 30, 1923, one was seen near Lake Lily by members of the Delaware Valley Ornithological Club.   The song was heard at the time but the bird was not found again although looked for all summer.   On June 8, 1924, another individual, attracted by the cries of a pair of Ovenbirds with a nest of young, flew close to me in the woods to the west of the lake and I watched it for some time.   The long bill and heavy black stripes on the sides, recalling those of the Black-and-white Warbler, were striking field marks.

On July 5, 1925, Julian Potter saw one west of Lake Lily which was in full song, probably the bird seen there on May 30, previous, by Henry Collins, while I watched one, possibly still the same individual, in the pine woods east of the lake on August 27, following, which fed among the pine needles like a Pine Warbler and sometimes hung to them like a Chickadee. Later observations are: April 7, 1929, by Julian Potter; May 24, 1931, by Mrs. John Gillespie; May 27–30, 1931, by Julian Potter; August 27, 1931, by Julian Potter (these three possibly the same bird); April 24, 1932, by Conrad Roland; March 29, 1936, by Harvey Moore. All of these were single birds except in Roland's case when two were seen together. Moore's record, the earliest that we have, probably indicates the normal time of first arrival as the bird is known to be an early migrant.

The occurrence of this bird at the Point is of particular interest as, like the Mockingbird, it gives a distinctly southern tinge to the bird life of the region.

## CHESTNUT-SIDED WARBLER

### Dendroica pensylvanica (Linnaeus)

Apparently a rather rare transient, occurring both at Cape May and at the Point. Our records follow:

In autumn:

| | | | |
|---|---|---|---|
| 1920. | September 4, two. | 1928. | September 27, one. |
| 1921. | August 15, several. | 1932. | August 29–30, several. |
| 1922. | August 21, one. | 1932. | September 17, several. |
| 1924. | September 10, one. | 1934. | August 27, one. |
| 1927. | August 25, one. | | |

In spring:

| | | |
|---|---|---|
| 1927.   May 20. | 1928.   May 10. | 1934.   May 5. |

In the northern half of the state the Chestnut-sided Warbler is a summer resident and has been found breeding as far south as Plainfield (Miller) and probably Princeton (Babson) while Turner McMullen found a nest and four eggs at Haddonfield, on May 30, 1914, with the female incubating.

## BAY-BREASTED WARBLER

### Dendroica castanea (Wilson)

A rare transient at Cape May and the Point as in other parts of the state. Our autumn records are:

| | | | |
|---|---|---|---|
| 1920. | September 2, several. | 1928. | September 30, one. |
| 1921. | September 14, one. | 1932. | September 17, several. |
| 1925. | September 22 and 29, one each. | | |

In spring: May 10, 1924, one; May 26, 1929, one; and two seen by Richard Miller at Cape May Court House, May 21, 1916.

## BLACK-POLL WARBLER

**Dendroica striata** (Forster)

A regular transient; never so numerous as in the Delaware Valley; apparently more common in spring. Spring records:

| | | | |
|---|---|---|---|
| 1892. | May 24, several. | 1925. | May 30, two. |
| 1915. | May 16, two. | 1927. | May 20, abundant. |
| 1916. | May 21. | 1927. | May 22, two. |
| 1918. | May 24, one. | 1928. | May 13, two. |
| 1919. | May 25. | 1928. | May 30, several. |
| 1921. | May 29, one. | 1930. | May 13. |
| 1922. | May 30. | 1932. | May 5. |
| 1923. | May 20. | 1933. | May 12. |
| 1923. | May 25–27, one. | 1935. | May 19. |
| 1924. | May 10 and 30, one each. | | |

Autumn records:

| | | | |
|---|---|---|---|
| 1924. | October 2, several. | 1931. | October 17. |
| 1925. | October 11, one. | 1931. | September 17 and 25. |
| 1928. | September 27. | 1933. | September 28. |
| 1929. | October 5 and 25. | | |

The Black-poll breeds entirely north of New Jersey.

## PINE WARBLER

### Dendroica pinus pinus (Wilson)

Few birds are as restricted in habitat as the Pine Warbler. True to its name it is found almost exclusively in pines; and about Cape May its range is limited to the pond pine woods at the Point. Here throughout the summer some of these birds are always present. Farther north in the Pine Barrens it is, of course, everywhere an abundant summer resident. In the northern half of the state it is a very local breeder and a colony was found by Dr. F. M. Chapman at High Knob on June 10, 1890.

The action of the Pine Warblers in the trees is deliberate, and they hop from one limb to another and creep about the cone clusters like mice. The wings usually droop slightly so that the tips are a trifle below the base of the tail. One bird (July 13, 1921) searched the larger limbs and apparently fed exclusively from the clumps of needles; more usually however they are out on the ends of the limbs among the clusters of small twigs and bunches of cones. One was seen to pull an insect of some sort from the scales of a cone and smash it against a limb. Sometimes they will fly clear of the tree in pursuit of prey and flutter in the air for a moment or two, or will descend to the ground after it.

On their first arrival in spring they often feed on the ground, and on April 2, 1922, half a dozen males were found in an old field near the pine woods feeding diligently. They hopped about pecking at dead leaves and scattered pieces of bark, deliberately putting the bill under them and turning them over, so as to expose such insects as were lurking beneath. When disturbed they flew into low shrubs, three or four feet in height, and rested, hopping down again in a few minutes. Again on April 1, 1933, they were feeding in a field with Juncos. A female was seen feeding on the ground in the woods August 22, 1925, and another August 6, 1927, but they usually do so only in early spring.

The song, a long, nearly monotone trill, is most strongly emphasized on the first two notes while the trill seems to rise during the first three pulsations and then gradually descend—*zit, zit, ziz-ziz-ziz-ziz-ziz-ziz-ziz-ziz-ziz-ziz*, at a distance it sounds like a clear monotone, somewhat like that of a Chipping Sparrow. When the bird sings his whole body seems to vibrate in unison. One studied (April 4, 1924) would sit on one twig and trill four to six times and then fly to another perch. He raised his head as he sang and the entire body trembled.

Several times I have found them feeding full-fledged young,—July 6, 1925; July 22, 1923; August 17, 1920. In the last instance the female dropped like a plumet to the ground at my feet as I paused beneath the tree; this behavior is seen when they are disturbed at the nest—an action akin to the "broken wing" ruse of ground nesting birds.

A young bird, July 13, was in full juvenal plumage, while a young male, August 5, another July 28, and a female, August 17, were molting to the adult dress, which was completely acquired by other individuals by August 18 and 27. An adult female on the latter date had not begun to molt and was dull sooty brown and very much worn, as was still another seen on August 17. An adult male September 1, was in full winter plumage, of unusually bright yellow. The yellow of the male Pine Warbler is not the usual yellow of our warblers but a sort of wax yellow and often rather dull but, even so, the plain dull brown female with only a shade of light yellow on the breast, if any, is quite a different looking bird. The gray, not white, wing bands however form an excellent identification mark for both.

Our earliest arrival dates for the Pine Warbler at Cape May Point are:

| | | |
|---|---|---|
| 1925. March 21. | 1921. April 3. | 1930. April 6. |
| 1923. March 25. | 1924. April 4. | 1932. March 25. |
| 1922. April 2. | 1928. April 1. | 1935. March 23. |
| | 1929. March 18. | |

Latest autumn dates recorded:

| | | |
|---|---|---|
| 1924. October 2. | 1929. October 5. | 1935. October 5. |
| 1925. October 10. | | |

In the Pine Barrens occasional individuals remain throughout the winter and one was seen at Haddonfield by Samuel Rhoads on January 30, 1898.

Julian Potter found the only nest at Cape May Point of which we have record on May 27, 1931. A number of pairs of the birds must breed there every summer but the nests are exceedingly hard to find as they are usually situated on limbs near the tops of the pine trees and well screened by clusters of cones or needles.   In the Pine Barrens, at Chatsworth, Turner McMullen has found nests with sets of three and four eggs on May 12 and 13 of different years, and one at Mays Landing on May 9, while George Stuart found a nest with four eggs at the former locality as late as May 24, 1918.   McMullen also found young in nests there on May 13, 1934.

Robert T. Moore, describing a nesting of the Pine Warbler in Griscom's Swamp in the Pine Barrens, May 22, 1908, writes: "With my glass I surveyed the supposed nest for several minutes.   No sign of a bird was visible, but a knock on the tree brought her down, tumbling almost into my arms. Like a dropping plumet she fell straight to the earth, fluttering to a log a few yards distant from my feet.   On it she crouched acting the broken wing in motion, a pathetic picture of trembling love boldly acting deception. During several hours spent about this nest I only once saw the male, and never heard a note from either bird.****   The cones on the tree were bunched near the top, and the nest was placed directly in their midst, not dissimilar from them in breadth at the bottom.   A thick network of pine spills, five to six inches long, screened it below and above, forming a mass of umbrage impossible to pierce.   This considered with the secretive movements and surprising artifices of the bird make it clear why the nest is so seldom discovered."   (Cassinia, 1908, p. 39.)

Philip Laurent records Pine Warblers as common in the woods of Five Mile Beach in the eighties.

## PRAIRIE WARBLER

Dendroica discolor discolor (Vieillot)

Prairie Warblers are common summer residents in the pine woods and oak scrub of Cape May Point and in similar situations in the peninsula to the northward, occurring also throughout the Pine Barrens where they are one of the most characteristic species. In northern New Jersey they seem to be rare and local. They increase in numbers in the latter part of August when the young have molted and migrants are drifting down from farther north. At this time, too, they appear on the Fill and even in the trees and shrubbery of Cape May gardens.

They are normally birds of the scrub and undergrowth and in the pine groves of the Point we often find them seeking minute insects in the clumps of wild indigo, while some of them actually feed on the ground. The low branches of huckleberry and bayberry bushes are favorite resorts and when disturbed they may fly up into the trees, and occasionally one will be seen feeding there twenty feet from the ground. They are active birds and their movements from twig to twig are accompanied by a constant up and down tilt of the tail, such as we see in the Palm Warbler but not so energetic. Sometimes, too, there is a nervous flutter of the wings and tail, both being spread to some extent so that the white marks on the rectrices come prominently into view. Sometimes they will pursue one another vigorously through the woods long after the excitement of the breeding season is over.

Data on twelve nests found by Richard Miller about Rio Grande, a few miles north of Cape May, show that the usual number of eggs is four, rarely five. Full sets of fresh eggs were noted on May 27, June 3 and 10, of various years while some on June 3 were partly incubated and three nests on June 10, contained recently hatched young. Other nests found on May 20 and 31 had incomplete sets. The nests were located from eighteen inches to four feet from the ground in holly, azalea, huckleberry and oak bushes.

Turner McMullen reports twelve nests in the same neighborhood found from May 20 to 27, most of which contained four eggs, one five, while three held also an egg of the Cowbird. Another found on May 30, contained young birds.

I have found adult Prairie Warblers feeding fledglings in the bushes on July 15 and August 5, and young were molting into the winter plumage on July 15, while the molt had been completed by August 5, 1921, and August 7, 1925. Our earliest spring records of the Prairie Warbler are April 30, 1923; May 8, 1925; May 1, 1926; April 30, 1927; May 2, 1927. In the autumn we have recorded it as late as October 16, 1921; October 2, 1924; October 1, 1925; September 30, 1928; October 5, 1929; October 13, 1935.

This active little warbler with its wheezy insect-like notes which Dr. Coues has likened to those of "a mouse with a tooth-ache," and its ever moving tail, is one of the most characteristic summer birds of the Point.

## WESTERN PALM WARBLER

### Dendroica palmarum palmarum (Gmelin)

Palm Warblers, recognized at once by their exaggerated tail dipping, arrive at Cape May about the middle of September and are present through October in varying numbers while a few individuals remain during the winter.

Unfortunately it is impossible to refer all of our sight records of these birds subspecifically. It is generally conceded that the vast majority of the duller colored western race travel north along the Mississippi Valley and as all of our spring birds have the bright yellow breasts of the eastern form— the Yellow Palm Warbler, it is certain that they represent that race. In autumn, however, the case is not so simple as both forms apparently occur, but it is my belief that the western form is the more abundant, immediately along the coast, especially in the earlier flights, and Julian Potter while making a careful study of the birds of the Cape region, September 20 to October 2, 1925, came to the same conclusion. All wintering individuals seem also to be referable to this race, as also the one seen on March 13, 1921, which was probably a winter resident.

Both races breed far north of New Jersey.

These little birds are distinctly ground birds found in old bushy fields and in low shrubbery or along the roadsides, always in open country, and alight in low trees or bushes only when disturbed at their feeding. Winter individuals have been found in company with Bluebirds along old fence rows back of the town, or seeking shelter under the deserted boardwalk on the beach front.

Our arrival dates in autumn are:

| 1893. September 11. | 1927. September 25. | 1930. September 21. |
| 1922. September 16. | 1928. September 23. | 1932. September 7. |
| 1925. September 20. | 1929. September 21. | 1934. September 28. |
| 1926. September 26. | | |

While most of them have passed on by the middle of October we have five records for November—November 14 and 21, 1920; November 26, 1922; November 22, 1929; November 9, 1930.

In winter it has been recorded as follows:

| 1920. December 12 and 26. | 1922. December 31. | 1924. January 19. |
| 1921. December 31. | 1923. December 2. | 1926. December 26. |

Usually these have been single birds but on December 2, two were seen and on the Christmas census of the Delaware Valley Club the combined observations of a number of men yielded four individuals on December 23, 1934; ten on December 22, 1935; ten on December 27, 1936.

## YELLOW PALM WARBLER

*Dendroica palmarum hypochrysea* Ridgway

This race of the Palm Warbler is the prevalent form in the East and the only one that we have seen in the spring. It occurs throughout the latter half of April and in the southward migration occurs a little later than the western race, our records being mostly in October. While all wintering birds at Cape May seem referable to the latter, one collected by Samuel Rhoads at Mays Landing in the Pine Barrens on December 2, 1892, is unquestionably the yellow-bellied eastern form.

## OVENBIRD

*Seiurus aurocapillus* (Linnaeus)

PLATE 114, p. 838

A typical bird of moist deciduous woodland, the Ovenbird is a common summer resident farther north in the peninsula but is not abundant immediately about Cape May. A pair or two nest at the Point between Lake Lily and the Bay and others in the woods bordering Pond Creek Meadows, while they occur also in the wooded strip back of the marshes on the ocean side of the peninsula from opposite Bennett northward and the bird is a common summer resident throughout the state.

A nest found at the Point by William Baily on May 31, 1924, contained five young and when I examined them on June 8 they were arranged in two tiers completely filling the mouth of the domed nest, the birds in the rear looking out over the backs of those in front. Their bills with yellow swollen

( 832 )

gapes were very conspicuous, while their brown plumage, so different from the olive green of the adults, blended beautifully with the surrounding dead leaves. The parents were greatly excited and flew about, one with food in its beak, calling *tick; tick; tick;* and with each utterance there was a sudden elevation of the tail.

An hour or two after studying them I found the nest empty, the young being apparently concealed in the adjoining thicket as the old birds were still very anxious. They are always extremely solicitous and the cries of any bird in distress will bring Ovenbirds if there are any in the vicinity.

Nests were examined by Turner McMullen as follows:

Mayville, May 16, 1915, three eggs.     Rio Grande, May 30, 1925, four eggs.
Rio Grande, May 17, 1925, five eggs.     Rio Grande, June 3, 1923, five young.
Rio Grande, May 25, 1925, four eggs.

A bird that I found in the pines on July 12, 1929, was walking and jumping along the limbs and seemed much disturbed. It gave utterance to alarm notes similar to those of the other pair but which at a little distance sounded more like *chip; chip; chip;* with a distinct pause after each note. This bird stretched its neck to the fullest extent and erected the dull orange feather of the crown, and its pale pink tarsi were conspicuous against the dark limb of the tree. It apparently had young somewhere in the vicinity in spite o the lateness of the date.

Another individual on August 16, 1921, acted in much the same way, calling and walking along the limbs of a pine tree, and the nesting season being long past, its actions could hardly have had anything to do with the care of young. It had a peculiar habit of squatting down on the limb every few minutes.

The Ovenbird is one of those species that is more frequently heard than seen and the loud ringing crescendo of its song: *cher, téa-cher, téa-cher, téa-cher, téa-cher,* announces its presence during the nesting season wherever it may be. With the wane of the singing period the bird seems to disappear, so secretive are its habits, and we realize that we had been in the habit of noting its presence more by ear than by eye. I have heard the song as late as July 6, 1925; July 6, 1928; July 9, 1921.

In late August there seems to be an influx of Ovenbirds from farther north—August 21, 1922; August 27, 1923; August 27, 1924; after which they fluctuate in numbers until the middle of September. Our latest records are:

1921. September 13.     1924. September 11.     1932. September 25.
1925. September 29.     1930. September 28.

Dates of first arrival in spring are:

1923. April 30.     1926. April 24.     1932. May 2.
                 1927. April 30.

## NORTHERN WATER-THRUSH

Seiurus noveboracensis noveboracensis (Gmelin)

The Water-Thrush is the first transient land bird to be seen in the Cape May district on the southward migration. Any time after the first of August, or even a few days earlier, we may expect to hear its metallic *pink, pink,* from the black muddy banks of Cape Island Creek where it winds through the meadows between Cape May and the Point and to see the bird perched on some projecting snag or overhanging branch with tail wagging up and down like a veritable wagtail.

Coming from its breeding grounds along the clear mountain brooks and cascades of the north it seems strangely out of place on these foul smelling tidewater creeks, which, where they flow through coastwise towns, are little better than open sewers. Yet here the Water-Thrushes remain through August and September and seem to find an abundance of food.

They have several times been flushed from the edge of the open salt meadows, near some shallow pool, flying at once to the nearest bushes for shelter, and a shady thicket at the Point, where a sewage pipe empties into the Lighthouse Pond, is a favorite resort. On September 1, 1920, two Water-Thrushes and two Solitary Sandpipers took possession of a small rain water pool well surrounded by weeds, on a vacant lot in the town, and remained until the water had entirely dried up. At best the pool was only three feet in diameter. Another Water-Thrush was seen feeding with a Least Sandpiper on the dry mud of a shallow pond, running this way and that and darting its bill right and left to the ground. Every summer a few of them take up their residence in the gardens in the heart of Cape May and we see their characteristic tail-tilting as they walk about among the flower beds. On September 7, 1924, I watched one feeding on the bottom of a dried up pool in the woods east of Bennett where a long arched wood road leads from a farm out to the salt meadows. The spot was covered with a carpet of dried decaying leaves left as the water evaporated, and the bird was diligently turning these over with its bill and tossing them to one side as it sought for insects beneath.

In a thicket where other birds are present in August, the alarm cry of a Catbird, Vireo or Towhee will at once bring all the Water-Thrushes in the vicinity to the scene of trouble and they fly nervously from branch to branch adding their cries to the miniature babel. Frequently, too, they will pursue one another vigorously through the thicket, turning and twisting with remarkable agility. When very close at hand the sharp emphatic note of the bird seems to lose the metallic quality that we note when farther off and I have recorded it as *pist!, pist!*

The Water-Thrush can be readily identified when flying in the open. Not only is it darker and apparently blacker than any other small bird seen against the sky or the meadows, but its flight is characteristic. The body is long and slender and the long swoops between the series of short wingbeats produce a diving, somewhat undulatory movement, but more irregular and less pronounced than that of the Goldfinch. I once saw a Water-Thrush hover for at least a minute in and over a bunch of cattails growing in water where there was no opportunity for the bird to alight.

Usually one sees not more than one or two Water-Thrushes together, but in the thicket about the sewer opening at the Point I have had six in view at once, and in a morning's walk on August 20, 1922, I listed twenty-five.

Our dates of arrival on the southward flight are:

| | | | | | |
|---|---|---|---|---|---|
| 1920. | August 2. | 1925. | July 30. | 1931. | August 8. |
| 1921. | August 5. | 1926. | August 4. | 1932. | July 26. |
| 1922. | August 7. | 1927. | July 29. | 1933. | August 5. |
| 1923. | August 9. | 1928. | July 29. | 1934. | July 23. |
| 1924. | August 4. | 1929. | July 27. | 1935. | August 1. |
| | | 1930. | July 30. | 1937. | July 15. |

Latest observations in autumn are:

| | | | | | |
|---|---|---|---|---|---|
| 1914. | September 13. | 1925. | September 30. | 1930. | September 28. |
| 1921. | September 14. | 1926. | September 11. | 1931. | September 7. |
| 1923. | September 16. | 1927. | September 11. | 1932. | September 25. |
| 1924. | September 14. | 1928. | September 8. | 1935. | October 5. |
| | | 1928. | September 29. | | |

In spring we have but two records: May 22, 1927, two seen by Julian Potter and May 6, 1928, one.

While a common transient in most parts of the state the Northern Water-Thrush nests in the mountains of Sussex and Passaic Counties.

## *GRINNELL'S WATER-THRUSH

### Seiurus noveboracensis notabilis Ridgway

Two specimens of this western race of the Water-Thrush have been recorded from New Jersey—Raritan, May 30, 1889 (Southwick, Auk, 1892, p. 303), and Princeton, September 10, 1879 (W. E. D. Scott, Babson, Birds of Princeton). Its slightly larger size, larger bill and darker coloration are not easily recognized in life.

## LOUISIANA WATER-THRUSH

### Seiurus motacilla (Vieillot)

A very rare transient with similar distribution to that of the Worm-eating and Kentucky Warblers and rare anywhere in southern New Jersey. I saw one on the shore of Lake Lily on August 9, 1932, and William Rusling reported one in the same place on September 7, 1935.

One was found in a swamp near Cape May Court House by Richard Miller on June 6, 1920, and David Harrower once found a pair apparently nesting in Timber and Beaver Swamp at South Dennis.

This Water-Thrush is a summer resident in some of the northern counties —along the upper Delaware and lower Hudson and at Lake Hopatcong (Dwight), also in Essex and Union Counties, and possibly Princeton (Babson).

## KENTUCKY WARBLER
### Oporornis formosus (Wilson)

A very rare transient in the Cape May district and my only records are one seen by Julian Potter in the woods near Lake Lily on May 26, 1918, and a single individual that I saw in the undergrowth of the pine woods at Cape May Point on May 13, 1928, as it hopped about the roots and lower branches of the bayberry bushes.

The distribution of the Kentucky Warbler corresponds closely with that of the Worm-eating Warbler, a common summer resident of southeastern Pennsylvania but absent from southern New Jersey. Richard Harlow did, however, find a pair in the extensive low woodland at Manahawkin in the coastal strip which seemed to be located for the nesting season, and Chreswell Hunt found a few breeding on Pensauken Creek nine miles from Camden. Dr. F. M. Chapman found it nesting at Englewood on the lower Hudson and there are records for Essex and Union Counties (Eaton and Urner).

## CONNECTICUT WARBLER
### Oporornis agilis (Wilson)

A rare transient, in autumn. Our only records are birds found dead at the Lighthouse; three on September 24, 1932, reported by Conrad Roland; one found the next day by Julian Potter, one on September 20, 1936, by John Hess and Hampton Carson and another by Hess on September 23, 1937.

The Connecticut Warbler is a common autumn transient locally throughout the state to the north and west of the Pine Barrens but very rare in spring. Samuel Rhoads secured a male at Haddonfield on May 20, 1882.

## *MOURNING WARBLER
### Oporornis philadelphia (Wilson)

The Mourning Warbler has never been seen in Cape May County so far as I am aware and the nearest occurrence was one shot by George Morris when with me and others on the Pensauken Creek, near its mouth above Camden, on May 30, 1897. Specimens have also been taken in the more northern counties at Englewood, Morristown, Summit etc. It does not breed in the state and would appear to migrate along the Delaware Valley.

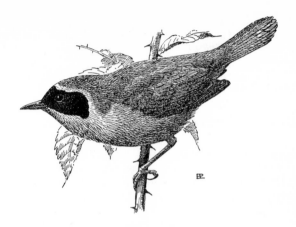

## MARYLAND YELLOW-THROAT

### Geothlypis trichas brachidactyla (Linnaeus)

The Maryland Yellow-throat is a generally distributed summer resident throughout the Cape May Peninsula. It is common in the bramble patches and moist thickets between Cape May and the Point; in the denser thickets of the latter locality; around the borders of the various ponds; and even in bayberry thickets on the edge of the meadows and in plum and sumac thickets behind the dunes of the Bay shore. They also come into the gardens of the town, especially where they back upon the meadows or on the Fill. On Two Mile Beach and the other coast islands they are common. In days past when there were almost continuous thickets along the turnpike to the Point one could hear six or eight Yellow-throats singing along the two mile stretch and a like number if one followed the coast line behind the dunes.

The Maryland Yellow-throat is not a bird that can be approached undisturbed. Ever alert he usually sees us before we can catch a glimpse of him and our first knowledge of his presence is his sharp complaining *shick*, *shick*, as he hops about in the thicket near the ground watching our every move. It is only when the male is singing that one has an opportunity to study him at rest. I saw one perched on a telegraph wire along the turnpike singing with vigor and quite oblivious to the traffic passing almost below him. Another was sitting on a dead twig at the base of a bush at the edge of a thicket not more than a foot from the ground and well surrounded by tall grass. He would glance first to one side and then to the other, occasionally picking at something on a leaf or twig within reach. Then he would raise his head and pour forth his familiar warble. The flight song is more elaborate and is uttered as the bird mounts six or eight feet into the air from his perch and flutters gradually down again. I have heard it as late as July 7.

If one thinks that all Yellow-throats sing alike it will pay him to jot down some careful records of their songs. I have gathered several at Cape May and no two are alike, although each carries a similar phrase which is characteristic, and gives to all the songs the impression of identity.

It was moreover quite easy to identify individual birds after their songs had once been memorized. Here are some of them:

Group I

    1. *Tzu-za-wítsky, tzu-za-wítsky, tzu-za-wítsky.*
    2. *Tsivit-swéeah, tsivit-swéeah, tsivit-swéeah, tsivít.*
    3. *Chit-wissa-whít, chit-wissa-whít.*
    3a. *Chissa-wissa-whít, chissa-wissa-whít.*
    4. *Chissa-wítso, tsu-wítso, tsu-wítso.* [*tsu-wítso*]

Group II

    5. *Wisset, seé-wisset, seé-wisset, seé-wisset.*
    6. *Sit-seea, weét-see-a, weét-see-a, weét-see-a.*

Group III

    7. *Tse-wítsa-seéa, tse-wítsa-seéa, tse-wít.*
    7a. *Tse-wítsa-séea, tse-wít.*
    8. *Tsi-vít-sa-vía, tse-vít-sa-vía, tse-vít.*
    9. *Tsi-vít-sa-réah, tsi-vít-sa-réah, tsi-vít-sa-réah.*
    10. *Tsi-vít-sa-wée, tsi-vít-sa-wée, tsi-vit-sa-wée, tsi-vit-sa-wée.*
    11. *Tsu-wítsua-weéah, tsu-wítsua-weéah, tsu-wít-su* [or *tsu-wit*].

I last heard the song of the Yellow-throat on July 27, 1920; August 4, 1923; July 28, 1924. These probably marked the last nestings of the season though early broods were of course on the wing long before this. I noticed bobtailed young with their parents on July 23, while birds, probably young of the year, were full-fledged and in close association with Prairie Warblers and Yellow Warblers, in a mixed flock, on August 26, 1920, while on August 13, 1922, and August 18, 1924, they were in all stages of molt.

The actions of the adults with the brood of bobtailed young were studied for some time. The male was very active, jumping from twig to twig, and flitting from one bush to another. He held the body well up with the tibio-tarsal joint clearly exposed, head down and tail cocked up while the bill was slightly elevated. There was a constant flirt of the tail to one side or the other accompanied by a nervous flap of the wings, so rapid as almost to escape detection, and a chirp of alarm uttered at regular intervals but not so frequent as the flirt of the tail.

Nests with fresh eggs have been found on May 13, partly incubated sets on May 22 and June 15, and young on June 8. The usual number is four.

After the singing ceases the Yellow-throat figures much less frequently in the bird life of the Cape district, but it can readily be called forth from

PLATE 114

*W. L. Baily*

*W. L. Baily*

1. NEST AND EGGS OF THE YELLOW WARBLER.
2. NEST AND EGGS OF THE OVENBIRD.

PLATE 115

*R. T. Peterson*

*W. L. Baily*

1. YOUNG RED-WINGED BLACKBIRD ON LILY POND, CAPE MAY POINT.

2. NEST AND EGGS OF MEADOWLARK.

its favorite thicket by the sucking sound used to attract birds—along with Catbirds, and certain other species which respond to this sound with equal alacrity.  The rich olive green of the upper parts of August Yellow-throats is conspicuous in contrast with the dull brownish gray of breeding individuals, and marks the full-plumaged young of the year or early molted adults.

About the middle of August (August 16, 1921; August 17, 1927; August 18, 1924; etc.) there seems to be a great influx of Yellow-throats and from then on they vary greatly in abundance, as each succeeding migratory wave brings additional hosts until one is astounded that so many of the birds exist.  They throng the countryside and the town gardens as well, and yet between flights it is sometimes difficult to find a single Yellow-throat!

During the great migratory flight of September 1 and 2, 1920, Yellow-throats fairly swarmed, and up on the Fill to the northeast of the town, as well as in the fields about the Race Track Pond, they arose like grasshoppers from the ground and low brambles as one advanced.  On September 25, 1926, I noted but one in a morning's walk about the Point, while the next day when the wind shifted to the north they were present by hundreds.

Our latest autumn dates run:

| | | | | | |
|---|---|---|---|---|---|
| 1921. | October 9. | 1927. | October 23. | 1931. | October 18. |
| 1923. | October 21. | 1928. | October 21. | 1932. | October 14. |
| 1924. | October 2. | 1929. | October 25. | 1934. | October 19. |
| 1925. | October 18. | 1930. | October 5. | 1935. | October 26. |

The bulk has left by October 5 but on December 27, 1931; December 22, 1935; December 27, 1936; single individuals were seen which indicate that a few may winter.

Dates of spring arrival, kept up to 1920 by Walker Hand, with subsequent records by others are:

| | | | | | |
|---|---|---|---|---|---|
| 1908. | April 26. | 1916. | April 28. | 1923. | April 22. |
| 1909. | April 29. | 1917. | April 23. | 1926. | April 24. |
| 1910. | April 16. | 1918. | April 30. | 1927. | April 24. |
| 1911. | April 27. | 1919. | April 23. | 1932. | April 23. |
| 1912. | April 25. | 1920. | April 25. | 1933. | April 30. |
| 1913. | April 30. | 1921. | April 24. | 1934. | April 20. |
| 1915. | April 20. | 1922. | April 23. | | |

The Maryland Yellow-throat is a common summer resident throughout the state.  Whether both races *G. t. trichas* and *brachidactyla* occur in the state has not been definitely determined the differences are very slight and not recognizable in the field while New Jersey covers the area of intergradation between the two.  Dr. H. C. Oberholser informs me that it seems probable that all New Jersey Yellow-throats are referable to *brachidactyla* the more northern race.

## YELLOW-BREASTED CHAT

### Icteria virens virens (Linnaeus)

The Chat is a familiar summer resident of the Cape May Peninsula as well as all other parts of southern New Jersey, arriving a little later than most of our summer birds and leaving somewhat earlier. It is an inhabitant of low scrub growth both in dry areas and on the borders of swamps, but is never found in the woodland nor is it seen in protracted flight, indeed we are lucky to see it on the wing at any time.

A pair or two are to be found every year established in some of the more remote thickets of the Point and there will be others on the borders of Pond Creek Meadow, as well as along the edges of the wooded strip on the ocean side of the peninsula from Brier Island and Cold Spring northward, while in the vicinity of Rio Grande they seem always to be particularly plentiful. Nesting pairs are usually scattered at intervals and do not colonize nor do the birds associate in groups after the breeding season is over, so that we do not see more than one or two at a time, although when in full song I have listed twenty Chats in a morning's walk back through the country north of Cape May.

The Chat is probably the most eccentric and erratic of our passerine birds both in postures and in vocal expression. He is far more often heard than seen, yet few birds are more certainly identified by voice alone. We hear his characteristic medley of notes coming from some dense thicket but we strive in vain to get a glimpse of him; restless and ever alert he manages to keep the thick foliage between us and, while watching our every move, he keeps himself unseen. He is likely to be calling at any time of day, or even at night, but in the heat of midday when most other voices are stilled his modest efforts dominate the scene. As one approaches his haunts amid the greenbriers he utters a deliberate *kuk-kuk-kuk-kuk* in a high key and then on a much lower note, and still more deliberately, *caw-caw-caw* followed by several whistles and a high pitched *kek-kek-kek-kek*. There is a long pause and we stealthily approach to gain a view of the performer when suddenly, from another clump of briers farther on, comes a derisive *tscheet, tscheet, tscheet, tscheet*, in a low almost guttural tone, if such is possible in a bird. He has been keeping a watchful eye upon us and has slipped deftly out on the far side of the thicket to a new place of shelter farther on. If we persist in following him it becomes largely a game of hide and seek among the brier patches at which the Chat is well able to hold his own, dodging about with much agility and occasionally uttering a *chuck* of satisfaction. Should we remain perfectly quiet we may excite his curiosity and as he approaches closer and closer we get a glimpse through the foliage of the brilliant yellow of his breast, the bright green of his back and the strong black and white markings about the eye, and realize more clearly what a beautiful bird he is.

After the young are hatched the vocal efforts of the Chat begin to wane and we hear but scraps of his spring repertoire while some of the sounds that he does produce seem different from those heard earlier in the year. On July 13, 1920, I found a Chat at the Point which was much excited and probably had young in the immediate vicinity as, contrary to custom, he kept in plain view for some time. As he shifted his position, hopping from one perch to another, he would elevate his tail with each jump and allow it to drop slowly back again, while he kept up a continuous series of calls such as I had never heard a Chat utter before—*scape, scape, scape*, etc., about two seconds intervening between the calls. The note more closely resembled the cry of a Nighthawk that any other bird call that I could think of. With each cry he would turn his head sharply to one side or the other, ducking the body slightly at the same time. This individual, or possibly another, seen a few days later in the same vicinity, acted in exactly the same manner but had an altogether different note—*tuck, tuck, tuck*, at intervals, and then much more rapidly *tuck-tuck-tuck-tuck*, and finally the call of the previous day but with a break in the middle of each note *skee-uk, skee-uk, skee-uk*, etc.

Another peculiar cry was uttered by a bird in the pine woods at the Point (July 24, 1920)—*whit, whit*, he called and then a quick *keu, keu, keu, keu*, like the rapid cry of the Osprey, finally relapsing into the familiar Chat call *tscheeet, tscheeeet, tscheeeet, tscheeet*.

Another bird still singing the medley of the nesting season had in addition a rapid call like that of the Kingfisher *ki-ki-ki-ki-ki-ki-ki* followed by several flute-like notes and a single *tlut* and finally the characteristic *tscheeet, tscheeet, tscheeet*. On June 5, 1923, one bird had a single cry possibly in the nature of an alarm note—*whee-to-lit*.

In spring (May 10, 1924), perhaps before the birds were mated, I found three Chats together in a thick hedgerow. One singing from inside a wild cherry bush had a trill like that of a tree toad, a *pheu, pheu*, call like a Greater

Yellow-legs, and a strange note resembling a distant automobile horn. One of the other birds sat on the top of a dead bush in full view, all hunched up as if its back were broken and with tail hanging straight down. Every now and then it would stretch up its neck, which appeared very thick and out of proportion, with feathers all ruffled up and on end, and utter a triple note *hoo-hoo-hoo*.

In the spring more than at other times I have come upon Chats up in trees, especially in the open pine grove of the Point, and on May 25 one was seen diligently exploring the ends of the pine branches apparently for food, jumping clumsily from one twig to another. On July 3, 1921, another bird launched forth from the top of a rather tall tree with his characteristic flight song, wings flapping lazily and feet hanging straight down and wide spread. I have seen this performance as late as July 8, 1923, and the regular song until July 14, 1927, and July 11, 1930.

Turner McMullen has found nests of the Chat at Rio Grande on June 3, 1923, and May 31, 1924, with three and four eggs respectively and one at Court House on June 6, 1920, with two eggs. The usual number of eggs seems to be four. The nests have been placed in oak scrub, bayberry bushes and greenbrier thickets. Recently hatched young have been found on June 16 and 19 in different years.

I have found young birds out of the nest on July 5, 1932, and July 15, 1922, dull gray birds with a lemon yellow suffusion on the center of the breast. On the former occasion a parent was feeding them. Other young, molting to the winter plumage, were seen on July 20, 1929, and August 4, 1923, and showed new bright yellow feathers coming in as an inverted V on the breast.

Our dates for spring arrival of the Chat are:

| | | |
|---|---|---|
| 1924. May 10. | 1927. May 8. | 1931. May 10. |
| 1925. May 8. | 1928. May 6. | 1933. May 7. |

I have never seen an adult Chat in the molt and as we rarely see them after the middle of August, and not often after the first week of the month, I sometimes think that they must move south before they molt, if not they certainly become very secretive. Our latest records are August 23, 1923, and August 26, 1927, but we have found several dead birds at the Lighthouse and in Cape May, at later dates, which were probably all migrants from somewhat farther north. They were picked up on September 21, 1934; September 29, 1935; all in full winter plumage. As New Jersey is about the northern limit of the Chat's range they could not have come from far.

While rare in the northern half of the state the Chat has been found breeding north to the state line on the lower Hudson as well as at Summit (Holmes), Morristown (Thurber), Lake Hopatcong (Dwight), Greenwood and Beaver Lakes (Rhoads) and High Knob (Chapman).

## HOODED WARBLER

**Wilsonia citrina** (Boddaert)

This beautiful warbler is a summer resident of swampy woodlands all over the Cape May Peninsula as far south as the borders of the Pond Creek Meadows, and on the edge of the cedar swamps of the Pine Barrens farther north. In the Pond Creek area Julian Potter counted twenty on June 21, 1923, but I have never found it so abundant there in recent years. Immediately about the Point I have never found it until mid-August when birds from a little farther north move down the peninsula and, with the first Black and White Warblers and Redstarts, mark the beginning of the autumn flight. Occasionally in migrations they have been seen in the gardens of Cape May.

I first made the acquaintance of the Hooded Warbler on its breeding ground in May, 1891, when with Harris Reed and Charles Voelker I spent some days in the heart of the Timber and Beaver Swamp at South Dennis where the birds abounded. Here among thickets of sweet pepper bush and swamp magnolia, bordered on the one hand by brown cedar water of the lake and on the other by the sandy upland covered with oak scrub and holly, I came to know it intimately. The swamps resound with the song of the bird throughout May and June—a full toned emphatic warble, quite different from the lisping buzzing song of the Parula or the still more wiry strain of the Prairie, which are here its most intimate associates. *Swee, swee, tsip, tsip, se-wit-su*, I interpreted it; now on this side, now on that, it breaks the solitude of the swamp and suddenly right in front of us appears the bright yellow face and frontlet of the bird framed in its velvety black hood. With tail partly spread he gazes intently at us for a moment and then with a sharp *tschip* he has plunged back again into the shelter of the bushes and presently he once more voices his song, over on the far side of the swamp; or perhaps he has changed it to a shorter rendering, lacking the two preliminary notes, with which he is wont to vary his performance. In the fork of a holly four feet from the ground is the nest and four eggs and now the female appears on the scene, usually duller of plumage and with less of the black hood developed. The male abandons his song and both birds resort to the sharp *tschip* of alarm. While singing the male is very active moving constantly from bush to bush and covering a wide area so that with the song coming now from one angle, now from another, the performer is difficult to locate. Every moment or two there is a sudden nervous flirt of the tail as the bird hops from one twig to another and a great show of white when the feathers are widely spread. Sometimes I have seen a Hooded Warbler cling for a moment to the trunk of a pine tree, as the Pine Warblers often do, in pursuit of insects.

The nest in the Beaver Swamp contained four eggs on May 27, 1891, and two others near the same spot on June 1, 1907, held three and four eggs respectively. At Rio Grande, a few miles north of Cape May, Turner McMullen found nests with three and four eggs on May 27, 31, and June 8, in different years, and other nests containing young on May 30 and 31, 1924. Richard Miller found one at Rio Grande with two eggs as early as May 23, 1923, while I found a female in a swamp on the Rutherford farm northeast of the Point which gave every indication of having young in the vicinity as late as July 8, 1925.

The dates of the appearance of Hooded Warblers in the pine groves at the Point, which may usually be interpreted as the first indication of the southward migration, are:

| | | | | | |
|---|---|---|---|---|---|
| 1920. | August 5. | 1923. | July 26. | 1931. | August 6. |
| 1921. | August 11. | 1925. | July 30. | 1932. | August 18. |
| 1922. | August 9. | 1927. | August 3. | 1934. | July 28. |
| | | 1929. | August 17. | | |

Our latest records are: September 27, 1928; September 7, 1931; October 5, 1935 (William Rusling).

First arrival dates for the spring migration are:

| | | | | | |
|---|---|---|---|---|---|
| 1912. | April 30. | 1915. | May 4. | 1926. | April 25. |
| 1913. | April 30. | 1919. | May 5. | 1932. | May 7. |
| 1914. | May 1. | 1920. | April 25. | 1933. | May 7. |

Over much of New Jersey outside of Cape May and the Pine Barrens the Hooded Warbler is a casual transient as at Princeton and Plainfield but at Englewood on the lower Hudson Dr. Chapman has found it a regular summer resident and it breeds at Demarest (Bowdish) and apparently at Alpine (Rhoads).

## WILSON'S WARBLER

### Wilsonia pusilla pusilla (Wilson)

A rather rare transient at Cape May Point during September and the last few days of August, and in late May. Once seen in shade trees of Cape May. Autumn records are:

| | | | |
|---|---|---|---|
| 1917. | September 29. | 1928. | September 5. |
| 1920. | September 2. | 1929. | August 31 and October 5. |
| 1922. | August 21. | 1930. | August 28 and 30. |
| 1924. | September 11. | 1932. | August 29 and 30; |
| 1925. | September 29. | | September 17 and 18. |

In spring we have only a single record, a bird in full song observed by Julian Potter on May 22, 1927, while quite extraordinary is the observation of another on June 4, 1933, on Seven Mile Beach, by John Gillespie, also in song but evidently a belated migrant.

Many of the birds seen in autumn at the Point show only a slight trace of the black cap and some lack it altogether. They are easily identified by their small size and nearly uniform greenish yellow coloration above and below which covers both breast and belly. The Wilson's Warblers are active little birds when feeding in the bushes, with a nervous flip of the wings and an irregular wag to the tail.

They breed entirely north of New Jersey.

## CANADA WARBLER

### Wilsonia canadensis (Linnaeus)

A regular transient in the Cape May district, more common on the southward flight. Practically all of our records are at the Point:

| | | | |
|---|---|---|---|
| 1920. | September 2. | 1927. | August 17 and 25. |
| 1921. | August 15. | 1928. | August 13. |
| 1922. | August 21, 28 and 29. | 1929. | August 17 and September 6. |
| 1923. | August 26. | 1931. | September 1. |
| 1924. | August 27, 29. | 1932. | August 29 and 30. |
| 1924. | September 3 and 7. | 1934. | August 27. |
| 1926. | August 27 and September 1. | 1935. | August 31 and September 3. |

On August 17, 1927, five were seen and on September 3, 1935, two, all other records are of single birds. The dates of August 13, 15 and 17, indicate how early some of the transient warblers from far northward reach localities as far south as Cape May although as some individuals nest in the mountains of northern New Jersey they may have come from there. Over most of the state the Canada Warbler is a common transient.

We have but three spring records—May 20, 1917; May 24, 1892; May 20, 1927.

# REDSTART

Setophaga ruticilla (Linnaeus)

The Redstart is a regular and abundant transient in the Cape May area and throughout the peninsula while it appears to breed sporadically in Cumberland and probably also in northwestern Cape May Counties. It is, however, unusual in the nesting season anywhere in southern New Jersey.

About the first of August Redstarts appear in varying numbers in the pine woods at Cape May Point and are present, off and on, until the end of September. With the Black and White and Hooded Warblers and the Northern Water-Thrush they usher in the southward flight of land birds at Cape May and are the most regular and consistant of our migrant warblers. During most of August and September they occur regularly in the shade trees of Cape May as well as throughout the woodlands of the interior upland.

The days of marked flights are always days with wind out of the northwest and one has but to glance at the pine groves of the Point to learn whether a migration is on, so conspicuous are the fluttering yellow and salmon colors of the Redstarts against the somber blue green of the trees. Throughout the day the birds seem to be everywhere and as they pass on only a few stray individuals will be seen until the next great wave arrives. As we see him in our late summer woodlands the Redstart is the very embodiment of nervous activity, flirting the tail to the right and left as he darts this way and that and then spreads wide the feathers like a fan. Some birds are always fluttering at the ends of the branches where the rapid movements of wing and tail make a constant flicker.

On August 21, 1922, a typical Redstart day, the birds were abundant both in the trees and in the shrubbery while along an old wood road through the pines dozens of them fed on the ground, darting a few inches up into the air, now and then, to catch a passing insect and dropping back again, all the while flaring their fan-tails and jerking them from side to side. Others were constantly coming down from the trees in a sort of "tail spin" and as the sun struck them the light areas of the wings and tail seemed almost transparent. Occasionally a bird would cling for a moment to the tree trunks like a creeper.

Again on August 29 of the same year Redstarts were swarming at the Point. They hopped from limb to limb as they passed through the pine trees and, after two or three hops, would flutter out into the air in a spiral, keeping at about the same level, or continuing in a prolonged flutter almost to the ground, in pursuit of some escaping insect. I have seen them whirl down in this manner for a distance of ten or twelve feet, but in any case they return to the tree and resume their feeding. When working their way through the foliage, with wings and tail closed, they seem so sleek and slender that we take them for a different kind of bird until the tell-tale yellow fan is flashed out and their identity proclaimed. In deciduous trees the actions of the Redstart are somewhat concealed by the foliage and they are not always so conspicuous, but wherever they are, in the tree tops, on the ground, or in the air, they are graceful in every movement and the personification of nervous energy.

Our evidence of nearby nesting of the Redstart is not extensive. On June 19, 1914, Julian Potter found a pair feeding young in a wooded swamp two miles west of South Vineland, Cumberland County, and Walker Hand saw a female feeding a full-fledged young at Eldora, Cape May County, on July 24, 1932. The occurrence of a single bird in the Physick garden on July 15, 1933, seems too early for a northern migrant and probably was a bird that had bred or been raised somewhere in the southern part of the state, and the same may have been the case with those seen at the Point in four years, on August 1 and 2.

While the bulk of the Redstarts seen in the southward flight are females or young, with pale yellow on the wings, tail and breast, the bright salmon and black males are by no means uncommon and a number of them may be seen on a single day. In spring while old males and yellow females make up the bulk of the flight there are some deep yellow males in their first breeding plumage with scattered black spots on the breast and back.

Arrival dates on the southward migration run as follows:

| | | |
|---|---|---|
| 1920. August 5. | 1925. July 30. | 1930. August 11. |
| 1921. August 11. | 1926. August 14. | 1931. August 1 (next 18) |
| 1922. August 9. | 1927. July 30. | 1932. August 1 (next 9). |
| 1923. July 26. | 1928. August 13. | 1934. August 2. |
| 1924. August 8. | 1929. August 2. | 1935. August 12. |

Latest autumn dates of occurrence:

| | | |
|---|---|---|
| 1921. September 16. | 1926. September 27. | 1931. September 27. |
| 1922. September 17. | 1927. September 25. | 1932. October 8. |
| 1923. October 1. | 1928. September 30. | 1934. September 19. |
| 1924. October 2. | 1929. October 5. | 1935. September 21. |
| 1925. October 2. | 1930. September 28. | |

In spring Walker Hand has recorded their arrival on May 5, 1914, and May 8, 1908, while I have records of May 8, 1925; May 7, 1932; May 8 and 9, 1925; May 20, 1927; May 14, 1928; May 27, 1931; while they have been seen as late as May 30 in 1912, 1921 and 1928. They are not nearly so abundant on the northward flight as in the autumn, and I have seen them common on only one occasion—May 20, 1927.

While mainly a transient in New Jersey the Redstart breeds in the northern half of the state—at Plainfield (Miller), Patterson (Clark), Summit (Holmes) etc., and has occurred in the nesting season sporadically at a number of localities farther south.

## ENGLISH SPARROW

### Passer domesticus domesticus (Linnaeus)

The English Sparrow had become abundant at Cape May long before I first visited the town and I have never been able to ascertain just when it first put in an appearance. The paving of the streets has probably had some effect in reducing their numbers, but not to the extent that we have seen in the large cities, and the advent of the Starling has also been a factor in the same direction. Sparrows are most evenly distributed in the town at nesting time in early spring, and by winter have gathered into several rather well defined flocks with definite roosting places, especially on ivy clad walls of buildings. I doubt if there is any actual change in the numbers of the bird at different seasons of the year except for the advent of young in early summer.

After the harvest they go out on the grain and hay fields and mingle with Red-wings, Starlings and Grackles as they feed among the stubble, or gather immediately on the new mown hay and alfalfa where insects abound. They are also to be seen about Schellenger's Landing where the shores of the Harbor furnish a variety of food and, after the young are on the wing, great flocks visit the various piggeries on the edge of Pond Creek Meadows and elsewhere. Not missing any possible source of food they come frequently to the sea beach where they catch blowflies on the lines of trash washed up by the waves and search the latter for bits of refuse. They alight on the wet portion of the beach just above the water and, when a wave rolls up a little farther than usual, they flutter back to safety. I never have seen one hop away from an oncoming wave, they always take wing. One day a ghost crab (*Ocypoda*) came out of his burrow for food and passed within an inch or two of a sparrow without any interest being shown on either side.

When on the ground the English Sparrow hops and never walks or runs, while it assumes an attitude quite different from that of any of our native species. The body is held erect with the head high and the tail just touching the ground and the bird seems, at times, almost to lean over backward in its exaggerated erectness. Sometimes when certain insects are abundant in the shade trees I have seen the sparrows clinging upright to the trunks like woodpeckers in their efforts to catch their prey. This habit and their attitude on the ground emphasize the fact that they have no near kinship with the true sparrows and that, as is shown by their anatomy, they are really related to the Weaver Finches of Africa.

In spite of their usual unsavory reputation I have seen the English Sparrow devouring mature Japanese beetles, clinging meanwhile to the flower stems and shrubbery in our yard. Surely they deserve some of the credit that is so lavishly accorded to that greater nuisance, the Starling, for devouring the larvae of this imported pest; had neither of the *three* pests been brought to America we should have been far better off!

By mid-summer the English Sparrows gathered in the evening at the Martin and Grackle roost. Some of them went in as early as July 2 while later they flocked there by thousands taking up their positions in the trees before any of the other species had arrived and making a prodigious noise by their continued chirping.

They nest about houses, under the eves or in any cavity or shelter that may be offered, and not infrequently build a globular nest in the top of an evergreen tree—another Weaver Finch character. One nest at Cold Spring as large as a peck measure was well out on top of a horizontal limb of a tulip poplar tree and was constructed in a few days after an old nest in a shed had been destroyed. I have seen them busy carrying nesting material as early as March 18 and by June 30 flocks composed wholly of young birds are on the wing. On the other hand I have seen parents feeding young as late as August 15, 1935, and September 6, 1927, illustrating the fecundity of the species, as they must build several nests in a season. While they are notorious for occupying the nest boxes erected for other birds I have seen a pair or two sharing a large Martin house with the rightful owners without any apparent conflict, each pair, of course, using its own apartment, while several times I have seen sparrows nesting in the lower parts of the Fish Hawks' great nests, going in and out between the larger branches which composed the structure while the Fish Hawks paid them no attention whatever.

The English Sparrows are pugnacious and resent the intrusion of other birds on their feeding grounds and I have seen them attack Goldfinches and native sparrows of several sorts. Those that come to feed on scraps of bread thrown out in our garden for other bird visitors defer to Starlings, Grackles and Red-wings but they do not leave the field and by watching their opportunity will snatch up a crust from under the very bill of one of the larger birds and fly off with it.

Sparrows are by no means confined to the town and may be seen even in winter flying far afield in search of food and I have seen them about closed cottages at South Cape May in mid-winter associated with Juncos, and out on the Fill at all seasons.

Back in the country there will be a good sized colony about every house or barnyard, smaller nesting groups being formed about dwellings where winter forage and shelter are not so plentiful. About the home of Otway Brown at Cold Spring and the adjacent farm buildings of David McPherson there is a flock which is doubtless characteristic of many others. About two hundred birds winter here and probably the summer residents number about the same. They nest about the various buildings and constantly seek shelter in the privet hedges, often escaping the pursuit of a Sharp-shinned Hawk in this manner, in autumn or winter. They also frequent loose piles of brush in the orchard and as I approached one of these I have counted upwards of one hundred leaving in small bunches. Sometimes the entire winter flock will fly in a dense mass from one shelter to another and once, on February 1, 1931, a bitter cold day, the birds arose *en masse* and circled overhead for nearly half an hour following exactly the same oval course and maintaining their dense flock formation. This performance seemed so unusual that I was in some doubt at first whether they really were English Sparrows. There seemed to be no cause for their action unless it was the cold. They finally settled in the trees by the house and on the barn roof.

Even this familiar bird would seem to warrant further study!


## BOBOLINK

### Dolichonyx oryzivorus (Linnaeus)

In the Reedbird plumage the Bobolink is an abundant transient from mid-August to late September traveling mainly by day and crossing at the Point to the coast of Delaware, while little groups stop for a few days on the marshes and in old fields west of the town. The Delaware River marshes, with their abundant growth of wild rice, have always been notable as hunting grounds for Reedbirds, when this sport was permissible, and the birds are as abundant there as ever, down to the head of the Bay. Whether the Cape May migrants come from the Delaware or along the coast from their breeding grounds to the north I am unable to say.

In spring the Bobolink is not nearly so abundant and occurs mainly farther back in the farming country, in fields of clover or alfalfa, occurring, as always, in flocks. Otway Brown tells me that some twenty years ago a flock of Bobolinks established themselves in an old brier field close to his home at Cold Spring and evidently bred there, the males singing all season from his apples trees, and on May 9, 1935, a flock of some twenty-five settled in an alfalfa field in almost the same spot and remained for two weeks, but when the crop was cut the birds immediately departed. There was every indication that they would have bred there. As additional evidence of the probable breeding of the birds in the Cape May district may be mentioned the arrival of eight individuals, still in breeding dress, on the marshes back of South Cape May on July 18, 1924, and fifteen on July 24, 1925. They remained for a week or more. In the latter group, when I first discovered them, were three males in full black and white plumage, one in an interesting molting condition with broad buff bands on the breast forming a great inverted V, while the rest were females and young of the year. It seems hardly likely that these birds would have traveled far before the molt was completed and I am inclined to think that they had nested in some out of the way field on one of the farms immediately to the north. Julian Potter also saw six on July 25, 1930.

The late August birds that we come across immediately about the town are often found perching on the tops of bayberry or marsh elder bushes, or among patches of reeds and tall grass, and swing back and forth in the wind bracing themselves to maintain their position. When they obtain a secure perch, they crane the neck up clear of the foliage to get a better view of the surroundings, and eventually either drop to the ground to feed or take wing to some more distant point. The striped buff and brown pattern of plumage makes the Reedbird really very conspicuous among the sparrows with which it may be associated and when the head is stretched upward the stripes seem to run continuously from bill to tail. The perching birds that we see are resting rather than feeding and, although they do feed on seeds of weeds and ranker grasses, we never see them stripping seeds from the tall stalks of wild rice which is a familiar sight on the Delaware marshes, as this plant does not grow about Cape May, being a strictly fresh water species. The *spink, spink,* call of the Reedbird is heard both from birds at rest and from flocks passing overhead.

The flight of the Reedbird somewhat resembles that of the Goldfinch in that there is a flicker of several short wingbeats followed by a drop of the body and then another series of beats causing a rising and falling, undulating motion in the flock. The Reedbird, however, swerves from side to side making its flight far more erratic and quite different from the straightaway course of the Goldfinch. Two that I saw on August 20, 1927, pitched down from a considerable height in zigzag drops to the tops of some bayberry bushes where they rested for a long time. They were apparently migrants which hesitated to cross the Bay, although on August 30, 1920, I saw several flocks of from one hundred to one hundred and fifty individuals put out across the water without a moment's hesitation.

On some late August or early September days I have seen a number of flocks passing between Cape May and the Point but have never kept count of them for any considerable period. In 1935, however, William Rusling made almost daily counts of their numbers and their flights and he tells me that they fly most frequently during north or northeast winds and upon reaching the Bay shore often circle about several times before crossing.

Those that come on a northwest wind, however, fly north along the Bay as do all other birds under similar conditions, and do not cross until later. His counts are as follows:

August 23, 800.

August 24, 1,000.

August 28, 75.

August 29, 175.

August 30, 4,000.

September 2, 350.

September 6, 2,615.

September 7, 1,575.

September 8, 150.

September 10, 330.

September 12, 35.

September 13, 250.

September 16, 66.

September 17, 391.

September 21, 350.

September 23, 121.

September 29, 27.

October 4, 4.

My dates of arrival of Reedbirds on the southward flight are:

| | | | | | |
|---|---|---|---|---|---|
| 1920. | August 16. | 1925. | August 22. | 1931. | August 25. |
| 1921. | August 15. | 1926. | August 25. | 1932. | August 20. |
| 1922. | August 14. | 1927. | August 20. | 1933. | August —. |
| 1923. | August 24. | 1928. | September 1. | 1934. | August —. |
| 1924. | August 27. | 1929. | August 25. | 1935. | August 23. |
| | | 1930. | August 17. | | |

In spring we have Walker Hand's dates of observation for seven years:

| | | | | | |
|---|---|---|---|---|---|
| 1907. | May 11. | 1909. | May 13. | 1916. | May 7. |
| 1908. | May 8. | 1910. | May 11. | 1917. | May 2. |
| | | 1914. | May 6. | | |

I have but few spring records for Cape May and am inclined to think that the birds travel farther inland on their northward journey.

Seven were present at Cold Spring on May 29, 1933, and I heard one in full song on the Fill on May 20, 1927, while another individual was seen on May 30, 1923, but appeared sick and emaciated, and was probably unable to travel further.

While most conspicuous as transients Bobolinks nest locally in several of the northern counties.

# MEADOWLARK

**Sturnella magna magna** (Linnaeus)

PLATE 115, p. 839

The Meadowlark is a common resident bird of the open grasslands about Cape May, from the farms of the upland down to the brackish marshes, and on the grass-covered dunes of the coast islands, while it strays occasionally onto the salt meadows themselves. For some years after the formation of the Fill it was common among the grass and clover which covered the original dredgings but as this has been succeeded by a forest of bayberry bushes it has to a great extent disappeared. Not infrequently we see Meadowlarks flying back and forth over the housetops of Cape May in their passage from the Fill to the golf links and in autumn and winter we may flush them from vacant lots and garden patches in the town.

All through the spring and early summer Meadowlark song is in the air as we sit on our porch, or it may come floating in at the open window, and we come to regard the bird as a familiar everyday species rather than an inhabitant of the more remote open fields with which, in most localities, it is associated.

While habitually a ground bird the Meadowlark frequently alights on the top of a small isolated tree or bush or on fence posts, or even on telegraph wires along the roadside. I have also seen them on several occasions perched on the peak of a cottage roof in full song, and on December 12, 1920, a flock of fifteen that flushed from the Fill lined up on the ridge pole of a closed cottage near the beach. When perched on a wire the Meadowlark settles its head well down on its shoulders and at intervals flirts its short tail as if to steady itself against the wind, for it is a heavy-bodied bird and it must be no easy matter for it to hold its balance on a slender wire. They sing from their perches at regular intervals and between songs I have frequently seen a bird bend its head over until the bill almost touched the breast and apparently gaze at something below it or at its feet, then the head will be raised again, the mouth will open, and the clear call floats out over the meadows.

On the ground the Meadowlark is by no means easy to study as its back is a fine example of protective coloration and effectively conceals it so long as it remains quiet, and it is usually careful to keep its brilliant yellow breast turned the other way. A mixed flock of Meadowlarks and Starlings feeding in an old field back of the town, on January 19, 1924, was an interesting study. The Starlings in their more or less black plumage, stood out clearly while the Larks with their mottled brown and buff backs were almost invisible against the dead grass that formed the turf. Even after I thought I had counted all that were present half as many more were disclosed as they took wing.

When moving about in a field of grass stubble the Meadowlark humps its back, draws its head down close on its shoulders and runs, almost like a rail, in and out among the tufts and roots, but its gait is not so rapid or direct as that of a rail and is rather more of a waddle. Now and then it will pause and holding the body nearly vertical will crane its neck upward giving it a slight twist and pointing the bill skyward as if straining every muscle to see over the top of the surrounding grass; but curiously enough I have seen them do exactly the same thing when perched on a wire. In winter too I have seen them acting in much the same way, walking rapidly with head and neck extended and back humped, when suddenly they pause and the vertical craning of the neck follows with an instantaneous flicking of the tail feathers, open and shut, displaying for a moment the white edgings. One bird walked about with the tail about half spread and nervously jerked it farther open and then shut again, showing the white very conspicuously.

In early July I have on several occasions observed Meadowlarks carrying insects about in the bill and later flying off apparently to feed young in the nest. On July 7, 1931, I watched two pairs of Meadowlarks with six young in a low grassy meadow back of the golf links. The adults were walking about like quail their heads moving back and forth with each step and were catching young grasshoppers on the ground sometimes flying up a foot or two in pursuit of prey. The young, while they could fly perfectly well, remained stationary and were apparently still being fed by their parents.

The contrast between young and old was striking. The latter had white or pale gray head stripes, quite different from the rich buffy stripes of the young, while the short almost conical bill of the young birds and their generally suffused buff plumage were characteristic. A curious melanistic specimen in the collection of the Academy of Natural Sciences of Philadelphia, which was secured at Haddonfield, on October 6, 1857, has all of the yellow breast plumage replaced by black.

PLATE 116

*Wharton Huber*

*Wharton Huber*

NEST AND EGGS OF RED-WINGED BLACKBIRD AND TWO VIEWS OF MALE BIRDS ON
  DEAD CATTAILS, CORSON'S INLET, N. J.

PLATE 117

*Wharton Huber*

*W. L. Baily*

1. RED-WINGED BLACKBIRD, CORSON'S INLET, N. J.
2. NEST AND EGGS OF FIELD SPARROW WITH EGG OF COWBIRD.

A bird noticed pluming itself on July 2, 1921, poked the bill down among the feathers and spreading its shoulders ruffled up all the plumage. It also spread its tail feathers and while holding them so, shook the tail forcibly from side to side.

Except for perching birds our experience with Meadowlarks is usually limited to flushing them from the grass as we walk through the old fields, and watching them sail away to alight again on the ground farther on, and it requires some care and keenness of sight to see them first and to study them before they take wing. When taking flight from the ground the Meadowlark vibrates its wings rapidly three times and takes a short sail followed by another series of vibrations and another sail, all the time ascending at a slight angle with the head held out in front and turned from side to side in constant observation. When hurried, the bird sometimes flaps its wings continuously for a moment or two, like a Starling, and the rapidity of its wingstrokes is about the same as in that species. Having attained a moderate altitude there is a long descending sail and sometimes a resumption of the short periods of beats and sails as if the bird had changed its mind about alighting at that particular spot and was extending its flight a little farther.

When a strong wind is blowing I have noticed that a Meadowlark will take off against it and, gaining a little altitude, will veer off and, on set wings, sail a long distance with neck stretched out and up, giving one the impression that the heavy body is drawing the bird down and that it is trying desperately to keep afloat. Other individuals going straight away, on flights of a quarter of a mile or more, kept up a pretty continuous flapping with an occasional short sail and one watched on August 20, 1920, flapped its wings continuously for nearly seventy-five yards, gaining altitude all the time and then began the alternate sailing and flapping with a gradual descent.

The song of the Meadowlark is usually rendered by the words *can't see me* but in reality there are four notes, not three, and it seems to me that the syllables *see—aar see—eee*, the second descending and the third and fourth on the same pitch, better represent it. The song is rendered either from the ground or from a perch and I have heard it as late as August 13, while its revival in late February is one of the first signs of spring. The Meadowlark has another call or song, which it utters from a perch. There is a single *tzud* or *zhud* followed by a sibilant trill *dzzzzzzzzzzzzz* then a pause and the notes are repeated, sometimes with the opening *tzud* duplicated. At other times this note is repeated at appreciable intervals without the trill.

The Meadowlark nests in grassland especially in old fields or in open places on the Fill and nests have been found as early as May 21, 1921, with five heavily incubated eggs and May 22, 1920, with four fresh eggs, and as late as June 17, 1922, and June 20, 1909, with three and five fresh eggs respectively. Another nest found on May 31, 1926, by members of the Delaware Valley Club, contained three normal eggs, one runt and four smaller eggs apparently those of a Sharp-tailed Sparrow! Young birds have been seen on the wing with their parents as early as June 18.

On the evening of July 6, 1923, and on two evenings previously, about dusk, a Meadowlark was seen to fly several times in a circle over a field where its mate apparently had a nest and finally to alight on a nearby telegraph wire; doubtless a courtship display. On another occasion in early spring I came upon two Meadowlarks, presumably rival males, tumbling about on the ground on their backs with feet firmly locked together as they reared up and struck at each other with their bills.

The best identification mark of the Meadowlark, aside from its song and manner of flight, is the flash of white in the tail as the bird takes wing. The bright yellow breast with its black crescent is only seen when the bird is perched on a bush or wire, and even then it does not seem nearly so bright as we might expect unless the sunlight strikes it at the proper angle. In winter the yellow is largely obscured by brownish edgings to the feathers, the back is browner, and the whole bird gives one the impression of being larger and fluffier, as if in a shaggy winter coat.

From April to July or early August the Meadowlarks are scattered in pairs but by August 15 they begin to collect in flocks and parties of twenty to twenty-five are not uncommon. Often at this season they gather on fields of second-crop hay, recently cut, or on patches of black grass mowed and left lying on the marsh. Later in August or in early September they may become very scarce so that only two or three are seen on a day's walk or perhaps none at all. The disappearance being possibly coincident with the gathering of the late hay crop or to retirement of the birds during the molt, both old and young having a complete change of plumage at this time.

From October on through the winter, however, Meadowlarks occur in large flocks. On October 19, 1924, Walker Hand and I flushed no less than three hundred from an old weed-covered field near the old toll gate. They arose, as they normally do, in small bunches one after another, not all together. On October 21, 1923, a similar flock of one hundred was seen; on October 23, 1927, sixty-five; one hundred on October 19, 1931; and on October 27 and 28, 1928, at Cold Spring, flocks of twenty, thirty and fifty. One flock flew directly over Cape May travelling from one feeding ground to another. The birds when on the ground, wherever they could be approached closely, seemed to be catching grasshoppers.

While many of these large October flocks pass on farther south some remain throughout the winter, associating with Cowbirds, Grackles and Red-wings and forming a single mixed flock which drifts here and there over the uplands and may be missed entirely by those who make single day trips to the shore at this season. We have records of a flock of one hundred on November 14, 1926; seventy-five on January 25, 1925; sixty on February 8, 1925. The counts of the Christmas census of the Delaware Valley Club are as follows:

| | |
|---|---|
| 1922. December 24, ten | 1930. December 28, seventy-two |
| 1923. December 23, 200 | 1931. December 27, 246 |
| 1926. December 26, 135 | 1932. December 26, 100 |
| 1927. December 26, 115 | 1933. December 24, 300 |
| 1928. December 23, 275 | 1934. December 23, 123 |
| 1929. December 22, 158 | 1935. December 22, 294 |
| | 1936. December 27, sixty-seven |

Sometimes the October flocks fly in a regular stream in passing from one spot to another and on October 31, 1920, fifty passed over the marsh back of South Cape May in a long line. Later, upon being disturbed where they were feeding, they flew back again picking up other individuals which had not been seen before. The flock then divided and each section settled to feed. Sometimes in midwinter I have seen flocks acting in the same way.

The most frequent associate of the Meadowlark is the Starling but I am inclined to think that the companionship is always sought by the latter which is a notoriously social bird, while the Meadowlark seems perfectly satisfied to associate with its own kind. On September 1, 1920, I found on an open space on the Fill two Meadowlarks and about a thousand Starlings. The former kept some distance in advance as if trying to escape from the black throng which constantly followed them up, rolling over one another like a flock of blackbirds in spring. Cowbirds and Flickers are sometimes associated with Meadowlarks when feeding on stubble fields or on freshly cut grass. A curious association was that of a couple of Kingbirds which persistently attacked a pair of Meadowlarks that had flushed from the grass near where their nest tree was located. All four birds alighted on a telegraph wire each Kingbird close to his Lark and as soon as the latter took wing the attack was renewed.

In winter Meadowlarks become much tamer than at other times, especially when food is scarce and it is then that they most frequently enter the town. On one occasion I found six feeding with English Sparrows on a vacant lot close to the street and at another time I approached within fifteen feet of some that were feeding in an old cabbage patch. During the severe blizzard of January, 1918, Walker Hand reported a single Meadowlark living in a narrow alleyway alongside of the post office on Ocean Street and feeding on some old bones that had been left there. During a storm on March 11, 1934, when the whole countryside was covered with snow, two Meadowlarks rested in an orchard at Cold Spring with a flock of Grackles and I have seen them doing the same thing during ice storms although in that case they had much trouble perching on the ice-covered twigs.

While I presume that Meadowlarks roost on the ground at night we really know little about the matter. On January 8, 1922, I flushed fifteen of the birds on the Fill and at the spot where one of them took wing I found a form in the grass much like those used by cotton-tail rabbits but it contained many droppings of the bird which seemed to demonstrate that it was used as a shelter or roosting place. On August 21, 1920, too, I flushed several young Larks from the edge of the marsh which took wing just as I was about to step upon them and I found that each one was resting in a grass form similar to the one just mentioned. As evidence of a possible roosting in another situation, a single Meadowlark was seen to enter the Martin and Grackle roost on the Physick place in the heart of the town on the evening of August 18, 1921, doubtless attracted by the tremendous flight of various birds that was pouring into the trees but I have no evidence that it remained through the night. Throughout New Jersey the Meadowlark is a summer resident or resident retiring to the river valleys or coast districts in winter, with possibly some migrants from states to the north.

I regret to see a definite decrease in Meadowlarks not only about Cape May but elsewhere in southern New Jersey. The uncalled for draining operations have ruined many of their haunts as have the recent "developments" and I cannot but wonder whether the Starling, a bird of much the same size and feeding habits, and which is fitted to fill the same ecologic niche, may not have been a factor in the matter. One species may effect the decrease and even extermination of another without active antagonism.


## YELLOW-HEADED BLACKBIRD

### Xanthocephalus xanthocephalus (Bonaparte)

Several individuals of this bird of the prairie lands of the North Central States have wandered as far east as New Jersey having doubtless become associated with flocks of Red-wings which were bound for the Atlantic Coast, or blown by storms from their normal migration route. One was shot by a gunner at Tuckerton about 1890, and later secured for the Delaware Valley Club Collection at the Academy of Natural Sciences. Another was shot on Newton Creek near Audubon by J. Kelton on September 1, 1917, and was shown to me by Joseph Tatum.

A third individual was seen in mid-August, about 1923, by Fletcher Street on the meadows between Cape May and the Point. All three were in immature plumage with duller colors than those shown by the adult males.

## RED-WINGED BLACKBIRD

*Agelaius phoeniceus phoeniceus* (Linnaeus)

PLATES 115–117, pp. 839, 854, 855

Red-winged Blackbirds are to be found about Cape May in every month of the year but from the time that the last young are on the wing, in mid-July, until the arrival of the males on their breeding grounds, in February, they occur in roving flocks of varying size and there may be many days in autumn and winter when none can be found in the immediate vicinity of the Cape. The appearance of the first migrant male swinging on the top of some dead cattail on the marsh, or perched on a bayberry bush on the Fill, and the sound of his gurgling, wheezing song give us the first intimation of the passing of winter; for it is the Red-wing rather than the Bluebird that is the harbinger of spring at Old Cape May.

There is often a large flock of "blackbirds" composed of Red-wings, Grackles, Cowbirds, and latterly Starlings, wintering on the open fields north of the town, especially about Cold Spring, but most of these roving winter assemblages seem to drift farther south, although they always linger longer on the shores of Delaware Bay and may be found on the extensive river marshes in the vicinity of Salem long after they have left the ocean side of

( 859 )

the peninsula. I saw one of these flocks near Elmer on November 28, 1926, which was typical of such gatherings. It consisted of probably five thousand birds which fairly blackened the ground as they alighted in close ranks and advanced over the fields in a rolling progress, the rear lines constantly rising and settling in front of the flock, the others following in regular sequence. When large detachments would occasionally fly up into the bare trees of some orchard or grove of swamp maples it appeared at a distance as if the branches were once more clothed in dense foliage. As the mixed flock went streaming past against the background of winter woods the bright epaulets of the male Red-wings would flash in the sunlight giving a touch of color to the black horde while a solitary albino looked strangely out of place. On March 8, 1919, I saw a similar flock at Bombay Hook on the Delaware shore which was rolling over the marsh in the same manner but when the birds settled in the trees they burst into the great blackbird medley of song so characteristic of early spring.

When the Red-wings start to move northward in February, and apparently during most of the winter, the males and females are, for the most part, in separate flocks. Of winter gatherings I remember one in late October at Mauricetown which contained one hundred females and a single male while another smaller group at Cape May in late January, 1891, was wholly composed of females. The males are the first to reach the nesting grounds in spring and it may be several weeks before the females arrive, so there may be a long interval between the appearance of the first migrants and the actual beginning of nesting operations. As early as February 21, 1926, solitary males were singing on the Fill as well as on the marshes at South Cape May and back of Schellenger's Landing, while on March 14, 1931, they were singing in the same way on the cattail marshes of the Lighthouse Pond, spreading both wings and tail as they gave vent to their characteristic vocal efforts. The extent to which the wings were spread, and the consequent amount of red shoulders to be exposed, varied greatly in different individuals but in every case the display was best seen from the front.

Walker Hand's dates for the arrival of singing males with some later records are:

| | | | |
|---|---|---|---|
| 1903. | February 26 | 1921. | February 10 |
| 1904. | March 9 | 1923. | February 22 |
| 1905. | March 1 | 1925. | February 14 |
| 1908. | February 16 | 1926. | February 21 |
| 1911. | February 27 | 1928. | February 14 |
| 1912. | February 21 | 1929. | February 15 |
| 1913. | February 23 | 1931. | February 9 |
| 1914. | February 27 | 1932. | February 22 |
| 1915. | February 15 | 1933. | February 19 |
| 1916. | February 18 | 1934. | February 10 |
| 1917. | February 22 | 1935. | February 23 |
| 1918. | February 12 | | |

In the very cold Februaries of several recent years the Red-wings were much later than usual, and even if an early arrival came before the freezing temperature or the ice and snow storms, he disappeared again.

All through March additional Red-wings take up their positions about the nesting grounds but as late as March 20, 1924, and March 21, 1925, no females were in evidence although on the latter date two flew rapidly over the marsh at South Cape May and were vigorously pursued by a male which, however, soon gave up the chase and returned to his stand.  During this same period some males will be found still associated with other blackbirds feeding out in the fields.  On March 19, 1924, six were feeding with Cowbirds and Starlings just back of the town, and on February 14, 1925, there were ten associated with thirty Starlings and fifty Meadowlarks in the same place, while at Cape May Point on March 13, 1921, there was a typical flock of spring migrants such as we often see moving through to points farther north.  There were twenty-eight Red-wings, five Cowbirds and two Starlings, all feeding on a damp piece of ground near a swampy thicket, a favorite resort at this time of year.  Presently they swirled up into the low trees and broke into a medley of blackbird music.  The spring song of the Red-wings—the *o—car—ée* and their liquid gurgle and harsh *chuck* note mingled with the coarser efforts of the Cowbirds, and some whistles from the Starlings.

Transient flocks of Red-wings seen as early as February 6, 1932, settled in the wooded borders of the New England Creek marshes and broke into song in the same way, while as late as April 2, 1922, and on the same date in 1924, I saw feeding flocks composed of males only, which seemed evidently to be migrants passing through.  By the end of the month, however, both sexes are established on the breeding grounds and there is a scene of wild excitement as the males leave their perches to pursue females or rival males, while the air is full of their songs and cries of alarm.

The Red-wings have many notes and there is in addition great variation in their expression.  Most characteristic is the song of the male so frequently interpreted as *o—car—ée* but which to me, especially when heard near at hand sounds more like *kill—géeze;* then there is a delightful liquid, flute-like gurgle difficult to represent syllabically which is usually uttered as the bird settles down on its perch—*zhu-lu-lu-lu-lu-lu-lu.*  Another "song" consists of two similar notes followed by a series of short notes uttered rapidly on a descending scale *zhurr, zhurr, chip-chip-chip-chip-chip-chip-chip-chip,* the short notes repeated sometimes as many as twenty times.  When one approaches a breeding colony early in the season, so as to arouse the birds' suspicion, the males will lapse into an occasional interrogatory *tuk, tuk, tuk.*

On April 29, 1923, there were some thirty Red-wings about a cattail pool on the Fill and some of them were evidently mating.  One male sitting near a female on the branch of a low tree was uttering the *kill—géeze* song.  At each utterance he would begin by bending the head over forwards and spreading the tail, at the same time bringing it forward under the perch.

Then, just as the song began he would swell up his shoulders and the brilliant red epaulets would flash out in a wonderful display of color, which was conspicuous for quite a distance, but which immediately disappeared as the bird resumed his normal attitude, with only the buffy edges of the shoulder patches in evidence. Several times the performer would drop to the ground and was immediately followed by the female who had been perched close by. Another male, with no female near, sang the *kill—géeeze* song continually from his perch, with wings drooping slightly and tail spread and with a little of the scarlet shoulder patch in evidence all the time, even between his songs, but he never attempted the spectacular display of the other individual.

When feeding on the ground the male Red-wing walks slowly about with tail elevated at an angle of 45° and every now and then will flirt it up and down uttering a harsh *chuck*. Sometimes when walking on soft ooze he will flap the wings suddenly and perhaps rise a few inches into the air to keep his feet from sinking in the mud. When perched among the cattails both males and females will grasp the stems with both feet one above the other while they hold the body close against the stalk and when they wish to descend nearer to the ground or water they will allow themselves to slide gradually down. At other times a bird will support itself on two stems holding one in each foot and spreading its legs widely, and I have seen a male perched thus on two stalks of wild carrot.

The pugnacity of the Red-wing is always in evidence during the nesting season, and not only does he resent human intrusion but woe betide other birds that venture near. I have seen five males vigorously pursue a Marsh Hawk which had inadvertently approached their territory and as he beat a hasty retreat and passed other colonies of Red-wings they too took up the chase. A passing Crow also invites attack and even a Grackle, with which most friendly association is maintained at other times of year, may be viciously set upon during the nesting season. On July 6, 1931, a pair of Red-wings even pursued a Bald Eagle which ventured to cross the meadows back of Five Mile Beach, where they had established a colony.

Red-wings formerly occurred in great abundance throughout the extensive cattail swamps that stretched away from Cape May to the Lighthouse and around the borders of the Race Track Pond and Pond Creek Meadows, but with the ruin of most of this territory by draining operations and real estate speculation, birds have sadly decreased in numbers. The Red-wings have not been entirely exterminated, as have some of the other marsh loving species, but persist in much smaller numbers on the edges of the old marshes where some available spots remain, and back of the town where some small ponds and marshy ground still are to be found. The Fill which has in the course of time developed some small cattail pools of its own, has been a favorite breeding place, but more recently the oiling of these waters has driven the birds away. The tall privet hedges and thickets of Japanese cane (*Arundinaria*) on the Physick place, which backs on the Fill, continue to be a favorite nesting place for the Red-wings as they are not so particular about building over water or wet ground, providing that such environment is not far away. Therefore we find both old and young frequenting the wet spots on the Fill after the latter are on the wing and also the lawns of the Physick garden and sheltered yards of adjoining or nearby properties, and coming up to the kitchen door in search of food. In Walker Hand's garden one male Red-wing came regularly to the chickenyard and entered a large coop through a hole in the top of the wirework to share the food furnished to the young chickens and he later brought his family to the spot. During July Red-wings, Grackles and Starlings come regularly to our garden for scraps of bread that are thrown out for them and to use the bird bath. A female Red-wing repeatedly carried bread from the ground to young birds on nearby telegraph wires which later came down and fed themselves. The Red-wings usually peck at the bread on the ground tossing it about this way and that until a piece is broken off, but occasionally they will hold it down with their feet as the Grackles always do.

A deserted nursery north of Schellenger's Landing, which flanks the salt meadows, is another favorite nesting place for Red-wings and here, too, they make use of the privet bushes while rows of English Holly are entirely neglected. The earliest date for eggs that I have is May 22, but by the 30th most nests have full sets. Richard Miller has found eggs as late as June 20 and I saw two nests with eggs in a cattail swamp on the Race Track Pond as late as July 3, 1920; whether there are two broods in a season I am not sure but am inclined to think that these late nestings are by birds whose first nests were destroyed. I have found young just hatched on June 9 and also as late as July 6, while full-fledged birds were on the wing and being fed by their parents by June 18, and other families, still in care of adults in thickets along the marsh edges, on July 7, 9 and 10 in different years.

Richard Miller has submitted a record of nests examined on Seven Mile Beach where the birds build mainly in bayberry bushes and generally in colonies:

May 14, 1916, one nest with three eggs.
May 18, 1924, three nests with four eggs, one with one.
May 26, 1929, four with two eggs, four with three.
May 30, 1911, one with one egg and one with two, others just begun.
May 30, 1913, two with four eggs, one with two.
May 30, 1915, one nest with three eggs just pipped.
May 30, 1919, one with three young.
June 2, 1929, two with three eggs.
June 7, 1925, one with four eggs.
June 22, 1924, one with three young.
July 3, 1927, two with three.

Other Cape May County nests examined by Turner McMullen are:

May 23, five nests with eggs (Corson's Inlet).
May 25, 1924, four nests with eggs (Court House).
May 30, 1921, eleven nests with young (Cape May Point).
May 30, 1926, one nest with three eggs (Ocean City).
June 2, 1935, three nests with young (Ludlam's Beach).
June 7, 1934, one nest with four young (Ludlam's Beach).
June 8, 1919, one nest with four eggs and one with young (Cape May Point).
June 14, 1925, one nest with three eggs (Corson's Inlet).

Nests have been found in various locations besides the privet hedges. Bayberry bushes, marsh elders (*Iva frutescens*), rose bushes and tussocks of sedge are all used and I saw one in a clump of goldenrod six inches from the ground and another in a small cedar bush one foot up. The most attractive nests are those swung between cattail stalks over the water and I have seen similar ones in marsh elder bushes six feet from the ground swung from the branches like nests of the Orchard Oriole.

After the nests have been completed and contain either eggs or young the parent birds become exceedingly agitated upon the approach of an intruder and their vocal efforts are redoubled. As one approaches the nesting site the male launches into the air and begins to call *sheep; sheep, sheep; sheep;* each call separated from the next by an interval. Then as the excitement increases there is a long drawn *zeeet* interpolated irregularly thus: *sheep; sheep; sheep; sheep; zeeet; sheep; sheep; sheep; zeeet; sheep; sheep; zeeet* etc. the bird all the while poised on rapidly beating wings directly overhead, and now and then swooping down still closer. The female, arising from her perch on a cattail, has a similar note but less harsh than the *sheep* of the male, and she also utters a much more rapid and differently pitched series of notes; *chip-chip-chip-chip; chip-chip-chip-chip-chip;* etc., then both birds alight on a bayberry bush and call together, the female seeming to relieve the male entirely from the first part of his cry and to her repeated *chip-chip-chip-chip* etc. he contributes only the long drawn *zeeet* at regular intervals so that the combination is almost like his opening effort. Taking wing again the male varies his cry. It is now *tuk; tuk; tuk;* etc. at intervals of several seconds or perhaps better rendered *put; put; put;* with the same interpolated *zeeet* as before. Another bird had both of these notes and used them together, thus: *sheep; sheep; tuk; tuk; sheep; tuk; tuk;* etc., while his long wheezy note was so very thin as to be hardly audible a few yards away and sounded like a whisper. In the distance, where the birds were not disturbed I could hear the *kill—géeeze* and the liquid *lul-lul-lul-lul-lul-lul-lul-* with a slight pause after the first note. On another occasion I have recorded the male's alarm note as *tseeet; tseeet; tseeet;* and the wailing cry as *tzeeee* while the cry of the female as she takes wing was written *sh-sh-sh-sh-sh-sh* etc. I have heard the *kill—géeez* song as late as July 3; the gurgle to July 16 and 26 and the long drawn *zeeeet* to July 17 and once on August 3. As they sit on the bushes uttering their alarm cries both male and female give a spasmodic flirt to the tail with every call.

By early July many young Red-wings are collected in bushes along the edge of the marshes where they sit rather stupidly, with their legs wide spread, quietly pluming themselves and paying no heed to the frantic cries of their parents, occasioned by our approach. When they finally realize the presence of danger they utter a low *chuck; chuck;* and fly straightaway for some distance, generally flapping their wings rapidly and ascending at a rather steep angle. They seem to be anxious to gain considerable altitude and then make for some thicket or group of low trees to which they gradually descend. The launching forth of the young always caused renewed clamor on the part of their parents and sometimes they accompany them. Usually, however, they remain at the nest site, possibly to protect other young birds still hiding in the vicinity.

Bobtailed young were being fed by parents in bayberry bushes on the Fill on June 24, 1928, and full-fledged young birds on July 7, 1921, were also apparently under the care of the adults, as a female was present with a green grasshopper in her bill nervously flirting her tail. These young were very sluggish and remained in the bushes, only flying when approached quite closely. They were very red buff below with broad buff edgings to the plumage of the upper parts which easily distinguished them from the duller, more worn adult females. In a group of five young the males were distinguished by their larger size, being larger indeed than the adult female. A female on August 19, 1927, was still carrying food and showed much concern at my presence but I did not locate any young. If they were present, as seems likely, I think that they must have represented a second brood. In spite of these late observations of parental feeding I found young Redwings shifting for themselves and feeding about a stable on the edge of the town with no adults about on July 3, 1920.

From about the first of August, or earlier in some years, many Red-wings repaired to the roost at the Physick place at dusk, along with the Martins, Grackles and Robins, but they also gathered in the cattail swamps just behind the town and later in the season most of the Cape May Red-wings apparently went there to spend the night and were seen rising in large flocks early in the morning. During late August and early autumn similar flocks pass high overhead bound apparently for the shores of the Delaware or marshes near the head of the Bay. Julian Potter observed them coming into a thicket of wild rice and reed grass on Oldman's Creek near Pedricktown on August 10, 1935, at 6:40 p. m. and estimated that for three quarters of an hour one thousand birds came in every minute.

There may be days at this time when it is difficult to find any Red-wings immediately about Cape May and my notes show that only a single individual was seen during a morning's walk on September 6, 1924, while on October 1 and 2 of that year and September 25, 1927, there were none at all.

When the molt is completed the Red-wings have practically all left to form the characteristic winter flocks, but during its progress they have certain haunts in which they may be found regularly. One of these is a thicket at the head of the Lighthouse Pond where they flush from the muddy flats surrounded by cattails and resort to the low trees, peering down at the intruder with little thought of danger.  On August 23 the old males in this gathering were in all stages of molt and on August 21, 1922, a young bird was seen with a newly acquired red shoulder patch although his wings and tail were still in the brown streaked juvenal plumage.

On September 9 and 10, 1921, a flock still resorting to the Physick roost used to stop every evening to feed in a patch of neglected corn close to my window.  There were in addition to the Red-wings many Grackles, Cowbirds and Starlings.  The Red-wings were for the most part tail-less, adult males in full molt.  Every now and then they would jump at one another or at one of the other birds like little game chickens.  This corn patch was finally cut down and after visiting the site the next evening, and eating the grain on the ground, the flock came no more.  We must give them credit where due, however, for not only do they destroy many a grasshopper but I have seen a Red-wing busy on an ear of corn pull out and devour a large fat caterpillar that was feeding on the grain.

Red-wings do much damage to patches of corn that are planted in out of the way places or close to the edge of the meadows.  The husks are ripped down and the exposed grain devoured while still in the milk.  Earlier in the year they feed on open mud flats often in company with Killdeers and Spotted Sandpipers, retiring to the surrounding cattails upon the approach of danger.  In the same way those that nest near the salt meadows will drop down into the grass to feed and fly up to the thickets where their nests are located.  These birds are, I think, searching for insects or minute crustacea and those that I see hovering over the surface of the Lighthouse Pond, with the swallows, must be seeking a similar diet.  When they have gathered in flocks the Red-wings frequent the grain and hay fields both before and after harvest and haymaking.

I have never noticed Red-wings visiting the sea beach for food as the Grackles do but they come to the dunes and hover like Sparrow Hawks catching grasshoppers in the dune grass and flying off with them to feed their young.  Red-wings have always been shot in the autumn when the great flocks are formed, and by erecting poles and branches on the marshes near to his blind, the gunner was able to kill three or four dozen at a shot according to "Homo" writing in "Forest and Stream" in August 1881.  He adds that dead birds were stuck on the branches as decoys.

The Red-winged Blackbird is an abundant summer resident throughout the state and becomes resident at many places along the shore or in the river valleys, while many of the birds that make up the great flocks of autumn must, I think, come from much farther north, finding their goal, or winter quarters, in southern New Jersey, Delaware and Maryland.

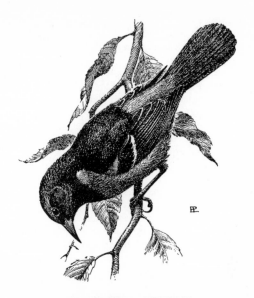

# ORCHARD ORIOLE

### Icterus spurius (Linnaeus)

Two or more pairs of Orchard Orioles nest regularly about Cape May Point and in some years there is a pair established in the heart of Cape May while back in the farming district to the north they are of regular occurrence in orchards. Walker Hand has recorded their arrival in spring as follows:

| | | | | | |
|---|---|---|---|---|---|
| 1907. | May 4. | 1912. | May 1. | 1915. | May 4. |
| 1908. | April 21. | 1913. | May 3. | 1917. | May 6. |
| 1910. | May 8. | 1914. | May 5. | 1920. | May 1. |

On the southward migration they seem to leave early and my latest dates are August 28, 1922; August 21, 1923; August 24, 1924; August 26, 1926; August 25, 1927.

During May and June the Orioles are in full voice, a rollicking song somewhat reminiscent of the Bobolink. A fine old chestnut and black male used to sing continually from the topmost branch of a giant silver poplar on Washington Street near the Martin roost, during June of 1925, and once at 8 p. m. I heard the song coming from the roost itself. At the Point I have heard a bird singing as late as July 11. On May 27, 1929, I listened for a long time to a singing bird in an orchard in West Cape May and after recording and checking it a number of times I regarded the following as an exact syllabic representation: *teétle—to—wheéter-tit-tíllo-wheétee, chip, chip, cheer.* The song varies with different individuals, however, and one that I

( 867 )

heard at the Point, on July 6, 1927, called *choop, choop, choolik* as if trying to start a song and failing in the effort.

By July 1 in some years the young are on the wing and we soon find family parties traveling along the fence rows and hedges ahead of us, the olive yellow young very quiet but the parents much excited, flirting the tail up and down but never spreading it.  One female on July 18, 1923, was particularly disturbed and kept up an almost continuous *chi-chi-chi-chi-chi,* etc. accompanied by exaggerated tail action.  Sometimes these parties are headed by a chestnut and black male and sometimes by an olive green one with a black throat, a bird in its first breeding season.  Such individuals have been seen quite as frequently as the older chestnut and black ones. The young birds are fed by the parents for some time after they are perfectly capable of finding their own food.  Even as late as July 12 and August 7, in different years, I have seen a female feeding young and in the latter case the young bird rested quietly in a bush and awaited the visits of the parent. During August I have seen young Orchard Orioles perched on the large red flowers of the trumpet creeper feeding on something that they picked from the outside of the corolla near the base, probably minute insects.  I have also seen them feeding among the flowers in the garden.

A nest with five eggs was examined by Turner McMullen at Cape May Court House on June 18, 1922.

While a summer resident in most parts of the state the Orchard Oriole is much more plentiful in the southern counties.


## BALTIMORE ORIOLE

### Icterus galbula (Linnaeus)

The Baltimore Oriole is a regular transient during late August and early September and much less numerous in spring.  The south-bound birds are partly gray-coated young of the year and partly old birds in burnt orange plumage.  They occur in some numbers in the orchards and shade trees of the town and country and in moist woods at the Point, where I have seen them feeding on the trumpet creeper flowers like the Orchard Oriole, apparently seeking small insects.  In May, 1928, there was an unusual number present, four being seen at a time in the trees on Washington Street.

There are reports of the Baltimore Orioles nesting in tall trees in the town in former years, but I have been unable to verify this and they certainly have not done so in the past twenty years.

Dates of spring occurrence are:

| | | | |
|---|---|---|---|
| 1924. | May 10. | 1932. | May 1. |
| 1925. | May 10. | 1934. | May 12. |
| 1930. | May 6 and 15. | 1928. | May 12 and 15. |
| 1931. | May 9. | | |

In autumn:

| 1922. | August 21. | 1930. | September 4. |
| 1924. | September 4, 5 and 12. | 1931. | September 1, 2, 3, 5. |
| 1927. | August 25, 26. | 1932. | August 29, September 17. |
| 1928. | September 1, 5, 8. | 1934. | August 27. |
| 1929. | August 30, 31, September 2, 3. | 1935. | August 29, September 7, 8. |

Exceptional dates are single birds seen on September 21, 1925, at the Point by William Rusling and on October 5, 1929, at Cold Spring, by myself.

I have seen twenty-five feeding on apple boughs in an orchard back of our cottage on August 29, 1932, while William Rusling saw 125 passing at Cape May Point at the height of migration on September 7, 1935.

It is a transient in the Pine Barrens and southward, and a summer resident only in the northern counties and the upper Delaware Valley.

## RUSTY BLACKBIRD
### Euphagus carolinus (Muller)

Curiously enough I have been unable to find a Rusty Blackbird at the Cape although there are several sight records by others. On the Delaware Meadows below Philadelphia, they occur regularly in both spring and autumn, especially at the latter season when they are present in flocks, often mingling with the abundant assemblages of Red-winged Blackbirds which at that time are feeding in the rank growth of weeds and coarse grasses. Single individuals have also been seen in winter with flocks of sparrows.

I have carefully examined many mixed flocks of blackbirds about Cape May in autumn and winter in the hope of finding a Rusty but without success. Julian Potter, however, saw two near Cape May Courthouse on December 24, 1935, which is our only definite record for the county.

## BOAT-TAILED GRACKLE
### Cassidix mexicanus major (Vieillot)

Philip Laurent states (Ornithologist and Oologist, 1892, p. 88) that "Two birds of this species made their appearance on Five Mile Beach in company with a number of Purple Grackles; one was shot by Samuel Ludlam who had it mounted." This, so far as I know, is the only occurrence of the Boat-tailed Grackle in New Jersey. It is a southern species and until quite recently was not known to breed north of Virginia. It is everywhere a coastal bird and I have seen large flocks on the marshes at Chincoteague, Virginia, composed of the big black males and the smaller brown females.

In 1930, Herbert Buckalew saw one of these Grackles near Milford, Delaware, and in 1933, found a pair near Cedar Beach on the shore of Delaware Bay, opposite Cape May, while on May 5, he found four pairs present and located a nest with three eggs. Young birds were on the wing by June 18. On May 30, 1934, I visited the spot with other members of the Delaware Valley Club and saw the birds as well as a nest containing young. This colony was doubtless the source of the birds that visited Five Mile Beach.

# PURPLE GRACKLE

Quiscalus quiscula quiscula (Linnaeus)

Purple Grackles may be seen at Cape May in every month of the year, though they occur less frequently, or with less regularity, during November, December and January, and it is by no means certain, or even probable, that the same individuals are permanently resident.

There may be a few Grackles about the town in winter, in spots where food and shelter are to be found, or there may be scattered individuals in the great roving bands of Red-wings, Cowbirds and Starlings that course over the bare fields, while occasional flocks composed entirely of Grackles visit the vicinity of the Cape in the heart of winter often following a snow storm that has driven them from some favorite feeding ground. A flock of several hundred birds arrived on the meadows back of South Cape May on the day following such a storm in mid-January, 1922, and drifted about in search of bare ground and then disappeared, probably moving farther south. On December 26, 1927, Julian Potter saw a flock of some five hundred birds and on December 27, 1929, Otway Brown tells me that upwards of one thousand flew over Cold Spring, traveling northward in detached flocks and long lines, taking some fifteen minutes to pass. During a snow storm a few days previously, probably this same flock devoured practically all of the corn left on the cob in a nearby field. On December 26–27, 1932, a flock of seventy-five remained about Cold Spring roosting in a maple swamp but later disappeared.

The variability in the number of Grackles present in the Cape May district in winter is shown by the counts on the Christmas census of the Delaware Valley Ornithological Club which are as follows:

| | | | |
|---|---|---|---|
| 1927. | December 26, 500. | 1932. | December 26, 450. |
| 1928. | December 23, 121. | 1933. | December 24, eleven. |
| 1929. | December 27, 1,000. | 1934. | December 23, five. |
| 1930. | December 30, three. | 1935. | December 22, seventeen. |
| 1931. | December 27, fifty. | 1936. | December 27, sixteen |

The possibility of many of these winter Grackles being Bronzed Grackles is discussed elsewhere. Dr. Frank M. Chapman, who has made an exhaustive study of the Grackles, considers that there is a recognizable race intermediate between the breeding birds of New Jersey and the Bronzed and that the name proposed for the former belongs to this. He has therefore named the New Jersey bird Stone's Grackle (*Quiscalus q. stonei*) (cf. Auk, 1935, pp. 21–29).

It is mid-February before the regular northward migration of Grackles at Cape May begins and we find them present continually either at their usual haunts or passing overhead in small or large detachments. Even then weather conditions have much to do with the time of their arrival.

Walker Hand's records of arrival of migrants at Cape May to 1917 and those of others in later years are as follows:

| | | | | | |
|---|---|---|---|---|---|
| 1904. | February 29. | 1910. | February 23. | 1918. | February 27. |
| 1905. | March 5. | 1911. | February 27. | 1921. | February 10. |
| 1906. | February 22. | 1912. | February 27. | 1923. | February 22. |
| 1907. | February 2. | 1913. | February 26. | 1926. | February 21. |
| 1908. | February 21. | 1915. | February 15. | 1932. | February 28. |
| 1909. | February 13. | 1916. | February 18. | 1933. | February 19. |
| | | 1927. | February 22. | | |

In 1934 and 1935 when February was marked by sub-zero weather with much snow the Grackles did not put in an appearance until March. Even after the flight is well underway a change in weather may halt them or drive them back again. So on March 10, 1924, a storm covered most of the peninsula with a deep coating of snow and a flock of one thousand Grackles settled down in the orchards at Cold Spring and remained for an hour or more as if uncertain where to go. From March on, however, Purple Grackles become a regular and conspicuous feature of the bird life of the Cape. Like the drifting assemblages of winter these early spring flocks are often associated with Red-wings, Cowbirds and Starlings and one gathering, resting in a field near Schellenger's Landing, on March 25, 1923, contained in addition a Meadowlark, a Flicker and some fifty English Sparrows.

While the transient flocks of March are passing to the northward smaller groups of Grackles establish themselves about the nesting sites of former years—in the shade trees of the Physick place on Washington St., in a grove of pond pines at Cape May Point, and about old farm houses a little farther north where they seem particularly fond of evergreens. The actions of these nesting communities are interesting. The flock at the

Point is constantly changing its position; now the birds are streaming out in a long line bound for plowed ground near the Lighthouse to feed, or out to the edge of the salt meadow, where the last year's crop of black grass was cut, and then suddenly back they go to the pine grove. As they approach the trees they sail down on set wings which form a triangular, kite-like outline, with the long tails of the males deeply depressed into the characteristic boat or keel. As early as March 13, many of the Grackles are flying in pairs, the male just behind the female and at a slightly lower level. They are noisy, too, about the nest trees and there is a constant chorus of harsh alarm calls; *chuck; chuck; chuck;* like the sound produced by drawing the side of the tongue away from the teeth, interspersed with an occasional long-drawn, *seeek*, these calls being uttered by birds on the wing as well as those that are perching. Then at intervals from a perching male comes the explosive rasping "song" *chu-séeeek* accompanied by the characteristic lifting of the shoulders, spreading of the wings and tail, and swelling up of the entire plumage.

As early as March 5 I have seen evidence of mating and sometimes two males have been in pursuit of a single female, resting near her in the tree tops, where they adopted a curious posture with neck stretched up and bill held vertically. On April 1 the birds in the Physick yard were in pairs, the males going through their courtship "song" but every now and then they all flew off together in true gregarious fashion although they always separated in pairs on their return.

By April 21 (1921) there were flimsy skeleton nests in the pine tops at the Point but even though nest building was under way the flock would often stream away to the feeding grounds. Grackles are walkers and as they stalk about the ground they carry the tail, at this season of the year at least, cocked up at an angle of 45° and the wings of the males slightly drooped. The head is bent over toward the ground and they turn it continually as they walk deliberately about. Sometimes one of them will turn his head completely around so that he looks back over his shoulders or, pointing the bill up nearly vertically with neck still twisted, he will gaze intently at some other bird passing overhead. Those feeding on the marsh were observed to jump a few inches clear of the ground every now and then, as if something below had alarmed them.

While I have no data on time of laying at Cape May, three nests seen by Richard Miller on Seven Mile Beach, contained six, four and six eggs on May 12, 1934, and two in Salem County, May 4 and 9, held four and five respectively. Farther north in West Jersey dates for complete sets range from April 20 to May 12 and the sets seem to be normally six or five eggs.

By May 20 the young in the colony at the Point had apparently hatched as the adults were flying back and forth from the feeding grounds to the nests, individually or in small bunches, and there seemed to be always Grackles in the air. Those nesting in Cape May evidently had young by June 21 in 1932, in the trees or still in the nests, as they were constantly coming in with green cherries, grasshoppers etc.

The birds of this colony may seek food on the Fill, in the gardens, or on the streets, and especially about the refuse dumps, while some individuals regularly visit the sea beach and the shores of the Harbor, and even as late as July, I have seen birds coming from inland colonies to the beach for food and returning northward with their bills full. They usually fed on the beach early in the morning and on July 19, 1925, there was a flock of thirty so engaged. They walked down onto the wet beach, and when shallow water flowed over their feet, they merely fluttered their wings or hopped up into the air for a moment. Larger waves caused them to run clumsily or fly a few feet up the beach but they came back after the retreating wave in true beachcomber fashion. On June 26, 1932, there were six feeding on the beach; they walked into the shallow water with their tails elevated and allowed them to wag from side to side as they progressed. One of them caught a small crab and retreated to the hard sand to eat it. In June I have seen them taking cherries from trees in the town and carrying them to the house tops to eat. On July 16, they were catching May beetles on the golf links, hopping vigorously with a peculiar rushing gait, in an attempt to overtake the flying insects. And once a Grackle was seen pursuing a flying beetle on the street, an unusual performance; the bird was exceedingly clumsy in turning on the wing and after following its erratic prey for several minutes without result it gave up the chase. On August 31, several Grackles were observed darting up in the air from the tree tops in pursuit of flying ants in which activity they also proved very clumsy.

Favorite feeding places visited by both old and young Grackles, until well into the summer, are the piggeries on the edge of the meadows where scraps of refuse food are always to be had. Many Grackles in the town also learn to come to gardens where scraps of bread are thrown out for them and for some years I have seen the birds in July and August, pick up bits of bread and deliberately fly up onto our bird bath and after soaking them for a few moments fly off with them to their young or eat them on the spot. Later the young came to the garden and were fed on the wires and fence tops, fluttering their wings and begging for food, although perfectly able to pick it up for themselves. I have seen this food solicitation on the part of full-fledged young on the Fill as late as June 25 and July 12, in other years.

Young are out of the nest by the early part of June and one family was seen as early as May 22, 1927. On June 30, 1920, thirty young, with perhaps a few adult females, were seen in a cattail swamp on the edge of the town holding their bills wide open as they often do on very hot days. There were also scattered bunches of old males, three to six together, feeding by themselves or passing overhead. Later in the day the entire colony from the Point, old and young to the number of sixty, joined forces and located in a nearby cornfield from which came their familiar *chuck, chuck*, though the "song" of springtime had long since been silenced. On July 3, the same flock was in a grassfield a little to the west where they were joined by four Domestic Pigeons, all of them feeding on the ground. On July 26, what was presumably the same gathering was feeding with Red-wings and Starlings in a field of new cut hay along the railroad, where grasshoppers and other insects abounded. When disturbed the Grackles always took to the thickets and hedgerows while the Red-wings resorted to a nearby cattail swamp. On another occasion the Cape May Point flock was feeding on the shores of a pond dug in the dunes of the Bay side where sand had been removed.

The flocks of old and young drift farther afield as the summer advances in search of new feeding grounds, although some few may remain about the refuse dumps during August, and some old males may be seen on shady lawns along Washington Street. Here they walk about looking particularly sleek in their glossy plumage. As we view them from the rear their legs stand wide apart and they seem almost bowlegged. They are busy investigating the dead leaves, turning them deftly with the bill and tossing them to this side or that to see what prey may be lurking beneath, their yellow eyes gleaming all the while.

By August 10, foraging flocks have scattered so widely that there may be days when no Grackles are to be seen from dawn to dark but at night they always come in to roost with the Martins, Robins, Cowbirds etc., which form the great summer roost of Cape May. For years this was located on the Physick place, then in West Cape May, and lately in the bayberry thickets of the Fill. The Grackles come in as early as July 1, if not earlier, apparently as soon as the young are on the wing, and probably the first to gather at the roost are birds that have bred in the vicinity, but as the season advances the roosting movement becomes more pronounced and definite. Early in the season the birds generally arrive from 7:00 to 7:30 p. m., while by mid-August they come in as early as 6:00 p. m. the actual time however varies considerably according to weather conditions and they always gather earlier on dark rainy days. Many Grackles, especially local birds, gather on the golf links or in nearby cornfields or orchards before entering the roost to feed on pears, or other fruit, or corn on the stalk. A neglected corn patch close to our cottage on Queen Street was a favorite rendezvous for flocks bound for the roost in early September 1921. Here Red-wings and Cowbirds, old and young in all sorts of molting plumages, gathered every evening for a hasty attack on the stunted ears of corn. With them were molting Grackles, some brown with patches of glossy black feathers coming in on the breast, others with scarcely a tail feather left and others, still, with necks almost denuded. Now and then they sprang at one another like miniature gamecocks when one encroached on the food of another. Flocks arriving at the roost from more distant points seemed to come at a higher altitude and when over the trees plunged precipitately down and at once took up their position for the night. On August 18, 1921, and succeeding evenings, I watched them from a location on the Fill which commanded a wide view from north of Schellenger's Landing to the roost. The birds could be detected coming in from far away to the north as tiny specks, then the wing action could be distinguished and finally they streamed past, one long flock after another. From 6:15 to 6:42, 854 Grackles entered the roost, there were 326 in the first five minutes, 150 in the next, and 297 in the next, making 773 in fifteen minutes. On August 20 they began to arrive a little earlier and I missed a part of the flight but from 6 to 6:40, 810 birds were counted. They flew much lower than on the previous evening and paused in the trees about the Landing. The next night the wind changed from southwest to northeast and not a bird came in from the north, like the other roosting birds they seemed always to come in against the wind.

In the morning they leave the roost at daybreak, or before, and Walker Hand has seen Grackles feeding under the electric lights on Washington Street before they were turned off at dawn. Often, especially on rainy mornings, they linger about town and on September 15, 1921, at 6 a. m., I saw about a thousand gathered on the golf links which rolled up in a great sheet of birds onto the wires and trees on Lafayette Street. Grackles continued to come to the roost until the middle of September but by October 1 all had left. Probably the presence of foliage on the trees has something to do with the length of their occupancy. The roost was entirely abandoned in 1936.

The progress of the molt in Grackles can easily be noted by the appearance of the wings and tail as the birds fly overhead, although the new and old body plumage of the adults are the same. They show gaps in the flight feathers as early as July 18 and some are still molting as late as September 8, 11 and 16 in different years. When the tail molt begins the long central feathers drop out first so that the tail appears split or forked, this gap becomes wider as successive pairs of feathers are lost, but by the time the outer pair is dropped the new central feathers have grown out and the outline of the tail is pointed or wedge-shaped. Young birds show a similar molt of the flight feathers and in addition experience a distinct change in the color of the body plumage, from dull brown to glossy black, and birds were seen on August 10, 24 and 17, in different years, with large patches of the new plumage supplanting the worn sooty juvenal dress. Whole flocks of birds in this transition plumage have been seen walking about on the lawns of the Physick place early in the evening before taking up their position in the trees for the night. There is considerable variation in the color of the glossy feathers of the head and neck and I have seen birds showing blue, green and purplish reflections all in the same flock. One albinistic male that visited our garden in July 1927 had the secondaries grayish white.

Grackles are of regular occurrence in flocks of varying dimensions about Cape May until the middle of October, at least, but soon after that they pass on to the southward and we have left only the shifting winter representatives. These seem to be more abundant in West Jersey toward the Delaware River and northwest of the Cape May Peninsula, and the great autumn and winter flocks seem to linger there longer, possibly finding more abundant food along the river swamps and their tributaries than in the pinelands farther east, and the occasional Cape May flocks may drift over from this area. On November 28, 1926, I saw a great flock near Elmer which contained many thousand birds. They covered the ground in great black sheets, the rear ranks constantly arising and flying over to take their place in the van which gave the impression of rolling over the ground. When they took wing in force the long procession streamed past shutting off from view all that lay beyond and when they alighted in the trees the bare branches appeared to be clothed with a dense black foliage.

With the departure of the October and November flocks from the Cape May region the Grackle becomes no longer one of the characteristic birds of the town until on some fine morning in February we awake to hear the familiar harsh call and find them once more in the tops of the ornamental spruce trees in the gardens of Washington Street or in the pines of the Point and when we once more listen to their guttural attempts at song and witness the grotesque swelling up of the body plumage we are apt to forget their ravages of the cornfield as we welcome them back and delight in the familiar voices which usher in another spring.

## BRONZED GRACKLE

### Quiscalus quiscula aeneus Ridgway

This northern and western race of the Grackle has been detected several times in the Cape May region in autumn and winter. On March 11, when the ground was covered with snow, a dozen or more Grackles which had been perching in the orchard at Cold Spring came down into the driveway to feed on the bread that had been thrown out for the birds. They were carefully studied from a window of the house at a distance of twenty feet or less and every one proved to be a Bronzed Grackle. It therefore seems likely that a fair proportion of the wintering Grackles of southern New Jersey, possibly all of them, belong to this race.

When we studied the birds referred to above we could distinguish at a glance the brassy bronze color of the back and rump sharply separated from the greenish or purplish blue of the head. The Purple Grackle on the other hand has the back bottle green and the rump purplish, both with iridescent bars or spots, making a varied or broken pattern in sharp distinction to the plain, uniform bronze of the other bird.

The Bronzed Grackle, the bird of the Mississippi Valley, has extended its range eastward to the coast of New England and far to the north, and in autumn a number of these birds come southeast of the Alleghanies on migration and evidently winter with us.

# COWBIRD

Molothrus ater ater (Boddaert)

Throughout the year Cowbirds may be found about Cape May. In April and May we come upon single birds or bunches of two or three, sometimes several males in pursuit of a single female. They usually are seen flying overhead or perched on the tops of trees but sometimes they are on the ground and on April 24, 1921, I came upon two pairs feeding in a plowed field. On May 7, 1933, I saw a solitary female skulking about the shrubbery in the Physick garden evidently seeking nests in which to deposit her eggs and on May 9, 1931, another female similarly engaged was closely attended by a male. Cowbirds' eggs have been found in the nests of several species of birds about Cape May. A deserted Field Sparrow's nest found on May 27 contained one as did a Parula Warbler's nest, on May 26, 1892, and I have been puzzled to know how the Cowbird managed to deposit an egg in such a delicate structure with only a small side entrance (pl. 117, p. 855).

The Prairie Warbler is another favorite victim of the Cowbird and Turner McMullen has examined nests of this little bird each of which contained an egg of the parasite—on May 31, 1934, four eggs of the warbler; May 24 and 27, 1925, with five eggs. He also found a nest of the Hooded Warbler with a Cowbird's egg on May 27, 1928.

Julian Potter came upon a young Cowbird in the woods at the Point which was calling lustily for food on July 4, 1928, and on August 3, 1927, and again on August 5, 1929, in the same woods, I found a full-fledged young Cowbird following a pair of White-eyed Vireos, which were busy supplying him with green caterpillars. On August 5, 1933, I was surprised to find a pair of these Vireos, also at the Point, busy feeding two young Cowbirds which were apparently full-grown and perfectly able to fly. As early as August 2 in 1934, four young Cowbirds were found feeding in a plowed field which showed scattered black feathers beginning to appear in the gray brown juvenal plumage and feeding with them were three adult males. On August 22, 1929, a flock of forty young were found in a rag-weed field back of the town which were feeding together on the ground and which flushed in a compact flock, flying for three or four yards and settling again. They were in true flock formation and arose and wheeled to right or left like Starlings or sandpipers. Their wings appeared curiously translucent as the sunlight struck them and about half of them were males showing black feathers here and there in their plumage; the rest were either females or males that had not yet begun to molt. They were pecking at the ground and apparently feeding entirely upon grass or weed seed. It is remarkable how these young Cowbirds, which are widely scattered when they leave the nest, and which have been reared by fosterers of different species and habits, are able so quickly to find and recognize their fellows and form into definite flocks. Other flocks of molting birds both young and adult have been found on August 18, 1921; August 28, 1924; August 17, 1925; on lawns on Washington Street in the early evening where they were waiting to enter the Grackle and Martin roost for the night. Another large flock of very much mottled individuals was seen in a barn yard near Erma on August 31, 1928, and a number of birds about half-molted used to come every night with Red-wings in a similar condition to a neglected corn patch close to a window in our cottage during the first week of September 1921.

Flocks of Cowbirds were seen entering the roost as early as July 5, 1923, and July 11, 1927, and they continued to do so until September 29, sometimes numbering one hundred or more to a flock. After the first of October most of the other roosting birds had departed and the foliage of the trees had to a great extent fallen, but a flock of twenty-five Cowbirds continued to come in at night as late as October 18 and joined some Starlings in a row of Norway maples on the sidewalk which still retained their leaves. Some of the birds also roosted on the tops of nearby houses. In the summer flocks we find both males and females and sometimes young mingled indiscriminately, although there is a tendency for the young to flock separately at first, and for the sexes to separate later in the season.

During the daytime these Cowbird flocks are usually found in attendance on cattle in the open fields or cowyards close to the barns. I have observed them so associated from early July to the end of October, and on two occasions, in April, when other Cowbirds were still flocking in the fields with Starlings and Red-wings. I think that the reason for not seeking the companionship of the cattle from November to March is due to the fact that the stock is not turned out in the fields during the cold weather, and not to any disinclination on the part of the birds. The association is peculiar and has generally been explained on the ground that the cattle, as they walk along and browse, stir up insects upon which the birds may feed. As a matter of fact, however, after many careful studies of such flocks with the binoculars at close quarters, I have been unable to detect the birds in the act of catching any insects nor have I seen the cattle stir up any form of insect life from the short grass of the pastures. On one occasion (October 8, 1932) when I was but a few yards away, I could see that the feet of the cows were covered with flies but the Cowbirds continued to peck at the ground and paid not the slightest attention to them nor were the flies disturbed by the progress of the cows. Again, on April 27, 1931, when a strong cold wind was blowing, there was no trace of insects on the ground of the pasture yet the Cowbirds were there feeding apparently on grass or weed seeds as usual.

While the birds sometimes walk quite close to the nose of the browsing cow, or to its feet, I could not see that they derived any benefit from the association. Most of the birds, moreover fed some feet away and seemed to pay but little attention to the activities of the cattle, except that, when the latter were slowly walking along as they browsed, the birds would walk in the same direction and if outdistanced they would fly on a few yards and settle again in front of the cattle. Sometimes I have seen Cowbirds in attendance on cattle that were lying down in the field, in which cases they wandered off from them and fed several yards away. Once I saw a small flock in attendance on a horse that had been turned out to pasture.

When on the ground the Cowbirds always walk and both males and females hold their tails more or less erect, sometimes almost vertical with wings slightly drooped or with the tips below the base of the tail. The appearance of one hundred or more of these rather small birds walking about with tails in the air is striking. I have never seen a Cowbird alight on the back of a cow as they are reported to do in some localities in the Middle West. Starlings often associate with Cowbirds in the fields or cowyards where cattle are gathered, having apparently learned the habit from them.

After the cattle have been retired to their winter quarters the Cowbirds continue to feed in the open fields throughout the cold weather. There is usually one large flock numbering perhaps, five hundred individuals which shifts from place to place between Cold Spring and Cape May and with which numerous Starlings, Red-wings and Meadowlarks associate, while smaller bands of Cowbirds may be found in large flocks of Red-wings or Grackles that now and then drift across the country.

On January 19, 1924, a flock of one hundred and fifty was found in fields just behind the town which contained a single pure white albino. This flock would fly up into the trees that grew along the fence row, or onto the telegraph wires, and later drop back to feed on the ground. The birds were still there on March 19 having moved but little during the winter. Snow, when heavy enough to cover the ground, disturbs the Cowbird flocks not a little and on March 11, 1934, a number of them were forced to repair to the orchard on Otway Brown's place at Cold Spring and flew down close to the house to feed on scraps that we threw out to them. A heavy snow on February 5, 1933, drove a flock of five hundred Cowbirds out on the beach at Cape May Point, about the only spot in the entire countryside where bare ground could be found. These winter flocks seem to be made up of both males and females although one sex or the other will sometimes predominate. While Cowbirds are common in Cape May County in winter their occurrence farther north in the state at this season is more or less sporadic but they have been recorded at Princeton, Plainfield, Yardville, etc.

The young birds in juvenal plumage are much brighter and browner than the drab gray females and have all of the feathers bordered by rich buff, while they are somewhat streaked below. They have acquired the adult plumage, however, by early September.

## SCARLET TANAGER

### Piranga erythromelas Vieillot

A regular but not abundant transient, apparently more plentiful in the autumn flight. In the pine woods of the Point the spring males, in their gorgeous scarlet, stand out most conspicuously against the dark foliage though I have never seen more than one or two at a time. Philip Laurent saw a few in the spring migration on Five Mile Beach in the eighties and Fletcher Street saw one in spring on Seven Mile Beach in 1916. We have records for spring arrival as follows:

| 1928. | May 5. | 1929. | May 9. | 1934. | May 5. |
| 1924. | May 10. | 1932. | May 5. | | |

and earlier records by Walker Hand.

In the autumn they have been seen on:

| 1913. | October 13. | 1925. | September 26. | 1933. | October 28. |
| 1924. | October 2. | 1929. | October 5. | 1934. | September 19. |
| | | 1932. | September 17–18. | 1937. | August 22. |

We do not often see old males in autumn and one that I observed on October 8, 1932, is therefore of special interest. It was very bright yellow olive with jet black wings in contrast to the young of the year with darker green back and wings and only the shoulders black.

The Scarlet Tanager occurs as an occasional summer resident farther north in the peninsula, since it has been seen on May 30, near the Court House by Richard Miller, while two were detected in the woods between there and the Bay Shore Road and one near Seaville by Fletcher Street on June 7, 1936. In the northern half of the state it is a more common summer resident.

## SUMMER TANAGER

Piranga rubra rubra (Linnaeus)

The Summer Tanager seems to have been very much more plentiful in southern New Jersey one hundred years ago than it is today and we have but meager information on its decrease. Alexander Wilson writing in 1807 says: "In Pennsylvania they are a rare species, having myself sometimes passed a whole summer without seeing one of them; while in New Jersey, even within half a mile of the shore opposite the city of Philadelphia, they may generally be found during the season (May to August)." He adds: "it delights in a flat sandy country covered with wood, and interspersed with pine trees * * * I have frequently observed both male and female, a little before sunset, in parts of the forest clear of underwood, darting after winged insects, and continuing thus engaged till it was almost dusk." He also alludes to its fondness for "whortle-berries" and for "humble bees."

In 1857, Beesley gives it as a rare breeder in Cape May County and in 1869 Turnbull lists it as rather rare. George N. Lawrence (Ann. N. Y. Lyceum of Nat. Hist. VIII, p. 286) states that he found it as late as 1866 in magnolia swamps near Atlantic City, but no farther north. Charles C. Abbott writing in 1868, says that up to 1850 it was as abundant as the Scarlet Tanager but that he had seen no nest since 1855 and no bird since 1862. His statements are rendered unsatisfactory by his later mention in 1870, that it was abundant until 1857 (Amer. Nat., IV, p. 536) but he still later records a pair nesting near Trenton in June, 1884! John Krider states that he had found the nest in New Jersey in former years. Thurber (1887) mentions it as an accidental visitant at Morristown in the northern part of the state and Babson (Birds of Princeton) mentions one taken by W. E. D. Scott at Princeton on August 5, 1880.

Mrs. Cordelia H. Arnold saw a Summer Tanager at Somers Point during a great flight of spring migrants on May 8, 1935. She writes: "Our greatest find was a young male Summer Tanager. He had much bricky red but his wings were yellowish green. We had near views for at least five minutes. On May 9, he was near the same spot. We studied him a long time and finally came away and left him. He was singing a low throaty song. In the twenty years that I have been hunting for birds at Somers Point never before have I seen a Summer Tanager." This is the only recent record for southern New Jersey.

Whether it was as plentiful as Wilson infers may be open to question as it is difficult to explain how such a bird should have been practically exterminated. We have a few records from the Pennsylvania side of the Delaware in more recent years and the bird still occurs in Delaware and along the Choptank River though even there it does not seem plentiful.

## CARDINAL
### Richmondena cardinalis cardinalis (Linnaeus)

Cardinals are common residents all over the Cape May Peninsula where swampy thickets overgrown with wild grape, or congenial wood edgings, afford them satisfactory shelter. They will also come close about the farmhouses to pick up food thrown out for the chickens and we hear the clear whistle of the male from the trees in the orchard. There are usually several pairs at the Point and others in thickets bordering Pond Creek Meadows and in the dense tangle surrounding the buildings at Higbee's Beach. There is usually a pair nesting in one of the gardens along Washington Street in Cape May and Miss Mary Doak informs me that in 1935 she was sure that three broods were raised by the pair that nested back of her house and whose activities she had watched carefully. Stray cats left behind by departing summer visitors to the resort have on one or two occasions been responsible for the death of one or more of the Cardinals of the town and for the rest of that year none will be in evidence. In the summer of 1936, a small boy with a gun destroyed the male Cardinal of the local pair but the female continued to come to our yard and eat the scraps of bread that were thrown out, and eventually a male appeared from somewhere.

The Cardinals of the town become quite tame but the birds of the countryside are very secretive and hold pretty well to their cover and when one is fortunate enough to come upon them unawares they leave precipitately the moment they detect our presence. Sometimes we may come upon a pair feeding out in the middle of a road, usually in the early morning, but this habit is becoming rarer as the delightful old shady sand and gravel roads are being replaced by concrete "boulevards" upon which the birds find little but spots of gasoline or oil!

I came upon one female Cardinal in the heart of a thicket busily picking at some sumac berries. She was very active and with each movement would spread her tail and flirt it from side to side. One fine day in March, 1932, Otway Brown and I entered a sheltered cornfield near Cold Spring in which the crop had proved a failure and had never been gathered, while many of the stalks had broken or fallen down. There were no less than twelve Cardinals busily engaged in eating the corn from the ears thereby demonstrating their right to the sobriquet of "corn bird" bestowed upon them in parts of the South. They made a wonderful display of color as we saw them against the dark swamp which bordered the field. Usually however when we see a male Cardinal flying from one thicket to another or venturing a flight in the open it is surprising, especially when the light is behind him, how inconspicuous his brilliant color appears. Indeed he seems to be only red when there is a suitable background to show him off.

Otway Brown tells me that, before the law was enacted forbidding the caging and sale of Cardinals, there was a woman at Cold Spring who raised Canaries and who made a standing offer to the boys of her neighborhood of two dollars for every male Cardinal that they could catch. What she received for them from dealers in Philadelphia was not revealed. The boys made little criscross cages of light cedar splints which were used as deadfalls, the trigger being baited with the end of an ear of ripe corn and grains of corn scattered about. They also had a pair of buckskin gloves handy with which to take the bird from the trap as the Cardinal's powerful beak can inflict a bite that will be remembered. Many of the birds that they caught were females which had no market value whatever.

The Cardinal has quite a repertoire but all of his vocal efforts come under the head of whistles rather than songs. There is the loud emphatic call—which I have recorded as *whoit, whoit, whoit*, often followed directly by the longer drawn out *cheer, cheer, cheer*, and sometimes a bird utters quite a different call *cheedle, cheedle, cheedle, cheedle*. On one occasion a bird called rapidly and continuously *whit, whit, whit, whit, whit*, etc., like the Flicker's rapid call, while another had a very low modification of the *cheer* call—*pheu, pheu, pheu*.

Nesting records furnished by Richard Miller and Turner McMullen are as follows: full sets of three eggs on May 10, 16, 25 and 27 in different years with one of two on May 25 and another of three on June 10. They were all about six feet from the ground in greenbrier thickets or holly bushes.

The Cardinals formerly nested in the forest on Seven Mile Beach and were present also on Five Mile Beach but recent "developments" have apparently driven them from these islands.

I have seen females feeding young on June 19, 1933, and August 14, 1935, and on September 2, 1920, I found a young male in a most interesting phase of molt; most of the dull juvenal plumage remained but the red crest and irregular patches of red on the body had already been assumed. Otway Brown saw two young in a similar condition in the Physick garden on September 1, 1921.

There is no migration of Cardinals since the bird is resident wherever found and southern New Jersey is near to the northern limit of its distribution as a regular and common species. In most of the northern counties it is absent or rare but nests have been found as far north as Plainfield and South Orange.

The counts of Cardinals in mid-winter are shown in the records of the Christmas census at Cape May.

| | |
|---|---|
| December 24, 1922, two. | December 27, 1931, forty-two. |
| December 23, 1923, twenty. | December 26, 1932, twenty-five. |
| December 26, 1926, four. | December 24, 1933, fifty-four. |
| December 23, 1928, forty-five. | December 23, 1934, thirty-five. |
| December 22, 1929, fifty-two. | December 22, 1935, fifty-nine. |
| December 28, 1930, nine. | December 27, 1936, twenty-one. |

The "Redbird" is one of the birds that give a distinctly southern touch to the avifauna of Cape May and, although it does not occur in quite the abundance that it attains in the lowlands of Virginia and the Carolinas, it is sufficiently plentiful to constitute one of the most characteristic resident species, while its outstanding color and voice are ever a delight, whether in the green of summer or in the snowy days of winter.

## ROSE-BREASTED GROSBEAK

### Hedymeles ludovicianus (Linnaeus)

The Rose-breasted Grosbeak is a transient at Cape May but by no means common. As a rule only one is observed at a time and in many years none is recorded. Philip Laurent saw two on Five Mile Beach on May 11, 1890, but it was rare there even then.

Dates of occurrence at Cape May are as follows:

| | | | |
|---|---|---|---|
| 1927. | May 20. | 1932. | September 17–18. |
| 1931. | May 10. | 1934. | September 19. |
| 1925. | September 22. | 1935. | September 7, 29, 30, and October 1. |

It nests in the more northern counties, south to Haddonfield and Beverly while a single bird was seen and photographed at Rutherford, by Clarence Brown from January 26 to February 13, 1908, which had doubtless been injured and was unable to migrate (Bird Lore, 1908, p. 82).

## BLUE GROSBEAK

Guiraca caerulea caerulea (Linnaeus)

We have but a single record of the Blue Grosbeak at Cape May, a female seen at Cape May Point by Julian Potter on the unseasonable date of November 11, 1923. He says: "While looking for birds at Cape May Point, N. J., I heard a loud metallic call which I soon found came from a bird in a nearby thicket which I had no trouble in identifying as a female Blue Grosbeak (*Guiraca caerulea caerulea*) I approached to within fifteen feet of it and studied it for fifteen or twenty minutes as it showed no disposition to fly away. The large heavy bill, reddish brown of the wings and all the details of brown markings on the plumage were clearly made out. Previous acquaintance with the western race in Arizona precluded any possibility of mistake and skins of the bird were examined the next day which agreed in the minutest detail with my observations." (Auk, 1924, p. 159).

Audubon describes in detail a nest with young which he found near Camden, N. J., in the summer of 1829, and which appears in the plate of this species in his "Birds of America." Thurber (1887) records a specimen seen by Mr. Fairchild at Morristown and there are records for the vicinity of New York and Philadelphia, mainly without details, but nothing further as to the occurrence of this distinctly southern bird in New Jersey.

It is of casual occurrence in Delaware and doubtless breeds in that state. Charles Pennock and Samuel Rhoads recorded a specimen taken near Dover in 1882 by Walter D. Bush (Auk, 1905, p. 202) and John Emlen and Benjamin Hiatt saw one at Rehobeth across the Bay from Cape May, on May 12 and 13, 1928. On the Choptank River, near the Delaware-Maryland line it is known to breed. John Carter found a male, female and young there on July 3, 1904, and Clifford Marburger saw one in full song on June 26, 1932.

## INDIGO BUNTING

Passerina cyanea (Linnaeus)

The Indigo Bunting is a decidedly rare summer resident about Cape May and but slightly more plentiful in the migrations, nor is it common anywhere in the peninsula or in the pinelands of southern New Jersey. Usually we have a pair nesting in the thickets along the edge of the meadows at Brier Island below Mill Lane where I have heard the male in song in early July in several years. One found singing on the wires along the railroad at Rutherford's Branch, a little to the west, on July 3, 1935, doubtless was one of these. Another pair is usually to be found in thickets along the southern edge of the Pond Creek Meadows and possibly two pairs bred there in the summer of 1928. A brilliant male found bathing in a rain water pool in the pine grove at the Point on July 2, 1930, probably came from there as I never saw it at the Point again. Still another pair was located in an orchard on the Town Bank Road on May 29, 1921. Others were seen in the same vicinity or at the Point on May 26, 1929, May 30, 1925, and 1928 all of which may well have been migrants.  Undoubted migrants were males recorded at Cold Spring on May 8, 1927; May 10, 1929; May 8, 1932; May 6, 1933, May 7, 1934.  One of these was feeding with Goldfinches on dandelion seed on a lawn.

In the autumn a few are seen nearly every year especially at Cape May Point and our records follow:

| | | | |
|---|---|---|---|
| 1921. | October 9. | 1928. | September 30. |
| 1923. | October 1. | 1929. | September 29. |
| 1924. | October 2, three. | 1930. | September 28. |
| 1925. | September 22, two. | 1932. | September 25, several. |
| 1926. | September 27, several. | 1933. | October 9, two. |
| 1927. | October 10, three. | | |

In those parts of the state north and west of the Pine Barrens the Indigo Bunting is a common summer resident.

## DICKCISSEL

### Spiza americana (Gmelin)

So far as I am aware the Dickcissel has only once been found in Cape May, a male bird trapped on the edge of waste ground in the town by James Tanner, Audubon Association representative during the autumn of 1936, on September 28, when trapping English Sparrows.  In adjoining counties it has occurred as an erratic transient.  The history of the species in the East, its former local abundance and later disappearance, has been treated by Samuel Rhoads in "Cassinia" for 1903.  It has always been primarily a bird of the Middle West.

Recent nearby records are as follows: Maurice River, September 18, 1890, William L. Baily; Bridgeton, January 18, 1925, B. K. Matlack; Sharpstown, Salem Co., June 10–11, 1928, one seen in an alfalfa field by Leland I. Warner.  (Auk, 1928, p. 509).

Curiously enough on May 26, 1928, Miss Mary Wood Daly found a pair of Dickcissels breeding in a clover field in Delaware County, Pennsylvania (Auk, 1928, pp. 507 and 509) and on June 23, 1934, Victor Debes found several Dickcissels in song near Mt. Pleasant, Delaware, and again on May 19, 1935, a single bird was singing at the same spot.

The last nesting in New Jersey was July 3, 1904, when Waldron Miller found a pair with young at Plainfield (Auk, 1904, p. 487).

PLATE 118

*J. K. Potter*

*J. K. Potter*

1. THE "FILL" EAST CAPE MAY; FORMER SITE OF CAPE ISLAND SOUND, 1923.

2. NEST AND YOUNG OF THE SAVANNAH SPARROW, FOUND ON THE "FILL" BY J. K. POTTER, JUNE 19, 1923.

## EVENING GROSBEAK

Hesperiphona vespertina vespertina (Cooper)

The first record of the Evening Grosbeak at Cape May was a female picked up dead on the grounds of the Physick place on Washington Street by Otway Brown on January 14, 1930, which is now in the collection of the Academy of Natural Sciences of Philadelphia. This so far as I am aware constitutes the farthest south record for the range of this far north species, in the East.

On March 30, 1932, Raymond Otter saw a pair of Evening Grossbeaks at his home in West Cape May and identified them at once by comparing them with the plate in Eaton's "Birds of New York." They were seen again in the same vicinity by two other residents of the neighborhood on April 16, and 25, and finally on May 1. There are a number of box elder trees at the spot which undoubtedly attracted the birds as the seeds of this tree are their favorite food. Our third local record is of four birds found by Conrad Roland on December 24, 1933, during the Christmas census of the Delaware Valley Club. They were perched in a tree on the edge of the dunes along the Bay shore, north of Cape May Point, and were studied by several other members of the Club. They were so tame that Roland was able to sketch one of them. Strangely enough in one of the years in which these grosbeaks occurred at Cape May they were not recorded anywhere else in the state. There have however been many other New Jersey records and a resumé of them seems of interest in connection with the Cape May occurrences.

*1890.* A flock of eight was found at Summit on March 6, 1890, by W. O. Raymond (Ornithologist and Oölogist, 1890, p. 46).

*1910–1911.* A flock of eight seen by Blanche Hill at Andover, Sussex Co. on December 13, 17 and 18. Mary F. Knouse saw them at Newton in the same county on January 6, 1911, and Stephen D. Inslee reported a flock of twenty-five at the same place on February 5. Waldron DeWitt Miller found a flock of thirteen near Plainfield on January 29 and on February 12 and 19 at least twenty were present. They lived in a grove of red cedars and flowering dogwood and fed on the berries of the latter rejecting the soft part and cracking open the stones with their powerful beaks to get at the kernels. On April 26, Belle C. Cooke found three feeding on cherry buds at Fair Haven on the Shrewsbury River four miles from the coast. They sat in stolid quiet for fifteen minutes at a time.

*1916–1917.* The flight this winter was more extended. On December 3 Charles Evans saw one at Cinnaminson, Burlington Co. They were at Smithville, Burlington Co., on December 24; at Mt. Holly on the same day (Pumyea); Westville December 25, six (Potter); Browns Mills, January 10, 1917, sixty-five (Darlington); New Lisbon, January 29, seventy-four (Scoville). They were seen again at the last locality February 11 (forty), 17 (thirty), February 22, March 2 (fifty), March 12 (thirty), March 20 (six) (Scoville and Huber). They were at Ham-

monton February 22 (Bassett) to March 26 and April 18.   Birmingham
March 2 (five) and 6 (four) (Huber).  Lumberton, March 21 (Clayberger).
Lakewood March 21 (twelve) (N. C. Brown).   The latest records were,
April 2, Wenona (Erskine); Rancocas, April 11–12 (Miss E. Haines);
Mt. Holly, April 8 (six), 26 (eight) (Pumyea); Yardville, May 7, (Rogers).
Also recorded from Blairstown, Morristown and Hackettstown in the
northern counties from January to March.

*1918–1919.*  New Lisbon, a flock of twenty-seven, February 22, 1919.  Lakewood, February 20, 1919 (N. C. Brown).

*1919–1920.*  Princeton, February 16, 1920 (four) to March 13 (eight) (H. L.
Eno).  Pt. Pleasant, early February, a pair came in a snow storm and
remained for some days (A. P. Richardson).  Vineland, February 21 to
May 7, a flock of from six to forty on different days (Price).  Morestown,
April 16-23, a flock of twenty-six.  Mt. Holly April 21, two pairs (Pumyea).

*1921–1922.*  Mt. Holly, November 20, a male (Pumyea).  Elizabeth, November a flock of 121 (Urner).  Vineland, January 5 to March 18, from
twelve to forty (Prince).  Moorestown, April 21, 25, 27 (Linton).

*1922–1923.*  Mt. Holly, November 20, 1921, a flock of 110 (Pumyea).

*1926–1927.*   Elizabeth, January 16 and February 6 (Urner).

*1929–1930.*  Tuckerton, February 2, a small flock (J. Emlen).

*1933–1934.*  Mount Holly, December 15—April 18, forty (Pumyea).  Moorestown, February 22, twelve (Street).  Medford, April 13–30, fifty-two
(Quay).

No doubt there are other records but probably all the winters of Grosbeak invasion are mentioned.


## PURPLE FINCH

### Carpodacus purpureus purpureus (Gmelin)

The Purple Finch is an autumn transient and somewhat irregular winter resident.   In the spring we have but one record, three birds one in full
song observed by William Yoder on March 6, 1927.

In 1935, when William Rusling was present at the Point in the interests of the Audubon Association, he recorded Purple Finches on nineteen
days between September 16 and November 14, usually less than a dozen
although on October 14, twenty-five were seen.   Whether his observations
represented a flock constantly present or small bunches on migration it is
difficult to say.

Our records are as follows:

    1922–1923.   November 12, two; January 14.
    1923.   November 11, six; December 23.
    1925.   February 8.
    1925–1926.   September 22 and 26, two; October 18, three; February 8.
    1926–1927.   November 21, six; December 26, two; March 6.

1927.  October 23, seven; November 6, fourteen; December 26, two.
1928.  October 27, December 23, two.
1929.  October 25, December 22, 26, five.
1931.  October 18; November 7, two; December 27.
1933.  October 28, two.
1935.  September 16; 17, sixteen; 20; 21, ten; 23, eleven; 29, twelve; October
         2; 4; 7; 10, 12, twenty-five; 14; 15; 24; 25; November 1; 3; 6; 14.
1936.  December 22, December 27, seven.

While mainly a transient or winter visitant the Purple Finch has bred at several localities in the northern counties.


## *PINE GROSBEAK

### Pinicola enucleator leucura (Muller)

The Pine Grosbeak is a rare visitant from the Far North in severe winters. It has been recorded on several occasions in the northern parts of the state but has never, so far as I am aware, occurred in Cape May County; indeed the most southern record seems to be a flock seen at Princeton by Prof. A. H. Phillips in 1886 (Babson, Birds of Princeton).  There were notable south-ward flights of these birds in the winters of 1836–37; 1884–85; 1899–1900; 1903–04; but they only reached the northern edge of New Jersey.

Charles Urner records them present in Union County in the winters of 1916–1917 and 1929–1930, a flock of forty on January 5, 1930 and they were present in Essex and Hudson Counties in December, 1913.


## *BRITISH GOLDFINCH

### Carduelis carduelis britannica (Hartert)

This bird was introduced at Hoboken according to Warren Eaton in 1878 and a few were still to be seen as late as 1913.  John T. Nichols found them at Englewood, a little farther north, from 1912 to 1915 and thought that they probably bred there.  He says "a flock of about eight on January 28, 1912 (at Englewood); about six at Leonia on February 16, 1913; one on February 21, 1915, seven, one in full song, in a heavy wet snow storm on March 6; a flock of about five at Coytesville on March 13, unusually common in the Englewood region this year, singing on March 23, 1915." (Auk, 1936, p. 429.)

They were also introduced on Long Island but do not seem to have spread beyond the immediate vicinity of New York City.

## COMMON REDPOLL

### Acanthis linaria linaria (Linnaeus)

The Redpoll is a rather rare and irregular winter visitant over most of the state but seldom ranges south of the Pine Barrens. Notable flights have been recorded in the winters of 1836–1837; 1878–1879, March 1888, 1899–1900, 1906–1907 and 1908–1909. Prior to 1930 Charles Urner had found them in Union County in seven out of twelve years from October 18 to March 21 (extreme dates).

Redpolls have occurred as far south as Haddonfield in 1888 (Rhoads) Swedesboro in 1909 (Lippincott) and down the coast to Brigantine where Brooke Worth found four with Siskins on February 22, 1936, during a spell of exceptionally cold weather and after a six inch fall of snow on the 21st. They were in bayberry bushes at the southern point of the island with Snow Buntings also present.

On the same day, a flock of fifty was seen at Beverly by members of the Delaware Valley Club. They appeared very dark-colored against the snow differing from the Goldfinches in this respect just as do the Siskins. Indeed the Redpolls are essentially Siskins with crimson crowns and a pink flush on the breast and rump, and even these marks are absent in the female, but they always lack the yellow wing flashes of the latter bird.

So far as I am aware we have but a single record of the Redpoll in Cape May County—two seen by John Carter and Edward Marshall on Seven Mile Beach on March 26, 1937.


## *GREATER REDPOLL

### Acanthis linaria rostrata (Coues)

Babson, in his "Birds of Princeton" has recorded two specimens of this slightly larger race of the Redpoll which were shot at Princeton on February 6, 1872. Prof. A. H. Phillips and Charles Rogers have assured me that they were correctly identified and thanks to Mr. Rogers I have been able to examine the birds and quite agree with them.


## PINE SISKIN

### Spinus pinus pinus (Wilson)

For the most part the occurrence of the Siskin in the Cape May region is irregular. Some individuals may occur every autumn but in only a few years has there been a large flock present throughout the winter. Several times there has been a notable migration of these birds down the coast but whether this is a regular occurrence I have been unable to determine. On November 12, 1922, Julian Potter saw them passing down the coast at intervals, all day long, in flocks of from ten to two hundred. They did not alight and scarcely any were seen except on the wing. On November 16, 1929, unaware of this record, I saw exactly the same thing. The flocks, consisting of from ten to one hundred birds, kept passing me all morning between South Cape May and the Point traveling in rapid flight along the dunes or the edge of the meadows just behind. They looked very dark but were difficult to study as they never paused or rested either on the ground or on bushes. I was unable to ascertain whether they came in off the ocean, as the Robin flocks do at the same spot, or whether they crossed the Bay immediately or cruised up the western side of the peninsula. On November 7, 1931, a similar flight occurred and I estimated that at least five hundred passed in an hour or two. Some of these birds alighted on the bayberry bushes by the Lighthouse and then continued on their way. On October 18, 1925, we have record of one hundred Siskins along the beach and 1500 observed at Barnegat by Charles Urner, on November 29 of that year, which may have been part of another of these flights.

In only the winters of 1922–1923 and 1925–1926, did they remain at Cape May as winter visitants and on the former occasion they were present until April 30. They associated with Goldfinches on the dunes and meadows back of South Cape May where Spencer Trotter and I found them feeding on cockleburs on December 30, 1922. We had a few present on November 6 and 11, 1921; October 7, 1922; November and December 27, 1931 (two); December 22, 1935 (two).

The most striking features of the Siskins are their general dark coloration and very heavy streaking below and, when they fly, their long pointed wings and flash of yellow as they are successively spread and closed again.

Throughout New Jersey the Siskin is a transient and irregular winter visitant varying in numbers in different years. While their occurrence in West Jersey along the Delaware Valley is usually between October 15 and April 25 I have seen considerable flocks as late as May 17.

## GOLDFINCH

### Spinus tristis tristis (Linnaeus)

The Goldfinch is a resident about Cape May but of somewhat irregular occurrence in the town and about the Point and not a bird that will be seen on every day afield. It is often seen or heard as it passes overhead in its undulating flight or pauses for a moment on a telegraph wire or tree top. In spring or early summer pairs or small flocks may come into the gardens or to the shade trees along the streets, and a pair or two are usually established on the Fill where they doubtless nest, as also in the fruit trees of the Physick place, where a few usually summer.

Occasionally we see a male Goldfinch flying high in the air more or less in circles, and after covering this imaginary track several times he will relapse into the usual undulating flight and drop back to his perch. This performance is apparently a display, incident to the mating season. I saw it once on July 9, 1923, and again on August 1, 1926, when the bird was tossing himself through the air in perfect abandon. Out on the Fill I watched other Goldfinches going through this display on June 26, 1928; August 6, 1925; June 30, 1935; circling high over the dense growth of bayberry bushes where the female was concealed.

I have watched Goldfinches in May feeding on dandelion seeds on the lawns of dwellings in the open country while in July and August they may be found feeding on thistles and chicory in waste ground near the town, or along the roadsides, and in late August and September they frequent sunflowers, picking the seeds from the great round heads and often feeding them to young birds already full-fledged and on the wing. These youngsters, apparently perfectly able to shift for themselves, have been seen begging for

food and twittering their wings as they followed their parents, as late as
September 12 and 29 in different years.   In wintertime the Goldfinches
feed in flocks on cockleburs along the dunes or edges of the marshes while
I have watched some individuals exploring pine cones in the groves at the
Point, and others in the center of a tall woods at Cold Spring picking seeds
from the burs of the Sweet Gum trees.   Yellow males resting against the
sunflowers and primroses in the garden are almost invisible and would
easily be passed by.

By the middle or end of August, but more especially from October to
March, Goldfinches gather in larger flocks and drift about the country,
often leaving the Cape May district entirely in midwinter when snow and
ice render food difficult to obtain.   Dr. William L. Abbott and I found an
immense flock largely birds of the year along the roadsides near Higbee's
Beach on August 27, 1918.   On November 21, 1926, John Gillespie saw
a flock of one hundred or more and I encountered a similar large gathering on March 15, 1931, while on December 30, 1922, there was a great
flock associated with Siskins on the marshes below the town where they
remained all winter and were present as late as April 30 though in much
reduced numbers.   Walker Hand records a flock of over two hundred on
February 9, 1919, and refers to "thousands" present, November 21–25,
1918.   While usually forming their own flock scattered winter individuals
will join a miscellaneous assemblage of sparrows along the fence rows and
thickets and feed with them on the ground.

I have seen males in the yellow and black breeding plumage as late as
September 7, which showed no sign of molting but others observed on
October 8 had undergone the change to the gray-brown winter dress.
Spring birds were molting on March 25, 1933, while others by April 30 were
essentially in full nuptial plumage.

The variation in the number of Goldfinches present in midwinter is
indicated by the counts on the Christmas census of the Delaware Valley Club.

December 30, 1922, 100.             December 27, 1931, 145.
December 26, 1926, thirty-one.      December 26, 1932, 300.
December 26, 1927, forty-one.       December 24, 1933, 144.
December 23, 1928, fifty-seven.     December 23, 1934, 210.
December 22, 1929, 120.             December 22, 1935, 154.
December 28, 1930, seventy-six.     December 27, 1936, ninety.

Elsewhere in the state the occurrence of the Goldfinch is similar to that
at Cape May—a resident species most abundant during the migrations.

## RED CROSSBILL

### Loxia curvirostra pusilla Gloger

We have but one record of the Red Crossbill at Cape May, one found
dead at the Point by Turner McMullen on March 4, 1923.   Julian Potter
found some at Barnegat on December 21, 1919, and it has been recorded at

various times and places in the northern parts of the state although always
irregular and erratic in its occurrence.

Dr. William E. Hughes found a flock of about two dozen of these birds
at Forked River on June 6, 1900, which were feeding on the pine cones
while on May 10, 1894, he saw three at Lewes, Delaware. These very late
records might indicate the breeding of the birds in the pine lands were it
not for their well-known erratic habits. William Evans saw some at Han-
over on May 6, 1900; George E. Hix in northern Somerset County, July 6,
1903; and Samuel Rhoads at Wawayanda Lake, June 5, 1909.

Nelson Pumyea has found them wintering at Mt. Holly, where they
were observed from January 21 to March 18, 1923.

## WHITE-WINGED CROSSBILL

### Loxia leucoptera Gmelin

A female White-winged Crossbill was brought in to Walker Hand by a
pet cat on February 5, 1909, the specimen is now in the collection of the
Academy of Natural Sciences of Philadelphia. No others have been seen
at any time in Cape May County.

Elsewhere in the state they have occurred as irregular winter visitants
especially in the northern counties. Audubon writing at Camden, in the
first week of November, 1827, says: "they are so abundant that I am able
to shoot, every day, great numbers out of the flocks that are continually
alighting in a copse of Jersey scrub pine, opposite my window." John
Cassin states that they were present in the winter of 1836–1837, and were
not seen again until the winter of 1854–1855 when they were unusually plentiful among the pines about Camden, and so tame that they could be killed
with stones. Samuel Rhoads found a small flock at Haddonfield in the
winter of 1896–1897 and in that of 1899–1900 they were abundant at
Plainfield, Princeton, Englewood, etc. On December 25, 1906, Charles
Rogers records four at Leonia, while Nelson Pumyea saw some at Mt. Holly
on January 21, 1923, which, as is often the case, were associated with the
Red Crossbills.

## RED-EYED TOWHEE

Pipilo erythrophthalmus erythrophthalmus (Linnaeus)

The Towhee or Chewink is a common summer resident of scrubby woods and clearings throughout Cape May County and northward. It is plentiful at Cape May Point and along the wood edges on the eastern side of the peninsula as far south as Cold Spring and Brier Island. It spends much of its life in the heart of the thickets from which comes its loud metallic alarm note "*chewink*" whenever one approaches its domain, for it is ever alert and we are lucky if we are able to steal a march on it. Occasionally we may manage to creep up unawares and get a view of the bird busily scratching a living from the dead leaves that cover the woods floor. His relatively large feet seem to be well adapted for the work as he jumps up a few inches and kicks out with both at once.

In early spring, and throughout the nesting season, the male Chewink will mount to the top of some small tree or occasionally a larger one, such as a Thrasher might select, and with head erect give voice to his familiar song. His usual habitat, however, is close to the ground and as we pass along some wooded road, where the present deplorable craze for clearing has left a fringe of underbrush, we may catch a glimpse of him crossing ahead of us on the wing and get a momentary flash of his striking black, white and chestnut livery, or he may cross on foot with head and neck extended and making prodigious hops. In the short flights of the Chewink the tail is always flailing up and down as if hinged at the base, producing a sort of broken-backed flight such as we are familiar with in the Song Sparrow. When perched for singing, however, the tail is pendent and the feathers of the crown are slightly elevated, while one bird hopping along the horizontal limb of a tree held the tail cocked up at an angle and kept flapping the wings as if to balance itself. In many of its actions, especially in its infrequent sustained flight, the Chewink recalls the Cardinal.

The normal song of the bird may be represented as *chúck, burr, chéeeeeee* the second note lower than the first and the following trill higher than either. This, however, is subject to much variation in different individuals. One seemed, to my ear, to say, *seé, tschu, chéeeeee* while the song of a third I have recorded *whíp, o, shéeeee*. Still another added a second trill *chíck, o, chéeee, chéeee*, and in one song that I heard the unaccented note came first *che, sék, chée* while in another there was only a single note before the trill, *chúck, chéeeee*. Then there was a bird with a peculiarly harsh preliminary note somewhat like the single call note of the Flicker, *skéuk chéeeee* and one which sang the first two notes on exactly the same pitch. There is practically no variation in the alarm note although I once heard two birds, perhaps a pair, calling alternately with a slightly different pitch and in a way supplementary to one another, one call rising and the other falling, *ka-wéek; che-wínk; ka-wéek; che-wínk*. Young birds, still in the dull gray brown juvenal plumage, have an alarm note like the latter part of the parent's call but weaker, *wink, wink;* while an adult female, heard on August 24, 1927, uttered an entirely different alarm note, a rapidly repeated *shwee, shwee, shwee, shwee,* etc. which immediately brought a dozen birds to the spot—Carolina Wrens, White-eyed Vireos, Thrashers and Catbirds.

I have heard the Towhee's song as late as July 16, 1927; July 23, 1926; July 27, 1922; July 29, 1924; while the *che-wínk* call may be uttered at any time, even by the occasional winter resident birds.

Richard Miller has examined a number of nests of the Towhee in the Cape May district and states that they are usually on the ground, often at the base of a bush or small tree, but one that I found at Erma, on July 29, 1924, evidently a delayed nesting, was in a huckleberry bush three feet from the ground and contained only two eggs. All full sets consisted of four eggs; and of Miller's nests three were found on May 27 and one each on May 25, 30, June 6 and 10; two nests found on May 27 and one on May 31 contained four young each.

Young birds in full juvenal plumage were seen on the wing on July 15, 1920 and 1922; July 31, 1921; July 28, 1934; looking, except for the tail, like plump gray brown sparrows. Some in the same condition were seen on August 9 and August 27, while on August 17, 1891; August 29, 1922; September 1, 1931; September 2, 1920; birds were found that were in all stages of molt. Some had black collars on a gray brown plumage and others irregular patches of black and chestnut producing a remarkable piebald pattern A little later old and young become indistinguishable.

Walker Hand's arrival dates are as follows up to 1920 with other records for more recent years:

| 1902. | March 10. | 1911. | March 11. | 1916. | April 18. |
|-------|-----------|-------|-----------|-------|-----------|
| 1903. | March 9. | 1912. | March 27. | 1928. | April 1. |
| 1904. | April 4. | 1920. | April 20. | 1929. | April 7. |
| 1905. | April 9. | 1921. | April 24. | 1930. | April 6. |
| 1906. | April 3. | 1922. | April 23. | 1932. | March 25. |
| 1907. | March 18. | 1923. | April 22. | 1933. | April 1. |
| 1908. | March 14. | 1924. | April 20. | 1934. | April 20. |
| 1909. | March 8. | 1925. | March 22. | | |

Some, at least, of the March dates probably refer to wintering individuals. Our latest autumn dates are:

| 1921. | October 16. | 1927. | October 27. | 1931. | October 19. |
|-------|-------------|-------|-------------|-------|-------------|
| 1922. | October 1. | 1928. | October 23. | 1932. | October 12. |
| 1923. | October 21. | 1929. | October 25. | 1934. | October 19. |
| 1924. | October 2. | 1930. | October 5. | 1935. | October 29. |
| 1925. | October 18. | | | | |

We have several records of single birds in November, and for February 22, 1923; February 8 and 14, 1925; February 6, 1932; while the counts on the Christmas census show the probable number of birds that wintered:

| 1922. | December 24, six. | 1932. | December 26, five. |
|-------|-------------------|-------|--------------------|
| 1923. | December 23, one. | 1933. | December 24, two. |
| 1928. | December 23, one. | 1934. | December 23, three. |
| 1929. | December 22, two. | 1935. | December 22, four. |
| 1930. | December 28, eleven. | 1936. | December 27, two. |
| 1931. | December 27, ten. | | |

Additional winter records are one seen on Five Mile Beach December 27, 1903 (Baily) and one at Moorestown, December 25, 1907 (Evans).

Like many other summer resident birds Towhees seem to start southward rather early and often about the middle or end of August there are days when none are to be found—August 27, 1925; August 28, 1926; August 17, 1929; August 29, 1932; while later they again become common or even abundant as hordes of migrants from farther north throng the woods, usually to stay a few days and then pass on, while their places are taken by later visitors.

## IPSWICH SPARROW

Passerculus princeps Maynard

This striking pale sparrow of the dunes has an interesting history. It was first obtained by Alexander Wilson on the New Jersey coast, probably on Peck's Beach where Ocean City now stands, the region known to the older ornithologists as "Great Egg Harbor." Wilson considered his bird as merely a fully adult male of the Savannah Sparrow and figured it under that name in his classic "Ornithology." In 1892 my friend Norris DeHaven called my attention to the similarity of Wilson's plate to the Ipswich Sparrow and I saw at once that he was right and that what we had always regarded as an exaggerated representation of a Savannah was in reality an excellent portrait of this interesting bird (cf. Osprey, 1898, p. 117). It had meanwhile been "rediscovered" on Ipswich Beach in Massachusetts by Charles J. Maynard who described and named it and his appellation still stands. The next New Jersey specimen is one found in the collection of Bernard Hoopes, without data but probably also from Great Egg Harbor, doubtless secured in the "sixties." No others were recorded from this state until Dr. W. L. Abbott shot one on Five Mile Beach, December 30, 1879, and Samuel Rhoads got another at Atlantic City on March 15, 1888. On April 3, 1889, John Sterner obtained one on Five Mile Beach for Philip Laurent and I secured two on January 29, 1892, at Cape May and two more on January 5, 1893. Since that time many more specimens have been obtained and many others seen, as ornithologists increased in numbers and the bird became better known.

It was later discovered that the summer home of the Ipswich Sparrow was Sable Island on the coast of Nova Scotia.

The Ipswich Sparrow is a winter resident of the sand dunes close to the beach and probably no other bird has such a restricted range. It runs like a mouse through the yellow dune grass or occasionally rests on logs or trash washed up by the waves. When standing still the light colors of the bird exactly match the tints of the sand and it is hard to distinguish it from its surroundings. Some individuals, probably young of the year, have brighter bay tints on the wings and the cheeks are deeper buff, while spring birds have the yellow eyebrow much more conspicuous. Ipswich Sparrows occur at Cape May singly, as a rule, and not more than four have been seen during a day's tramp but on the wilder stretches of Seven Mile Beach Dr. William E. Hughes found them present in greater numbers and secured as many as nine on January 1, 1899. He has recorded them as present from November 14, 1897, to March 27, 1898 and from November 13, 1898, to January 2, 1899. His interesting series of specimens is now in the collection of the Philadelphia Academy.

The earliest dates of autumn arrival of the Ipswich Sparrow for the Cape May region are: November 21, 1926; October 23, 1927; October 27, 1928; November 16, 1929; November 7, 1931.

The latest dates of observation in spring: March 31, 1921; March 12, 1922; March 20, 1924; March 18, 1927; April 12, 1930.

To show the variation in the midwinter population we may quote the figures of the Delaware Valley Club's Christmas census:

| | |
|---|---|
| December 31, 1921, one. | December 28, 1930, eight. |
| December 30, 1922, three. | December 27, 1931, two. |
| December 23, 1923, four. | December 26, 1932, four. |
| December 26, 1926, one. | December 23, 1934, two. |
| December 26, 1927, four. | December 22, 1935, three. |
| December 23, 1928, four. | December 27, 1936, four. |
| December 25, 1929, one. | |

## SAVANNAH SPARROW

Passerculus sandwichensis savanna (Wilson)

PLATE 118, p. 886

The Savannah Sparrow is a common winter visitant to the brushy marshes and old fields of Cape May County as well as on the dunes and open sandy spots of the coast from about September 7 to May 10.

A specimen secured by F. D. Stone, Jr., on the borders of Cape Island Sound on July 6, 1891, raised the question of its possible occurrence as a breeder at Cape May and in 1921 I found two pairs established on the Fill, which had replaced the old Sound, and for several summers thereafter one or more pairs evidently bred on the edge of the swampy spots that had developed there. Finally Julian Potter found a nest on the Fill on June 19, 1923, containing four fully fledged young which promptly took wing. The nest was in a slight depression in the ground. A male was still in full song on July 4, 1927, in the same locality. Meanwhile Waldron De Witt Miller had found a nest and three young on Seven Mile Beach, on July 8, 1903, and W. B. Crispin one near Salem and on June 3, 1934, Edward Reiman found one with four eggs at Brigantine farther up the coast. While these are the only nests so far recorded for southern New Jersey, Charles Pennock obtained an adult and a young bird in the juvenal plumage at Delaware City, Del., on June 24, 1911.

Savannah Sparrows are most plentiful in the spring and autumn migrations but a few remain through every winter and in some seasons they occur in large numbers, as in the week of January 29, 1891, when Samuel Rhoads and I found them fairly swarming on the meadows between Cape May and the Point during a spell of extremely cold weather with a gale from the northwest. Like many other sparrows they always take wing as individuals, not in concentrated flocks, and fly from the ground in a low somewhat undulating but direct flight, soon dropping down to the ground again. They usually crouch perfectly still like a Snipe and flush again before one can get near to them. Their flight is totally unlike that of the Song Sparrow lacking the tail action while the tail itself appears distinctly shorter. Compared with the Grasshopper Sparrow the Savannah lacks the twisting character of flight as it takes wing, and the tail is longer. The migrant and winter birds run like mice through the grass and it is almost impossible to study them on the ground, but summer breeding birds, resenting one's intrusion on nest or young, are much more in evidence. They run rapidly with tail slightly elevated and after taking wing will alight on the top of a bayberry bush or weed stalk from which perch I have heard them sing as late as July 21, 1921. On January 17, 1932, I followed a single bird which I found feeding in an old bean field, for fifty yards, walking at a medium gait some fifteen feet behind it. The bird would pause when I did and then run on, sometimes giving a slight flip to the wings or spreading them a little to steady itself and maintain its balance. It never attempted flight although it would, of course, have done so had I quickened my pace. Other birds that were flushed later alighted on bushes giving an instantaneous flirt to the tail, as they reached their perch, so quick that the eye could scarcely catch it.

The breeding Savannahs appear very pure white below and the black streaks stand out boldly while the yellow eyebrow is conspicuous. In winter there is more of a buff tint on the breast and whitish edgings to the feathers of the back emphasize the streaked appearance, while there is an olive yellow cast to the sides of the head. The young are darker than the adults with a strong buff suffusion on the breast and heavier streaking below. The feet in all are pinkish flesh-color.

Spring migrants that I saw feeding on an open sandy flat on Ludlam's Beach on May 9, 1925, seemed to spread the legs very far apart as if to bring the head nearer to the ground as they picked up food, flirting the tail nervously all the time. They ran with a jerky gait.

Autumn dates for arrival of migrants are:

| | | | | | |
|---|---|---|---|---|---|
| 1921. | September 9. | 1925. | September 22. | 1929. | September 21. |
| 1922. | September 17. | 1926. | September 25. | 1930. | September 21. |
| 1923. | August 21. | 1927. | September 25. | 1932. | September 17. |
| 1924. | September 7. | 1928. | September 23. | 1935. | September 19. |

The variation in numbers recorded on the Christmas census are shown below:

| | |
|---|---|
| December 28, 1921, three. | December 28, 1930, twenty. |
| December 24, 1922, six. | December 27, 1931, nine. |
| December 23, 1923, twenty. | December 26, 1932, seven. |
| December 26, 1926, sixteen. | December 24, 1933, forty-two. |
| December 26, 1927, ninety-two. | December 23, 1934, forty-nine. |
| December 23, 1928, nine. | December 22, 1935, twelve. |
| December 27, 1929, two. | December 27, 1936, nineteen. |

While mainly a transient in New Jersey the Savannah Sparrow breeds at various localities in the northern counties—Morristown, Patterson etc.

## GRASSHOPPER SPARROW

### Ammodramus savannarum australis Maynard

The Grasshopper Sparrow is a common summer resident in old fields of the uplands and ranges down almost to the edge of the salt meadows. It also occurs on sandy grassy areas back of the dunes and is abundant on the Fill, although becoming less common there as the bayberry bushes overgrow the open grassy spots.

It is essentially a ground bird and progresses by quick hops intermingled with running steps and occasionally breaking into a regular run. When it stops it often ducks the body nervously like a wren. The head and neck seem out of proportion to the rest of the body and as the bird leans far forward, in running, the legs seem set too far behind and it looks as if it were about to fall over. The tail is very short and slender and is elevated at an angle of 45°.

When feeding or resting in the short grass the bird will hold its position until almost trodden upon and then dart away in its characteristic erratic, twisting flight, apparently turning on one side or the other like a Snipe. After a short flight it drops back to the ground. During the nesting season both parents and young will perch on the bushes or weed tops and the former will utter their insect-like buzzing song from such positions. While singing the body is scarcely raised but the head is thrown back a little as the song is uttered. One individual, singing from a telegraph wire, where it could be seen more clearly, threw back its head and simultaneously spread its tail, the feathers standing out like a semicircle of bristles which closed as soon as the song ended.

The most characteristic markings of the Grasshopper Sparrow are the "strings" of round black spots on the wing-coverts, the yellow on the bend of the wing, the plain unspotted buff breast and the pale pinkish feet. The young with their spotted breasts look quite different but they have the same top-heavy build, and the black spots on the coverts.

The nest is placed in a shallow depression in the ground alongside a tussock of grass and is often so arched over that it is impossible to see into it from above. From observations of Richard Miller, Turner McMullen and myself I have prepared the following summary of nests:

> May 20, one nest of four eggs.
> May 22, one nest of four eggs.
> May 30, four of four eggs and two of five.
> June 17, 20, 21, one set of four each.
> June 29 and July 10, one set of five each.

Nests with young were found on June 8 (five young) and July 19 (four young). Young birds are on the wing by June 18 and 30 in different years while the juvenal plumage is retained until August 5.

First observations in spring are April 29, 1923; May 9, 1924; May 10, 1929; but judging from the nest data most of these must be late.

Last dates for autumn are: September 16, 1921; October 21, 1923; October 2, 1924; October 5, 1929; September 28, 1930.

In build and habits the Grasshopper Sparrow can be compared only with Henslow's but the chestnut tints on the back and the streaked breast of the adults of the latter will distinguish it.

Through most of the state it is a regular summer resident in open country.

PLATE 119

*W. L. Baily*

*W. L. Baily*

1. YOUNG HENSLOW'S SPARROW, JUNE 16, 1900.
2. CHIPPING SPARROW FEEDING YOUNG.

# HENSLOW'S SPARROW

Passerherbulus henslowi susurrans Brewster

PLATE 119, p. 902

Henslow's Sparrow is a common summer resident of the Cape May Peninsula but distinctly local in its distribution and sometimes associates in little colonies. Old fields overgrown with patches of bayberry, brambles and wild rose, interspersed with little moist or boggy spots, and reaching down to the edge of the salt marshes are the home of Henslow's Sparrow—that region where upland and meadow meet. The Fill also offered attractive quarters before the bushes grew so tall. The range of the bird, however, is not entirely coastwise as it is found in similar spots far inland.

If we stop for a moment on the edge of one of these boggy spots that the Henslow's frequents we shall hear immediately the explosive ventriloquial note of the bird and scanning the field we shall see him perched on the top of some dead weed stalk standing perhaps a foot above the surrounding grass and sedge or on some briar twig. If approached he will fly to another similar perch, for he has several regular singing stands, and as long as we are in the vicinity he will continue to move from one to another. The female seems rarely to flush unless we almost tread upon her and this trait helps to make the nest so difficult to find.  The young, when first on the wing, may roost in the lower branches of some nearby bush but once the nesting season is past Henslow's Sparrow becomes exclusively a ground bird but does not move far from its breeding spot.  As we cross the field we may flush them repeatedly but they fly only a few yards and plunge back into the grass.  They apparently run a few steps after alighting, as they never arise from the spot where we expect them to be, and after a while they may fail to flush at all and run like mice through the tufts of grass until a safe shelter is found where they crouch until danger is past, and our best efforts fail to dislodge them.

Henslow's Sparrow presents a peculiar appearance but is in many respects an exaggerated Grasshopper Sparrow.  The bill is very heavy and the head large in proportion to the body which tapers rapidly to a slender wisp of a tail.  As the bird perches, hunched up, perhaps, on the top of a wild carrot plant, he appears to be all head and neck but when excited the tail is cocked up at an angle and there is a nervous twitch of both body and wings.  As he flies with his short rapidly pulsating wings the tail is all but lost sight of and he looks decidedly bobtailed.  When seen in good light, the rich mahogany brown tints of the back contrasted with the olive of the head and the minute streaking of the sides of the breast, distinguish the Henslow's from any other of our sparrows; but color aside, its peculiar build, its perch on the weed stalks and its never to be forgotten note will always identify it.

The note of the Henslow's Sparrow has been variously transcribed but after long and careful study of the Cape May birds the syllables *chís-eck* seem to my ear best to describe it.  The accent is surely on the first syllable although there is not really much question of accent about it as the two syllables often almost run together into a single—*chisk*.  Only once have I seen a female perch out in the open.  She took up a position near a singing male and uttered a weak almost inaudible *tick, tick*, evidently an alarm note.  Her life seems to be spent almost entirely on the ground.  Conrad Roland has frequently heard the note of the Henslow's Sparrow at night.

The young are strikingly different in color from the adults having plain yellow buff breasts with no trace of streaks, but there is the same top heavy appearance as if the bird had run entirely to neck and head.  I have found them barely able to fly, in fields by the old Race Track Pond, on June 8, 1919, while they were still in the juvenal plumage as late as July 20.  Two nests found by Turner McMullen on May 30, contained newly hatched young.

Nests with three or four eggs have been found at Cape May on May 22, May 24, May 30 and one on July 7, and at Ocean View on June 7 and 17.

Our earliest spring records for the bird at Cape May have been:

April 24, 1921.                  April 24, 1926.
April 29, 1923.                  April 24, 1927.

and Richard Miller found it at Pennsville on April 17. Our latest Cape May dates are September 16, 1921; October 1, 1923; September 28, 1924; October 7, 1928.

This interesting little bird entirely escaped the notice of Alexander Wilson nor did Audubon know it from New Jersey except for the information given him by James Trudeau and Edward Harris who obtained a specimen as early as 1838. The next definite record of the occurrence of the bird in New Jersey was of specimens obtained on Seven Mile Beach in June 1875 by John McIlvain, a notable Philadelphia collector of early days (Atlantic Slope Naturalist, I, p. 79). Harry G. Parker records a nest on this same beach on May 27, 1885 (O. and O., XI, p. 140) while Sylvester D. Judd secured a young bird at Boonton, Morris County (Auk, 1897, p. 326). Frank L. Burns found a nest on Peck's Beach on May 30, 1895 (Auk, 1895, p. 189) and W. E. D. Scott obtained several specimens near Princeton prior to 1900, while Thurber (1887) recorded it as a local summer resident at Morristown. Waldron Miller found Henslow's Sparrow breeding in the mountains north of Plainfield and located colonies at various locations in the Passaic Valley, Great Swamp etc. in the same vicinity. A specimen had been obtained by Dr. Amos P. Brown at Point Pleasant on August 16, 1886. I visited the spot with Dr. William E. Hughes on May 30, 1895, and we found quite a colony although we failed to locate a nest. Subsequently Samuel Rhoads and I found a colony near Bayside; Stewardson Brown at Forked River; and William Baily at Ocean View, while I detected a few in a bog at Lindenwold, Camden County. Of course they may have increased very much in later years but I am inclined to think that they have always been in these haunts as their secretive nature would make it very easy to overlook them and ornithological knowledge of southern New Jersey land birds was never very extensive until comparatively recent times.

Samuel Rhoads has published an excellent history of the Henslow's Sparrow in New Jersey, in "Cassinia" for 1902, pp. 6–14.

Later nests have been found at Marlton (Carter); Millville (Hunt), and New Lisbon (Stuart) etc.

## SHARP-TAILED SPARROW

*Ammospiza caudacuta caudacuta* (Gmelin)

This bird like the Seaside Sparrow is entirely limited to the salt meadows and has suffered the same restriction in range immediately about
Cape May through the influence of man.  I found it quite as abundant as
the other species in 1891, nesting in the same areas south of the town and
about Cape Island Sound and on the meadows above and below the Harbor.
I have been able to detect little if any difference in the habits of the two
species except that the Sharp-tail seems to prefer the rather dryer spots,
where the grass is shorter, while the Seaside frequents the taller vegetation
along the tide-water creeks, although both nest in areas of short grass.

The Sharp-tail perches on the grass stems with its head protruding just
as does the other species and runs rapidly through the grass cover with
neck extended and head held low while it has the same heavy flight for short
distances.  Its song is much less powerful than that of the Seaside Sparrow
and does not carry well nor does the bird seem to sing so frequently and is
rarely heard after the first of July.  A late singer heard early in the morning
just back of the town on July 7, 1923, had four notes in its song: *chuck, char-
éee-zik*.  The first separated by a short interval and the accent on the third.
Julian Potter who has given the species much study describes the note as a
faint wheezy ditty scarcely audible at fifteen yards, suggestive of the song
of the Grasshopper Sparrow but of much less volume.

When in good light the Sharp-tail is a handsome bird and very different
from the somber gray Seaside.  It has the usual white underparts of most
sparrows with dusky streaks while the upper parts have a yellow brown

( 906 )

tone with a bright orange yellow patch on the side of the head. The young of the year are entirely different being suffused with ruddy buff above and below, the back striped with brown, and the breast plain.

There seems to be an influx of migrants in the autumn and on September 3, 1925, I counted upwards of one hundred on the edge of the meadows opposite Bennett. On the meadows back of Atlantic City in 1894 and 1895 I found the growth of tall grass and sedges along the salt creeks simply swarming with Sharp-tailed and Seaside Sparrows which the boatmen of the sounds used to refer to indiscriminately as "meadow wrens" and were disgusted that anyone should regard them as game when they found us collecting some specimens! The Seasides of these assemblages were doubtless mainly of local origin as the New Jersey coast is close to the northern range of the species but many of the Sharp-tails probably came from farther north as they range up along the coast of New England. Turner McMullen and Richard Miller have furnished me with many records of nests of the Sharp-tailed Sparrow and I have found a number myself. Four eggs seem to form the regular set and nests with full complements have been examined on:

| | | |
|---|---|---|
| May 22, one. | June 18, one. | June 29, one. |
| May 26, two. | June 20, two. | July 3, one. |
| May 30, one. | June 22, two. | July 4, one. |
| June 2, two. | June 25, one. | July 15, one. |
| June 4, one. | June 26, one. | July 19, one. |
| June 12, three. | June 28, one. | |

Three sets of five were found on May 30, June 10 and June 24.

Sets of three were found from June 9 to July 22, most of them doubtless incomplete.

Young birds were found in nests on June 2, 4, 10, 15, 17, 22, July 1 and 11 while they have been seen on the wing by July 1.

I have few records of the spring arrival of the Sharp-tails at Cape May but have found them present in small numbers on March 31, 1921, and April 11, 1926. In the autumn, last dates of observation are September 5, 1921; October 21, 1923; September 28, 1924; October 18, 1925; October 25, 1929; October 12, 1932.

Single birds have been seen on January 13, 1924; January 25, 1925; January 23, 1927; while the Christmas census shows:

| | |
|---|---|
| December 28, 1921, one. | December 26, 1932, two. |
| December 24, 1922, three. | December 24, 1933, seven. |
| December 23, 1923, one. | December 23, 1934, fifteen. |
| December 22, 1929, one. | December 22, 1935, eight. |
| December 28, 1930, two. | December 27, 1936, fourteen. |
| December 27, 1931, two. | |

## ACADIAN SPARROW

Ammospiza caudacuta subvirgata (Dwight)

In the large flocks of Sharp-tailed Sparrows that occur late in summer or early autumn, specimens of the smaller Acadian Sharp-tail which breeds in Nova Scotia are to be found every year. They are grayer and duller in color than the native race and lack the white streaks on the back.

Specimens have been taken as follows:

Atlantic City meadows, October 1 and 2, 1892, four (I. N. DeHaven and W. Stone).
Atlantic City meadows, October 21, 1894, I. N. DeHaven.
Point Pleasant, May 30, 1895, W. L. Baily.

They have been recorded in Essex and Hudson Counties (Eaton) and in Union County (Urner).

I have seen them at South Cape May on several occasions in October.

## * NELSON'S SPARROW

Ammospiza caudacuta nelsoni (Allen)

Nelson's Sharp-tail is a fresh water race which breeds in the upper Mississippi Valley and on rare occasions individuals are to be found in the mixed Sharp-tail flocks on the Atlantic coast. While I have never detected this bird at Cape May it must occur there as Norris DeHaven and I have taken specimens at Atlantic City as follows:

Atlantic City meadows, October 2, 1892, three, I. N. DeHaven and W. Stone.
Atlantic City meadows, October 21, 1894, I. N. DeHaven.
Atlantic City meadows, September 27 1896, W. Stone.
Atlantic City meadows, May 9, 1892, I. N. DeHaven.

Charles Urner records one on the marshes of Union County.

## SEASIDE SPARROW

*Ammospiza maritima maritima* (Wilson)

The Seaside and Sharp-tailed Sparrows are the only breeding land birds peculiar to the maritime environment and both are absolutely restricted to the salt meadows where they are regular summer residents, and where a few individuals usually manage to remain throughout the winter. Up to 1890, when I first visited Cape May, and for some years later, the Seaside Sparrow bred abundantly on the meadows between Cape May and the Lighthouse as well as on the more extensive meadows surrounding Cape Island Sound, the body of water that later disappeared when the great Fill was created. This operation drove practically all of the sparrows from the latter area although for a few years several persisted in marshy spots that developed temporarily on the filled-in land. Then began the draining and "development" of the marshes to the west until today not a single pair of Seaside Sparrows is left of the thousands that once nested about Cape May, except a few pairs immediately behind the golf links along Cape Island Creek, and with draining activities started there, during 1936, they too will probably be doomed. The same thing has been going on all along the coast until this species, the Sharp-tail and the Marsh Wrens are actually threatened with extinction so far at least, as most of the New Jersey coast, is concerned.

The Seaside Sparrows perch on the tops of marsh elder bushes, or more frequently, on the stems of the grass and rushes, grasping them low down so that most of the bird is concealed by the surrounding vegetation, and all that we see is the head stretched upward to get a view of the surroundings. When perched among the grass a bird will often grasp a different stem with each foot and as they sway apart in the wind its legs are drawn out almost at right angles to the body. When resting on a more substantial perch the slender tail is often held parallel to the ground, otherwise it hangs vertically.

When the male sings the head is thrown well back and the bill pointed upward and the harsh explosive note *che-zheéeege* bursts forth—after which the bird drops back into its normal position.   This song coming often from a dozen different throats at once is one of the most characteristic sounds of the marsh.   There is also, of course, the clapper of the Mud Hens, heard mainly at dusk or at night, the whistle of the Fish Hawk, and the cry of the Common Tern, but the two latter belong more properly to the mainland and to the strand respectively, but the humble efforts of the Seaside Sparrow we hear on all sides and all day long at the proper season, and more than all the others it is to me the voice of the marsh.   I have recorded it at different times as: *che-zhée; che-wéege; chur-zhée;* and *too-szhéee*, the first syllable is short and the other long drawn and accented.   One bird that I studied for twenty minutes, very close at hand, seemed to have a very short preliminary note, which may be characteristic of all the songs, and a curious sound— *let, let, let*, like water breaking through a pipe as the air escapes, which was uttered simultaneously with the last long note and gave the impression that it came from some entirely different source.   The bird really seemed to be producing two sounds at once.   In its entirety this performance might be written *e-dulllt-tzéeee, let, let, let*.   Sometimes a male will mount a few feet into the air and give utterance to a slightly more complicated flight song dropping down again as the spluttering vocal effort is completed.   As we gaze over the meadows we can see the dark heads of the birds stretched up from the grass on every side, while later in the season, when the southward migration is about to start, they concentrate in the taller growth of sedge along the tidewater creeks.   The ordinary flight of the Seaside Sparrow strikes one as laborious, the impression being of a heavy body that is being dragged along, while the rapid wing beating seems necessary to keep it afloat.   The body really is heavy and the short and rounded wings seem not to be built for a long flight so that the bird usually makes only short efforts, low over the tops of the grass, and drops back quickly into shelter. It seems strange that a bird that makes no further attempts at flight during the entire summer will, when the proper time arrives, launch forth on the long journey to its winter quarters many miles to the south.

While making but little show in the air the Seaside Sparrow is very much at home on the muddy bottom of the marsh and its large feet are well adapted for running over the soft ooze while they, as well as the short tail, shape of the body, and somewhat elongated bill, all recall the structure of the rails, which are co-tenants of the meadows.   The Seaside Sparrow can run very swiftly, threading its way in and out among the coarse stalks of the Spartina grass that grows along the edges of the creeks.   As it runs the legs seem rather long and the body is held well up from the ground while the tail is always pointed downward.   Occasionally we see it slow down and pick at food on the edge of the water.

As we look at the perching Seaside it appears very dark, almost black, indeed, and stands forth very clearly.   This is due largely to counter shading produced by the uniform darkness of the under surface; for in white-bellied birds the light on the dark upper surface and the shadow on the white under parts equalize each other and the bird appears unicolor and is not conspicuous. When we are reasonably close to one of the birds in full nuptial plumage we can see the light loral spot and the gray streaks on the lighter gray breast, while the white throat is often quite conspicuous. The wearing effect of the constant contact with the harsh grass stems is very pronounced and by August most of the birds are almost uniform sooty gray. The new autumn plumage shows richer tones and more olive on the back.

The totally different young birds, with brown backs and streaked breasts, somewhat resembling young Song Sparrows appear on the wing by early July and parents were seen feeding them on July 14, 1920, and August 18, 1924, although the latter date was very unusual and was probably due to a delayed nesting.

Richard Miller and Turner McMullen have given me data on a number of nests of this species which were all built in the grass either on the ground or over shallow water at an elevation of from three to eight inches. The normal number of eggs is four but one nest found on May 26, contained five and some of those holding three were apparently complete sets. Sets of four were found as follows:

| | | |
|---|---|---|
| May 18, one. | June 17, one. | June 28, two. |
| May 30, two. | June 18, two. | June 30, one. |
| May 31, one. | June 19, one. | July 1, one. |
| June 2, three. | June 20, two. | July 2, two. |
| June 7, three. | June 21, five. | July 3, one. |
| June 9, two. | June 22, one. | July 4, one. |
| June 11, two. | June 23, two. | July 5, one. |
| June 12, ten. | June 24, six. | July 15, one. |
| June 16, five. | June 26, two. | July 19, one. |
| | June 27, one. | |

Sets of three were found from May 30 to July 22, many doubtless incomplete but no less than six were observed on the last date. A second nest found on the early date of May 18 held two eggs. Young birds were found in nests on May 26, June 7, 8, 11, 12, 14, 17, 24, 26, July 2 and 4.

I have no satisfactory data on the arrival dates of the Seaside Sparrow at Cape May in spring but they are established there by early May and doubtless by late April. In the autumn we have recorded them as late as October 7, 1923; October 25, 1929; October 19, 1931 and 1934; while birds seen on November 9, 1930, and November 21, 1926, may have been wintering individuals; as was one observed on January 23, 1927. William Baily who found the bird on Five Mile Beach on February 22, 1892, was the first to establish the species as a winter resident. The counts on the Christmas census follow:

December 26, 1927, one.           December 26, 1932, six.
December 23, 1928, three.         December 24, 1933, eleven.
December 22, 1929, two.           December 22, 1935, two.
December 27, 1931, three.         December 27, 1936, three.

The Seaside Sparrow was discovered and named by Alexander Wilson who, however, termed it a finch and not a sparrow, and probably got his specimens near where Ocean City now stands about 1810. He writes of it as follows:

"It inhabits the low, rush covered sea islands along our Atlantic coast, where I first found it; keeping almost continually within the boundaries of tide water, except when long and violent east or northeasterly storms, with high tides, compel it to seek the shore. On these occasions it courses along the margin, and among the holes and interstices of the weeds and sea wrack, with a rapidity equalled only by the nimblest of our Sandpipers, and very much in their manner. At these times also it roosts on the ground, and runs about after dusk.

"Amidst the recesses of these wet sea marshes it seeks the rankest growth of grass, and sea weed, and climbs along the stalks of the rushes with as much dexterity as it runs along the ground, which is rather a singular circumstance, most of our climbers being rather awkward at running." (American Ornithology, Vol. IV, p. 68.)

## VESPER SPARROW

Pooecetes gramineus gramineus (Gmelin)

The Vesper Sparrow is a regular but not very abundant transient, more plentiful in autumn than in spring, while a few remain throughout the winter. We have no records during the breeding season and no evidence of its nesting in the county but that it does nest sporadically not very far to the north of Cape May is suggested by the following observations. One was heard on May 30, 1925, near Cold Spring by Julian Potter; another was seen by William Yoder near Cape May on July 18, 1926; and several on the meadow below Higbee's Beach on August 12, 1932, by James Bond and Conrad Roland. At Ocean View one was seen by Eliot Underdown on May 20, 1928, and another by myself on July 27, 1932, while Fletcher Street saw one near Goshen station on June 7, 1936. It is a common summer resident of west Jersey as far south as Vineland, Bridgeton and Franklinville (Potter).

Vesper Sparrows occur during migration in open areas about the Lighthouse and elsewhere at the Point; in old fields along the railroad back of the town and at Cold Spring and Higbee's Beach. On April 4, 1924, moreover, I found a spring flock feeding among the dune grass in front of Congress Hall Hotel.

When flushed these sparrows will usually alight in a tree or bush where they are easily studied. The most striking characteristics are the prominent line of black spots on the wing coverts and the clear cut line separating the streaked breast from the white abdomen, all the streaks stopping at the same point and not running farther back on the sides as in the Song Sparrow. Then there is the chestnut on the bend of the wing and white on the outer tail feathers; although this last, is considered the best field mark, it is not always so easily seen as might be supposed unless the bird is below our line of vision and flying away from us.

Our records of autumn arrival are:

| | | |
|---|---|---|
| 1921. October 30. | 1924. October 19. | 1929. October 25. |
| 1922. October 22. | 1925. October 15. | 1930. October 12. |
| 1923. October 21. | 1928. October 13. | 1932. October 12. |

Last dates in spring are: April 4, 1924; March 21, 1925; March 18, 1933. Midwinter records are as follows, mainly from the Christmas census:

| | |
|---|---|
| February 22, 1923, five. | December 26, 1932, three. |
| December 23, 1923, two. | December 24, 1933, three. |
| December 26, 1927, one. | December 23, 1934, four. |
| December 28, 1930, seven. | December 22, 1935, twenty-one. |
| February 6, 1932, twelve. | |

I first determined the Vesper Sparrow to be a winter resident at the Cape on January 27, 1892, when I found a flock of twenty in a field close to the town.

North of the Pine Barrens the Vesper Sparrow is a regular summer resident and has been found occasionally in winter as far north as Princeton (January 21, 1879, Scott), Haddonfield (December 29, 1880, Rhoads), etc.

## LARK SPARROW

Chondestes grammacus grammacus (Say)

This western bird was first detected in Cape May County by Brooke Worth who found one in the hotel yard at Avalon on Seven Mile Beach, on August 21, 1927, and studied it with a glass for some time at a distance of fifteen feet. On September 10, following, I flushed an unfamiliar sparrow from the roadside near the Lighthouse at the Point and as it alighted on a wire and later on a fence post I had ample opportunity to study it at short range. I recognized it at once as a Lark Sparrow. The head markings were rather indistinct but distinguishable with the glass as was the rounded shape of the tail and the white edgings to all the rectrices but the middle pair. The back reminded one of that of a female English Sparrow the rump and lower back were plain brownish ash, breast pale gray with a central black spot. The feathers of the crown appeared to be slightly raised. After a short time the bird plunged again into the thicket and could not be flushed. Julian Potter and I saw another at the same place on August 15, 1937. On May 12, 1935, Victor Debes saw a Lark Sparrow on the Bay side of the peninsula near Price's Pond.

Daniel Lehrman reported one at Brigantine farther north on August 15, 1935. The first New Jersey specimen was taken by Dr. Frank M. Chapman at Schraalenburg, in the extreme northeastern corner of the state on November 26, 1885. There is a record for Essex County, September 19, 1934 (Eaton) and one for Union County, October 28, 1928 (Urner).

## SLATE-COLORED JUNCO

### Junco hyemalis hyemalis (Linnaeus)

A common winter visitant throughout the peninsula occurring somewhat irregularly in the town itself and frequent at the Point and along the coast and marshes from there to Cape May. "Snowbirds" as they are usually termed, here, always occur in flocks, sometimes by themselves, sometimes mingled with the various winter sparrows and often drifting about with flights of Myrtle Warblers in windy weather and in snow flurries. Like the Tree Sparrows they are essentially ground birds and only fly up into the trees when disturbed. Their slaty blue plumage and white outer tail feathers make them conspicuous and easily recognized, and they are therefore better known to the residents of the Cape than are any of the other sparrows.

On December 12, 1920, I watched a large flock of Juncos feeding in the open pine woods of the Point. While I remained perfectly still they hopped close around me, picking up food from the ground among the grass and dead plant stems, causing a rustling among the fallen leaves and a constant movement of the tops of the dead vegetation all about. Upon the first alarm they swarmed up into the trees and I presently saw several of them hopping out along the pine branches and pecking at the cone clusters. There are days during the southward migration when they are particularly abundant and on November 7, 1931, I counted two hundred at the Point while all along the stretch of Seven Mile Beach they fairly swarmed.

The earliest autumn records that we have are:

| | | | | | |
|---|---|---|---|---|---|
| 1921. | October 30. | 1927. | October 10. | 1932. | September 30. |
| 1922. | November 12. | 1928. | September 30. | 1933. | October 28. |
| 1923. | October 1. | 1929. | October 5. | 1934. | September 28. |
| 1924. | October 19. | 1930. | September 25. | 1935. | October 12. |
| 1925. | September 29. | 1931. | October 19. | | |

In spring we have recorded them as late as:

| | | | | | |
|---|---|---|---|---|---|
| 1922. | April 2. | 1928. | April 1. | 1933. | April 1. |
| 1923. | March 25. | 1929. | April 7. | 1934. | March 25. |
| 1924. | April 20. | 1930. | April 12. | 1935. | March 23. |
| 1926. | April 24. | 1932. | March 26. | | |

Mid-winter counts on the Christmas census are as follows:

December 24, 1922, twenty.
December 23, 1923, twenty-three.
December 26, 1926, eleven.
December 26, 1927, forty.
December 23, 1928, 412.
December 22, 1929, fifty.
December 28, 1930, 170.

December 27, 1931, 112.
December 26, 1932, 120.
December 24, 1933, 366.
December 23, 1934, 256.
December 22, 1935, 463.
December 27, 1936, fifty-six.

The Junco does not nest in New Jersey but is everywhere a winter visitant.

## TREE SPARROW

Spizella arborea arborea (Wilson)

The Tree Sparrow is a common winter visitant along wood edges, fence rows and swampy thickets in the Cape region and to the north, but not in the town itself, as it is distinctly a bird of the open and not of the gardens or door yards. It is frequent on the Fill and in thickets along the edge of the meadows back of Cape May, and north of Schellenger's Landing. The Tree Sparrow is found in flocks all winter long and sometimes as many as two hundred may be found together. It forms the bulk of most of the mixed sparrow flocks of winter but is as frequent in flocks of its own. I have found Field, Song, Swamp, Savannah and Chipping Sparrows mingling with the Tree Sparrows in the winter assemblages along with White-throats, Juncos, Myrtle Warblers and an occasional Cardinal or Bluebird.

We usually come upon flocks of Tree Sparrows feeding on the ground and they fly up into the bushes or trees as we approach dropping back again when assured that danger has passed. This habit was the basis for the name of Tree Sparrow given to them by Alexander Wilson. As they perch they give a nervous flirt to the tail and the neck is craned up with the feathers of the crown slightly elevated. Other individuals settle themselves in a hunched attitude with all the plumage fluffed up. The prominent wing bars, chestnut crown and black breast spot, and the yellow under mandible, are their most striking field marks.

We have records of Tree Sparrows in autumn as early as:

1921.  November 11.
1926.  November 21.

1928.  October 28.
1929.  November 16.

1931.  November 28.
1934.  November 25.

Our latest spring dates are:

1924.  April 2.
1932.  March 26.

1934.  March 11.
1931.  March 15.

Some doubtless remain every year until early April.

The Christmas census gives some idea of the numbers in the Cape May area in midwinter:

December 29, 1921, six.
December 24, 1922, twenty.
December 23, 1923, fifty-four.
December 26, 1927, 110.
December 23, 1928, 165.
December 22, 1929, 300.
December 28, 1930, 135.

December 27, 1931, eighty-five.
December 26, 1932, 120.
December 24, 1933, 360.
December 23, 1934, 256.
December 22, 1935, 463.
December 27, 1936, 153.

Elsewhere in the state the Tree Sparrow, as in Cape May, is a regular winter visitant.

## CHIPPING SPARROW

Spizella passerina passerina (Bechstein)

PLATE 119, p. 902

The "Chippy" is a common summer resident in the open farming country north of the town; every year there is a pair or two about the home of Otway Brown at Cold Spring, feeding on the lawn and nesting in the shrubbery or in the apple trees in the orchard, and the same is true at every farm house or country residence in the peninsula. The Chippies range south as far as the turnpike to the Point, and a few pairs nest about the houses at the Point itself, but strangely enough on only three occasions has a pair bred in Cape May although one would suppose that the shady lawns with gardens and abundant shrubbery would furnish ideal quarters for them.

In the summer of 1921 a pair bred on Lafayette Street near Queen and on July 9 an adult was feeding a full-fledged young in our garden nearby, on July 2 the birds were seen pairing so that they probably raised two broods. No others were seen in the town in summer until 1932 when a pair nested in a yard on Washington and were seen feeding young on July 1. Another pair was seen in July 1937. Occasional transients have been noted in the Physick garden and elsewhere in spring and fall but they passed on at once.

When Five Mile was a "wild beach," back in the eighties, Philip Laurent found Chipping Sparrows nesting in the numerous cedar trees.

Richard Miller has examined a nest at Mayville which contained three eggs on May 25, and another at the Court House with four eggs on May 21 while one at Cape May Point held half grown young on June 8. The last nest was on the branch of a pine tree twenty-one feet up, the others in cedars five and six feet from the ground.

Walker Hand has recorded the arrival of Chipping Sparrows in the country north of the town from March 9 to April 8, with an average of March 21, and I have seen them at Cape May or the Point on:

1921. April 3.
1922. April 2.

1924. April 2.
1925. March 22.
1928. April 1.

1932. March 26.
1933. April 1.

Our latest dates for southbound migrants have been:

| | | | |
|---|---|---|---|
| 1921. | October 30. | 1928. October 27. | 1933. October 28. |
| 1924. | October 2. | 1929. October 25. | 1930. November 9. |
| 1923. | October 18. | 1932. October 12. | 1931. November 7. |

The striped-breasted young are on the wing as early as June 8 and are seen frequently during July and early August. By this time the Chippies have gathered in flocks and mingled with the Field Sparrows along the brushy fence rows, but while most of them pass on to the south some remain every winter in the mixed sparrow flocks about the Cape as well as in gardens and door yards at Cold Spring.

We have the following Christmas census and other winter records:

| | |
|---|---|
| December 24, 1922, one. | December 22, 1929, two. |
| December 28, 1924, one. | December 28, 1930, seven. |
| February 21, 1926, one. | February 1, 1931, one. |
| December 26, 1926, one. | February 6, 1932, one. |
| December 26, 1927, six. | December 22, 1935, seven. |
| | December 27, 1936, one. |

The Chipping Sparrow is a common summer resident throughout the state.

## *CLAY-COLORED SPARROW

### Spizella pallida (Swainson)

While there is no record of the occurrence of this western bird at Cape May, Charles Urner and James Edwards saw one below Beach Haven on May 8, 1932, and, as it has occurred in New England and in Florida, there is always a possibility of its presence here.

The Beach Haven bird was recognized by both observers as something with which they were unfamiliar. They immediately noted that it was unstreaked below but with a definite dark wash on the sides of the breast, a medial line through the darker crown and a white line over the eye. The upper parts showed little if any rufous and were finely striated with dusky and creamy buff, the general effect was a rather light-colored bird.

A Field Sparrow, to which species it is most closely related, was near where this bird was feeding and offered an opportunity for comparison (cf. Auk, 1932, p. 491).

## FIELD SPARROW

### Spizella pusilla pusilla (Wilson)

PLATE 117, p. 855

A common and universally distributed summer resident species through-out the dry sandy fields and thickets of the interior down to the very edge of the salt meadows, the numerous bramble-covered stretches on neglected farms being ideal cover for them. Immediately about Cape May one finds them along the railroads and highways while they approach the outskirts of the town at Schellenger's Landing and along the south side of Broadway. When we walk down the beach Field Sparrows are encountered as soon as one reaches the Lighthouse and they are common all over the Point in the pine and oak scrub. For some reason they never adapted themselves to the Fill as did the Song and Grasshopper Sparrows but, taking all things into consideration, I am inclined to think that the Field Sparrow out-numbers the Song Sparrow in the Cape May Peninsula and is probably our most adundant sparrow.

The Field Sparrow's song is heard on every side in spring and early sum-mer at the Point and from the roadsides and fence rows of the open country. As it sounds to me it may be expressed in three double and one single notes and a final trill *sée-o, sée-o, sée-o, see-sesesesesesesese* although when very close there seems to be a slight preliminary unaccented note so that the first note above might be written *se-sée-o* on other occasions I have recorded it as *fée-o, fée-o, fée-o, trrrrrrr*, the fourth note being absorbed in the trill, and again, there have been four notes all on the same pitch followed by the trill *chíp, chíp, chíp chíp, trrrrrrrrr* or the four have seemed very slightly broken, approaching the first form, *féu, féu, féu, féu, feffffffffffffff*. The trill is always ascending and gradually wears out as it were. I have heard the song as late as August 7, 9, 11, 18, 20 and 28 in different years but the birds are usually silent after August 1; and they have been heard singing in spring by March 13.

From the records of Richard Miller and Turner McMullen I have compiled the following data on nesting. Four eggs are the usual complement and nests with that number have been found on:

| | | |
|---|---|---|
| May 16. | May 24. | May 27 |
| May 22, three. | May 25. | May 30. |
| May 23, two. | May 26. | |

One nest with five eggs was found on May 21 and sets of three, often doubtless incomplete, on:

| | | |
|---|---|---|
| May 17 | May 22, three. | June 3, three. |
| May 20, two. | May 30. | |

Nests with young were examined on May 20, 22, 23 and 29.

I have recorded what appeared to be arrivals of Field Sparrows from farther south on:

| | | |
|---|---|---|
| 1921. April 3. | 1924. April 2. | 1929. March 31. |
| 1922. April 2. | 1925. March 22. | 1930. April 6. |
| 1923. March 25. | 1928. April 1. | 1933. April 1. |

The Field Sparrow is regularly present in winter in varying numbers. Sometimes it is in little flocks of its own but is more often found joining forces with the composite sparrow flocks which one finds feeding on the ground in the winter sunshine, in the lee of some wood edge or fence row, and which may contain Juncos and Cardinals and a few Bluebirds as well as the somber colored sparrows. It is therefore difficult to determine when the migrant Field Sparrows leave but the following dates seem to mark the last of the transient flocks:

| | | |
|---|---|---|
| 1921. November 21. | 1929. November 17. | 1933. October 28. |
| 1922. November 12. | 1931. November 7. | |
| 1927. October 30. | 1932. November 12. | |

The numbers of wintering individuals is well shown by the Christmas census of the Delaware Valley Club.

| | |
|---|---|
| December 30, 1922, twenty. | December 28, 1930, ten. |
| December 22, 1923, thirty-five. | December 27, 1931, twenty. |
| December 26, 1926, twenty-six. | December 24, 1933, twenty-three. |
| December 26, 1927, six. | December 23, 1934, twenty-four. |
| December 23, 1928, fourteen. | December 22, 1935, fifty-four. |
| December 26, 1929, twelve. | December 27, 1936, twenty-eight. |

Elsewhere in New Jersey the Field Sparrow is a common summer resident and individuals have been seen in winter in many localities.

## WHITE-CROWNED SPARROW

### Zonotrichia leucophrys leucophrys (Forster)

A rather rare transient seen more frequently in autumn. While adult males have been seen in spring most of our autumnal records are birds of the year in their olive gray plumage strongly contrasting with the rusty tints of the Song Sparrows with which they have been found feeding. The sides of the neck appear quite gray and there is narrow streaking on the saddle of the back; the tail appears long and the bill quite pink and small in proportion to the size of the bird. I have watched them feeding on the ground at the Point, where most of our observations have been made. They scratch vigorously and can run rapidly.

Our records are as follows:

Autumn:

1923. September 30.
1924. October 2, several, nineteen.
1928. October 13, two; 15, two; 21, two; 28.
1929. October 13, two.

1930. October 11, two.
1931. October 18.
1932. October 8; 12, four.
1935. October 27.

Spring:

1924. May 10, two.

1933. May 7, 14.

In other parts of the state the White-crowned Sparrow is a rather uncommon transient.

## WHITE-THROATED SPARROW

### Zonotrichia albicollis (Gmelin)

This large plump sparrow is a regular winter visitant to the Cape region and a more abundant transient in autumn. Small flocks take up their residence in dense greenbrier thickets along the wood edges, old brush heaps in orchards and gardens, or other similar shelters, even in the town itself; and while they may venture out into open ground to feed they do not stray far from their favorite retreats into which they fly at the first approach of danger. Usually there are not more than six to twenty in these winter resident flocks but in the migrations they throng the thickets and woods, although their numbers vary from day to day. On October 10–11, 1927, they were to be seen everywhere on the Bay shore but on October 16, following, none could be found.

The brilliant coloration of the old males with their black heads, and conspicuous white crown stripes is in strong contrast to the duller females and young males and has caused more than one novice to take them for the

White-crowned Sparrow, but the white throat in distinct contrast to the gray breast will always identify them as will the yellow spot before the eye.

Our earliest autumn dates are:

| | | | | | |
|---|---|---|---|---|---|
| 1923. | October 1. | 1926. | September 27. | 1931. | September 26. |
| 1924. | October 2. | 1929. | October 4. | 1932. | September 25. |
| 1925. | September 22. | 1930. | September 28. | 1935. | September 29. |

Latest spring dates of observation are:

| | | | | | |
|---|---|---|---|---|---|
| 1917. | May 20. | 1927. | April 30. | 1932. | May 7. |
| 1924. | May 10. | 1928. | May 14. | 1933. | May 6. |
| 1926. | May 2. | 1931. | May 10. | 1934. | May 5. |

Numbers counted on the Christmas census are:

| | |
|---|---|
| December 22, 1923, ten. | December 27, 1931, fifty-seven. |
| December 26, 1926, twenty-four. | December 26, 1932, seventy-five. |
| December 26, 1927, 100. | December 24, 1933, 174. |
| December 23, 1928, 255. | December 23, 1934, 105. |
| December 22, 1929, fifty. | December 22, 1935, 870. |
| December 28, 1930, eighty-four. | December 27, 1936, ninety-three. |

The White-throat is a common transient throughout the state wintering more or less frequently especially in the southern half. One was heard in song on July 7, 1935, in the Secancus Swamp, Hudson Co. (Eaton).

## FOX SPARROW

**Passerella iliaca iliaca** (Merrem)

This, the largest of our sparrows, seems to be a regular transient in March and November while a varying number remain through the winter. The migratory flight would seem to pass quickly and in some years, at least, is very heavy and concentrated immediately along the shore. In the vicinity of West Creek, Ocean County, farther up the coast I have found them fairly swarming in early March, 1906, when every thicket seemed full of them and they alighted all over fences, chicken houses and elsewhere along the roads. I have never had the opportunity to see such a flight at Cape May but others have found them abundant on November 16–17, 1929, and at other times.

Our records for Cape May are as follows:

Autumn:

| | | | |
|---|---|---|---|
| 1921. | November 6, eleven. | 1929. | November 16–17, abundant. |
| 1922. | November 12. | 1931. | November 7, several. |
| 1923. | December 2, five. | 1932. | November 13, ten. |
| 1926. | November 21, twenty. | 1933. | October 21, six. |

Spring:

| | | | |
|---|---|---|---|
| 1924. | March 19, six; April 3, three. | 1931. | March 15. |
| 1928. | March 25, two. | 1932. | March 5, two; 25, |
| 1930. | March 22, six. | 1934. | March 11. |

The counts of the Christmas census show how many of these birds remain through the winter:

| | |
|---|---|
| December 11, 1921, two. | December 27, 1931, thirty-nine. |
| December 30, 1922, six. | December 26, 1932, nineteen. |
| December 26, 1927, twelve. | December 24, 1933, fifteen. |
| December 23, 1928, twenty-one. | December 23, 1934, ten. |
| December 22, 1929, nine. | December 22, 1935, forty. |
| December 28, 1930, thirty-three. | |

We have also records for January 14, 1923 (one) and January 25, 1925 (four).

I have seen Fox Sparrows several times in gardens along Washington Street where they seem to enjoy digging in the flower beds, jumping several inches in the air and scratching with both feet at once among the dead leaves like the Towhee. Like the White-throat the Fox Sparrow seems to spend most of the time of his winter sojourn in some favorite thicket and does not wander far afield.

Elsewhere in the state it is a common transient wintering in small numbers at least as far north as Princeton.

## LINCOLN'S SPARROW

### Melospiza lincolni lincolni (Audubon)

We have but one record of this rare sparrow in the Cape May district, a single bird found at the Point by Julian Potter and Conrad Roland, on October 12, 1932, on the lawn at the Lighthouse where it was studied for some time.

Lester Walsh found another at Seaside Park on the upper part of the coast on September 12, 1926, which, so far as I am aware, is the only other record for the coastal region. It would seem probable that this and many other "inland" species cross the state north of the Pine Barrens in a south-westerly direction and proceed south along the Delaware Valley.

Lincoln's Sparrow is a rare transient in New Jersey. Specimens have been taken at Princeton on October 25, 1875; September 21, 1878; and October 7, 1879, (Scott) and May 8, 1894 (Phillips), and it has been seen several times in the northern counties.

## SWAMP SPARROW

### Melospiza georgiana (Latham)

A regular transient, most plentiful in autumn, while some remain through the winter. It is an inhabitant of swampy spots where there is a shelter of sedges or low bushes, but during large flights it may be found in almost any situation. Such flights were observed on October 1, 1923; October 18, 1925;

September 27, 1926; October 4, 1929; October 12, 1932; and doubtless in other years as well had I been present at the time. On January 28–29, 1892, Samuel Rhoads and I found the meadows back of South Cape May simply swarming with Swamp Sparrows during a spell of very severe weather but I have not seen such an assemblage in winter again. Sometimes, however, a few individuals will be found in the mixed sparrow flocks of midwinter when they gather on moist ground.

We often see Swamp Sparrows in growths of tall reeds along some pond where they hold to the upright stalks and often flirt their wings and tail like a wren. At nesting time they are as characteristic of fresh water marshes or swamps as are the Seaside and Sharp-tailed Sparrows of the salt meadows and consequently are not found summering at Cape May. On the marshes of the Delaware, however, for some distance south of Philadelphia they breed commonly and Turner McMullen has examined nests at Marshalltown in Salem County; one on May 15, 1921, with two eggs; one on May 29 of the same year with four; and two on June 3, 1922, containing five and four eggs.

Our dates of observation in the Cape May area are as follows. In autumn:

| | | | |
|---|---|---|---|
| 1921. | October 16–November 11. | 1928. | September 30–October 21. |
| 1922. | November 26. | 1929. | September 21–October 25. |
| 1923. | September 30–November 11. | 1930. | October 5–November 9. |
| 1924. | October 2–19. | 1931. | October 18–November 7. |
| 1925. | September 23–October 18. | 1932. | September 25–November 13. |
| 1926. | September 27–November 21. | 1933. | October 28. |
| 1927. | September 25–October 23. | 1935. | October 5–November 3. |

In spring:

| | | | |
|---|---|---|---|
| 1921. | April 3. | 1929. | May 11–12, March 31. |
| 1924. | March 20–May 10. | 1930. | April 6. |
| 1926. | April 24–May 1. | 1931. | March 14. |
| 1927. | May 8. | 1932. | April 30–May 7. |
| 1928. | May 13–14, April 8. | 1933. | May 6. |

The counts of the Christmas census are:

| | |
|---|---|
| December 23, 1923, four. | December 26, 1932, seven. |
| December 26, 1927, four. | December 24, 1933, fourteen. |
| December 23, 1928, three. | December 23, 1934, twenty-four. |
| December 28, 1930, ten. | December 22, 1935, forty-four. |
| December 27, 1931, six. | December 27, 1936, three. |

Elsewhere in the state the Swamp Sparrow is a summer resident in suitable localities.

## EASTERN SONG SPARROW

### Melospiza melodia melodia (Wilson)

The Song Sparrow may be regarded as a regular resident about Cape May but whether the birds that we find in winter are the same as our summer breeding birds is open to question. There is a pronounced migration in autumn and in early spring when more Song Sparrows are in evidence than at any other time, and the summer population is greater than that of winter. But while the Song Sparrow may be the most generally distributed sparrow of summer it is doubtful it if exceeds the Field Sparrow in actual number of individuals.

It is an inhabitant of thickets all along the coast where it may be heard in song from mid-March to August; also in the gardens of the town and all about Cape May Point where moist thickets are to be found. Farther back in the country it is found everywhere in similar situations and, while not a woodland bird, may be found in shrubbery along the wood edges. In winter it collects in flocks, often associating with other sparrows, and seems to desert its ocean front habitats for less exposed shelters farther inland.

The relatively long tail of the Song Sparrow and its jerky "broken-backed" flight, as if the tail were hinged at the base, serve to distinguish it from our other sparrows, while the song is, of course, always characteristic and renders it familiar to many who do not trouble to study its markings.

In late March and April the air seems simply filled with Song Sparrow song and at this time we see male birds flying from bush to bush with neck stretched out, head and tail held high, and wings vibrating rapidly. This seems to be a part of the courtship display and as soon as the bird alights it bursts into song. On March 21, 1925, and April 2, 1914, I have noted this performance and the birds were evidently paired although at the same time there were flocks of migrant Song Sparrows present nearby. I have heard the song as late as August 10 and 21 in different years. Richard Miller and Turner McMullen have furnished me with data on the nesting of the Song Sparrow in the Cape May area upon which the following summary is based.

Nests with five eggs have been found on May 15, one; 23, one; 30, one; June 17, one. Four eggs: May 20, two; 21, one; 23, one; 26, three; 30, two; June 25, one. Three eggs: May 14, one; 18, two; July 5, one; 15, one. Young birds were found in the nest on May 10, 25, 30, June 6 and 7. Full grown young in juvenal plumage have been recorded on June 28, July 7 and 10 in different years.

The curious variation in the day by day numbers of the Song Sparrow is noticeable in autumn as in other species, due to the irregularity of the migratory flights or "waves" at the Point. On October 5, 1929, they were estimated to be present by the hundred while on the 13th, only two could be found. On October 13, 1928, I found but six while on the 15th and 21st they were abundant, but on the 27th only two could be found.

While we see Song Sparrows most frequently in their passage from one bush to another or perched conspicuously as they sing, or later when they protest our approach to nest or young, they spend much time when undisturbed feeding on the ground and it is there that we see them in winter and realize how well adapted they are for a terrestrial life and how rapidly they can run, mouse-like, through the grass.

With Song Sparrows present in varying numbers in every month of the year it is useless to try to designate dates of arrival and departure. The counts of the Christmas census will show the numbers present in mid-winter:

December 30, 1922, two.
December 23, 1923, four.
December 26, 1927, 100.
December 23, 1928, sixty-two.
December 22, 1929, forty-two.
December 28, 1930, forty.

December 27, 1931, forty-five.
December 26, 1932, thirty-two.
December 24, 1933, 172.
December 23, 1934, 108.
December 22, 1935, 446.
December 27, 1936, seventy-three.

The Song Sparrow is a common resident throughout the state.

## ATLANTIC SONG SPARROW

Melospiza melodia atlantica Todd

The study of the Song Sparrow at the Cape is further complicated by the fact that we have two races of the bird present as breeders, the only case of the sort in the bird life of New Jersey. In the interior is found the Eastern Song Sparrow, the same form that occurs all over the Eastern States but on the coast islands, and possibly the inner edge of the salt meadows as well, lives the larger, grayer Atlantic Song Sparrow, recognizably different when series of specimens are compared but not distinguishable in life, nor can the eggs be differentiated. This form would seem to be permanently resident while the bird of the interior is migratory and to the latter belong the migrant host that comes through in the autumn. Winter Song Sparrows naturally include both races as well as intermediates between the two, from areas where upland and meadow meet. To illustrate how environment affects the distribution of these birds it may be mentioned that a series of breeding Song Sparrows collected in 1891 on the edge of the old Cape Island Sound and on the salt meadows that formerly existed southwest of Cape May are all typical of the Atlantic Song Sparrow with its grayer coloration and much heavier bill. Since the Fill was formed and the meadows replaced by dry ground with thickets of bayberry, etc., the common Eastern Song Sparrows of the interior have spread out and occupied the area. Earl Poole's drawings of the two races show very clearly the difference in the size of the bill.

I have secured specimens from as far north as Atlantic City.

Nests supposed, from locality, to belong to this race are reported by Richard Miller and Turner McMullen: from Seven Mile Beach:

May 14, 1827, three eggs.
May 18, 1924, two with three eggs.
May 20, 1922, two with four eggs.
May 21, 1922, one with four eggs.
May 23, 1926, one with four eggs.

June 6, 1926, one with four young.
June 7, 1925, one with four eggs.
May 22, 1932, two with four eggs.
June 16, 1935, one with young.

## LAPLAND LONGSPUR

### Calcarius lapponicus lapponicus (Linnaeus)

An irregular winter visitant to the coasts of southern New Jersey, where a few might be seen every winter were competent observers present continuously. I first saw them on the strand of Seven Mile Beach on November 28, 1926, when in company with Richard Erskine. There were three of them in a flock of Horned Larks which seem to be their usual associates. They ran or walked like the Larks and were similar in all of their actions but easily recognized by their darker coloration and chunkier build. Against the light they looked quite black as compared with the grayer hue of the other birds, while in good view the chestnut tints of the back and the black of the breast could easily be seen with the glass. Once recognized, the Longspurs could readily be picked out whenever the flock took wing and settled again. On December 26, 1932, Joseph Tatum saw four Longspurs on the open sand flat on the southern part of Five Mile Beach.

On Brigantine Beach farther up the coast they seem to be of more frequent occurrence or else the bird watchers have given more attention to the spot. On December 26, 1930, Stuart Cramer saw twelve with twenty-five Horned Larks and Donald Carter found four present on February 15, following. On February 22, 1935, Joseph Tatum found a flock of thirty and on March 24 of the same year Julian Potter found the same flock some of them in song, "a medley of tinkling, sputtering notes recalling the Bobolink's song." It seems probable that in both these seasons the birds were winter residents there.

Elsewhere in the state it seems to be a rare winter visitant except on the salt meadows where it is more regular and more plentiful. Specimens have been taken at Princeton, February 13, 1895 (Phillips), Washington Park on the Delaware, February 14, 1895 (Reiff), Salem, December 28, 1898 (Warrington) and in Union County where Charles Urner has found it present on the meadows in five out of the seven years, 1921–1927, extreme dates being November 14 and March 22.

Across the river in Delaware Charles Pennock and I have found Longspurs on several occasions at Delaware City associated with Horned Larks on the marshes in midwinter.

## SNOW BUNTING

### Plectrophenax nivalis nivalis (Linnaeus)

An irregular winter visitant along the coast occurring on the sand dunes and upper beach or on the sand flats and marshes behind them.

Spencer Trotter and I came upon a pair on the dunes below South Cape May on December 30, 1922. They ran over the sand with head erect and jumped up at the seeds of the dune grass. When flushed they flew in long undulating sweeps showing to perfection the contrasting black and white of the plumage, the two colors being in approximately equal proportions.

The female was browner but the amount of white in flight was about the same. There were chains of delicate footprints in the sand where the birds had been feeding and the marks of the long hind claw were very evident.

The next day William Yoder and Henry Gaede saw a flock of fifty near the same spot while I saw a single female on December 26, 1929. Prior to these observations Julian Potter saw four at Cape May on December 18, 1921; and a flock of fifty on January 19, 1919, while he saw two flocks totalling twenty-eight birds on Seven Mile Beach on January 23, 1927 and Conrad Roland found them abundant there on February 16. He also saw them with Potter on January 19, 1919, and wrote me that their note was a trilled whistle and that on the ground they resembled rats as they crept along but "in flight they seemed to forget their terrestrial affinities and to impersonate the spirit of the wind their movements resembling wave crests although they seemed to ricochet rather than proceed in undulations. They had an erratic, lark-like habit of taking flight, not from alarm, but apparently to regale themselves by flying in the face of the unspeakably cold winds and frequently returned to the very spot from which they started."

The counts on the Christmas census of the Delaware Valley Club are as follow:

| | |
|---|---|
| December 23, 1928, one. | December 23, 1934, eighteen. |
| December 22, 1929, three. | December 22, 1935, one. |
| December 26, 1932, fifty-one. | December 27, 1936, six. |
| December 24, 1933, one. | |

Charles Page saw two at Cape May Point on November 27, 1922, and William Rusling one on November 6, 1935, two on the 10th and one on the 11th while Dr. Henry Wharton found them on the Salem marshes on the Bay side as early as November 7, 1919 and Richard Bender found a flock of thirty at Fortesque on December 7, 1930.

A favorite resort of late years has been the broad sand flats of Wildwood Crest (formerly Two Mile Beach) where 450 were seen on February 22, 1930, and seventy-five on December 2, 1933, by members of the Delaware Valley Club.

Farther north on the coast Julian Potter found a few at Corson's Inlet as late as March 12, 1922, and also on November 18, 1923. On Brigantine Clifford Marburger found a flock of seventy-five on November 15 and December 20, 1925, while Potter found fifty still there on February 22, following, which would indicate that the birds were winter residents there. Brooke Worth found a flock of twenty-nine at Brigantine in a blinding snow storm on February 21, 1929. They seem to be more abundant and regular on Barnegat Bay and John Emlen has found them there as early as November 2, 1923. On January 5, 1935, Arthur H. Howell, who had visited Ocean City, Maryland, on the day before, wrote me that he had seen great flocks of Snow Buntings flying north along the coast and wondered if the flight had been noticed at Cape May. Unfortunately none of our observers had been at the

Cape at the time and I could get no information from residents. It is of course possible that the Snow Buntings travel over the sea from Brigantine to the Delaware or Maryland coast, passing by the retreating shore line of the Cape May Peninsula which has been suggested in the case of several of the water birds.

Elsewhere in the state the Snow Bunting occurs as an irregular winter visitant. Large flocks were observed about Princeton in the winter of 1895–1896 and it has been recorded at various other localities, but it seems to be much more plentiful and regular in its occurrence on the shore and in Union County Charles Urner states that it occurs every year, his extreme dates being November 6 and March 18.

H. B.

# BIBLIOGRAPHY

A reasonably complete bibliography of books, magazine articles and short notes dealing with the ornithology of New Jersey from 1753 to 1909 was published in the author's "The Birds of New Jersey" (Ann. Rept. N. J. State Museum for 1908), while lists of later publications on the subject will be found in the several issues of "Cassinia" (Proc. Delaware Valley Ornithological Club) for subsequent years.

It seems unnecessary to republish this matter in the present volume and it is the intention to present below only such leading works on the subject as have been frequently quoted in the preceding pages and the journals upon which we have depended for local records.

ALEXANDER WILSON. American Ornithology, Vols. I–IX. Philadelphia, 1808–1814.
> This is the original edition of this classic work, the first publication to present an account of the bird life of the New Jersey coast. The author died before the work was completed and his young friend, George Ord, later president of the Academy of Natural Sciences of Philadelphia, superintended the publication of the last two volumes from Wilson's notes. (Cf. p. 29.)

GEORGE ORD. American Ornithology, Vols. I–IX. Philadelphia, 1808–1825 (= 1824–1825).
> This is the Ord reprint of Wilson's work. Vols. I–VI follow the original very closely and retain the original dates of publication. Vols. VII–IX, which contain most of the matter relating to the birds of the coast, were carefully revised by Ord and much original material incorporated. Vols. I to VIII were issued in 1824 and Vol. IX in 1825.
>
> Curiously enough the great works of Bonaparte, Audubon and Nuttall added very little to our knowledge of the birds of the New Jersey coast nor have any of the numerous sportsmen who later frequented the region left any record of the bird life. The next work dealing with coastal birds is the following:

J. P. GIRAUD. The Birds of Long Island. New York, 1844.
> Contains casual mention of New Jersey birds.

THOMAS BEESLEY. Catalogue of the Birds of the County of Cape May. (Appendix to "The Geology of the County of Cape May, N. J.," by William Kitchell.)
> A briefly annotated list of 196 species on pp. 138–145. The author was evidently personally acquainted only with the commoner species and records many birds as breeders in the county which do not even breed in the state. In the chapter of the work dealing with the history of Cape May by Dr. Maurice Beesley, there are several interesting references to birds observed by the early explorers.

CHARLES C. ABBOTT. Catalogue of the Vertebrate Animals of New Jersey. (In Cook's "Geology of New Jersey," App. E., pp. 751–830.) Trenton, 1868.
> Like the preceding author, Dr. Abbott has recorded many species as breeders in the state which occur only as migrants. In later publications (Amer. Nat., IV, 1870, pp. 536–550; and "A Naturalist's Rambles about Home," 1884), he

endeavors to substantiate some of these statements but presents no satisfactory data while he corrects or contradicts other statements.

WILLIAM P. TURNBULL. The Birds of East Pennsylvania and New Jersey. Philadelphia, 1869, pp. i–viii + 1–50.

An exceedingly accurate and painstaking list, the first reliable work to cover the region. We can only regret that he did not amplify his comments and present more individual records.

JOHN KRIDER. Forty Years Notes of a Field Ornithologist. Philadelphia, 1879, pp. [4] + xl + 84.

Had the author possessed more literary ability this could have been made a work of the greatest importance as he had wide experience, but it was compiled by another, apparently from the recollections by the famous gunsmith in his later years when his memory was fading, and it contains many obvious errors.

W. E. D. SCOTT. Notes on Birds Observed at Long Beach, New Jersey. *Bull. Nuttall Ornith. Club*, 1879, pp. 222–228.

This is a most important paper dealing exclusively with coastal New Jersey but at this date the abundant bird life of earlier times had suffered a great decrease from over-shooting and millinery collecting was at its height.

CHARLES S. SCHICK. Birds Found Breeding on Seven Mile Beach, New Jersey. *The Auk*, 1890, pp. 326–329.

An important picture of the bird life of this famous island before it had been ruined as a bird haven by draining and "developments." Unfortunately the paper was never finished. The author was primarily an egg collector and a few of his identifications may be open to question.

PHILIP LAURENT. Birds of Five Mile Beach, N. J. *Ornithologist and Oölogist*, 1892, pp. 43, 53, 88.

An excellent and thoroughly reliable account of the birds of this island at a time when most of it was a "wild beach." Mr. Laurent's collection is now in the Reading, Pa., Museum.

WITMER STONE. The Birds of Eastern Pennsylvania and New Jersey. Philadelphia, 1894. Pp. i–vi + 1–176.

A publication of the Delaware Valley Ornithological Club in which the attempt was made to bring our knowledge of the birds of the region up to date. Unfortunately the members of the Club had as a rule very little personal acquaintance with the birds of the coast at this time.

WITMER STONE. The Birds of New Jersey. (Annual Report of the New Jersey State Museum for 1908.) Trenton, 1909. Pp. 11–347.

Published, like the preceding, at a time when bird students were very few in New Jersey, especially along the coast, while modern methods of observation and transportation had not developed and information was lacking or difficult to obtain. Nevertheless it presents a fairly accurate summary of conditions as they were at the time.

GRISCOM, LUDLOW. Birds of the New York Region.

This work, like its predecessors by Dr. F. M. Chapman, 1894 and 1906, includes many records from New Jersey, mainly from the northern part of the coastal strip.

THE AUK. Organ of the American Ornithologists' Union. 1884–1937. A Quarterly Journal of Ornithology.

Many articles and short notes from this journal are quoted in the text almost always with direct reference.

BIRD-LORE. Organ of the National Association of Audubon Societies. New York. 1899–1937.

Most of our quotations from "Bird-Lore" are from the Philadelphia section of "The Season" compiled by Julian K. Potter and including records from the New Jersey coast; and from the Christmas Censuses. Most of these are observations of members of the Delaware Valley Ornithological Club and the Linnaean Society of New York.

CASSINIA. Proceedings of the Delaware Valley Ornithological Club. Philadelphia, 1891–1934.

Most of the records from "Cassinia" are from the annual migration records kept by members of the Club and others, covering southeastern Pennsylvania and southern New Jersey.

PROCEEDINGS OF THE LINNAEAN SOCIETY OF NEW YORK. 1889–1936.

Records quoted from this journal are mainly from the annual summary of observations for the New York region.

In No. 39–40 will be found Charles A. Urner's "Birds of Union County" and in No. 47 the late Warren F. Eaton's "Birds of Essex and Hudson Counties," excellent accounts of the bird-life of the extreme northern part of the coastal region of New Jersey.

---

Migration and occurrence records taken from these three journals are simply credited to the observer; in many cases they have been published in two journals; the place of publication if desired may readily be found by looking up the month in "Bird-Lore's" "The Season" or the yearly list in the other journals. Many records of this sort, however, are first published in the present volumes.

For information on the birds of the mountainous portion of the state one should consult:

WILLIAM L. BAILY. Breeding Birds of Passaic and Sussex Counties, N. J. *Cassinia*, 1909, pp. 29–36.

WALDRON DEW. MILLER. The Summer Birds of Northern New Jersey. *Natural History*, October, 1925, pp. 450–458.

# INDEX

[This comprehensive index covers both volumes of the work. Volume I contains pages 1 through 484 and Volume II contains pages 485 through 932.]

# CATALOGUE OF DOVER BOOKS

# Books Explaining Science and Mathematics

**WHAT IS SCIENCE?, N. Campbell.** The role of experiment and measurement, the function of mathematics, the nature of scientific laws, the difference between laws and theories, the limitations of science, and many similarly provocative topics are treated clearly and without technicalities by an eminent scientist. "Still an excellent introduction to scientific philosophy," H. Margenau in PHYSICS TODAY. "A first-rate primer . . . deserves a wide audience," SCIENTIFIC AMERICAN. 192pp. 5⅜ x 8.　　S43 Paperbound **$1.25**

**THE NATURE OF PHYSICAL THEORY, P. W. Bridgman.** A Nobel Laureate's clear, non-technical lectures on difficulties and paradoxes connected with frontier research on the physical sciences. Concerned with such central concepts as thought, logic, mathematics, relativity, probability, wave mechanics, etc. he analyzes the contributions of such men as Newton, Einstein, Bohr, Heisenberg, and many others. "Lucid and entertaining . . . recommended to anyone who wants to get some insight into current philosophies of science," THE NEW PHILOSOPHY. Index. xi + 138pp. 5⅜ x 8.　　S33 Paperbound **$1.25**

**EXPERIMENT AND THEORY IN PHYSICS, Max Born.** A Nobel Laureate examines the nature of experiment and theory in theoretical physics and analyzes the advances made by the great physicists of our day: Heisenberg, Einstein, Bohr, Planck, Dirac, and others. The actual process of creation is detailed step-by-step by one who participated. A fine examination of the scientific method at work. 44pp. 5⅜ x 8.　　S308 Paperbound **75¢**

**THE PSYCHOLOGY OF INVENTION IN THE MATHEMATICAL FIELD, J. Hadamard.** The reports of such men as Descartes, Pascal, Einstein, Poincaré, and others are considered in this investigation of the method of idea-creation in mathematics and other sciences and the thinking process in general. How do ideas originate? What is the role of the unconscious? What is Poincaré's forgetting hypothesis? are some of the fascinating questions treated. A penetrating analysis of Einstein's thought processes concludes the book. xiii + 145pp. 5⅜ x 8.　　T107 Paperbound **$1.25**

**THE NATURE OF LIGHT AND COLOUR IN THE OPEN AIR, M. Minnaert.** Why are shadows sometimes blue, sometimes green, or other colors depending on the light and surroundings? What causes mirages? Why do multiple suns and moons appear in the sky? Professor Minnaert explains these unusual phenomena and hundreds of others in simple, easy-to-understand terms based on optical laws and the properties of light and color. No mathematics is required but artists, scientists, students, and everyone fascinated by these "tricks" of nature will find thousands of useful and amazing pieces of information. Hundreds of observational experiments are suggested which require no special equipment. 200 illustrations; 42 photos. xvi + 362pp. 5⅜ x 8.　　T196 Paperbound **$2.00**

**THE UNIVERSE OF LIGHT, W. Bragg.** Sir William Bragg, Nobel Laureate and great modern physicist, is also well known for his powers of clear exposition. Here he analyzes all aspects of light for the layman: lenses, reflection, refraction, the optics of vision, x-rays, the photoelectric effect, etc. He tells you what causes the color of spectra, rainbows, and soap bubbles, how magic mirrors work, and much more. Dozens of simple experiments are described. Preface. Index. 199 line drawings and photographs, including 2 full-page color plates. x + 283pp. 5⅜ x 8.　　T538 Paperbound **$1.85**

**SOAP-BUBBLES: THEIR COLOURS AND THE FORCES THAT MOULD THEM, C. V. Boys.** For continuing popularity and validity as scientific primer, few books can match this volume of easily-followed experiments, explanations. Lucid exposition of complexities of liquid films, surface tension and related phenomena, bubbles' reaction to heat, motion, music, magnetic fields. Experiments with capillary attraction, soap bubbles on frames, composite bubbles, liquid cylinders and jets, bubbles other than soap, etc. Wonderful introduction to scientific method, natural laws that have many ramifications in areas of modern physics. Only complete edition in print. New Introduction by S. Z. Lewin, New York University. 83 illustrations; 1 full-page color plate. xii + 190pp. 5⅜ x 8½.　　T542 Paperbound **95¢**

**THE STORY OF X-RAYS FROM RONTGEN TO ISOTOPES, A. R. Bleich, M.D.** This book, by a member of the American College of Radiology, gives the scientific explanation of x-rays, their applications in medicine, industry and art, and their danger (and that of atmospheric radiation) to the individual and the species. You learn how radiation therapy is applied against cancer, how x-rays diagnose heart disease and other ailments, how they are used to examine mummies for information on diseases of early societies, and industrial materials for hidden weaknesses. 54 illustrations show x-rays of flowers, bones, stomach, gears with flaws, etc. 1st publication. Index. xix + 186pp. 5⅜ x 8. T622 Paperbound **$1.35**

**SPINNING TOPS AND GYROSCOPIC MOTION, John Perry.** A classic elementary text of the dynamics of rotation — the behavior and use of rotating bodies such as gyroscopes and tops. In simple, everyday English you are shown how quasi-rigidity is induced in discs of paper, smoke rings, chains, etc., by rapid motions; why a gyrostat falls and why a top rises; precession; how the earth's motion affects climate; and many other phenomena. Appendix on practical use of gyroscopes. 62 figures. 128pp. 5⅜ x 8. T416 Paperbound **$1.00**

**SNOW CRYSTALS, W. A. Bentley, M. J. Humphreys.** For almost 50 years W. A. Bentley photographed snow flakes in his laboratory in Jericho, Vermont; in 1931 the American Meteorological Society gathered together the best of his work, some 2400 photographs of snow flakes, plus a few ice flowers, windowpane frosts, dew, frozen rain, and other ice formations. Pictures were selected for beauty and scientific value. A very valuable work to anyone in meteorology, cryology; most interesting to layman; extremely useful for artist who wants beautiful, crystalline designs. All copyright free. Unabridged reprint of 1931 edition. 2453 illustrations. 227pp. 8 x 10½. T287 Paperbound **$3.00**

**A DOVER SCIENCE SAMPLER, edited by George Barkin.** A collection of brief, non-technical passages from 44 Dover Books Explaining Science for the enjoyment of the science-minded browser. Includes work of Bertrand Russell, Poincaré, Laplace, Max Born, Galileo, Newton; material on physics, mathematics, metallurgy, anatomy, astronomy, chemistry, etc. You will be fascinated by Martin Gardner's analysis of the sincere pseudo-scientist, Moritz's account of Newton's absentmindedness, Bernard's examples of human vivisection, etc. Illustrations from the Diderot Pictorial Encyclopedia and De Re Metallica. 64 pages. **FREE**

**THE STORY OF ATOMIC THEORY AND ATOMIC ENERGY, J. G. Feinberg.** A broader approach to subject of nuclear energy and its cultural implications than any other similar source. Very readable, informal, completely non-technical text. Begins with first atomic theory, 600 B.C. and carries you through the work of Mendelejeff, Röntgen, Madame Curie, to Einstein's equation and the A-bomb. New chapter goes through thermonuclear fission, binding energy, other events up to 1959. Radioactive decay and radiation hazards, future benefits, work of Bohr, moderns, hundreds more topics. "Deserves special mention . . . not only authoritative but thoroughly popular in the best sense of the word," Saturday Review. Formerly, "The Atom Story." Expanded with new chapter. Three appendixes. Index. 34 illustrations. vii + 243pp. 5⅜ x 8. T625 Paperbound **$1.60**

**THE STRANGE STORY OF THE QUANTUM, AN ACCOUNT FOR THE GENERAL READER OF THE GROWTH OF IDEAS UNDERLYING OUR PRESENT ATOMIC KNOWLEDGE, B. Hoffmann.** Presents lucidly and expertly, with barest amount of mathematics, the problems and theories which led to modern quantum physics. Dr. Hoffmann begins with the closing years of the 19th century, when certain trifling discrepancies were noticed, and with illuminating analogies and examples takes you through the brilliant concepts of Planck, Einstein, Pauli, Broglie, Bohr, Schroedinger, Heisenberg, Dirac, Sommerfeld, Feynman, etc. This edition includes a new, long postscript carrying the story through 1958. "Of the books attempting an account of the history and contents of our modern atomic physics which have come to my attention, this is the best," H. Margenau, Yale University, in "American Journal of Physics." 32 tables and line illustrations. Index. 275pp. 5⅜ x 8. T518 Paperbound **$1.50**

**SPACE AND TIME, E. Borel.** Written by a versatile mathematician of world renown with his customary lucidity and precision, this introduction to relativity for the layman presents scores of examples, analogies, and illustrations that open up new ways of thinking about space and time. It covers abstract geometry and geographical maps, continuity and topology, the propagation of light, the special theory of relativity, the general theory of relativity, theoretical researches, and much more. Mathematical notes. 2 Indexes. 4 Appendices. 15 figures. xvi + 243pp. 5⅜ x 8. T592 Paperbound **$1.45**

**FROM EUCLID TO EDDINGTON: A STUDY OF THE CONCEPTIONS OF THE EXTERNAL WORLD, Sir Edmund Whittaker.** A foremost British scientist traces the development of theories of natural philosophy from the western rediscovery of Euclid to Eddington, Einstein, Dirac, etc. The inadequacy of classical physics is contrasted with present day attempts to understand the physical world through relativity, non-Euclidean geometry, space curvature, wave mechanics, etc. 5 major divisions of examination: Space; Time and Movement; the Concepts of Classical Physics; the Concepts of Quantum Mechanics; the Eddington Universe. 212pp. 5⅜ x 8. T491 Paperbound **$1.35**

# Nature, Biology

**NATURE RECREATION: Group Guidance for the Out-of-doors, William Gould Vinal.** Intended for both the uninitiated nature instructor and the education student on the college level, this complete "how-to" program surveys the entire area of nature education for the young. Philosophy of nature recreation; requirements, responsibilities, important information for group leaders; nature games; suggested group projects; conducting meetings and getting discussions started; etc. Scores of immediately applicable teaching aids, plus completely updated sources of information, pamphlets, field guides, recordings, etc. Bibliography. 74 photographs. + 310pp. 5⅜ x 8½. **T1015 Paperbound $1.75**

**HOW TO KNOW THE WILD FLOWERS, Mrs. William Starr Dana.** Classic nature book that has introduced thousands to wonders of American wild flowers. Color-season principle of organization is easy to use, even by those with no botanical training, and the genial, refreshing discussions of history, folklore, uses of over 1,000 native and escape flowers, foliage plants are informative as well as fun to read. Over 170 full-page plates, collected from several editions, may be colored in to make permanent records of finds. Revised to conform with 1950 edition of Gray's Manual of Botany. xlii + 438pp. 5⅜ x 8½. **T332 Paperbound $2.00**

**HOW TO KNOW THE FERNS, F. T. Parsons.** Ferns, among our most lovely native plants, are all too little known. This classic of nature lore will enable the layman to identify almost any American fern he may come across. After an introduction on the structure and life of ferns, the 57 most important ferns are fully pictured and described (arranged upon a simple identification key). Index of Latin and English names. 61 illustrations and 42 full-page plates. xiv + 215pp. 5⅜ x 8. **T740 Paperbound $1.35**

**MANUAL OF THE TREES OF NORTH AMERICA, Charles Sprague Sargent.** Still unsurpassed as most comprehensive, reliable study of North American tree characteristics, precise locations and distribution. By dean of American dendrologists. Every tree native to U.S., Canada, Alaska, 185 genera, 717 species, described in detail—leaves, flowers, fruit, winterbuds, bark, wood, growth habits etc. plus discussion of varieties and local variants, immaturity variations. Over 100 keys, including unusual 11-page analytical key to genera, aid in identification. 783 clear illustrations of flowers, fruit, leaves. An unmatched permanent reference work for all nature lovers. Second enlarged (1926) edition. Synopsis of families. Analytical key to genera. Glossary of technical terms. Index. 783 illustrations, 1 map. Two volumes. Total of 982pp. 5⅜ x 8. **T277 Vol. I Paperbound $2.25**
**T278 Vol. II Paperbound $2.25**
**The set $4.50**

**TREES OF THE EASTERN AND CENTRAL UNITED STATES AND CANADA, W. M. Harlow.** A revised edition of a standard middle-level guide to native trees and important escapes. More than 140 trees are described in detail, and illustrated with more than 600 drawings and photographs. Supplementary keys will enable the careful reader to identify almost any tree he might encounter. xiii + 288pp. 5⅜ x 8. **T395 Paperbound $1.35**

**GUIDE TO SOUTHERN TREES, Ellwood S. Harrar and J. George Harrar.** All the essential information about trees indigenous to the South, in an extremely handy format. Introductory essay on methods of tree classification and study, nomenclature, chief divisions of Southern trees, etc. Approximately 100 keys and synopses allow for swift, accurate identification of trees. Numerous excellent illustrations, non-technical text make this a useful book for teachers of biology or natural science, nature lovers, amateur naturalists. Revised 1962 edition. Index. Bibliography. Glossary of technical terms. 920 illustrations; 201 full-page plates. ix + 709pp. 4⅝ x 6⅜. **T945 Paperbound $2.35**

**FRUIT KEY AND TWIG KEY TO TREES AND SHRUBS, W. M. Harlow.** Bound together in one volume for the first time, these handy and accurate keys to fruit and twig identification are the only guides of their sort with photographs (up to 3 times natural size). "Fruit Key": Key to over 120 different deciduous and evergreen fruits. 139 photographs and 11 line drawings. Synoptic summary of fruit types. Bibliography. 2 Indexes (common and scientific names). "Twig Key": Key to over 160 different twigs and buds. 173 photographs. Glossary of technical terms. Bibliography. 2 Indexes (common and scientific names). Two volumes bound as one. Total of xvii + 126pp. 5⅝ x 8⅜. **T511 Paperbound $1.25**

**INSECT LIFE AND INSECT NATURAL HISTORY, S. W. Frost.** A work emphasizing habits, social life, and ecological relations of insects, rather than more academic aspects of classification and morphology. Prof. Frost's enthusiasm and knowledge are everywhere evident as he discusses insect associations and specialized habits like leaf-rolling, leaf-mining, and case-making, the gall insects, the boring insects, aquatic insects, etc. He examines all sorts of matters not usually covered in general works, such as: insects as human food, insect music and musicians, insect response to electric and radio waves, use of insects in art and literature. The admirably executed purpose of this book, which covers the middle ground between elementary treatment and scholarly monographs, is to excite the reader to observe for himself. Over 700 illustrations. Extensive bibliography. x + 524pp. 5⅜ x 8. **T517 Paperbound $2.45**

**COMMON SPIDERS OF THE UNITED STATES, J. H. Emerton.** Here is a nature hobby you can pursue right in your own cellar! Only non-technical, but thorough, reliable guide to spiders for the layman. Over 200 spiders from all parts of the country, arranged by scientific classification, are identified by shape and color, number of eyes, habitat and range, habits, etc. Full text, 501 line drawings and photographs, and valuable introduction explain webs, poisons, threads, capturing and preserving spiders, etc. Index. New synoptic key by S. W. Frost. xxiv + 225pp. 5⅜ x 8. **T223 Paperbound $1.45**

**THE LIFE STORY OF THE FISH: HIS MANNERS AND MORALS, Brian Curtis.** A comprehensive, non-technical survey of just about everything worth knowing about fish. Written for the aquarist, the angler, and the layman with an inquisitive mind, the text covers such topics as evolution, external covering and protective coloration, physics and physiology of vision, maintenance of equilibrium, function of the lateral line canal for auditory and temperature senses, nervous system, function of the air bladder, reproductive system and methods—courtship, mating, spawning, care of young—and many more. Also sections on game fish, the problems of conservation and a fascinating chapter on fish curiosities. "Clear, simple language . . . excellent judgment in choice of subjects . . . delightful sense of humor," New York Times. Revised (1949) edition. Index. Bibliography of 72 items. 6 full-page photographic plates. xii + 284pp. 5⅜ x 8. **T929 Paperbound $1.65**

**BATS, Glover Morrill Allen.** The most comprehensive study of bats as a life-form by the world's foremost authority. A thorough summary of just about everything known about this fascinating and mysterious flying mammal, including its unique location sense, hibernation and cycles, its habitats and distribution, its wing structure and flying habits, and its relationship to man in the long history of folklore and superstition. Written on a middle-level, the book can be profitably studied by a trained zoologist and thoroughly enjoyed by the layman. "An absorbing text with excellent illustrations. Bats should have more friends and fewer thoughtless detractors as a result of the publication of this volume," William Beebe, Books. Extensive bibliography. 57 photographs and illustrations. x + 368pp. 5⅜ x 8½. **T984 Paperbound $2.00**

**BIRDS AND THEIR ATTRIBUTES, Glover Morrill Allen.** A fine general introduction to birds as living organisms, especially valuable because of emphasis on structure, physiology, habits, behavior. Discusses relationship of bird to man, early attempts at scientific ornithology, feathers and coloration, skeletal structure including bills, legs and feet, wings. Also food habits, evolution and present distribution, feeding and nest-building, still unsolved questions of migrations and location sense, many more similar topics. Final chapter on classification, nomenclature. A good popular-level summary for the biologist; a first-rate introduction for the layman. Reprint of 1925 edition. References and index. 51 illustrations. viii + 338pp. 5⅜ x 8½. **T957 Paperbound $1.85**

---

**LIFE HISTORIES OF NORTH AMERICAN BIRDS, Arthur Cleveland Bent.** Bent's monumental series of books on North American birds, prepared and published under auspices of Smithsonian Institute, is the definitive coverage of the subject, the most-used single source of information. Now the entire set is to be made available by Dover in inexpensive editions. This encyclopedic collection of detailed, specific observations utilizes reports of hundreds of contemporary observers, writings of such naturalists as Audubon, Burroughs, William Brewster, as well as author's own extensive investigations. Contains literally everything known about life history of each bird considered: nesting, eggs, plumage, distribution and migration, voice, enemies, courtship, etc. These not over-technical works are musts for ornithologists, conservationists, amateur naturalists, anyone seriously interested in American birds.

**BIRDS OF PREY.** More than 100 subspecies of hawks, falcons, eagles, buzzards, condors and owls, from the common barn owl to the extinct caracara of Guadaloupe Island. 400 photographs. Two volume set. Index for each volume. Bibliographies of 403, 520 items. 197 full-page plates. Total of 907pp. 5⅜ x 8½. Vol. I **T931** Paperbound **$2.50**
Vol. II **T932** Paperbound **$2.50**

**WILD FOWL.** Ducks, geese, swans, and tree ducks—73 different subspecies. Two volume set. Index for each volume. Bibliographies of 124, 144 items. 106 full-page plates. Total of 685pp. 5⅜ x 8½. Vol. I **T285** Paperbound **$2.50**
Vol. II **T286** Paperbound **$2.50**

**SHORE BIRDS.** 81 varieties (sandpipers, woodcocks, plovers, snipes, phalaropes, curlews, oyster catchers, etc.). More than 200 photographs of eggs, nesting sites, adult and young of important species. Two volume set. Index for each volume. Bibliographies of 261, 188 items. 121 full-page plates. Total of 860pp. 5⅜ x 8½. Vol. I **T933** Paperbound **$2.35**
Vol. II **T934** Paperbound **$2.35**

---

**THE LIFE OF PASTEUR, R. Vallery-Radot.** 13th edition of this definitive biography, cited in Encyclopaedia Britannica. Authoritative, scholarly, well-documented with contemporary quotes, observations; gives complete picture of Pasteur's personal life; especially thorough presentation of scientific activities with silkworms, fermentation, hydrophobia, inoculation, etc. Introduction by Sir William Osler. Index. 505pp. 5⅜ x 8. **T632 Paperbound $2.00**

# Puzzles, Mathematical Recreations

**SYMBOLIC LOGIC and THE GAME OF LOGIC, Lewis Carroll.** "Symbolic Logic" is not concerned with modern symbolic logic, but is instead a collection of over 380 problems posed with charm and imagination, using the syllogism, and a fascinating diagrammatic method of drawing conclusions. In "The Game of Logic" Carroll's whimsical imagination devises a logical game played with 2 diagrams and counters (included) to manipulate hundreds of tricky syllogisms. The final section, "Hit or Miss" is a lagniappe of 101 additional puzzles in the delightful Carroll manner. Until this reprint edition, both of these books were rarities costing up to $15 each. Symbolic Logic: Index. xxxi + 199pp. The Game of Logic: 96pp. 2 vols. bound as one. 5⅜ x 8. T492 Paperbound **$1.50**

**PILLOW PROBLEMS and A TANGLED TALE, Lewis Carroll.** One of the rarest of all Carroll's works, "Pillow Problems" contains 72 original math puzzles, all typically ingenious. Particularly fascinating are Carroll's answers which remain exactly as he thought them out, reflecting his actual mental process. The problems in "A Tangled Tale" are in story form, originally appearing as a monthly magazine serial. Carroll not only gives the solutions, but uses answers sent in by readers to discuss wrong approaches and misleading paths, and grades them for insight. Both of these books were rarities until this edition, "Pillow Problems" costing up to $25, and "A Tangled Tale" $15. Pillow Problems: Preface and Introduction by Lewis Carroll. xx + 109pp. A Tangled Tale: 6 illustrations. 152pp. Two vols. bound as one. 5⅜ x 8. T493 Paperbound **$1.50**

**AMUSEMENTS IN MATHEMATICS, Henry Ernest Dudeney.** The foremost British originator of mathematical puzzles is always intriguing, witty, and paradoxical in this classic, one of the largest collections of mathematical amusements. More than 430 puzzles, problems, and paradoxes. Mazes and games, problems on number manipulation, unicursal and other route problems, puzzles on measuring, weighing, packing, age, kinship, chessboards, joiners', crossing river, plane figure dissection, and many others. Solutions. More than 450 illustrations. vii + 258pp. 5⅜ x 8. T473 Paperbound **$1.25**

**THE CANTERBURY PUZZLES, Henry Dudeney.** Chaucer's pilgrims set one another problems in story form. Also Adventures of the Puzzle Club, the Strange Escape of the King's Jester, the Monks of Riddlewell, the Squire's Christmas Puzzle Party, and others. All puzzles are original, based on dissecting plane figures, arithmetic, algebra, elementary calculus and other branches of mathematics, and purely logical ingenuity. "The limit of ingenuity and intricacy," The Observer. Over 110 puzzles. Full Solutions. 150 illustrations. vii + 225pp. 5⅜ x 8. T474 Paperbound **$1.25**

**MATHEMATICAL EXCURSIONS, H. A. Merrill.** Even if you hardly remember your high school math, you'll enjoy the 90 stimulating problems contained in this book and you will come to understand a great many mathematical principles with surprisingly little effort. Many useful shortcuts and diversions not generally known are included: division by inspection, Russian peasant multiplication, memory systems for pi, building odd and even magic squares, square roots by geometry, dyadic systems, and many more. Solutions to difficult problems. 50 illustrations. 145pp. 5⅜ x 8. T350 Paperbound **$1.00**

**MAGIC SQUARES AND CUBES, W. S. Andrews.** Only book-length treatment in English, a thorough non-technical description and analysis. Here are nasik, overlapping, pandiagonal, serrated squares; magic circles, cubes, spheres, rhombuses. Try your hand at 4-dimensional magical figures! Much unusual folklore and tradition included. High school algebra is sufficient. 754 diagrams and illustrations. viii + 419pp. 5⅜ x 8. T658 Paperbound **$1.85**

**CALIBAN'S PROBLEM BOOK: MATHEMATICAL, INFERENTIAL AND CRYPTOGRAPHIC PUZZLES, H. Phillips (Caliban), S. T. Shovelton, G. S. Marshall.** 105 ingenious problems by the greatest living creator of puzzles based on logic and inference. Rigorous, modern, piquant; reflecting their author's unusual personality, these intermediate and advanced puzzles all involve the ability to reason clearly through complex situations; some call for mathematical knowledge, ranging from algebra to number theory. Solutions. xi + 180pp. 5⅜ x 8. T736 Paperbound **$1.25**

**MATHEMATICAL PUZZLES FOR BEGINNERS AND ENTHUSIASTS, G. Mott-Smith.** 188 mathematical puzzles based on algebra, dissection of plane figures, permutations, and probability, that will test and improve your powers of inference and interpretation. The Odic Force, The Spider's Cousin, Ellipse Drawing, theory and strategy of card and board games like tit-tat-tee, go moku, salvo, and many others. 100 pages of detailed mathematical explanations. Appendix of primes, square roots, etc. 135 illustrations. 2nd revised edition. 248pp. 5⅜ x 8. T198 Paperbound **$1.00**

**MATHEMAGIC, MAGIC PUZZLES, AND GAMES WITH NUMBERS, R. V. Heath.** More than 60 new puzzles and stunts based on the properties of numbers. Easy techniques for multiplying large numbers mentally, revealing hidden numbers magically, finding the date of any day in any year, and dozens more. Over 30 pages devoted to magic squares, triangles, cubes, circles, etc. Edited by J. S. Meyer. 76 illustrations. 128pp. 5⅜ x 8. T110 Paperbound **$1.00**

**THE BOOK OF MODERN PUZZLES, G. L. Kaufman.** A completely new series of puzzles as fascinating as crossword and deduction puzzles but based upon different principles and techniques. Simple 2-minute teasers, word labyrinths, design and pattern puzzles, logic and observation puzzles — over 150 braincrackers. Answers to all problems. 116 illustrations. 192pp. 5⅜ x 8.
T143 Paperbound **$1.00**

**NEW WORD PUZZLES, G. L. Kaufman.** 100 ENTIRELY NEW puzzles based on words and their combinations that will delight crossword puzzle, Scrabble and Jotto fans. Chess words, based on the moves of the chess king; design-onyms, symmetrical designs made of synonyms; rhymed double-crostics; syllable sentences; addle letter anagrams; alphagrams; linkograms; and many others all brand new. Full solutions. Space to work problems. 196 figures. vi + 122pp. 5⅜ x 8.
T344 Paperbound **$1.00**

**MAZES AND LABYRINTHS: A BOOK OF PUZZLES, W. Shepherd.** Mazes, formerly associated with mystery and ritual, are still among the most intriguing of intellectual puzzles. This is a novel and different collection of 50 amusements that embody the principle of the maze: mazes in the classical tradition; 3-dimensional, ribbon, and Möbius-strip mazes; hidden messages; spatial arrangements; etc.—almost all built on amusing story situations. 84 illustrations. Essay on maze psychology. Solutions. xv + 122pp. 5⅜ x 8.
T731 Paperbound **$1.00**

**MAGIC TRICKS & CARD TRICKS, W. Jonson.** Two books bound as one. 52 tricks with cards, 37 tricks with coins, bills, eggs, smoke, ribbons, slates, etc. Details on presentation, misdirection, and routining will help you master such famous tricks as the Changing Card, Card in the Pocket, Four Aces, Coin Through the Hand, Bill in the Egg, Afghan Bands, and over 75 others. If you follow the lucid exposition and key diagrams carefully, you will finish these two books with an astonishing mastery of magic. 106 figures. 224pp. 5⅜ x 8. T909 Paperbound **$1.00**

**PANORAMA OF MAGIC, Milbourne Christopher.** A profusely illustrated history of stage magic, a unique selection of prints and engravings from the author's private collection of magic memorabilia, the largest of its kind. Apparatus, stage settings and costumes; ingenious ads distributed by the performers and satiric broadsides passed around in the streets ridiculing pompous showmen; programs; decorative souvenirs. The lively text, by one of America's foremost professional magicians, is full of anecdotes about almost legendary wizards: Dede, the Egyptian; Philadelphia, the wonder-worker; Robert-Houdin, "the father of modern magic;" Harry Houdini; scores more. Altogether a pleasure package for anyone interested in magic, stage setting and design, ethnology, psychology, or simply in unusual people. A Dover original. 295 illustrations; 8 in full color. Index. viii + 216pp. 8⅜ x 11¼.
T774 Paperbound **$2.25**

**HOUDINI ON MAGIC, Harry Houdini.** One of the greatest magicians of modern times explains his most prized secrets. How locks are picked, with illustrated picks and skeleton keys; how a girl is sawed into twins; how to walk through a brick wall — Houdini's explanations of 44 stage tricks with many diagrams. Also included is a fascinating discussion of great magicians of the past and the story of his fight against fraudulent mediums and spiritualists. Edited by W.B. Gibson and M.N. Young. Bibliography. 155 figures, photos. xv + 280pp. 5⅜ x 8.
T384 Paperbound **$1.35**

**MATHEMATICS, MAGIC AND MYSTERY, Martin Gardner.** Why do card tricks work? How do magicians perform astonishing mathematical feats? How is stage mind-reading possible? This is the first book length study explaining the application of probability, set theory, theory of numbers, topology, etc., to achieve many startling tricks. Non-technical, accurate, detailed! 115 sections discuss tricks with cards, dice, coins, knots, geometrical vanishing illusions, how a Curry square "demonstrates" that the sum of the parts may be greater than the whole, and dozens of others. No sleight of hand necessary! 135 illustrations. xii + 174pp. 5⅜ x 8.
T335 Paperbound **$1.00**

**EASY-TO-DO ENTERTAINMENTS AND DIVERSIONS WITH COINS, CARDS, STRING, PAPER AND MATCHES, R. M. Abraham.** Over 300 tricks, games and puzzles will provide young readers with absorbing fun. Sections on card games; paper-folding; tricks with coins, matches and pieces of string; games for the agile; toy-making from common household objects; mathematical recreations; and 50 miscellaneous pastimes. Anyone in charge of groups of youngsters, including hard-pressed parents, and in need of suggestions on how to keep children sensibly amused and quietly content will find this book indispensable. Clear, simple text, copious number of delightful line drawings and illustrative diagrams. Originally titled "Winter Nights Entertainments." Introduction by Lord Baden Powell. 329 illustrations. v + 186pp. 5⅜ x 8½.
T921 Paperbound **$1.00**

**STRING FIGURES AND HOW TO MAKE THEM, Caroline Furness Jayne.** 107 string figures plus variations selected from the best primitive and modern examples developed by Navajo, Apache, pygmies of Africa, Eskimo, in Europe, Australia, China, etc. The most readily understandable, easy-to-follow book in English on perennially popular recreation. Crystal-clear exposition; step-by-step diagrams. Everyone from kindergarten children to adults looking for unusual diversion will be endlessly amused. Index. Bibliography. Introduction by A. C. Haddon. 17 full-page plates. 960 illustrations. xxiii + 401pp. 5⅜ x 8½.
T152 Paperbound **$2.00**

# Entertainments, Humor

**ODDITIES AND CURIOSITIES OF WORDS AND LITERATURE, C. Bombaugh, edited by M. Gardner.** The largest collection of idiosyncratic prose and poetry techniques in English, a legendary work in the curious and amusing bypaths of literary recreations and the play technique in literature—so important in modern works. Contains alphabetic poetry, acrostics, palindromes, scissors verse, centos, emblematic poetry, famous literary puns, hoaxes, notorious slips of the press, hilarious mistranslations, and much more. Revised and enlarged with modern material by Martin Gardner. 368pp. 5⅜ x 8.                          T759 Paperbound **$1.50**

**A NONSENSE ANTHOLOGY, collected by Carolyn Wells.** 245 of the best nonsense verses ever written, including nonsense puns, absurd arguments, mock epics and sagas, nonsense ballads, odes, "sick" verses, dog-Latin verses, French nonsense verses, songs. By Edward Lear, Lewis Carroll, Gelett Burgess, W. S. Gilbert, Hilaire Belloc, Peter Newell, Oliver Herford, etc., 83 writers in all plus over four score anonymous nonsense verses. A special section of limericks, plus famous nonsense such as Carroll's "Jabberwocky" and Lear's "The Jumblies" and much excellent verse virtually impossible to locate elsewhere. For 50 years considered the best anthology available. Index of first lines specially prepared for this edition. Introduction by Carolyn Wells. 3 indexes: Title, Author, First lines. xxxiii + 279pp.
                                                                           T499 Paperbound **$1.35**

**THE BAD CHILD'S BOOK OF BEASTS, MORE BEASTS FOR WORSE CHILDREN, and A MORAL ALPHA-BET, H. Belloc.** Hardly an anthology of humorous verse has appeared in the last 50 years without at least a couple of these famous nonsense verses. But one must see the entire volumes—with all the delightful original illustrations by Sir Basil Blackwood—to appreciate fully Belloc's charming and witty verses that play so subacidly on the platitudes of life and morals that beset his day—and ours. A great humor classic. Three books in one. Total of 157pp. 5⅜ x 8.                                                       T749 Paperbound **$1.00**

**THE DEVIL'S DICTIONARY, Ambrose Bierce.** Sardonic and irreverent barbs puncturing the pomposities and absurdities of American politics, business, religion, literature, and arts, by the country's greatest satirist in the classic tradition. Epigrammatic as Shaw, piercing as Swift, American as Mark Twain, Will Rogers, and Fred Allen, Bierce will always remain the favorite of a small coterie of enthusiasts, and of writers and speakers whom he supplies with "some of the most gorgeous witticisms of the English language" (H. L. Mencken). Over 1000 entries in alphabetical order. 144pp. 5⅜ x 8.                  T487 Paperbound **$1.00**

**THE PURPLE COW AND OTHER NONSENSE, Gelett Burgess.** The best of Burgess's early nonsense, selected from the first edition of the "Burgess Nonsense Book." Contains many of his most unusual and truly awe-inspiring pieces: 36 nonsense quatrains, the Poems of Patagonia, Alpha-bet of Famous Goops, and the other hilarious (and rare) adult nonsense that place him in the forefront of American humorists. All pieces are accompanied by the original Burgess illustra-tions. 123 illustrations. xiii + 113pp. 5⅜ x 8.                           T772 Paperbound **$1.00**

**MY PIOUS FRIENDS AND DRUNKEN COMPANIONS and MORE PIOUS FRIENDS AND DRUNKEN COMPANIONS, Frank Shay.** Folksingers, amateur and professional, and everyone who loves singing: here, available for the first time in 30 years, is this valued collection of 132 ballads, blues, vaudeville numbers, drinking songs, sea chanties, comedy songs. Songs of pre-Beatnik Bohemia; songs from all over America, England, France, Australia; the great songs of the Naughty Nineties and early twentieth-century America. Over a third with music. Woodcuts by John Held, Jr. convey perfectly the brash insouciance of an era of rollicking unabashed song. 12 illustrations by John Held, Jr. Two indexes (Titles and First lines and Choruses). Introductions by the author. Two volumes bound as one. Total of xvi + 235pp. 5⅜ x 8½.
                                                                           T946 Paperbound **$1.25**

**HOW TO TELL THE BIRDS FROM THE FLOWERS, R. W. Wood.** How not to confuse a carrot with a parrot, a grape with an ape, a puffin with nuffin. Delightful drawings, clever puns, absurd little poems point out far-fetched resemblances in nature. The author was a leading physicist. Introduction by Margaret Wood White. 106 illus. 60pp. 5⅜ x 8.
                                                                           T523 Paperbound **75¢**

**PECK'S BAD BOY AND HIS PA, George W. Peck.** The complete edition, containing both volumes, of one of the most widely read American humor books. The endless ingenious pranks played by bad boy "Hennery" on his pa and the grocery man, the outraged pomposity of Pa, the perpetual ridiculing of middle class institutions, are as entertaining today as they were in 1883. No pale sophistications or subtleties, but rather humor vigorous, raw, earthy, imaginative, and, as folk humor often is, sadistic. This peculiarly fascinating book is also valuable to historians and students of American culture as a portrait of an age. 100 original illustrations by True Williams. Introduction by E. F. Bleiler. 347pp. 5⅜ x 8.
                                                                           T497 Paperbound **$1.35**

**THE HUMOROUS VERSE OF LEWIS CARROLL.** Almost every poem Carroll ever wrote, the largest collection ever published, including much never published elsewhere: 150 parodies, burlesques, riddles, ballads, acrostics, etc., with 130 original illustrations by Tenniel, Carroll, and others. "Addicts will be grateful . . . there is nothing for the faithful to do but sit down and fall to the banquet," N. Y. Times. Index to first lines. xiv + 446pp. 5⅜ x 8.
T654 Paperbound **$2.00**

**DIVERSIONS AND DIGRESSIONS OF LEWIS CARROLL.** A major new treasure for Carroll fans! Rare privately published humor, fantasy, puzzles, and games by Carroll at his whimsical best, with a new vein of frank satire. Includes many new mathematical amusements and recreations, among them the fragmentary Part III of "Curiosa Mathematica." Contains "The Rectory Umbrella," "The New Belfry," "The Vision of the Three T's," and much more. New 32-page supplement of rare photographs taken by Carroll. x + 375pp. 5⅜ x 8.
T732 Paperbound **$1.65**

**THE COMPLETE NONSENSE OF EDWARD LEAR.** This is the only complete edition of this master of gentle madness available at a popular price. A BOOK OF NONSENSE, NONSENSE SONGS, MORE NONSENSE SONGS AND STORIES in their entirety with all the old favorites that have delighted children and adults for years. The Dong With A Luminous Nose, The Jumblies, The Owl and the Pussycat, and hundreds of other bits of wonderful nonsense. 214 limericks, 3 sets of Nonsense Botany, 5 Nonsense Alphabets, 546 drawings by Lear himself, and much more. 320pp. 5⅜ x 8.
T167 Paperbound **$1.00**

**THE MELANCHOLY LUTE, The Humorous Verse of Franklin P. Adams ("FPA").** The author's own selection of light verse, drawn from thirty years of FPA's column, "The Conning Tower," syndicated all over the English-speaking world. Witty, perceptive, literate, these ninety-six poems range from parodies of other poets, Millay, Longfellow, Edgar Guest, Kipling, Masefield, etc., and free and hilarious translations of Horace and other Latin poets, to satiric comments on fabled American institutions—the New York Subways, preposterous ads, suburbanites, sensational journalism, etc. They reveal with vigor and clarity the humor, integrity and restraint of a wise and gentle American satirist. Introduction by Robert Hutchinson. vi + 122pp. 5⅜ x 8½.
T108 Paperbound **$1.00**

**SINGULAR TRAVELS, CAMPAIGNS, AND ADVENTURES OF BARON MUNCHAUSEN, R. E. Raspe,** with 90 illustrations by Gustave Doré. The first edition in over 150 years to reestablish the deeds of the Prince of Liars exactly as Raspe first recorded them in 1785—the genuine Baron Munchausen, one of the most popular personalities in English literature. Included also are the best of the many sequels, written by other hands. Introduction on Raspe by J. Carswell. Bibliography of early editions. xliv + 192pp. 5⅜ x 8.
T698 Paperbound **$1.00**

**THE WIT AND HUMOR OF OSCAR WILDE, ed. by Alvin Redman.** Wilde at his most brilliant, in 1000 epigrams exposing weaknesses and hypocrisies of "civilized" society. Divided into 49 categories—sin, wealth, women, America, etc.—to aid writers, speakers. Includes excerpts from his trials, books, plays, criticism. Formerly "The Epigrams of Oscar Wilde." Introduction by Vyvyan Holland, Wilde's only living son. Introductory essay by editor. 260pp. 5⅜ x 8.
T602 Paperbound **$1.00**

**MAX AND MORITZ, Wilhelm Busch.** Busch is one of the great humorists of all time, as well as the father of the modern comic strip. This volume, translated by H. A. Klein and other hands, contains the perennial favorite "Max and Moritz" (translated by C. T. Brooks), Plisch and Plum, Das Rabennest, Eispeter, and seven other whimsical, sardonic, jovial, diabolical cartoon and verse stories. Lively English translations parallel the original German. This work has delighted millions, since it first appeared in the 19th century, and is guaranteed to please almost anyone. Edited by H. A. Klein, with an afterword. x + 205pp. 5⅝ x 8½.
T181 Paperbound **$1.15**

**HYPOCRITICAL HELENA, Wilhelm Busch.** A companion volume to "Max and Moritz," with the title piece (Die Fromme Helena) and 10 other highly amusing cartoon and verse stories, all newly translated by H. A. Klein and M. C. Klein: Adventure on New Year's Eve (Abenteuer in der Neujahrsnacht), Hangover on the Morning after New Year's Eve (Der Katzenjammer am Neujahrsmorgen), etc. English and German in parallel columns. Hours of pleasure, also a fine language aid. x + 205pp. 5⅝ x 8½.
T184 Paperbound **$1.00**

**THE BEAR THAT WASN'T, Frank Tashlin.** What does it mean? Is it simply delightful wry humor, or a charming story of a bear who wakes up in the midst of a factory, or a satire on Big Business, or an existential cartoon-story of the human condition, or a symbolization of the struggle between conformity and the individual? New York Herald Tribune said of the first edition: ". . . a fable for grownups that will be fun for children. Sit down with the book and get your own bearings." Long an underground favorite with readers of all ages and opinions. v + 51pp. Illustrated. 5⅜ x 8½.
T939 Paperbound **75¢**

**RUTHLESS RHYMES FOR HEARTLESS HOMES and MORE RUTHLESS RHYMES FOR HEARTLESS HOMES, Harry Graham ("Col. D. Streamer").** Two volumes of Little Willy and 48 other poetic disasters. A bright, new reprint of oft-quoted, never forgotten, devastating humor by a precursor of today's "sick" joke school. For connoisseurs of wicked, wacky humor and all who delight in the comedy of manners. Original drawings are a perfect complement. 61 illustrations. Index. vi + 69pp. Two vols. bound as one. 5⅜ x 8½.
T930 Paperbound **75¢**

## Say It language phrase books

These handy phrase books (128 to 196 pages each) make grammatical drills unnecessary for an elementary knowledge of a spoken foreign language. Covering most matters of travel and everyday life each volume contains:

Over 1000 phrases and sentences in immediately useful forms — foreign language plus English.

Modern usage designed for Americans. Specific phrases like, "Give me small change," and "Please call a taxi."

Simplified phonetic transcription you will be able to read at sight.

The only completely indexed phrase books on the market.

Covers scores of important situations: — Greetings, restaurants, sightseeing, useful expressions, etc.

These books are prepared by native linguists who are professors at Columbia, N.Y.U., Fordham and other great universities. Use them independently or with any other book or record course. They provide a supplementary living element that most other courses lack. Individual volumes in:

| | | | |
|---|---|---|---|
| Russian 75¢ | Italian 75¢ | Spanish 75¢ | German 75¢ |
| Hebrew 75¢ | Danish 75¢ | Japanese 75¢ | Swedish 75¢ |
| Dutch 75¢ | Esperanto 75¢ | Modern Greek 75¢ | Portuguese 75¢ |
| Norwegian 75¢ | Polish 75¢ | French 75¢ | Yiddish 75¢ |
| Turkish 75¢ | | English for German-speaking people 75¢ | |
| English for Italian-speaking people 75¢ | | English for Spanish-speaking people 75¢ | |

Large clear type. 128-196 pages each. 3½ x 5¼. Sturdy paper binding.

## Listen and Learn language records

LISTEN & LEARN is the only language record course designed especially to meet your travel and everyday needs. It is available in separate sets for FRENCH, SPANISH, GERMAN, JAPANESE, RUSSIAN, MODERN GREEK, PORTUGUESE, ITALIAN and HEBREW, and each set contains three 33⅓ rpm long-playing records—1½ hours of recorded speech by eminent native speakers who are professors at Columbia, New York University, Queens College.

Check the following special features found only in LISTEN & LEARN:

● **Dual-language recording.** 812 selected phrases and sentences, over 3200 words, spoken first in English, then in their foreign language equivalents. A suitable pause follows each foreign phrase, allowing you time to repeat the expression. You learn by unconscious assimilation.

● **128 to 206-page manual** contains everything on the records, plus a simple phonetic pronunciation guide.

● **Indexed for convenience. The only set on the market** that is completely indexed. No more puzzling over where to find the phrase you need. Just look in the rear of the manual.

● **Practical.** No time wasted on material you can find in any grammar. LISTEN & LEARN covers central core material with phrase approach. Ideal for the person with limited learning time.

● **Living, modern expressions,** not found in other courses. Hygienic products, modern equipment, shopping—expressions used every day, like "nylon" and "air-conditioned."

● **Limited objective.** Everything you learn, no matter where you stop, is immediately useful. You have to finish other courses, wade through grammar and vocabulary drill, before they help you.

● **High-fidelity recording.** LISTEN & LEARN records equal in clarity and surface-silence any record on the market costing up to $6.

"Excellent . . . the spoken records . . . impress me as being among the very best on the market," **Prof. Mario Pei,** Dept. of Romance Languages, Columbia University. "Inexpensive and well-done . . . it would make an ideal present," CHICAGO SUNDAY TRIBUNE. "More genuinely helpful than anything of its kind which I have previously encountered," **Sidney Clark,** well-known author of "ALL THE BEST" travel books.

UNCONDITIONAL GUARANTEE. Try LISTEN & LEARN, then return it within 10 days for full refund if you are not satisfied.

Each set contains three twelve-inch 33⅓ records, manual, and album.

| | | | |
|---|---|---|---|
| SPANISH | the set $5.95 | GERMAN | the set $5.95 |
| FRENCH | the set $5.95 | ITALIAN | the set $5.95 |
| RUSSIAN | the set $5.95 | JAPANESE | the set $5.95 |
| PORTUGUESE | the set $5.95 | MODERN GREEK | the set $5.95 |
| MODERN HEBREW | the set $5.95 | | |

# Americana

**THE EYES OF DISCOVERY, J. Bakeless.** A vivid reconstruction of how unspoiled America appeared to the first white men. Authentic and enlightening accounts of Hudson's landing in New York, Coronado's trek through the Southwest; scores of explorers, settlers, trappers, soldiers. America's pristine flora, fauna, and Indians in every region and state in fresh and unusual new aspects. "A fascinating view of what the land was like before the first highway went through," Time. 68 contemporary illustrations, 39 newly added in this edition. Index. Bibliography. x + 500pp. 5⅜ x 8.                                                           T761 Paperbound **$2.00**

**AUDUBON AND HIS JOURNALS, J. J. Audubon.** A collection of fascinating accounts of Europe and America in the early 1800's through Audubon's own eyes. Includes the Missouri River Journals —an eventful trip through America's untouched heartland, the Labrador Journals, the European Journals, the famous "Episodes", and other rare Audubon material, including the descriptive chapters from the original letterpress edition of the "Ornithological Studies", omitted in all later editions. Indispensable for ornithologists, naturalists, and all lovers of Americana and adventure. 70-page biography by Audubon's granddaughter. 38 illustrations. Index. Total of 1106pp. 5⅜ x 8.                                                          T675 Vol I Paperbound **$2.25**
T676 Vol II Paperbound **$2.25**
The set **$4.50**

**TRAVELS OF WILLIAM BARTRAM, edited by Mark Van Doren.** The first inexpensive illustrated edition of one of the 18th century's most delightful books is an excellent source of first-hand material on American geography, anthropology, and natural history. Many descriptions of early Indian tribes are our only source of information on them prior to the infiltration of the white man. "The mind of a scientist with the soul of a poet," John Livingston Lowes. 13 original illustrations and maps. Edited with an introduction by Mark Van Doren. 448pp. 5⅜ x 8.
T13 Paperbound **$2.00**

**GARRETS AND PRETENDERS: A HISTORY OF BOHEMIANISM IN AMERICA, A. Parry.** The colorful and fantastic history of American Bohemianism from Poe to Kerouac. This is the only complete record of hoboes, cranks, starving poets, and suicides. Here are Pfaff, Whitman, Crane, Bierce, Pound, and many others. New chapters by the author and by H. T. Moore bring this thorough and well-documented history down to the Beatniks. "An excellent account," N. Y. Times. Scores of cartoons, drawings, and caricatures. Bibliography. Index. xxviii + 421pp. 5⅝ x 8⅜.                                                                       T708 Paperbound **$1.95**

**THE EXPLORATION OF THE COLORADO RIVER AND ITS CANYONS, J. W. Powell.** The thrilling first-hand account of the expedition that filled in the last white space on the map of the United States. Rapids, famine, hostile Indians, and mutiny are among the perils encountered as the unknown Colorado Valley reveals its secrets. This is the only uncut version of Major Powell's classic of exploration that has been printed in the last 60 years. Includes later reflections and subsequent expedition. 250 illustrations, new map. 400pp. 5⅝ x 8⅜.
T94 Paperbound **$2.25**

**THE JOURNAL OF HENRY D. THOREAU, Edited by Bradford Torrey and Francis H. Allen.** Henry Thoreau is not only one of the most important figures in American literature and social thought; his voluminous journals (from which his books emerged as selections and crystallizations) constitute both the longest, most sensitive record of personal internal development and a most penetrating description of a historical moment in American culture. This present set, which was first issued in fourteen volumes, contains Thoreau's entire journals from 1837 to 1862, with the exception of the lost years which were found only recently. We are reissuing it, complete and unabridged, with a new introduction by Walter Harding, Secretary of the Thoreau Society. Fourteen volumes reissued in two volumes. Foreword by Henry Seidel Canby. Total of 1888pp. 8⅜ x 12¼.             T312-3 Two volume set, Clothbound **$20.00**

**GAMES AND SONGS OF AMERICAN CHILDREN, collected by William Wells Newell.** A remarkable collection of 190 games with songs that accompany many of them; cross references to show similarities, differences among them; variations; musical notation for 38 songs. Textual discussions show relations with folk-drama and other aspects of folk tradition. Grouped into categories for ready comparative study: Love-games, histories, playing at work, human life, bird and beast, mythology, guessing-games, etc. New introduction covers relations of songs and dances to timeless heritage of folklore, biographical sketch of Newell, other pertinent data. A good source of inspiration for those in charge of groups of children and a valuable reference for anthropologists, sociologists, psychiatrists. Introduction by Carl Withers. New indexes of first lines, games. 5⅜ x 8½. xii + 242pp.                          T354 Paperbound **$1.75**

# Art, History of Art, Antiques, Graphic Arts, Handcrafts

**ART STUDENTS' ANATOMY, E. J. Farris.** Outstanding art anatomy that uses chiefly living objects for its illustrations. 71 photos of undraped men, women, children are accompanied by carefully labeled matching sketches to illustrate the skeletal system, articulations and movements, bony landmarks, the muscular system, skin, fasciae, fat, etc. 9 x-ray photos show movement of joints. Undraped models are shown in such actions as serving in tennis, drawing a bow in archery, playing football, dancing, preparing to spring and to dive. Also discussed and illustrated are proportions, age and sex differences, the anatomy of the smile, etc. 8 plates by the great early 18th century anatomic illustrator Siegfried Albinus are also included. Glossary. 158 figures, 7 in color. x + 159pp. 5⅝ x 8⅜.　　　　T744 Paperbound **$1.50**

**AN ATLAS OF ANATOMY FOR ARTISTS, F Schider.** A new 3rd edition of this standard text enlarged by 52 new illustrations of hands, anatomical studies by Cloquet, and expressive life studies of the body by Barcsay. 189 clear, detailed plates offer you precise information of impeccable accuracy. 29 plates show all aspects of the skeleton, with closeups of special areas, while 54 full-page plates, mostly in two colors, give human musculature as seen from four different points of view, with cutaways for important portions of the body. 14 full-page plates provide photographs of hand forms, eyelids, female breasts, and indicate the location of muscles upon models. 59 additional plates show how great artists of the past utilized human anatomy. They reproduce sketches and finished work by such artists as Michelangelo, Leonardo da Vinci, Goya, and 15 others. This is a lifetime reference work which will be one of the most important books in any artist's library. "The standard reference tool," AMERICAN LIBRARY ASSOCIATION. "Excellent," AMERICAN ARTIST. Third enlarged edition. 189 plates, 647 illustrations. xxvi + 192pp. 7⅞ x 10⅝.　　　　T241 Clothbound **$6.00**

**AN ATLAS OF ANIMAL ANATOMY FOR ARTISTS, W. Ellenberger, H. Baum, H. Dittrich.** The largest, richest animal anatomy for artists available in English. 99 detailed anatomical plates of such animals as the horse, dog, cat, lion, deer, seal, kangaroo, flying squirrel, cow, bull, goat, monkey, hare, and bat. Surface features are clearly indicated, while progressive beneath-the-skin pictures show musculature, tendons, and bone structure. Rest and action are exhibited in terms of musculature and skeletal structure and detailed cross-sections are given for heads and important features. The animals chosen are representative of specific families so that a study of these anatomies will provide knowledge of hundreds of related species. "Highly recommended as one of the very few books on the subject worthy of being used as an authoritative guide," DESIGN. "Gives a fundamental knowledge," AMERICAN ARTIST. Second revised, enlarged edition with new plates from Cuvier, Stubbs, etc. 288 illustrations. 153pp. 11⅜ x 9.　　　　T82 Clothbound **$6.00**

**THE HUMAN FIGURE IN MOTION, Eadweard Muybridge.** The largest selection in print of Muybridge's famous high-speed action photos of the human figure in motion. 4789 photographs illustrate 162 different actions: men, women, children—mostly undraped—are shown walking, running, carrying various objects, sitting, lying down, climbing, throwing, arising, and performing over 150 other actions. Some actions are shown in as many as 150 photographs each. All in all there are more than 500 action strips in this enormous volume, series shots taken at shutter speeds of as high as 1/6000th of a second! These are not posed shots, but true stopped motion. They show bone and muscle in situations that the human eye is not fast enough to catch. Earlier, smaller editions of these prints have brought $40 and more on the out-of-print market. "A must for artists," ART IN FOCUS. "An unparalleled dictionary of action for all artists," AMERICAN ARTIST. 390 full-page plates, with 4789 photographs. Printed on heavy glossy stock. Reinforced binding with headbands. xxi + 390pp. 7⅞ x 10⅝.　　　　T204 Clothbound **$10.00**

**ANIMALS IN MOTION, Eadweard Muybridge.** This is the largest collection of animal action photos in print. 34 different animals (horses, mules, oxen, goats, camels, pigs, cats, guanacos, lions, gnus, deer, monkeys, eagles—and 21 others) in 132 characteristic actions. The horse alone is shown in more than 40 different actions. All 3919 photographs are taken in series at speeds up to 1/6000th of a second. The secrets of leg motion, spinal patterns, head movements, strains and contortions shown nowhere else are captured. You will see exactly how a lion sets his foot down; how an elephant's knees are like a human's—and how they differ; the position of a kangaroo's legs in mid-leap; how an ostrich's head bobs; details of the flight of birds—and thousands of facets of motion only the fastest cameras can catch. Photographed from domestic animals and animals in the Philadelphia zoo, it contains neither semiposed artificial shots nor distorted telephoto shots taken under adverse conditions. Artists, biologists, decorators, cartoonists, will find this book indispensable for understanding animals in motion. "A really marvelous series of plates," NATURE (London). "The dry plate's most spectacular early use was by Eadweard Muybridge," LIFE. 3919 photographs; 380 full pages of plates. 440pp. Printed on heavy glossy paper. Deluxe binding with headbands. 7⅞ x 10⅝.　　　　T203 Clothbound **$10.00**

**THE AUTOBIOGRAPHY OF AN IDEA, Louis Sullivan.** The pioneer architect whom Frank Lloyd Wright called "the master" reveals an acute sensitivity to social forces and values in this passionately honest account. He records the crystallization of his opinions and theories, the growth of his organic theory of architecture that still influences American designers and architects, contemporary ideas, etc. This volume contains the first appearance of 34 full-page plates of his finest architecture. Unabridged reissue of 1924 edition. New introduction by R. M. Line. Index. xiv + 335pp. 5⅜ x 8.  T281 Paperbound **$2.00**

**THE DRAWINGS OF HEINRICH KLEY.** The first uncut republication of both of Kley's devastating sketchbooks, which first appeared in pre-World War I Germany. One of the greatest cartoonists and social satirists of modern times, his exuberant and iconoclastic fantasy and his extraordinary technique place him in the great tradition of Bosch, Breughel, and Goya, while his subject matter has all the immediacy and tension of our century. 200 drawings. viii + 128pp. 7¾ x 10¾.  T24 Paperbound **$1.85**

**MORE DRAWINGS BY HEINRICH KLEY.** All the sketches from Leut' Und Viecher (1912) and Sammel-Album (1923) not included in the previous Dover edition of Drawings. More of the bizarre, mercilessly iconoclastic sketches that shocked and amused on their original publication. Nothing was too sacred, no one too eminent for satirization by this imaginative, individual and accomplished master cartoonist. A total of 158 illustrations. Iv + 104pp. 7¾ x 10¾.  T41 Paperbound **$1.85**

**PINE FURNITURE OF EARLY NEW ENGLAND, R. H. Kettell.** A rich understanding of one of America's most original folk arts that collectors of antiques, interior decorators, craftsmen, woodworkers, and everyone interested in American history and art will find fascinating and immensely useful. 413 illustrations of more than 300 chairs, benches, racks, beds, cupboards, mirrors, shelves, tables, and other furniture will show all the simple beauty and character of early New England furniture. 55 detailed drawings carefully analyze outstanding pieces. "With its rich store of illustrations, this book emphasizes the individuality and varied design of early American pine furniture. It should be welcomed," ANTIQUES. 413 illustrations and 55 working drawings. 475. 8 x 10¾.  T145 Clothbound **$10.00**

**THE HUMAN FIGURE, J. H. Vanderpoel.** Every important artistic element of the human figure is pointed out in minutely detailed word descriptions in this classic text and illustrated as well in 430 pencil and charcoal drawings. Thus the text of this book directs your attention to all the characteristic features and subtle differences of the male and female (adults, children, and aged persons), as though a master artist were telling you what to look for at each stage. 2nd edition, revised and enlarged by George Bridgman. Foreword. 430 illustrations. 143pp. 6⅛ x 9¼.  T432 Paperbound **$1.50**

**LETTERING AND ALPHABETS, J. A. Cavanagh.** This unabridged reissue of LETTERING offers a full discussion, analysis, illustration of 89 basic hand lettering styles — styles derived from Caslons, Bodonis, Garamonds, Gothic, Black Letter, Oriental, and many others. Upper and lower cases, numerals and common signs pictured. Hundreds of technical hints on make-up, construction, artistic validity, strokes, pens, brushes, white areas, etc. May be reproduced without permission! 89 complete alphabets; 72 lettered specimens. 121pp. 9¾ x 8.  T53 Paperbound **$1.35**

**STICKS AND STONES, Lewis Mumford.** A survey of the forces that have conditioned American architecture and altered its forms. The author discusses the medieval tradition in early New England villages; the Renaissance influence which developed with the rise of the merchant class; the classical influence of Jefferson's time; the "Mechanicsvilles" of Poe's generation; the Brown Decades; the philosophy of the Imperial facade; and finally the modern machine age. "A truly remarkable book," SAT. REV. OF LITERATURE. 2nd revised edition. 21 illustrations. xvii + 228pp. 5⅜ x 8.  T202 Paperbound **$1.65**

**THE STANDARD BOOK OF QUILT MAKING AND COLLECTING, Marguerite Ickis.** A complete easy-to-follow guide with all the information you need to make beautiful, useful quilts. How to plan, design, cut, sew, appliqué, avoid sewing problems, use rag bag, make borders, tuft, every other aspect. Over 100 traditional quilts shown, including over 40 full-size patterns. At-home hobby for fun, profit. Index. 483 illus. 1 color plate. 287pp. 6¾ x 9½.  T582 Paperbound **$2.00**

**THE BOOK OF SIGNS, Rudolf Koch.** Formerly $20 to $25 on the out-of-print market, now only $1.00 in this unabridged new edition! 493 symbols from ancient manuscripts, medieval cathedrals, coins, catacombs, pottery, etc. Crosses, monograms of Roman emperors, astrological, chemical, botanical, runes, housemarks, and 7 other categories. Invaluable for handicraft workers, illustrators, scholars, etc., this material may be reproduced without permission. 493 illustrations by Fritz Kredel. 104pp. 6½ x 9¼.  T162 Paperbound **$1.00**

**PRIMITIVE ART, Franz Boas.** This authoritative and exhaustive work by a great American anthropologist covers the entire gamut of primitive art. Pottery, leatherwork, metal work, stone work, wood, basketry, are treated in detail. Theories of primitive art, historical depth in art history, technical virtuosity, unconscious levels of patterning, symbolism, styles, literature, music, dance, etc. A must book for the interested layman, the anthropologist, artist, handicrafter (hundreds of unusual motifs), and the historian. Over 900 illustrations (50 ceramic vessels, 12 totem poles, etc.). 376pp. 5⅜ x 8.  T25 Paperbound **$2.00**

# Fiction

**THE LAND THAT TIME FORGOT and THE MOON MAID, Edgar Rice Burroughs.** In the opinion of many, Burroughs' best work. The first concerns a strange island where evolution is individual rather than phylogenetic. Speechless anthropoids develop into intelligent human beings within a single generation. The second projects the reader far into the future and describes the first voyage to the Moon (in the year 2025), the conquest of the Earth by the Moon, and years of violence and adventure as the enslaved Earthmen try to regain possession of their planet. "An imaginative tour de force that keeps the reader keyed up and expectant," NEW YORK TIMES. Complete, unabridged text of the original two novels (three parts in each). 5 illustrations by J. Allen St. John. vi + 552pp. 5⅜ x 8½.
T1020 Clothbound **$3.75**
T358 Paperbound **$2.00**

**AT THE EARTH'S CORE, PELLUCIDAR, TANAR OF PELLUCIDAR: THREE SCIENCE FICTION NOVELS BY EDGAR RICE BURROUGHS.** Complete, unabridged texts of the first three Pellucidar novels. Tales of derring-do by the famous master of science fiction. The locale for these three related stories is the inner surface of the hollow Earth where we discover the world of Pellucidar, complete with all types of bizarre, menacing creatures, strange peoples, and alluring maidens—guaranteed to delight all Burroughs fans and a wide circle of adventure lovers. Illustrated by J. Allen St. John and P. F. Berdanier. vi + 433pp. 5⅜ x 8½.
T1051 Paperbound **$2.00**

**THREE MARTIAN NOVELS, Edgar Rice Burroughs.** Contains: Thuvia, Maid of Mars; The Chessmen of Mars; and The Master Mind of Mars. High adventure set in an imaginative and intricate conception of the Red Planet. Mars is peopled with an intelligent, heroic human race which lives in densely populated cities and with fierce barbarians who inhabit dead sea bottoms. Other exciting creatures abound amidst an inventive framework of Martian history and geography. Complete unabridged reprintings of the first edition. 16 illustrations by J. Allen St. John. vi + 499pp. 5⅜ x 8½.
T39 Paperbound **$1.85**

**TO THE SUN? and OFF ON A COMET!, Jules Verne.** Complete texts of two of the most imaginative flights into fancy in world literature display the high adventure that have kept Verne's novels read for nearly a century. Only unabridged edition of the best translation, by Edward Roth. Large, easily readable type. 50 illustrations selected from first editions. 462pp. 5⅜ x 8.
T634 Paperbound **$1.75**

**FROM THE EARTH TO THE MOON and ALL AROUND THE MOON, Jules Verne.** Complete editions of two of Verne's most successful novels, in finest Edward Roth translations, now available after many years out of print. Verne's visions of submarines, airplanes, television, rockets, interplanetary travel; of scientific and not-so-scientific beliefs; of peculiarities of Americans; all delight and engross us today as much as when they first appeared. Large, easily readable type. 42 illus. from first French edition. 476pp. 5⅜ x 8.
T633 Paperbound **$1.75**

**THREE PROPHETIC NOVELS BY H. G. WELLS, edited by E. F. Bleiler.** Complete texts of "When the Sleeper Wakes" (1st book printing in 50 years), "A Story of the Days to Come," "The Time Machine" (1st complete printing in book form). Exciting adventures in the future are as enjoyable today as 50 years ago when first printed. Predict TV, movies, intercontinental airplanes, prefabricated houses, air-conditioned cities, etc. First important author to foresee problems of mind control, technological dictatorships. "Absolute best of imaginative fiction," N. Y. Times. Introduction. 335pp. 5⅜ x 8.
T605 Paperbound **$1.50**

**SEVEN SCIENCE FICTION NOVELS, H. G. Wells.** Full unabridged texts of 7 science-fiction novels of the master. Ranging from biology, physics, chemistry, astronomy to sociology and other studies, Mr. Wells extrapolates whole worlds of strange and intriguing character. "One will have to go far to match this for entertainment, excitement, and sheer pleasure . . . ," NEW YORK TIMES. Contents: The Time Machine, The Island of Dr. Moreau, First Men in the Moon, The Invisible Man, The War of the Worlds, The Food of the Gods, In the Days of the Comet. 1015pp. 5⅜ x 8.
T264 Clothbound **$4.50**

**28 SCIENCE FICTION STORIES OF H. G. WELLS.** Two full unabridged novels, MEN LIKE GODS and STAR BEGOTTEN, plus 26 short stories by the master science-fiction writer of all time. Stories of space, time, invention, exploration, future adventure—an indispensable part of the library of everyone interested in science and adventure. PARTIAL CONTENTS: Men Like Gods, The Country of the Blind, In the Abyss, The Crystal Egg, The Man Who Could Work Miracles, A Story of the Days to Come, The Valley of Spiders, and 21 more! 928pp. 5⅜ x 8.
T265 Clothbound **$4.50**

**THE WAR IN THE AIR, IN THE DAYS OF THE COMET, THE FOOD OF THE GODS: THREE SCIENCE FICTION NOVELS BY H. G. WELLS.** Three exciting Wells offerings bearing on vital social and philosophical issues of his and our own day. Here are tales of air power, strategic bombing, East vs. West, the potential miracles of science, the potential disasters from outer space, the relationship between scientific advancement and moral progress, etc. First reprinting of "War in the Air" in almost 50 years. An excellent sampling of Wells at his storytelling best. Complete, unabridged reprintings. 16 illustrations. 645pp. 5⅜ x 8½.
T1135 Paperbound **$2.00**

# Music

**A GENERAL HISTORY OF MUSIC, Charles Burney.** A detailed coverage of music from the Greeks up to 1789, with full information on all types of music: sacred and secular, vocal and instrumental, operatic and symphonic. Theory, notation, forms, instruments, innovators, composers, performers, typical and important works, and much more in an easy, entertaining style. Burney covered much of Europe and spoke with hundreds of authorities and composers so that this work is more than a compilation of records . . . it is a living work of careful and first-hand scholarship. Its account of thoroughbass (18th century) Italian music is probably still the best introduction on the subject. A recent NEW YORK TIMES review said, "Surprisingly few of Burney's statements have been invalidated by modern research . . . still of great value." Edited and corrected by Frank Mercer. 35 figures. Indices. 1915pp. 5⅜ x 8. 2 volumes. **T36 The Set, Clothbound $12.50**

**A DICTIONARY OF HYMNOLOGY, John Julian.** This exhaustive and scholarly work has become known as an invaluable source of hundreds of thousands of important and often difficult to obtain facts on the history and use of hymns in the western world. Everyone interested in hymns will be fascinated by the accounts of famous hymns and hymn writers and amazed by the amount of practical information he will find. More than 30,000 entries on individual hymns, giving authorship, date and circumstances of composition, publication, textual variations, translations, denominational and ritual usage, etc. Biographies of more than 9,000 hymn writers, and essays on important topics such as Christmas carols and children's hymns, and much other unusual and valuable information. A 200 page double-columned index of first lines — the largest in print. Total of 1786 pages in two reinforced clothbound volumes. 6¼ x 9¼. **The set, T333 Clothbound $17.50**

**MUSIC IN MEDIEVAL BRITAIN, F. Ll. Harrison.** The most thorough, up-to-date, and accurate treatment of the subject ever published, beautifully illustrated. Complete account of institutions and choirs; carols, masses, and motets; liturgy and plainsong; and polyphonic music from the Norman Conquest to the Reformation. Discusses the various schools of music and their reciprocal influences; the origin and development of new ritual forms; development and use of instruments; and new evidence on many problems of the period. Reproductions of scores, over 200 excerpts from medieval melodies. Rules of harmony and dissonance; influence of Continental styles; great composers (Dunstable, Cornysh, Fairfax, etc.); and much more. Register and index of more than 400 musicians. Index of titles. General Index. 225-item bibliography. 6 Appendices. xix + 491pp. 5⅝ x 8¾. **T705 Clothbound $10.00**

**THE MUSIC OF SPAIN, Gilbert Chase.** Only book in English to give concise, comprehensive account of Iberian music; new Chapter covers music since 1941. Victoria, Albéniz, Cabezón, Pedrell, Turina, hundreds of other composers; popular and folk music; the Gypsies; the guitar; dance, theatre, opera, with only extensive discussion in English of the Zarzuela; virtuosi such as Casals; much more. "Distinguished . . . readable," Saturday Review. 400-item bibliography. Index. 27 photos. 383pp. 5⅜ x 8. **T549 Paperbound $2.00**

**ON STUDYING SINGING, Sergius Kagen.** An intelligent method of voice-training, which leads you around pitfalls that waste your time, money, and effort. Exposes rigid, mechanical systems, baseless theories, deleterious exercises. "Logical, clear, convincing . . . dead right," Virgil Thomson, N.Y. Herald Tribune. "I recommend this volume highly," Maggie Teyte, Saturday Review. 119pp. 5⅜ x 8. **T622 Paperbound $1.25**

*Prices subject to change without notice.*

*Dover publishes books on art, music, philosophy, literature, languages, history, social sciences, psychology, handcrafts, orientalia, puzzles and entertainments, chess, pets and gardens, books explaining science, intermediate and higher mathematics, mathematical physics, engineering, biological sciences, earth sciences, classics of science, etc. Write to:*

*Dept. catrr.*
*Dover Publications, Inc.*
*180 Varick Street, N.Y. 14, N.Y.*